An Introduction to Vectors, Vector Operators and Vector Analysis

Conceived as s a supplementary text and reference book for undergraduate and graduate students of science and engineering, this book intends communicating the fundamental concepts of vectors and their applications. It is divided into three units. The first unit deals with basic formulation: both conceptual and theoretical. It discusses applications of algebraic operations, Levi-Civita notation and curvilinear coordinate systems like spherical polar and parabolic systems. Structures and analytical geometry of curves and surfaces is covered in detail.

The second unit discusses algebra of operators and their types. It explains the equivalence between the algebra of vector operators and the algebra of matrices. Formulation of eigenvectors and eigenvalues of a linear vector operator are discussed using vector algebra. Topics including Mohr's algorithm, Hamilton's theorem and Euler's theorem are discussed in detail. The unit ends with a discussion on transformation groups, rotation group, group of isometries and the Euclidean group, with applications to rigid displacements.

The third unit deals with vector analysis. It discusses important topics including vector valued functions of a scalar variable, functions of vector argument (both scalar valued and vector valued): thus covering both the scalar and vector fields and vector integration

Pramod S. Joag is presently working as CSIR Emeritus Scientist at the Savitribai Phule University of Pune, India. For over 30 years he has been teaching classical mechanics, quantum mechanics, electrodynamics, solid state physics, thermodynamics and statistical mechanics at undergraduate and graduate levels. His research interests include quantum information, and more specifically measures of quantum entanglement and quantum discord, production of multipartite entangled states, entangled Fermion systems, models of quantum nonlocality etc.

An Introduction to Vectors, Vector Operators and Vector Analysis

Pramod S. Joag

CAMBRIDGE
UNIVERSITY PRESS

CAMBRIDGE
UNIVERSITY PRESS

4843/24, 2nd Floor, Ansari Road, Daryaganj, Delhi - 110002, India

Cambridge University Press is part of the University of Cambridge.

It furthers the University's mission by disseminating knowledge in the pursuit of education, learning and research at the highest international levels of excellence.

www.cambridge.org
Information on this title: www.cambridge.org/9781107154438

First published 2016

Printed in India by Shree Maitrey Printech Pvt. Ltd., Noida

A catalogue record for this publication is available from the British Library

Library of Congress Cataloging-in-Publication Data

Names: Joag, Pramod S., 1951- author.
Title: An introduction to vectors, vector operators and vector analysis /
    Pramod S. Joag.
Description: Daryaganj, Delhi, India : Cambridge University Press, 2016. |
    Includes bibliographical references and index.
Identifiers: LCCN 2016019490| ISBN 9781107154438 (hardback) | ISBN 110715443X
    (hardback)
Subjects: LCSH: Vector analysis. | Mathematical physics.
Classification:LCC QC20.7.V4 J63 2016 | DDC 512/.5–dc23 LC record available at
https://lccn.loc.gov/2016019490

ISBN 978-1-107-15443-8 Hardback

To Ela and Ninad
who made me write this document

Contents

Appendices

Figures

Tables

Preface

This is a textbook on vectors at the undergraduate/advanced undergraduate level. Its target readership is the undergraduate student of science and engineering. It may also be used by professional scientists and engineers to brush up on various aspects of vectors and applications of their interest. Vectors, vector operators and vector analysis form the essential background to and the skeleton of many courses in science and engineering. Therefore, the utility of a book which clearly builds up the theoretical structure and applications of vectors cannot be over-emphasized. The present book is an attempt to fulfill such a requirement. This book, for instance, can be used to give a course forming a common pre-requisite for a number of science and engineering courses. In this book, I have tried to develop the theory and applications of vectors from scratch. Although the subject is presented in a general setting, it is developed in 3-D space using basic vector algebra. A coordinate-free approach is taken throughout, so that all developments are free of any particular coordinate system and apply to all coordinate systems. This approach directly deals with vectors instead of their components or coordinates and combines these vectors using vector algebra.

A large part of this book is inspired by the geometric algebra of multivectors that originated in the 19th century, in the works of Grassmann and Clifford and which has had a powerful re-incarnation with enhanced applicability in the recent works of D. Hestenes and others [7, 10, 11]. This is one of the most general algebraic formulations of geometry of which vectors form a special case. Keeping the multivector geometric algebra at the backdrop makes the coordinate free approach for vectors emerge naturally. On a personal note, the book on classical mechanics by D. Hestenes [10], which introduced me to the multivector geometric algebra, has always been a source of joy and education for me. I have always enjoyed solving problems from this book, many of them are included here. In fact I have used Hestenes' work in various places throughout the book, without using or referring to the geometric algebra or geometric calculus.

While designing this book I was guided by two principles: A consistent development of the subject from scratch, and also showing the beauty of the whole edifice and extending the utility of the book to the largest possible cross-section of students. The book comprises three parts, one for each part of the title: First on the basic formulation, the second on vector operators and the third on vector analysis. Following is the brief description of each one of them.

The first part gives the basic formulation, both conceptual and theoretical. The first chapter builds basic concepts and tools. The first three sections are the result of my experience with students and I have found that these matters should be explicitly dealt with for the correct understanding of the subject. I hope that the first three sections will clear up the confusion and the misconceptions regarding many basic issues, in the minds of students. I have also given the applications and examples of every algebraic operation, starting from vector addition. Levi-Civita notation is introduced in detail and used to get the vector identities. The metric space structure is introduced and used to understand vectors in the context of the physical quantities they represent. Apart from the essential structures like basis, dimension, coordinate systems and the consequences of linearity, the curvilinear coordinate systems like spherical polar and parabolic systems are developed systematically. Vector fields are defined and their basic structure is given. The orientation of a linearly independent triplet of vectors is then discussed, also including the orientation of a triplet relative to a coordinate system and the related concept of the orientation of a plane, which is later used to understand the orientation of a surface. The second chapter deals with the analytical geometry of curves and surfaces emphasizing vector methods. The third chapter uses complex algebra for manipulating planar vectors and for the description and transformations of the plane curves. In this chapter I follow the treatment by Zwikker [26] which is a complete and rigorous exposition of these issues.

The second part deals with operators on vectors. Everything about vector operators is formulated using vector algebra (scalar and vector products) and matrices. The fourth chapter gives the algebra of operators and various types of operators, and proves and emphasizes the equivalence between the algebra of vector operators and the algebra of matrices representing them. The fifth chapter gives general formulation of getting eigenvectors and eigenvalues of a linear operator on vectors using vector algebra. The properties of the spectrum of a symmetric operator are also obtained using vector algebra. Thus, extremely useful and general methods are accessible to the students using elementary vector algebra. A powerful algorithm to diagonalize a positive operator acting on a 2-D space, called Mohr's algorithm, is then described. Mohr's algorithm has been routinely used by engineers via its graphical implementation, as explained in the text. The sixth chapter develops in detail orthogonal transformations as rotations or reflections. The generic forms for operators of reflection and rotation, as well as the matrices for the rotation operator are obtained. The relationship between rotation and reflection is established via Hamilton's theorem. The active and passive transformations and their connection with symmetry is discussed. The concept of broken symmetry is briefly discussed. The Euler angle construction for arbitrary rotation is then derived. The problem of finding the axis and the angle of rotation corresponding to a given orthogonal matrix is solved as the Euler's theorem. The second part ends with the seventh chapter on transformation groups and deals with the rotation group, group of isometries and the Euclidean group, with applications to rigid displacements.

The third part deals with vector analysis. This is a vast subject and a personal flavor in the choice of topics is inevitable. For me the guiding question was, what vector analysis a graduating student in science and engineering must have ? Again, the variety of answers to this question is limited only by the number of people addressing it. Thus, the third part gives my version of the answer to this question and the resulting vector analysis. I primarily develop the subject with geometric point of view, making as much contact with applications as possible. My aim is to enable the student to independently read, understand and use the literature based on vector analysis for the applications of his interest. Whether this aim is met can only be decided by the students who learn and try to use this material. This part is divided into five (Chapters 8–12). The eighth chapter outlines fundamental notions and preliminary start ups, and also sets the objectives. The ninth chapter consists of the vector valued functions of a scalar variable. Theories of space curves and of plane curves are developed from scratch with some physical applications. This chapter ends with the integration of such functions with respect to their scalar argument and their Taylor series expansion. The tenth chapter deals with the functions of vector argument, both scalar valued and vector valued, thus covering both the scalar and vector fields. Again, everything is developed from scratch, starting with the directional derivative, partial derivatives and continuity of such functions. A part of this development is inspired by the geometric calculus developed by D. Hestenes and others [7, 10, 11]. To summarize, this chapter consists of different forms of derivatives of these and inverse functions, and their geometric/physical applications. A major omission in this chapter is that of the systematic development of differential forms, which may not be required in an undergraduate course. The eleventh chapter concerns vector integration. This is done in three phases: the line, the surface and the volume integral. All the standard topics are covered, emphasizing geometric aspects and physical applications. While writing this part, I have made use of many books, especially the book by Courant and John [5] and that by Lang [15], for the simple reason that I have learnt my calculus from these books, and I have no regrets about that. In particular, my treatment of multiple integrals and matrices and determinants in Appendix A is inspired by Courant and John's book. I find in their book, the unique property of building rigorous mathematics, starting from an intuitive geometric picture. Also, I follow Griffiths while presenting the divergence and the curl of vector fields, which, I think, is possibly one of the most compact and clear treatments of this topic. The subsections 11.1.1 and 11.8.1 and a part of section 9.2 are based on ref [22]. The twelfth and last chapter of the book presents an assorted collection of applications involving rotational motion of a rigid body, projectile motion, satellites and their orbits etc, illustrating coordinate-free analysis using vector techniques. This chapter, again, is influenced by Hestenes [10].

Appendix A develops the theory of matrices and determinants emphasizing their connection with vectors, also proving all results involving matrices and determinants used in the text. Appendix B gives a brief introduction to Dirac delta function.

The whole book is interspersed with exercises, which form an integral part of the text. Most of these exercises are illustrative or they explore some real life application of the theory. Some of them point out the subtlties involved. I recommend all students to attempt all exercises, without looking at the solutions beforehand. When you read a solution after an attempt to get there, you understand it better. Also, do not be miserly about drawing figures, a figure can show you a way which thousand words may not.

I cannot end this preface without expressing my affection towards my friend and my deceased colleague Dr Narayan Rana, who re-kindled my interest in mechanics. Long evenings that I spent with him discussing mechanics and physics in general, sharing and laughing at various aspects of life from a distance, are the treasures of my life. We entered a rewarding and fruitful collaboration of writing a book on mechanics [19]. This collaboration and Hestenes' book [10] motivated me to formulate mechanics in a coordinate free way using vector methods. Apart from the book by Hestenes and his other related work, the book by V. I. Arnold on mechanics [3] has made an indelible impact on my understanding and my global view of mechanics, although its influence is not quite apparent in this book. I have always enjoyed discussing mechanics and physics in general with my colleagues Rajeev Pathak, Anil Gangal, C. V. Dharmadhikari, P. Durganandini, and Ahmad Sayeed. The present book is produced in LATEX and I thank our students, Dinesh Mali, Mukesh Khanore and Mihir Durve for their help in drawing figures and also as TEXperts.

Nomenclature

$\alpha, \beta, \gamma, \delta$ Scalars

$\angle\,(\mathbf{a}, \mathbf{b})$ Angle between vectors $\mathbf{a}, \mathbf{b}$

$\mathbf{a}, \mathbf{b}, \mathbf{x}, \mathbf{y}$ Vectors

θ, ϕ, ψ, χ Angles

$\mathcal{R}$ Region of 3-D space/plane

LHS Left hand side

RHS Right hand side

$\mathbb{R}^3$ Vector space comprising ordered triplets of real numbers

$\mathcal{E}_3$ 3-D vector space

$|\mathbf{a}|, a$ Magnitude of $\mathbf{a}$

$\|\mathbf{a}\|$ Norm of $\mathbf{a}$

A, B Matrices

$|A|, |B|$ Determinants

$\mathcal{R}(z), \mathcal{I}(z)$ Real and imaginary parts of a complex number

CM Center of mass

$\boldsymbol{\mu}$ Magnetic moment

L Magnitude of angular momentum, A linear differential form

$\mathbf{h}$ Angular momentum

H Specific angular momentum : Angular momentum per unit mass

M Moment of a force, Torque

B Magnetic field

E, $\mathcal{E}$ Electric field

κ Curvature

ρ Radius of curvature

p Semilatusrectum of a conic section

e Eccentricity of a conic section

m Moment of a line

$\mathcal{R}(\hat{\mathbf{n}}, \theta)$ Operator for rotation of vector **x** about $\hat{\mathbf{n}}$ by angle θ

$\mathcal{U}$ Canonical reflection operator, general orthogonal operator

S Similarity transformation on $\mathcal{E}_3$

$\mathcal{A}$ Affine transformation, skewsymmetric transformation

J Jacobian matrix

$|J|$, D Jacobian determinant

E, F, G Gaussian fundamental quantities of a surface

$\mathcal{I}$ Moment of Inertia operator/tensor

$\mathbf{g}(\mathbf{x}, t)$ Gravitational field of a continuous body

$\mathcal{Q}$ Gravitational quadrupole tensor

ω, Ω Rotational velocity

Part I

Basic Formulation

Models are to be used, not believed.
H. Theil (Principles of Econometrics)

Getting Concepts and Gathering Tools

1.1 Vectors and Scalars

In science and engineering we come across many quantities which require both magnitude and direction for their complete specification, e.g., velocity, acceleration, momentum, force, angular momentum, torque, electrical current density, electric and magnetic fields, pressure and temperature gradients, heat flow and so on. To deal with such quantities, we need laws to represent, combine and manipulate them. Instead of creating these laws separately for each of these quantities, it makes good sense to create a mathematical model to set up common laws for all quantities requiring both magnitude and direction to be specified. This idea is neither new nor alien: right from our childhood we deal with real numbers and integers which are the mathematical objects representing a value of 'something'. This 'something' is anything which can be quantified or measured and whose value is specified as a single entity: length, mass, time, energy, area, volume, curvature, cash in your pocket, the size of the memory and the speed of your computer, bank interest rates $\cdots$. The combination and manipulation of these values is effected by combining and manipulating the corresponding real numbers. Similarly, the values of the quantities specified by magnitude and direction are represented by vectors. A vector is *completely specified by its magnitude and direction*. Note that the magnitude of a vector is specified by a single real number ≥ 0, so if we wish to change only the magnitude of a vector, we must have the facility to multiply a vector by a real number, which we call a *scalar* in this context. Henceforth, in this book, by a scalar we mean a real number. Thus, in order to develop an algebra on the set of vectors, we need to associate with it the set of scalars and define the laws for multiplying a vector by a scalar. If we multiply a vector by -1 we get the vector with same magnitude but opposite in direction, which, when added to the original vector gives the zero vector, that is, a vector with zero magnitude and no direction. Two vectors are equal if *they have equal magnitudes and the same direction*.

In this book we are using boldfaced letters for vectors. A symbol which is not bold, may represent the magnitude of the corresponding vector, or a scalar.

1.2 Space and Direction

We have not attempted to formally define 'space' or 'direction' as these are the integral parts of our experience right from birth. By space we mean the space we live in and move around. We experience direction by our motion as well as by observing other moving objects. We call our space three dimensional, (3-D) because given any two different directions, we can always choose a third direction such that going through any sequence of displacements along any two of them, we will never move along the third and also because given any set of four different directions we can always find a sequence of displacements through any three of them, which will take us along the fourth. *In this book, any n-dimensional object is denoted n*-D. We also assume that space is a continuum, that is, any region of space can be divided arbitrarily and indefinitely into smaller and smaller regions. Further, we assume that space is an inert vacuum, whose sole purpose is to make room for different physical phenomena to occur in it. We denote this space by a symbol $\mathbb{R}^3$. You may wonder about this weird symbol. However, we will understand it in due course. For the time being we just view this symbol as a short name for our space with the above properties.

In order to incorporate the concept of direction in our model, we note that any straight line in space specifies two directions, each by the sense in which the line is traversed. In order to pick one of these two directions, we may put an arrow-head on the line, pointing in the direction we want to indicate. Thus, a straight line with an arrow is our first model for specifying direction in space (see Fig. 1.1(a)). We will refine it shortly. Note that if we parallelly transport a line with an arrow, (that is, the transported line is always parallel to the original one), it indicates the same direction. Thus, two different directions in space correspond to two intersecting straight lines with arrows appropriately placed on them. One of these directions (which we call 'reference direction') can be reached from the other by rotating the other direction about the line normal to the plane containing the two intersecting lines and passing through the point of intersection, until both, the lines and the arrows, coincide (see Fig. 1.1(b)). The angular advance made by the rotating line is simply the angle between the two directions. This angle can be measured by drawing a circle of radius r in the plane of two intersecting lines with its center at the point of intersection and measuring the length of the arc of this circle, say S, swept by the rotating line. The angle θ swept by the rotating line is then given by

$$S = r\theta.$$

Any arbitrary circle drawn in the specified plane can be used to get the value of angle θ via the above equation ($\theta = S/r$). In other words, the radius r is arbitrary. It is convenient to choose a unit circle, that is, a circle with radius unity, ($r = 1$), so that the arc-length and the angle swept by the rotating line are numerically equal (see Fig. 1.1(c)). Such a arc-length measure of angle is called 'radian measure'. Since the length of the circumference of a unit circle is 2π, the angle corresponding to one complete rotation is 2π. The angle corresponding to half the circumference is π and so on.

This procedure still leaves an ambiguity in defining the angle between two directions. We can rotate one of the directions (so as to coincide with the other direction) in two ways. The sense of one rotation is reverse to that of the other. Each of these rotations correspond to different angles, say θ and $2\pi - \theta$ (see Fig. 1.1(b)). Which of these rotations do we choose? We place a clock with its center at the point of intersection of the two lines so as to view it from the top. We then choose the rotation in the sense opposite to that of the hands of the clock. This is called counterclockwise rotation.

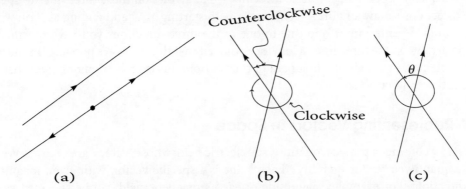

(a)   (b)   (c)

Fig. 1.1   (a) A line indicates two possible directions. A line with an arrow specifies a unique direction. (b) The angle between two directions is the amount by which one line is to be rotated so as to coincide with the other along with the arrows. Note the counterclockwise and clockwise rotations. (c) The angle between two directions is measured by the arc of the unit circle swept by the rotating direction.

The angle swept by a counterclockwise rotation is taken to be positive, while the angle swept by a clockwise rotation is negative. Note that we can always choose the angle between two directions to be $\leq \pi$ by choosing which direction is to be rotated counterclockwise towards which (see Fig. 1.2).

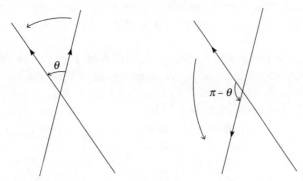

Fig. 1.2   We can choose the angle between directions $\leq \pi$ by choosing which direction is to be rotated (counterclockwise) towards which.

The angle between two directions is used to specify one direction relative to the other. If you reflect on your experience, you will realize that the only way to specify a direction is to specify it relative to some other reference direction which you can determine by observing something like a magnetic needle. To appreciate this, imagine that you are on a ship sailing in the mid-pacific. Suppose that you have no device like a magnetic compass or a gyroscope on the ship (I do not recommend this!) and that clouds block your vision of the pole star and the other stars. Then it is impossible to tell in which direction your ship is moving.

Exercise   Consider three different *non-coplanar lines*[1] intersecting at a point O. Take a point P which is not on any of these three lines. Put arrows on these three lines to specify three directions (Draw a figure). Construct a path starting at O and ending at P on which you are moving either in or opposite to one of the three directions you have specified by putting arrows on the three lines. Convince yourself that this is always possible. In the light of the statements made in the first para of this section, this exercise demonstrates that our space is three dimensional.   □

1.3   Representing Vectors in Space

Let us now consider a physical quantity, say electric field, whose 'values' are vectors. We call such a quantity, a 'vector quantity'. Each value is a specific vector, with given magnitude and direction. For example, magnitude of earth's magnetic field can be specified as say, 0.37 gauss and the direction can be given relative to that implied by earth's polar axis. Any such vector can be represented in space as follows. Given the magnitude and the direction of the vector, we draw a line in space in the direction of the vector. Then, we mark out a segment of this line whose length is proportional to the magnitude of the vector and then put an arrow at one of the ends of this segment to indicate the direction of the vector. For example, to represent a vector specifying a value of the electric field, we may choose a length of 1 cm to correspond to the magnitude of 1 volt/meter. An electric field vector of magnitude x volts/meter is then represented by a segment of length x cm. Once chosen, the same constant of proportionality must be used to represent all vectors corresponding to the electric field. Every vector giving a possible value of a vector quantity is completely represented in space by the corresponding segment with an arrow at one of its ends. Of course, the arrow can be placed anywhere on the line segment, not necessarily at one of its ends.

The end opposite to the arrow on the vector (drawn in space) is called its base point. Since a vector is completely specified by its magnitude and direction, it can be represented in space at any point as its base point, because changing the base point does not change the length or the direction of the vector. Two or more representations of the same vector based at different points in space are to be taken as the same vector (see Fig. 1.3).

---

[1] Any number of lines *all* of which fall on the same plane are called *coplanar*. A collection of lines which are not coplanar is called non-coplanar. A pair of intersecting lines is coplanar.

Fig. 1.3   Different representations of the same vector in space

Henceforth, by a vector, we will mean the representation of a value of a vector quantity in space, which is simply proportional to the actual value of the vector quantity it represents. *This enables us to specify every vector by its length and direction, without any reference to the physical quantity it represents. This gives us the freedom to set up the laws of combining two or more vectors in the same sense as we set up the laws for combining real or complex numbers without reference to the quantities they correspond to.* Thus, we can develop the theory of vectors independent of which physical quantity they represent and common to all applications of vectors. The vectors giving the possible positions of a point particle in space (relative to some origin) are called the *position vectors*. The set of all vectors is in one to one correspondence with the set of points in space.

In some applications, a vector has to be localized in space, that is, it has to be based at a particular point in space and cannot be parallel transported. A typical example is – the forces applied at a given set of points on a body which is in mechanical equilibrium, so that the net force on the body is zero, as well as the net torque about any point of the body is zero. Here, the set of applied forces are vectors fixed at the points of application. Such a localization of vectors can be effected by assigning them to the points in space or to the corresponding position vectors. If the number of vectors we are dealing with is finite and small, we can assign this set of vectors to the corresponding set of position vectors by giving an explicit table of assignment. If the vectors and the corresponding position vectors form a continuum, then the assignment takes the form of a vector valued function of the position vector variable, say $\mathbf{f}(\mathbf{x})$, which is called a vector field (see section 1.15).

Apart from the vectors representing the values of vector quantities in space, we need to draw another kind of vectors in space. These are called unit vectors whose length is always unity. Thus, two unit vectors differ only in direction. A unit vector replaces the 'line with an arrow' model to specify a direction in space. The sole purpose of a unit vector is to specify a direction in space. In particular, the length of a unit vector does not correspond to the magnitude of any physical quantity. We shall always denote a unit vector by a hat over it, so that you can recognize it as a unit vector even if that is not explicitly stated. Given a vector $\mathbf{a}$, $\hat{\mathbf{a}}$ will denote the unit vector in the direction of $\mathbf{a}$. Thus, every vector $\mathbf{a} \neq \mathbf{0}$ can be written as

$$\mathbf{a} = |\mathbf{a}|\hat{\mathbf{a}},$$

where $|\mathbf{a}|$ denotes the magnitude of $\mathbf{a}$.

The geometric interpretation of the set of real numbers is a straight line, that is, the set of real numbers is in one to one correspondence with the points on the line. Similarly, the set of vectors is in one to one correspondence with the points in the three dimensional space $\mathbb{R}^3$. To see this one to one correspondence, consider the set of vectors comprising all possible values of some vector quantity. We can construct the set containing the representatives of these vectors in space. One to one correspondence between these two sets is obvious by construction. To transfer this correspondence to the points in $\mathbb{R}^3$ we take an arbitrary point in space say O, called origin and represent every vector with O as the base point. Since the vectors have all possible magnitudes and directions, every point in space is at the tip of some vector based at O, representing a possible value of the vector quantity. In this way, a unique magnitude and direction is assigned to every point in space, establishing the one to one correspondence between the set of vectors and the set of points in space. We could have chosen any other point, say O' as the origin and base all vectors at O'. This gives a new representation for each vector in the set of vectors obtained by parallelly transporting each vector based at O to that based at O'. These two are the representations of the same set of vectors (values of a vector quantity). However, they generate two different one to one correspondences with the points in $\mathbb{R}^3$ as can be seen from Fig. 1.4. We see that changing the origin from O to O' makes a vector correspond to two different points in space (or, makes a point in space correspond to two different vectors) as we assign a vector (based at O or O') to a point in space. Thus, changing the origin changes the one to one correspondence between the set of vectors and the points in space. Later, we will have a closer look at the one to one correspondence between $\mathbb{R}^3$ and the set of vectors (values of a vector quantity).

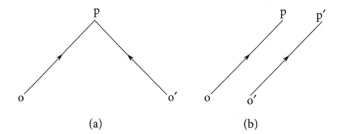

(a)   (b)

Fig. 1.4   Shifting origin makes (a) two different vectors correspond to the same point and (b) two different points correspond to the same vector

1.4 Addition and its Properties

Let us now see how to add two vectors. We will define the addition of vectors using the representatives of the values of a vector quantity in space. This frees vector addition from the corresponding vector quantities.

To add **a** and **b**, base the vector **b** at the tip of **a**. Then, the vector joining the base point of **a** to the tip of **b**, in that direction, is the vector **a** + **b**. You can check that **a** + **b** = **b** + **a** (see Fig. 1.5). Notice that the vectors **a**, **b** and **a** + **b** form a (planar) triangle and hence are coplanar.

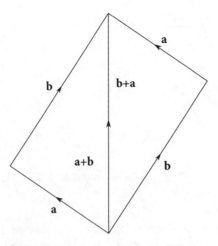

Fig. 1.5   Vector addition is commutative

The vector $\mathbf{a} + \mathbf{b}$ is sometimes called the resultant of $\mathbf{a}$ and $\mathbf{b}$. The rule of adding two or more vectors is motivated by the net displacement of an object in space, resulting due to many successive displacements. Thus, if we go from A to B by travelling 10 km NE (vector $\mathbf{a}$) and then from B to C by travelling 6 km W (vector $\mathbf{b}$) the net displacement, 8 km due North from A to C (vector $\mathbf{c}$), is obtained as depicted in Fig. 1.6(a), which is the same as that given by $\mathbf{c} = \mathbf{a} + \mathbf{b}$. Figure 1.6(b) shows the net displacement ($\mathbf{f}$) after four successive displacements ($\mathbf{a}, \mathbf{b}, \mathbf{c}, \mathbf{d}$) which is consistent with $\mathbf{f} = \mathbf{a} + \mathbf{b} + \mathbf{c} + \mathbf{d}$.

We can now list the properties of vector addition and multiplication by a scalar.

(1) *Closure*   If $\mathbf{a}, \mathbf{b}$ are in $\mathbb{R}^3$ then $\mathbf{a} + \mathbf{b}$ is also in $\mathbb{R}^3$. That is, addition of two vectors results in a vector.

(2) *Commutativity* $\mathbf{a} + \mathbf{b} = \mathbf{b} + \mathbf{a}$ (see Fig. 1.5).

(3) *Associativity*   For all vectors $\mathbf{a}, \mathbf{b}, \mathbf{c}$ in $\mathbb{R}^3$, $\mathbf{a} + (\mathbf{b} + \mathbf{c}) = (\mathbf{a} + \mathbf{b}) + \mathbf{c}$. Thus, while adding three or more vectors, it does not matter which two you add first, which two next etc, that is, the order in which you add does not matter (see Fig. 1.6(b)).

(4) *Identity*   There is a unique vector $\mathbf{0}$ such that for every vector $\mathbf{a}$ in $\mathbb{R}^3$, $\mathbf{a} + \mathbf{0} = \mathbf{a}$.

(5) *Inverse*   For every vector $\mathbf{a} \neq \mathbf{0}$ in $\mathbb{R}^3$, there is a unique vector $-\mathbf{a}$ such that $\mathbf{a} + (-\mathbf{a}) = \mathbf{0}$ and $\mathbf{0} \pm \mathbf{0} = \mathbf{0}$.

To every pair α and $\mathbf{a}$ where α is a scalar (i.e., a real number) and $\mathbf{a}$ in $\mathbb{R}^3$ there is a vector $\alpha \mathbf{a}$ in $\mathbb{R}^3$. If we denote by $|\mathbf{a}|$ the magnitude of $\mathbf{a}$, then the magnitude of $\alpha \mathbf{a}$ is $|\alpha| \, |\mathbf{a}|$. If $\alpha > 0$, the direction of $\alpha \mathbf{a}$ is the same as that of $\mathbf{a}$, while if $\alpha < 0$ then the direction of $\alpha \mathbf{a}$ is opposite to that of $\mathbf{a}$. If $\alpha > 0$, then $\alpha \mathbf{a}$ is said to be the *scaling* of $\mathbf{a}$ by α. Note that $\alpha = 1/|\mathbf{a}|$ produces unit vector $\hat{\mathbf{a}}$ in the direction of $\mathbf{a}$. We have, for the scalar multiplication,

(1) *Associativity* $\alpha(\beta \mathbf{a}) = (\alpha\beta)\mathbf{a}$.

(2) *Identity* $1\mathbf{a} = \mathbf{a}$.

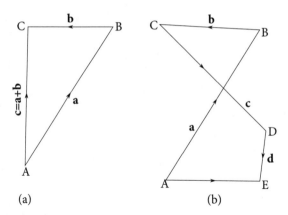

Fig. 1.6   (a) Addition of two vectors (see text). (b) Vector $\overline{AE}$ equals $\mathbf{a}+\mathbf{b}+\mathbf{c}+\mathbf{d}$. Draw different figures, adding $\mathbf{a},\mathbf{b},\mathbf{c},\mathbf{d}$ in different orders to check that this vector addition is associative.

Multiplication by scalars is distributive, namely,

(3) $\alpha(\mathbf{a}+\mathbf{b}) = \alpha\mathbf{a} + \alpha\mathbf{b}$.

(4) $(\alpha + \beta)\mathbf{a} = \alpha\mathbf{a} + \beta\mathbf{a}$.

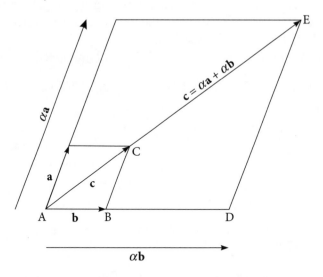

Fig. 1.7 $\alpha\mathbf{a} + \alpha\mathbf{b} = \alpha(\mathbf{a}+\mathbf{b})$

Note that these properties are shared by *all vectors independent of the context in which they are used and independent of which vector quantity they correspond to.* As explained in section 1.3, this is true of all the algebra of vectors and operations on vectors we develop in this book and will not be stated explicitly again.

Exercise   Draw vectors $\mathbf{a}, \mathbf{b}, \mathbf{c} = \mathbf{a} + \mathbf{b}, \alpha\mathbf{a}, \alpha\mathbf{b}, \mathbf{C} = \alpha\mathbf{a} + \alpha\mathbf{b}$ based at the same point A and check using elementary geometry that $\alpha\mathbf{a} + \alpha\mathbf{b} = \alpha(\mathbf{a} + \mathbf{b})$.

Solution   In Fig. 1.7 $\triangle ABC$ is similar to $\triangle ADE$ as two corresponding sides are parallel and the angle at A is common. Therefore,

$$\frac{AE}{AC} = \frac{AD}{AB} = \alpha\frac{|\mathbf{b}|}{|\mathbf{b}|} = \alpha.$$

Substituting $AC = |\mathbf{a} + \mathbf{b}|$ in the above equation, we get $AE = |\mathbf{C}| = \alpha|\mathbf{a} + \mathbf{b}| = \alpha|\mathbf{c}|$. However, the vectors $\mathbf{c}$ and $\mathbf{C}$ are in the same direction, so that $\mathbf{C} = \alpha\mathbf{c} = \alpha(\mathbf{a} + \mathbf{b})$. Finally, $\mathbf{C} = \alpha\mathbf{a} + \alpha\mathbf{b}$ giving $\alpha\mathbf{a} + \alpha\mathbf{b} = \alpha(\mathbf{a} + \mathbf{b})$. $\square$

To subtract vector $\mathbf{b}$ from vector $\mathbf{a}$ we add vector $-\mathbf{b}$ to vector $\mathbf{a}$, as shown in Fig. 1.8

$$\mathbf{a} - \mathbf{b} = \mathbf{a} + (-\mathbf{b}).$$

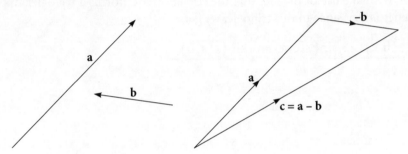

Fig. 1.8   Subtraction of vectors

Given any two non-zero vectors $\mathbf{a}$ and $\mathbf{b}$, their *linear combination* $\alpha\mathbf{a} + \beta\mathbf{b}$, ($\alpha, \beta$ scalars) is a vector in the plane defined by $\mathbf{a}$ and $\mathbf{b}$ (see Fig. 1.9). Given any set of N vectors $\{\mathbf{x}_1, \mathbf{x}_2, \ldots, \mathbf{x}_N\}$, their linear combination is defined iteratively. The resulting vector $\sum_{i=1}^{N} \alpha_i\mathbf{x}_i$ is common to the planes formed by all the pairs of vectors ($\sum_{i=1 i\neq k}^{N}$ $\alpha_i\mathbf{x}_i$, $\mathbf{x}_k$), $k = 1, \ldots, N$. You can verify this for $N = 3$.

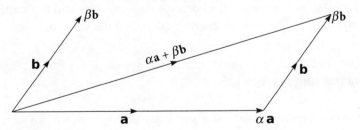

Fig. 1.9 $\mathbf{a}, \mathbf{b}, \alpha\mathbf{a} + \beta\mathbf{b}$ are in the same plane

How are the magnitudes of non-zero vectors $\mathbf{a}$, $\mathbf{b}$ and $\mathbf{a} + \mathbf{b}$ related? We know that the vectors $\mathbf{a}$, $\mathbf{b}$ and $\mathbf{a} + \mathbf{b}$ form a triangle. Applying the trigonometric *law of cosines* to this triangle, we get (see Fig. 1.10)

$$|\mathbf{a} + \mathbf{b}|^2 = |\mathbf{a}|^2 + |\mathbf{b}|^2 - 2\cos(\angle(\mathbf{a}, \mathbf{b}))|\mathbf{a}|\,|\mathbf{b}|,$$

where $\angle(\mathbf{a}, \mathbf{b})$ is the angle between the directions of $\mathbf{a}$ and $\mathbf{b}$. This also gives, for the angle between $\mathbf{a}$ and $\mathbf{b}$,

$$\cos(\angle(\mathbf{a}, \mathbf{b})) = \frac{|\mathbf{a}|^2 + |\mathbf{b}|^2 - |\mathbf{a} + \mathbf{b}|^2}{2|\mathbf{a}|\,|\mathbf{b}|}.$$

Later, you will prove the law of cosines as an exercise. Obviously, if the vectors $\mathbf{a}$ and $\mathbf{b}$ are perpendicular (also called *orthogonal*) then,

$$|\mathbf{a} + \mathbf{b}|^2 = |\mathbf{a}|^2 + |\mathbf{b}|^2,$$

which is nothing but the statement of the Pythagorean theorem. Let us now find the angle made by the vector $\mathbf{c} = \mathbf{a} + \mathbf{b}$ with $\mathbf{a}$ say, in terms of the attributes of vectors $\mathbf{a}$ and $\mathbf{b}$. Here again, we make use of the fact that the triplet $\{\mathbf{a}, \mathbf{b}, \mathbf{c}\}$ forms a triangle. Applying the trigonometric *law of sines* to this triangle, we get,

$$\frac{\sin(\angle(\mathbf{b}, \mathbf{c}))}{a} = \frac{\sin(\angle(\mathbf{c}, \mathbf{a}))}{b} = \frac{\sin(\angle(\mathbf{a}, \mathbf{b}))}{c}$$

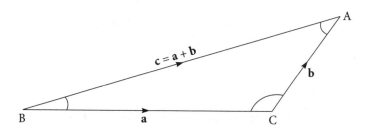

Fig. 1.10   An arbitrary triangle ABC formed by addition of vectors $\mathbf{a}, \mathbf{b}$; $\mathbf{c} = \mathbf{a} + \mathbf{b}$. The angles at the respective vertices A, B, C are denoted by the same symbols.

where (a, b, c) are the magnitudes of the corresponding vectors and the angles involved are between the directions of the vectors. Having calculated the value of c, we can use the last equality to get,

$$\sin(\angle(\mathbf{c}, \mathbf{a})) = \sin(\angle(\mathbf{a}, \mathbf{b}))\frac{b}{c}.$$

This gives $\angle(\mathbf{c}, \mathbf{a})$ as required. Again, if $\mathbf{a}$ and $\mathbf{b}$ are orthogonal, we can simplify by noting $\sin(\angle(\mathbf{c}, \mathbf{a})) = \frac{b}{c}$, or $\tan(\angle(\mathbf{c}, \mathbf{a})) = \frac{b}{a}$.

Exercise   If $\mathbf{a}$ and $\mathbf{b}$ are position vectors of points P and Q, based at the origin O, then show that the position vector $\mathbf{x}$ of a point X dividing PQ in the ratio $\lambda : (1 - \lambda)$ is given by

$$(1 - \lambda)\mathbf{a} + \lambda\mathbf{b}.$$

For what values of λ does the position vector correspond to the point on the ray in the direction of Q from P?

Solution   We have, (see Fig. 1.11),

$$\mathbf{x} - \mathbf{a} = \lambda \overrightarrow{PQ} = \lambda(\mathbf{b} - \mathbf{a}).$$

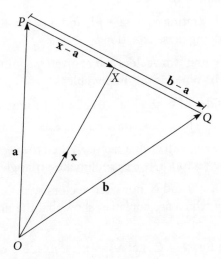

Fig. 1.11   Dividing PQ in the ratio $\lambda : (1 - \lambda)$

This gives,

$$\mathbf{x} = (1 - \lambda)\mathbf{a} + \lambda\mathbf{b}.$$

To answer the question, write

$$\mathbf{x} = \mathbf{a} + \lambda(\mathbf{b} - \mathbf{a}),$$

where $\mathbf{b} - \mathbf{a} = \overrightarrow{PQ}$, to see that $\lambda > 0$.   □

Exercise   Two spheres of masses m_1 and m_2 are rigidly connected by a massless rod. The system is rotating freely about its center of mass. Find the total angular momentum of the system about CM.

Answer   Let the position vector of m_1 relative to m_2 be $\mathbf{r}$, let the velocity of m_1 relative to CM be $\mathbf{v}$ and let $\mu = \frac{m_1 m_2}{m_1 + m_2}$ be the reduced mass of the system. Then the total angular momentum is $\mathbf{L} = 2\mu\mathbf{r} \times \mathbf{v}$.   □

1.4.1   Decomposition and resolution of vectors

Just as we can add two vectors $\mathbf{a}$ and $\mathbf{b}$ to get the vector $\mathbf{c} = \mathbf{a} + \mathbf{b}$, we can do the reverse, namely, given a vector $\mathbf{c}$ we can find two vectors $\mathbf{a}$ and $\mathbf{b}$ satisfying $\mathbf{c} = \mathbf{a} + \mathbf{b}$. To do this, we choose an arbitrary vector $\mathbf{a} \neq \mathbf{0}$ and then get $\mathbf{b} = \mathbf{c} - \mathbf{a}$. Thus, there are infinite, (in fact, uncountably many), pairs of vectors into which a given vector can be decomposed or resolved. In order to resolve a given vector $\mathbf{c}$ into a set of N vectors we first choose arbitrary sets $\{\alpha_i \neq 0\}$ and $\{\mathbf{x}_i \neq \mathbf{0}\}$, $i = 1,\ldots,N-1$ of $N-1$ scalars and vectors respectively and find the vector $\mathbf{x} = \sum_{i=1}^{N-1} \alpha_i \mathbf{x}_i$. Then, we choose α_N and $\mathbf{x}_N$ to satisfy $\alpha_N \mathbf{x}_N = \mathbf{c} - \mathbf{x}$. Thus, any vector can be resolved or decomposed in a set of N vectors in infinitely (uncountably) many ways.

Exercise Draw figures illustrating $\mathbf{c} = \alpha\mathbf{a} + \beta\mathbf{b}$ and $\mathbf{d} = \alpha\mathbf{a} + \beta\mathbf{b} + \gamma\mathbf{c}$ for different sets of scalars and vectors satisfying these equations. □

Exercise Given a vector $\mathbf{c}$ find two vectors $\mathbf{a}, \mathbf{b}$ of given magnitudes a, b respectively, such that $\mathbf{c}$ is the resultant of $\mathbf{a}, \mathbf{b}$. When is this impossible?

Answer Squaring both sides of $\mathbf{b} = \mathbf{c} - \mathbf{a}$ we get, for the angle between $\mathbf{a}$ and $\mathbf{c}$, $\hat{\mathbf{c}} \cdot \hat{\mathbf{a}} = \cos\theta = (c^2 + a^2 - b^2)/2ca$. Thus, if we draw vectors $\mathbf{c} = \overrightarrow{AC}$ and $\mathbf{a} = \overrightarrow{AB}$ making angle $\theta = \cos^{-1}[(c^2 + a^2 - b^2)/2ca]$ with each other at A, then the vector $\overrightarrow{BC}$ gives the required vector $\mathbf{b}$. This will fail if the vectors $\mathbf{a}, \mathbf{b}, \mathbf{c}$ cannot make a triangle, that is when $a + b < c$. □

Exercise Given a vector $\mathbf{a} \neq \mathbf{0}$ and N non-zero vectors $\mathbf{x}_i$, $i = 1,\ldots,N$, no two of which are parallel and no three of which are coplanar, show that the linear combination of $\{\mathbf{x}_i\}$'s that equals $\mathbf{a}$ is unique.

Solution We first show it for $N = 2$. Let $\mathbf{a} = \lambda\mathbf{x}_1 + \mu\mathbf{x}_2$. Note that both the coefficients cannot be zero, otherwise $\mathbf{a} = \mathbf{0}$. Now suppose that some other linear combination equals $\mathbf{a}$, say $\mathbf{a} = \lambda_1\mathbf{x}_1 + \mu_1\mathbf{x}_2$. Subtracting these two equations we get $(\lambda - \lambda_1)\mathbf{x}_1 + (\mu - \mu_1)\mathbf{x}_2 = \mathbf{0}$. Either both of these coefficients are non-zero, or both are zero, otherwise one of the vectors $\mathbf{x}_1, \mathbf{x}_2$ is zero, contradicting the assumption that both are non-zero. If both the coefficients are non-zero, then the vectors $\mathbf{x}_1, \mathbf{x}_2$ are simply proportional to each other, which means that they are parallel, in contradiction with the assumption that they are not. Therefore, both the coefficients $(\lambda - \lambda_1)$ and $(\mu - \mu_1)$ must vanish, proving that the linear combination of $\mathbf{x}_1$ and $\mathbf{x}_2$ which equals $\mathbf{a}$ is unique. This also means that a given linear combination specifies a unique vector $\mathbf{a}$. Now let $\mathbf{a}$ equal a linear combination of three non-zero and non-coplanar[2] vectors, say $\mathbf{a} = \lambda_1\mathbf{x}_1 + \lambda_2\mathbf{x}_2 + \lambda_3\mathbf{x}_3$. We know that the first two terms in this linear combination add up to a unique vector say $\mathbf{x}_{12} = \lambda_1\mathbf{x}_1 + \lambda_2\mathbf{x}_2$. Therefore, we can equivalently write this linear combination as $\mathbf{a} = \mathbf{x}_{12} + \lambda_3\mathbf{x}_3$ involving only two vectors which are not collinear because three vectors $\mathbf{x}_1, \mathbf{x}_2, \mathbf{x}_3$ are not coplanar, so that we know it to be unique. This fixes the coefficient λ_3 and hence makes the linear combination of three vectors giving $\mathbf{a}$ unique. Iterating the same argument we can show that a linear combination of non-zero, non-parallel and non-coplanar N vectors which equals $\mathbf{a}$ is unique. □

Exercise The *center of mass* of the vertices of a tetrahedron $PQRS$ (each with unit mass) may be defined as the point dividing MS in the ratio $1 : 3$, where M is the center of mass of the vertices PQR. Show that this definition is independent of the order in which the vertices are taken and it agrees with the general definition of the center of mass.

---

[2] Note that if three vectors are non-coplanar, then no two of them can be parallel.

Solution   Let $\mathbf{p}, \mathbf{q}, \mathbf{r}, \mathbf{s}, \mathbf{m}$ be the position vectors of the points P, Q, R, S, M respectively. Take the origin O at the point dividing MS in the ratio $1 : 3$. Thus, $\mathbf{s} = -3\mathbf{m}$. Since $\mathbf{m} = 1/3(\mathbf{p} + \mathbf{q} + \mathbf{r})$, it follows that

$$\frac{1}{4}(\mathbf{p} + \mathbf{q} + \mathbf{r} + \mathbf{s}) = \mathbf{0}.$$

Thus, O is the center of mass by the general definition and clearly does not depend on the order of the vertices.   □

Exercise   Two edges of a tetrahedron are called opposite if they have no vertex in common. For example, the edges PQ and RS of the tetrahedron of the previous exercise are opposite. Show that the segment joining the midpoints of opposite edges of a tetrahedron passes through the center of mass of the vertices.

Solution   Let the edges be PQ and RS so that in the notation of the preceding solution their midpoints have position vectors $\frac{1}{2}(\mathbf{p}+\mathbf{q})$ and $\frac{1}{2}(\mathbf{r}+\mathbf{s})$ respectively. From the solution to the previous exercise $\frac{1}{2}(\mathbf{p} + \mathbf{q}) = -\frac{1}{2}(\mathbf{r} + \mathbf{s})$; hence, the midpoints are collinear with center of mass O and equidistant from it.   □

Exercise   Let $\mathbf{a}_1, \mathbf{a}_2, \ldots, \mathbf{a}_n$ be the position vectors of n particles in space, with respect to the origin at the center of mass G of this system, with masses $m_1, m_2, \ldots, m_n$ respectively. Show that

$$m_1\mathbf{a}_1 + m_2\mathbf{a}_2 + \cdots + m_n\mathbf{a}_n = \mathbf{0}.$$

Solution   By definition, the left side gives the position vector of the center of mass G, which is chosen to be zero.   □

Collinear and coplanar vectors

Two non-zero vectors are *collinear* if they have same or opposite directions. Two such vectors can be made to lie on the same line because a line accommodates two opposite directions (orientations). Obviously, two collinear vectors $\mathbf{a}$ and $\mathbf{b}$ are proportional to each other: $\mathbf{b} = k\mathbf{a}$ with $|\mathbf{b}| = |k||\mathbf{a}|$ and $k > 0$ ($k < 0$) corresponds to the two vectors in the same (opposite) direction(s). We have to differentiate between collinear vectors we have just defined and the collinear points in space which are points lying on the same line.

Three non-zero vectors are *coplanar* if they lie or can be made to lie in the same plane. Three vectors are non-coplanar if they are not coplanar. Let $\mathbf{a}, \mathbf{b}, \mathbf{c}$ be three non-zero vectors such that $\mathbf{c}$ can be resolved along $\mathbf{a}$ and $\mathbf{b}$ so that $\mathbf{c}$ is a linear combination

$$\mathbf{c} = \alpha\mathbf{a} + \beta\mathbf{b} \tag{1.1}$$

for some non-zero scalars α and β. This means, the vectors $\mathbf{c}$, $\alpha\mathbf{a}$ and $\beta\mathbf{b}$ form a triangle. Since triangle is a planar figure, we conclude that vectors $\mathbf{a}, \mathbf{b}, \mathbf{c}$ are coplanar. More useful form of Eq. (1.1) is

$$\alpha\mathbf{a} + \beta\mathbf{b} + \gamma\mathbf{c} = \mathbf{0}. \tag{1.2}$$

On the other hand if $\mathbf{a}, \mathbf{b}, \mathbf{c}$ are given to be coplanar, it is possible to resolve one of them along the other two vectors, as shown at the beginning of this subsection, so that they satisfy Eq. (1.1) or Eq. (1.2) with α, β, γ not all zero. Thus, three non-zero vectors are coplanar if and only if they satisfy Eq. (1.2) with two or more non-zero coefficients. It follows immediately that if three non-zero vectors satisfy Eq. (1.2) only when all the coefficients are zero, then they aught to be non-coplanar.

Exercise   Show that three points with position vectors $\mathbf{a}, \mathbf{b}, \mathbf{c}$ are collinear if and only if there exist three non-zero scalars α, β, γ, $\alpha \neq \pm\beta$, such that

$$\alpha\mathbf{a} + \beta\mathbf{b} + \gamma\mathbf{c} = \mathbf{0}$$

and

$$\alpha + \beta + \gamma = 0.$$

Hint   From a previous exercise we can infer that if three points are collinear, the position vector of the middle point is $\mathbf{b} = \frac{\alpha\mathbf{c}+\gamma\mathbf{a}}{\alpha+\gamma}$ giving $\gamma\mathbf{a} + \alpha\mathbf{c} = (\alpha + \gamma)\mathbf{b}$ or $\beta + \alpha + \gamma = 0$. If the given conditions are assumed, we can show that $\mathbf{b}$ divides the line joining $\mathbf{a}$ and $\mathbf{c}$ in the ratio $\alpha : \gamma$. $\qquad\square$

Exercise   Four points P, Q, R, S have position vectors $\mathbf{a}, \mathbf{b}, \mathbf{c}, \mathbf{d}$ respectively, no three of which are collinear. Show that P, Q, R, S are coplanar if and only if there exist four scalars $\alpha, \beta, \gamma, \delta$ not all zero, satisfying

$$\alpha\mathbf{a} + \beta\mathbf{b} + \gamma\mathbf{c} + \delta\mathbf{d} = \mathbf{0} \text{ and } \alpha + \beta + \gamma + \delta = 0. \tag{1.3}$$

Solution   Let the given P, Q, R, S be coplanar and let the lines PQ and RS intersect at A with position vector $\mathbf{r}$, such that $PA : AQ = \lambda/\mu$ and $RA : AS = \rho/\tau$. By previous exercise this gives,

$$\frac{\mu\mathbf{a} + \lambda\mathbf{b}}{\lambda + \mu} = \mathbf{r} = \frac{\tau\mathbf{d} + \rho\mathbf{c}}{\rho + \tau},$$

or

$$\frac{\mu}{\lambda+\mu}\mathbf{a} + \frac{\lambda}{\lambda+\mu}\mathbf{b} - \frac{\rho}{\rho+\tau}\mathbf{c} - \frac{\rho}{\rho+\tau}\mathbf{d} = \mathbf{0}.$$

Replacing the coefficients by $\alpha, \beta, \gamma, \delta$ we see that conditions in Eq. (1.3) are satisfied. The proof of sufficiency is left to you. $\qquad\square$

Vector methods employed to prove simple results in Euclidean geometry may be found in [23].

1.4.2   Examples of vector addition

In this book we will draw examples from physics and engineering. This particularly suits vectors as vectors are almost exclusively used in physics and engineering.

As our first example, we calculate the acceleration of a particle of mass 0.2 kg moving on a frictionless, horizontal and rectangular table when subjected to a force of $\mathbf{F}_1 = 3$N along the breadth and $\mathbf{F}_2 = 4$N along the length of the table. We know that forces are vector quantities and the force $\mathbf{F}$ experienced by a particle subjected to several forces $\mathbf{F}_1, \mathbf{F}_2, \ldots, \mathbf{F}_N$ is simply the sum $\mathbf{F}_1 + \mathbf{F}_2 + \cdots + \mathbf{F}_N$. Thus, the force on the particle is $\mathbf{F} = \mathbf{F}_1 + \mathbf{F}_2$ and the magnitude of the resultant $\mathbf{F}$ is $|\mathbf{F}| = (F_1^2 + F_2^2)^{\frac{1}{2}} = 5$N and acts in a direction making angle ϕ with the breadth of the table where $\tan \phi = \frac{4}{3}$ (see Fig. 1.12). By Newton's law, $\mathbf{F} = m\mathbf{a}$, so the acceleration is in the same direction, with the magnitude $F/m = 25$ m/s/s.

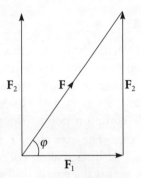

Fig. 1.12   Addition of forces to get the resultant.

In our second example we make use of the following principle. If an observer moving with velocity $\mathbf{v}_0$ with respect to the ground sees an object moving with an apparent velocity $\mathbf{v}_a$, then the velocity of the object with respect to ground say $\mathbf{v}_g$ is $\mathbf{v}_g = \mathbf{v}_a + \mathbf{v}_0$. Thus, consider a tank travelling due north at $\mathbf{v}_0 = 10$ m/s firing a shell at $\mathbf{v}_a = 200$ m/s in a direction which appears due west to an observer on the tank. Then, the ground velocity of the shell $\mathbf{v}_g$ has the magnitude $v_g = (200^2 + 10^2)^{\frac{1}{2}} = 205$ m/s and a direction making an angle ϕ north of due west where $\tan \phi = 10/200 = 0.05$ (see Fig. 1.13(a)). A more relevant question is to ask about the direction in which the gun should be aimed so as to hit a target due west of the tank. Here, the gun must be fired in a direction θ south of due west so that the total velocity is in the direction due west. Consulting Fig. 1.13(b) we see that the required angle is given by $\sin \theta = 0.05$.

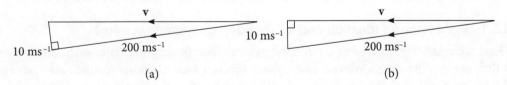

Fig. 1.13   (a) The velocity of a shell fired from a moving tank relative to the ground. (b) The southward angle θ at which the shell will fire from a moving tank so that its resulting velocity is due west.

Exercise   A river flows with a speed of 1 m/s. A boy wishes to swim across the river to the point exactly opposite to him on the other bank. He can swim relative to water at the speed of 2 m/s. At what angle θ should he aim relative to the bank?   □

Exercise   You travel from A to B with velocity $30\hat{\mathbf{i}}$ and travel back from B to A with velocity $-70\hat{\mathbf{i}}$, both measured in the same units. Find your (a) average velocity (b) average speed.

Answer   (a) **0** because the net displacement is **0**. (b) Average speed = distance travelled/time of travel = 42.   □

1.5   Coordinate Systems

Consider any three *non-coplanar* vectors based at a point in space. We call these vectors $\hat{\mathbf{i}}, \hat{\mathbf{j}}, \hat{\mathbf{k}}$. These vectors need not be mutually perpendicular, (orthogonal), vectors, but in most of the applications they are taken to be so. We will take these to be unit vectors, although this also is not necessary. Draw straight lines passing through these vectors. These lines pass through a single common point, (the point at which three vectors are based) and are called coordinate axes. The axes along $\hat{\mathbf{i}}, \hat{\mathbf{j}}, \hat{\mathbf{k}}$ are conventionally called x,y and z axes respectively. Such a set of lines, called *coordinate lines*, forms a *coordinate system*. The point common to all axes is the origin of the coordinate system, which is the point corresponding to zero vector. The planes defined by $(\hat{\mathbf{i}}, \hat{\mathbf{j}}), (\hat{\mathbf{j}}, \hat{\mathbf{k}})$ and $(\hat{\mathbf{k}}, \hat{\mathbf{i}})$ are called the *coordinate planes*. Since $\hat{\mathbf{i}}, \hat{\mathbf{j}}, \hat{\mathbf{k}}$ are any three non-coplanar vectors, we can have infinite such triplets of vectors based at origin, each resulting in a coordinate system. Thus, there are infinite coordinate systems based at the same origin. Given a coordinate system with its origin at some point in space, we can translate it, without rotating its axes, to some other point in space. Similarly, we can construct a new coordinate system with its origin displaced from that of the first one by a vector **X** with some new triplet of non-coplanar vectors based at the new origin. Note that, we can choose appropriate translation and rotation of any one of these coordinate systems to make it coincide with the remaining one, provided the corresponding coordinate axes can be made parallel by rotation. This condition is obviously fulfilled, if the three vectors defining the coordinate systems are mutually orthogonal.

Exercise   Draw figures to illustrate everything that is said in the above paragraph.   □

1.5.1   Right-handed (dextral) and left-handed coordinate systems

Here, we restrict ourselves to coordinate systems comprising mutually orthogonal axes which are straight lines. We call such systems rectangular *Cartesian coordinate systems*. All we have said in the above paragraph still leaves a gap in the complete specification of a coordinate system, given the axes x, y, z. Each of the vectors $\hat{\mathbf{i}}, \hat{\mathbf{j}}, \hat{\mathbf{k}}$ can be in one of the two possible directions along the corresponding axis. Which of the two possibilities we choose for each one of them? We need a relation between $\hat{\mathbf{i}}, \hat{\mathbf{j}}, \hat{\mathbf{k}}$ that will fix them. This is done by relating $\hat{\mathbf{k}}$ to the sense of rotation which takes $\hat{\mathbf{i}}$ towards $\hat{\mathbf{j}}$. Thus, the directions of

$\hat{\mathbf{i}}, \hat{\mathbf{j}}, \hat{\mathbf{k}}$ along their axes are chosen so that a rotation from $\hat{\mathbf{i}}$ to $\hat{\mathbf{j}}$ about z axis should advance a *right handed screw* in the direction of $\hat{\mathbf{k}}$ along the z axis. In the last statement you can cyclically permute $\hat{\mathbf{i}} \longrightarrow \hat{\mathbf{j}} \longrightarrow \hat{\mathbf{k}} \longrightarrow \hat{\mathbf{i}}$, with the corresponding change in the axis about which rotation takes place. The coordinate system so chosen is known as the *right handed* or *dextral* system. As against this, we can fix the $\hat{\mathbf{i}}, \hat{\mathbf{j}}, \hat{\mathbf{k}}$ vectors such that a rotation from $\hat{\mathbf{i}}$ towards $\hat{\mathbf{j}}$ advances a *left handed screw* in the direction of $\hat{\mathbf{k}}$. As you may know, the same sense of rotation advances right handed and left handed screws in opposite directions. This choice results in the *left handed* coordinate system. Having fixed the $\hat{\mathbf{i}}, \hat{\mathbf{j}}, \hat{\mathbf{k}}$ vectors, their directions are called the positive directions of the corresponding axes. All this is depicted in Fig. 1.14.

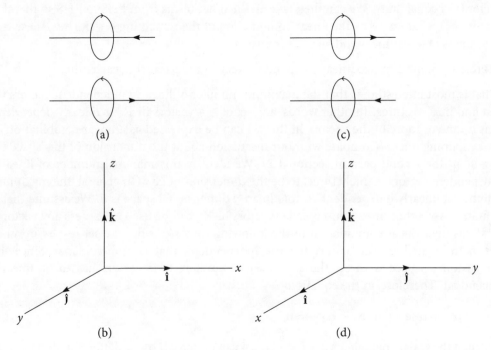

Fig. 1.14 (a) Left handed screw motion and (b) Left handed coordinate system. (c) Right handed screw motion and (d) Right handed (dextral) coordinate system. Try to construct other examples of the left and right handed coordinate systems.

1.6 Linear Independence, Basis

Why do we need the vectors $\hat{\mathbf{i}}, \hat{\mathbf{j}}, \hat{\mathbf{k}}$ to be *non-coplanar*? Because in that case, knowledge of one or two of them cannot be used to fix the remaining one(s), by combining the known ones using vector addition and multiplication by scalars. The most general linear combination we can prepare out of $\hat{\mathbf{i}}$ and $\hat{\mathbf{j}}$ say, is $\alpha_1\hat{\mathbf{i}} + \alpha_2\hat{\mathbf{j}}$ where α_1 and α_2 are scalars that we can choose. However, the vector $\alpha_1\hat{\mathbf{i}} + \alpha_2\hat{\mathbf{j}}$ is always in the plane defined by $\hat{\mathbf{i}}$ and $\hat{\mathbf{j}}$

(see subsection 1.4.1, Fig. 1.9) and can never be made to coincide with the non-coplanar vector $\hat{\mathbf{k}}$, irrespective of the values of α_1 and α_2 we choose. In other words, none of the non-coplanar vectors $\hat{\mathbf{i}}$, $\hat{\mathbf{j}}$, $\hat{\mathbf{k}}$ can be expressed as a linear combination of the remaining ones. Such a set of vectors is called a set of *linearly independent* vectors. If a set of vectors $\{\mathbf{v}_1, \mathbf{v}_2, \mathbf{v}_3\}$, $\mathbf{v}_i \neq \mathbf{0}$; $i = 1, 2, 3$ is linearly independent, then the equation

$$\alpha_1 \mathbf{v}_1 + \alpha_2 \mathbf{v}_2 + \alpha_3 \mathbf{v}_3 = \mathbf{0} \tag{1.4}$$

is satisfied only when all scalars are zero. Suppose $\alpha_i \neq 0$, $i \in \{1, 2, 3\}$ and still satisfies Eq. (1.4), (note that at least two of them have to be non-zero for this), then we can divide Eq. (1.4) by a non-zero coefficient (say α_1) making the coefficient of the corresponding vector ($\mathbf{v}_1$) equal unity. We can then take all the other terms from LHS to RHS so that this vector ($\mathbf{v}_1$) is expressed as the linear combination of the remaining ones. Thus, these two definitions of linear independence are equivalent.

Exercise   Show that two linearly dependent vectors are parallel to each other.   □

What is most interesting is that the maximum number of linearly independent vectors we can find in $\mathbb{R}^3$ is three. In other words, any set of ≥ 4 vectors in $\mathbb{R}^3$ is *linearly dependent*, that is, one or more of the vectors in this set can be expressed as a linear combination of the remaining ones. (Compare with our discussion about the dimension of the 'space we live in' in the second para of section 1.2). We identify this maximal number of linearly independent vectors, namely three, to be the *dimension* of $\mathbb{R}^3$. (In general, the maximum number of linearly independent vectors in an n dimensional space is n. We assume that n is finite). Any set of three non-coplanar vectors in $\mathbb{R}^3$ can be used to express any vector $\mathbf{v}$ in $\mathbb{R}^3$ as their linear combination in the following way. Consider the set $\{\mathbf{e}_1, \mathbf{e}_2, \mathbf{e}_3, \mathbf{v}\}$ of which the first three vectors are linearly independent, that is, non-coplanar. Since the dimension of space is three, the above set comprising four vectors has to be linearly dependent. Therefore, in the equation

$$\alpha_1 \mathbf{e}_1 + \alpha_2 \mathbf{e}_2 + \alpha_3 \mathbf{e}_3 + \alpha_4 \mathbf{v} = \mathbf{0},$$

not all of the scalar coefficients α_i, $i = 1, \ldots, 4$ can be zero. If $\alpha_4 = 0$, the equation reduces to

$$\alpha_1 \mathbf{e}_1 + \alpha_2 \mathbf{e}_2 + \alpha_3 \mathbf{e}_3 = \mathbf{0}$$

and not all these α's can be zero. This contradicts the fact that the set $\{\mathbf{e}_i,\ i = 1, 2, 3\}$ is linearly independent. Therefore, $\alpha_4 \neq 0$ and we can write

$$\mathbf{v} = \frac{-1}{\alpha_4} [\alpha_1 \mathbf{e}_1 + \alpha_2 \mathbf{e}_2 + \alpha_3 \mathbf{e}_3].$$

Note that we can trivially generalize this argument to any n dimensional space where the maximum number of linearly independent vectors is n.

We restrict ourselves to the case where the three linearly independent vectors $\hat{\mathbf{i}}, \hat{\mathbf{j}}, \hat{\mathbf{k}}$ are also mutually orthogonal, (although the following discussion in this section does not require it) and set up the corresponding Cartesian coordinate system. Given any vector $\mathbf{v}$ we want to find three scalars v_x, v_y and v_z such that the linear combination $v_x\hat{\mathbf{i}} + v_y\hat{\mathbf{j}} + v_z\hat{\mathbf{k}}$ equals $\mathbf{v}$. The successive terms in this linear combination are called the x, y, and z *components* of $\mathbf{v}$ or the components along the x, y, z axes respectively. The scalars v_x, v_y, v_z are the *coordinates* of the tip of the vector $\mathbf{v}$, (or the coordinates of $\mathbf{v}$ for brevity) based at the origin of the coordinate system corresponding to the mutually orthogonal unit vectors $\hat{\mathbf{i}}, \hat{\mathbf{j}}, \hat{\mathbf{k}}$ we have set up. (A way to get these coordinates is given in the next section). Given $\mathbf{v}$, the scalars v_x, v_y, v_z defined by the linear combination of $\mathbf{v}$ in terms of the three linearly independent vectors are unique. Suppose v_{x1}, v_{y1}, v_{z1} and v_{x2}, v_{y2}, v_{z2} are two sets of scalars such that both the corresponding linear combinations equal $\mathbf{v}$. This means

$$v_{x1}\hat{\mathbf{i}} + v_{y1}\hat{\mathbf{j}} + v_{z1}\hat{\mathbf{k}} = v_{x2}\hat{\mathbf{i}} + v_{y2}\hat{\mathbf{j}} + v_{z2}\hat{\mathbf{k}}$$

or,

$$(v_{x1} - v_{x2})\hat{\mathbf{i}} + (v_{y1} - v_{y2})\hat{\mathbf{j}} + (v_{z1} - v_{z2})\hat{\mathbf{k}} = \mathbf{0}.$$

Since $\hat{\mathbf{i}}, \hat{\mathbf{j}}, \hat{\mathbf{k}}$ are linearly independent, the last equation is satisfied only when $(v_{x1} - v_{x2}) = 0$ etc, that is, when $v_{x1} = v_{x2}, v_{y1} = v_{y2}$ and $v_{z1} = v_{z2}$. Thus, every vector in $\mathbb{R}^3$ corresponds to a unique triplet of scalars (real numbers, motivating the notation $\mathbb{R}^3$) *once we fix the mutually orthogonal set of vectors* $\hat{\mathbf{i}}, \hat{\mathbf{j}}, \hat{\mathbf{k}}$. (e.g., the triplet $0, 0, 0$ corresponds to the origin). The set of vectors $\{\hat{\mathbf{i}}, \hat{\mathbf{j}}, \hat{\mathbf{k}}\}$ has two properties: It is a maximal set of linearly independent vectors (i.e., contains three vectors) and every vector in $\mathbb{R}^3$ can be written as a unique linear combination of this set of vectors. Such a set of vectors is called a *basis*. Note that we may add a vector to the set of basis vectors and express every vector in $\mathbb{R}^3$ as a linear combination of this expanded set, but this linear combination can be written as a linear combination of the basis vectors alone, because the expanded set is a linearly dependent set of vectors. On the other hand, as we have seen above, given a linearly independent set smaller than a basis, we can find vectors that are not equal to any linear combination of vectors from this smaller set. Thus, a basis (that is, a maximal set of linearly independent vectors) is the minimal set of vectors required to span the space. Further, there are infinite possible bases as we can choose infinitely many sets of three mutually orthogonal vectors and each of them can be a basis, defining the corresponding coordinate system and the corresponding linear combinations for the vectors in $\mathbb{R}^3$. For different bases (coordinate systems), the linear combinations of basis vectors which equal a given vector are different, resulting in different coordinates for the same vector in different coordinate systems. A basis comprising three mutually orthogonal unit vectors is called an *orthonormal* basis.

Exercise   Let $\mathbf{a} = \sum_{k=1}^{3} \alpha_k \hat{\mathbf{i}}_k$ and $\mathbf{b} = \sum_{k=1}^{3} \beta_k \hat{\mathbf{i}}_k$ with respect to the same orthonormal basis $\{\hat{\mathbf{i}}_k\}$ $k = 1, 2, 3$. Show that $\mathbf{a} + \mathbf{b} = \sum_{k=1}^{3} (\alpha_k + \beta_k)\hat{\mathbf{i}}_k$.   □

Exercise   If any subset of a set of vectors is linearly dependent, then show that the whole set is linearly dependent.

Solution   Let $\{\mathbf{x}_i, \ i = 1,\ldots,k\}$ out of $\{\mathbf{x}_i, \ i = 1,\ldots,n\}$ $k < n$ be linearly dependent, so that $\sum_{i=1}^{k} \alpha_i \mathbf{x}_i = \mathbf{0}$ such that not all $\alpha_i = 0$. Consider $\sum_{i=1}^{k} \alpha_i \mathbf{x}_i + \sum_{j=k+1}^{n} 0\mathbf{x}_j = \mathbf{0}$ which is a linear combination of all the n vectors equated to zero such that not all the coefficients equal zero. Therefore, the whole set is linearly dependent.   □

From this result we conclude that every subset of a linearly independent set of vectors is linearly independent.   Thus, any three linearly independent vectors have to be non-coplanar, which in turn ensures that no two of them are collinear and hence no two of them are linearly dependent.

1.7   Scalar and Vector Products

Products of vectors can be defined in many ways, however, two definitions turn out to be physically significant. These are the so called scalar and the vector products. We learn about them one by one.   A third kind of product, called geometric product, unifies scalar and vector products, is defined on a set far larger than and containing the set of vectors called the set of multivectors and generates a beautiful algebra on this set[10, 7, 11]. However, we do not deal with multivectors and their geometric algebra in this book, as this will cause a long detour making us lose sight of our intended path and destinations.

1.7.1   Scalar product

We define a product of two vectors whose value is a scalar. Given two vectors $\mathbf{a}$ and $\mathbf{b}$ their *scalar* or *inner* or *dot* product is denoted $\mathbf{a} \cdot \mathbf{b}$ and is given by

$$\mathbf{a} \cdot \mathbf{b} = |\mathbf{a}||\mathbf{b}| \cos \theta = ab \cos \theta$$

where $a, |\mathbf{a}|$ $(b, |\mathbf{b}|)$ is the magnitude of $\mathbf{a}$ ($\mathbf{b}$) and θ is the angle between the directions of $\mathbf{a}$ and $\mathbf{b}$. (To get this angle, we have to base both the vectors at the same point). Note that the scalar product has different signs for $\theta < \pi/2$ and $\theta > \pi/2$. We can always take $\theta < \pi$ by choosing which direction is to be rotated counterclockwise towards which. If one of the two vectors (say $\hat{\mathbf{b}}$) is a unit vector, then $\mathbf{a} \cdot \hat{\mathbf{b}}$ is the projection of $\mathbf{a}$ on the direction defined by $\hat{\mathbf{b}}$. Thus, the scalar product is the product of the projection of $\mathbf{a}$ on the direction defined by $\hat{\mathbf{b}}$ with the magnitude of $\mathbf{b}$ which is the same as the product of the projection of $\mathbf{b}$ on the direction defined by $\hat{\mathbf{a}}$ with the magnitude of $\mathbf{a}$. This demonstrates the obvious symmetry of the result

$$\mathbf{a} \cdot \mathbf{b} = \mathbf{b} \cdot \mathbf{a}.$$

This shows that the dot product is commutative (see Fig. 1.15).

The magnitude of $\mathbf{a}$ is also called the *norm* of $\mathbf{a}$ and denoted $\|\mathbf{a}\|$. Note that $\mathbf{a} \cdot \mathbf{a} = a^2 = \|\mathbf{a}\|^2$ so that

$$\|\mathbf{a}\| = +\sqrt{\mathbf{a} \cdot \mathbf{a}}.$$

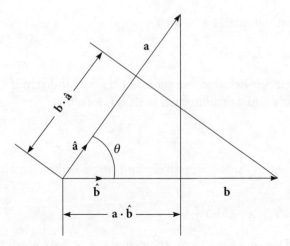

Fig. 1.15   Scalar product is commutative. The projections of **a** on **b** and **b** on **a** give respectively $\mathbf{a} \cdot \hat{\mathbf{b}} = |\mathbf{a}| \cos\theta$ and $\mathbf{b} \cdot \hat{\mathbf{a}} = |\mathbf{b}| \cos\theta$. Multiplication on both sides of the first equation by $|\mathbf{b}|$ and the second by $|\mathbf{a}|$ results in the symmetrical form $\mathbf{a} \cdot \mathbf{b} = |\mathbf{b}| \, \mathbf{a} \cdot \hat{\mathbf{b}} = |\mathbf{a}| \, \mathbf{b} \cdot \hat{\mathbf{a}}$

If **a** and **b** are parallel or antiparallel, their scalar product evaluates to $\pm ab$ respectively. In particular, $\mathbf{a} \cdot \mathbf{a} = a^2$.

If **a** and **b** are orthogonal,

$$\mathbf{a} \cdot \mathbf{b} = ab \cos\left(\frac{\pi}{2}\right) = 0.$$

Thus, the scalar product of two orthogonal vectors vanishes. Conversely, $\mathbf{a} \cdot \mathbf{b} = 0$ does not necessarily imply either $\mathbf{a} = \mathbf{0}$ or $\mathbf{b} = \mathbf{0}$.

The *inverse* of a non-zero vector **a** with respect to the dot product is

$$\mathbf{a}^{-1} = \frac{\mathbf{a}}{|\mathbf{a}|^2},$$

because $\mathbf{a}^{-1} \cdot \mathbf{a} = 1 = \mathbf{a} \cdot \mathbf{a}^{-1}$. We will denote by $\mathbf{a}^{-1}$ a vector like $\frac{\mathbf{a}}{|\mathbf{a}|^2}$ even if it does not occur as a factor in a dot product.

Exercise   Let **a** and **b** be two non-zero non-parallel vectors. Show that

$$\mathbf{c} = \mathbf{a} - \frac{\mathbf{a} \cdot \mathbf{b}}{|\mathbf{b}|^2}\mathbf{b} = \mathbf{a} - \mathbf{a} \cdot \mathbf{b}\mathbf{b}^{-1}$$

is perpendicular to **b**. The vector **c** is called the component of **a** perpendicular to **b**.

Solution   Note that $\mathbf{c} \neq \mathbf{0}$, otherwise **a** will be proportional to **b**, contradicting the assumption that they are not parallel. Now check that $\mathbf{b} \cdot \mathbf{c} = 0$.   □

If $\hat{\mathbf{i}}_1, \hat{\mathbf{i}}_2, \hat{\mathbf{i}}_3$ is an orthonormal basis, then

$$\hat{\mathbf{i}}_k \cdot \hat{\mathbf{i}}_l = \delta_{kl}; \; k, l = 1, 2, 3 \tag{1.5}$$

where δ_{kl} is the Kronecker delta, whose value is 1 if $k = l$ and zero if $k \neq l$.
   Consider a vector $\mathbf{v}$ and a orthonormal basis $\hat{\mathbf{i}}, \hat{\mathbf{j}}, \hat{\mathbf{k}}$ so that

$$\mathbf{v} = v_x \hat{\mathbf{i}} + v_y \hat{\mathbf{j}} + v_z \hat{\mathbf{k}}. \tag{1.6}$$

Dotting both sides with $\hat{\mathbf{i}}, \hat{\mathbf{j}}, \hat{\mathbf{k}}$ successively and using orthonormality of the basis (Eq. (1.5)), we get,

$$v_s = \mathbf{v} \cdot \hat{\mathbf{n}} \, ; \; s = x, y, z \, ; \; \hat{\mathbf{n}} = \hat{\mathbf{i}}, \hat{\mathbf{j}}, \hat{\mathbf{k}}. \tag{1.7}$$

Thus, coordinates of $\mathbf{v}$ along x, y, z axes (namely v_x, v_y, v_z) are given by its projections on these axes. If we put $\mathbf{v} = \mathbf{0}$ in Eq. (1.6), by Eq. (1.7) we get $v_s = 0$; $s = x, y, z$. This means that any orthogonal triplet of vectors is linearly independent.

Exercise   Show that $n > 1$ mutually orthogonal non-zero vectors are linearly independent.

Solution   Let $\{e_k, \; k = 1, \ldots, n\}$ be mutually orthogonal non-zero vectors, so that

$$\mathbf{e}_i \cdot \mathbf{e}_j = \delta_{ij} |\mathbf{e}_j|^2,$$

where δ_{ij} is the Kronecker delta. Consider the equation

$$\alpha_1 \mathbf{e}_1 + \alpha_2 \mathbf{e}_2 + \cdots + \alpha_n \mathbf{e}_n = \mathbf{0}$$

and take its scalar product successively with $\mathbf{e}_i$, $i = 1, \ldots, n$ to get $\alpha_i = 0$, $i = 1, \ldots, n$. Note that the converse is not true. We conclude that any four or more vectors in $\mathcal{E}_3$ cannot be mutually perpendicular.   □

Direction cosines

Given a vector $\mathbf{v}$ and an orthonormal basis $\hat{\mathbf{i}}_1, \hat{\mathbf{i}}_2, \hat{\mathbf{i}}_3$ we define the quantities

$$\xi_k = \frac{\mathbf{v} \cdot \hat{\mathbf{i}}_k}{\|\mathbf{v}\|} = \frac{v_k}{\|\mathbf{v}\|} = \hat{\mathbf{v}} \cdot \hat{\mathbf{i}}_k, \quad k = 1, 2, 3.$$

If $\alpha_1, \alpha_2, \alpha_3$ are the angles made by the direction of $\mathbf{v}$ with $\hat{\mathbf{i}}_1, \hat{\mathbf{i}}_2, \hat{\mathbf{i}}_3$ respectively, then

$$\xi_k = \cos \alpha_k, \quad k = 1, 2, 3.$$

ξ_k are called the *direction cosines* of the vector $\mathbf{v}$ with respect to the orthonormal basis $\hat{\mathbf{i}}_1, \hat{\mathbf{i}}_2, \hat{\mathbf{i}}_3$. Direction cosines unambiguously specify the direction of a non-zero vector. In particular, two or more vectors having the same direction cosines with respect to some orthonormal basis have the same directions. The only vector with all the direction cosines zero and hence having no direction, is the zero vector. Note that the coordinates of a unit vector are its direction cosines:

$$\hat{\mathbf{v}} = \xi_1\hat{\mathbf{i}}_1 + \xi_2\hat{\mathbf{i}}_2 + \xi_3\hat{\mathbf{i}}_3 \equiv (\xi_1, \xi_2, \xi_3) = (\cos\alpha_1, \cos\alpha_2, \cos\alpha_3),$$

where $\alpha_1, \alpha_2, \alpha_3$ are the angles made by $\hat{\mathbf{v}}$ with $\hat{\mathbf{i}}_1, \hat{\mathbf{i}}_2, \hat{\mathbf{i}}_3$ respectively, or with the positive directions of the x, y, z-axes respectively.

Distributive property

The dot product is distributive, that is,

$$(\alpha_1\mathbf{a}_1 + \alpha_2\mathbf{a}_2) \cdot \mathbf{b} = \alpha_1\,\mathbf{a}_1 \cdot \mathbf{b} + \alpha_2\,\mathbf{a}_2 \cdot \mathbf{b}.$$

This is seen from Fig. 1.16 where the projection of $(\alpha_1\mathbf{a}_1 + \alpha_2\mathbf{a}_2)$ on $\mathbf{b}$ equals the sum of the projections of $\alpha_1\mathbf{a}_1$ and $\alpha_2\mathbf{a}_2$ on $\mathbf{b}$. From Fig. 1.16 we get,

$$
\begin{aligned}
\alpha_1\mathbf{a}_1 \cdot \mathbf{b} + \alpha_2\mathbf{a}_2 \cdot \mathbf{b} &= (\alpha_1\mathbf{a}_1 \cdot \hat{\mathbf{b}} + \alpha_2\mathbf{a}_2 \cdot \hat{\mathbf{b}})|\mathbf{b}| \\
&= ((\alpha_1\mathbf{a}_1 + \alpha_2\mathbf{a}_2) \cdot \hat{\mathbf{b}})|\mathbf{b}| \\
&= (\alpha_1\mathbf{a}_1 + \alpha_2\mathbf{a}_2) \cdot \mathbf{b}
\end{aligned}
$$

Note that the vectors $\mathbf{a}_1, \mathbf{a}_2$ need not be coplanar with $\mathbf{b}$.

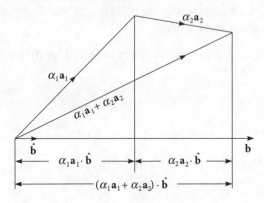

Fig. 1.16   The scalar product is distributive with respect to addition

We can use the distributive property of the dot product to express it in terms of the coordinates of the factors with respect to an orthogonal Cartesian coordinate system. Thus, let $\{x_1, x_2, x_3\}$ and $\{y_1, y_2, y_3\}$ be the coordinates of vectors $\mathbf{a}$ and $\mathbf{b}$ with respect to an orthogonal Cartesian coordinate system. Then we have,

$$
\begin{aligned}
\mathbf{a} \cdot \mathbf{b} &= (x_1\hat{\mathbf{i}}_1 + y_1\hat{\mathbf{i}}_2 + z_1\hat{\mathbf{i}}_3) \cdot (x_2\hat{\mathbf{i}}_1 + y_2\hat{\mathbf{i}}_2 + z_2\hat{\mathbf{i}}_3) \\
&= x_1x_2 + y_1y_2 + z_1z_2
\end{aligned}
$$

where we have used the distributive property and Eq. (1.5), that is, orthonormality of the basis. This is the desired result. Note that for unit vectors $\hat{\mathbf{a}}$ and $\hat{\mathbf{b}}$, we can replace the LHS of this equation by $\cos\theta$, θ being the angle between $\hat{\mathbf{a}}$ and $\hat{\mathbf{b}}$, and their coordinates by their respective direction cosines, say, $(\lambda_1, \mu_1, \nu_1)$ and $(\lambda_2, \mu_2, \nu_2)$. Thus, we get

$$\cos\theta = \lambda_1\lambda_2 + \mu_1\mu_2 + \nu_1\nu_2.$$

This equation expresses the well known relation in Solid Geometry that the cosine of the angle between two straight lines equals the sum of the products of the pairs of cosines of the angles made by the straight lines with each of the three (mutually perpendicular) coordinate axes.

Exercise (law of cosines) Consider triangle ABC. We denote by A, B, C the angles subtended at the vertices A, B, C respectively. Let a, b, c be the lengths of the sides opposite to the vertices A, B, C respectively (see Fig. 1.10). Show that

$$c^2 = a^2 + b^2 - 2ab\cos C.$$

which is true for any triangle.

Hint Let $\mathbf{a} = \vec{BC}, \mathbf{b} = \vec{CA}, \mathbf{c} = \vec{BA}$. Then $\mathbf{c} = \mathbf{a} + \mathbf{b}$ so that $c^2 = \mathbf{c}\cdot\mathbf{c} = (\mathbf{a}+\mathbf{b})\cdot(\mathbf{a}+\mathbf{b})$. Now use the distributive property and the definition of the dot product. When $C = \frac{\pi}{2}$, we recover the Pythagoras theorem.   □

Exercise Let P and Q be diametrically opposite points and R any other point on a sphere. Show that PR and QR are at right angles.

Solution Take the origin at the center of the sphere and let $\mathbf{p}, \mathbf{q}, \mathbf{r}$ be the position vectors of P, Q, R respectively. We have,

$$|\mathbf{p}|^2 = |\mathbf{q}|^2 = |\mathbf{r}|^2,$$

each equal to the square of the radius and $\mathbf{q} = -\mathbf{p}$. Consequently, (see Fig. 1.17),

$$(\mathbf{r}-\mathbf{p})\cdot(\mathbf{r}-\mathbf{q}) = (\mathbf{r}-\mathbf{p})\cdot(\mathbf{r}+\mathbf{p}) = |\mathbf{r}|^2 - |\mathbf{p}|^2 = 0.$$ □

Polar coordinates

Let us find a way to get the coordinates $v_x = \mathbf{v}\cdot\hat{\mathbf{i}}, v_y = \mathbf{v}\cdot\hat{\mathbf{j}}, v_z = \mathbf{v}\cdot\hat{\mathbf{k}}$ of a vector $\mathbf{v}$ based at the origin of a dextral rectangular Cartesian coordinate system. You have to refer to Fig. 1.18 to understand whatever is said until Eq. (1.8). Let $\mathbf{v}$ make angle θ with the positive direction of the z axis. this angle is called the *polar* angle. Take the projection of $\mathbf{v}$ on the $x - y$ plane and call the resulting vector $\mathbf{v}_p$. Let the angle made by $\mathbf{v}_p$ with the positive direction of the x axis be ϕ. This angle is called the *azimuthal* angle. The magnitude v_p of $\mathbf{v}_p$ is $v\cos(\frac{\pi}{2} - \theta) = v\sin\theta$. Project $\mathbf{v}_p$ on x axis to get $v_x = v_p\cos\phi = v\sin\theta\cos\phi$. Project $\mathbf{v}_p$ on y axis to get $v_y = v_p\cos(\frac{\pi}{2} - \phi) = v_p\sin\phi = v\sin\theta\sin\phi$. Now project $\mathbf{v}$ on z axis to get $v_z = v\cos\theta$. Thus the equation,

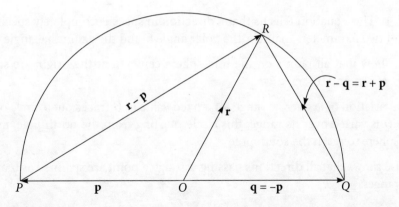

Fig. 1.17 Lines joining a point on a sphere with two diametrically opposite points are perpendicular

$$\mathbf{v} = v_x\hat{\mathbf{i}} + v_y\hat{\mathbf{j}} + v_z\hat{\mathbf{k}}$$

can be written as

$$\mathbf{v} = v\sin\theta\cos\phi\hat{\mathbf{i}} + v\sin\theta\sin\phi\hat{\mathbf{j}} + v\cos\theta\hat{\mathbf{k}}. \qquad (1.8)$$

If we use in Eq. (1.8) the unit vector $\hat{\mathbf{v}}$ specifying the direction of $\mathbf{v}$ we get

$$\hat{\mathbf{v}} = \sin\theta\cos\phi\hat{\mathbf{i}} + \sin\theta\sin\phi\hat{\mathbf{j}} + \cos\theta\hat{\mathbf{k}}.$$

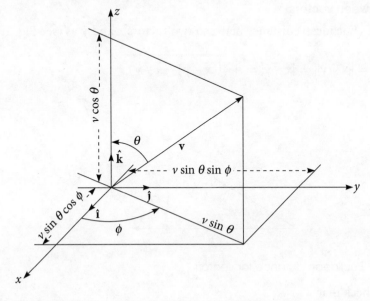

Fig. 1.18 Getting coordinates of a vector $\mathbf{v}$ (see text)

since $|\hat{\mathbf{v}}| = 1$. This equation tells us that a direction in space is completely specified fixing the values of two parameters, namely, the polar angle θ and the azimuthal angle ϕ.

Exercise   Show that all points on the unit sphere centered at the origin are scanned by varying $0 \le \theta \le \pi$ and $0 \le \phi < 2\pi$.

Solution   Variation of ϕ over its range for a fixed value of θ traces out a circle on the unit sphere. As θ is varied over its range, this circle, starting from the north pole, moves over the whole sphere to reach the south pole.   □

This exercise shows that all directions passing through a point are spanned as θ and ϕ vary over their ranges.

Cauchy–Schwarz inequality

In $\mathbb{R}^3$ Cauchy–Schwarz inequality is almost obvious. For any two vectors $\mathbf{x}$ and $\mathbf{y}$ we have

$$|\mathbf{x} \cdot \mathbf{y}| = \|\mathbf{x}\| \, \|\mathbf{y}\| \, |\cos\theta| \le \|\mathbf{x}\| \, \|\mathbf{y}\|.$$

because $|\cos\theta| \le 1$. Thus,

$$|\mathbf{x} \cdot \mathbf{y}| \le \|\mathbf{x}\| \, \|\mathbf{y}\|,$$

which is Schwarz Inequality. Schwarz inequality is extremely useful in obtaining various properties of vectors.

Distance between vectors

We define the (Euclidean) distance between two vectors $\mathbf{x}$ and $\mathbf{y}$ as (see Fig. 1.19),

$$d(\mathbf{x}, \mathbf{y}) = \|\mathbf{x} - \mathbf{y}\| = |\mathbf{x} - \mathbf{y}| = +\sqrt{(\mathbf{x} - \mathbf{y}) \cdot (\mathbf{x} - \mathbf{y})}. \tag{1.9}$$

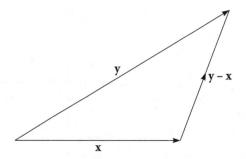

Fig. 1.19   Euclidean distance for vectors

Exercise   Check that

$$d^2(\mathbf{x}, \mathbf{y}) = \sum_{k=1}^{3} (x_k - y_k)^2,$$

where $\mathbf{x} \equiv (x_1, x_2, x_3)$ and $\mathbf{y} \equiv (y_1, y_2, y_3)$. $\qquad \square$

In order for $d(\mathbf{x}, \mathbf{y})$ to be called a distance (or a distance function), it should have the following properties.

(i) $d(\mathbf{x}, \mathbf{y}) = d(\mathbf{y}, \mathbf{x})$.

(ii) $d(\mathbf{x}, \mathbf{y}) \geq 0$; $d(\mathbf{x}, \mathbf{y}) = 0$ if and only if $\mathbf{x} = \mathbf{y}$.

(iii) $d(\mathbf{x}, \mathbf{y}) \leq d(\mathbf{x}, \mathbf{z}) + d(\mathbf{z}, \mathbf{y})$. This property is called triangle inequality.

(iv) $d(\mathbf{x}, \mathbf{y}) = d(\mathbf{x} + \mathbf{z}, \mathbf{y} + \mathbf{z})$.

Properties (i), (ii) and (iv) are obvious from the definition of $d(\mathbf{x}, \mathbf{y})$. We need to prove property (iii). Here is the proof.

We observe that

$$
\begin{aligned}
\|\mathbf{x} + \mathbf{y}\|^2 &= (\mathbf{x} + \mathbf{y}) \cdot (\mathbf{x} + \mathbf{y}) \\
&= \|\mathbf{x}\|^2 + 2\mathbf{x} \cdot \mathbf{y} + \|\mathbf{y}\|^2 \\
&\leq \|\mathbf{x}\|^2 + 2|\mathbf{x} \cdot \mathbf{y}| + \|\mathbf{y}\|^2
\end{aligned}
$$

The last expression can now be tamed using Schwarz inequality, so that

$$
\|\mathbf{x} + \mathbf{y}\|^2 \leq \|\mathbf{x}\|^2 + 2\|\mathbf{x}\|\,\|\mathbf{y}\| + \|\mathbf{y}\|^2 = (\|\mathbf{x}\| + \|\mathbf{y}\|)^2.
$$

Now replace $\mathbf{x}$ by $\mathbf{x} - \mathbf{z}$ and $\mathbf{y}$ by $\mathbf{z} - \mathbf{y}$ in the above inequality to get

$$
\|\mathbf{x} - \mathbf{y}\| \leq \|\mathbf{x} - \mathbf{z}\| + \|\mathbf{z} - \mathbf{y}\|
$$

and this is the same as property (iii). $\qquad \square$

Exercise Let $\hat{\mathbf{x}}$ and $\hat{\mathbf{y}}$ be two unit vectors. Show that distance between them is $\sqrt{2 - 2\cos\theta}$ where θ is the angle between $\hat{\mathbf{x}}$ and $\hat{\mathbf{y}}$. If $\hat{\mathbf{x}}$ and $\hat{\mathbf{y}}$ are mutually orthogonal, the distance between them is $\sqrt{2}$, consistent with the Pythagoras theorem. When $\mathbf{x}$ and $\mathbf{y}$ are not unit vectors,

$$
d(\mathbf{x}, \mathbf{y}) = \sqrt{\|\mathbf{x}\|^2 + \|\mathbf{y}\|^2 - 2\|\mathbf{x}\|\,\|\mathbf{y}\| \cos\theta}.
$$

Hint These results follow directly from the previous exercise in which you proved law of cosines. $\qquad \square$

Exercise Show that (a) $|\mathbf{a} + \mathbf{b}| \leq |\mathbf{a}| + |\mathbf{b}|$ and (b) $|\mathbf{a} - \mathbf{b}| \geq \big||\mathbf{a}| - |\mathbf{b}|\big|$.

Solution Part (a) is simply the statement of triangle inequality for the triangle formed by the vectors $\mathbf{a}, \mathbf{b}, \mathbf{a} + \mathbf{b}$. To get (b), we write $|\mathbf{a}| = |(\mathbf{a} - \mathbf{b}) + \mathbf{b}|$ and apply (a) to get $|\mathbf{a} - \mathbf{b}| + |\mathbf{b}| \geq |\mathbf{a}|$, or, $|\mathbf{a} - \mathbf{b}| \geq |\mathbf{a}| - |\mathbf{b}|$. If $|\mathbf{a}| > |\mathbf{b}|$, (b) follows. Otherwise interchange $\mathbf{a}$ and $\mathbf{b}$. $\qquad \square$

A distance function obeying conditions (i)–(iv) above is called a metric. The distance between two vectors, as we have defined via Eq. (1.9), is called the *Euclidean metric.* In 3-D space, it follows from its definition that the curve with minimum Euclidean distance joining two points is a straight line. Given a smooth surface in 3-D space (see section 10.12), the curve with 'shortest distance' joining two points on the surface is constrained to lie wholly on the surface. This restriction does not allow, in general, the curve with the shortest distance on a surface to be a straight line. However, given a smooth surface S, we can find a unique curve with shortest distance joining two distinct points on the surface, called a *geodesic* on S. Thus, if we stretch a thread between two points on a sphere S then this thread will lie along a great circle joining these two points and this is a geodesic on the sphere.

1.7.2   Physical applications of the scalar product

Consider the displacement **d** of an object under the action of a force **F**. The resulting work done by the force on the object, W, is the product of the displacement and the component of the force in the diction of displacement or, alternatively, product of the force and the component of the displacement in the diction of the force. From Fig. 1.20 this is

$$W = (F\cos\theta)d = Fd\cos\theta = \mathbf{F}\cdot\mathbf{d}.$$

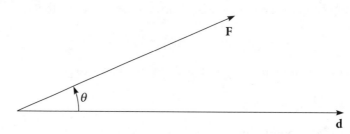

Fig. 1.20   Work done on an object as it is displaced by **d** under the action of force **F**

Exercise   A horse tows a barge along a two-path walking at 1 m/s. The tension in the rope is 300N and the angle between the rope and the walk direction is 30°. How much work is done by the horse per second? (That is, find the power produced by the horse).   ☐

When the work is done on the object, its energy is increased. This energy may be kinetic (if the object accelerates) or potential (e.g., energy stored due to the change of position) or it may be dissipated while doing work against frictional (dissipative) forces. Thus energy, in whatever form, is a scalar quantity. In many cases the potential energy is written as the scalar product of vector quantities. Examples are the potential energy of an electric dipole **p** in an electric field $\mathcal{E}$, (see Fig. 1.21)

$$V = -\mathbf{p}\cdot\mathcal{E}$$

and the potential energy of a magnetic dipole of moment μ in a magnetic field **B**

$$V = -\mu\cdot\mathbf{B}.$$

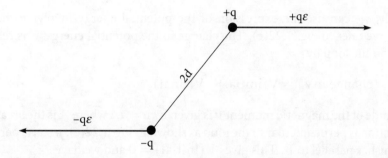

Fig. 1.21   Potential energy of an electric dipole p in an electric field $\mathcal{E}$

As an example, consider a square loop of wire of side L carrying a current i placed in a magnetic field B with the plane of the loop parallel to the field. Two possible realizations are depicted in Figs 1.22(a) and 1.22(b). We explicitly calculate the work done by the force due to the magnetic field B on the loop. We use Fig. 1.22(b). The force on a wire of length L carrying a current i in a field B is BiL in a direction given by Fleming's left hand rule. Thus, the forces acting on two of the sides of the loop give rise to the torque as in Fig. 1.22(b). As the loop rotates, each of these sides moves a distance $L/2$ in the direction of the force so that the work done is

$$W = 2FL/2 = BiL^2$$

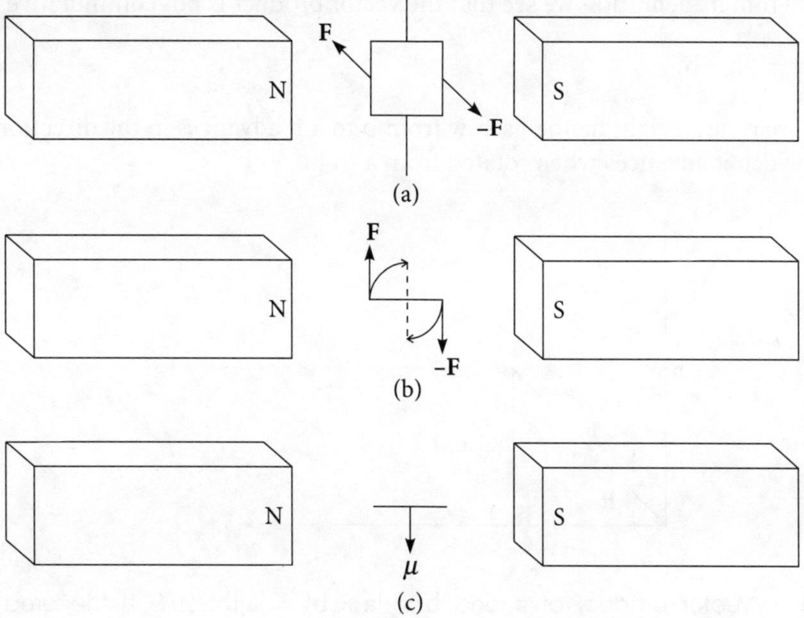

Fig. 1.22   Torque on a current carrying coil in a magnetic field

Alternatively, we can use the expression of the potential energy involving the magnetic moment μ. We refer to Fig. 1.22(c). The change in the potential energy V is related to the work done on the loop by

$$W = -(\text{change in} V) = V(\text{initial}) - V(\text{final}).$$

The magnitude of the magnetic moment μ is given by $\mu = iA$ where A is the area of the loop and its direction is perpendicular to the loop as shown in Fig. 1.22(c). μ starts perpendicular to **B** and finishes parallel to **B**. This gives $V(\text{initial}) = 0$ and we have

$$W = 0 - (-iAB) = BiL^2$$

Since both the expressions for W agree, we have better confidence in the formula $V = -\mu \cdot \mathbf{B}$.

1.7.3 Vector product

Given two vectors **a**, **b**, their *vector* or *cross* product is a *vector* $(\mathbf{a} \times \mathbf{b})$ with magnitude $ab \sin \theta$ $(a, b, \theta$ as defined while defining the scalar product) and in the direction (perpendicular to the plane of **a** and **b**) in which a right handed screw advances when **a** is rotated towards **b**. (see Fig. 1.23). We assume that both the vectors are based at the same point and take the angle between them to be $\leq \pi$. Thus, the magnitude of the vector product $|\mathbf{a} \times \mathbf{b}|$ is the same as the area of the parallelegram with adjacent sides **a** and **b** (see Fig. 1.23). From its definition we see that the vector product is not commutative. In fact,

$$\mathbf{b} \times \mathbf{a} = -\mathbf{a} \times \mathbf{b},$$

because if we rotate a right handed screw from **b** to **a** it advances in the direction opposite to that in which it advances when rotated from **a** to **b**.

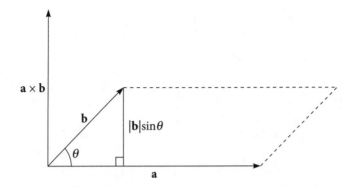

Fig. 1.23   Vector product of **a** and **b** : $|\mathbf{a} \times \mathbf{b}| = |\mathbf{a}||\mathbf{b}| \sin \theta$ is the area of the parallelogram as shown

Note that $\mathbf{a} \times \mathbf{b} = \mathbf{0}$ whenever **a** and **b** are parallel $(\theta = 0)$ or anti-parallel $(\theta = \pi)$. Both these cases are covered by requiring $\mathbf{b} = \alpha \mathbf{a}$, α a scalar. In particular, $\mathbf{a} \times \mathbf{a} = \mathbf{0}$. This shows that $\mathbf{a} \times \mathbf{b} = 0$ if and only if $\mathbf{a} \ne \mathbf{0}$ and $\mathbf{b} \ne \mathbf{0}$ are proportional to each other, that is, are linearly dependent.

The vector product is not associative as can be seen from

$$(\mathbf{a} \times \mathbf{a}) \times \mathbf{b} \ne \mathbf{a} \times (\mathbf{a} \times \mathbf{b})$$

with $\mathbf{a} \ne \mathbf{0}, \mathbf{b} \ne \mathbf{0}$, as the LHS is always zero, while RHS is never zero unless $\mathbf{b} = \alpha \mathbf{a}$. RHS is a vector in the plane of $\mathbf{a}, \mathbf{b}$ with magnitude $a^2 b \sin \theta$ (θ : angle between $\mathbf{a}$ and $\mathbf{b}$).

The vector product is distributive, that is,

$$\mathbf{a} \times (\mathbf{b} + \mathbf{c}) = \mathbf{a} \times \mathbf{b} + \mathbf{a} \times \mathbf{c},$$

and $\qquad (\mathbf{a} + \mathbf{b}) \times \mathbf{c} = \mathbf{a} \times \mathbf{c} + \mathbf{b} \times \mathbf{c}.$

We will prove this result later (see subsection 1.8.1).

From its definition, it follows that multiplying one of the factors of a vector product by a scalar amounts to multiplying the vector product itself by that scalar.

All of the above discussion leads immediately to the laws of vector multiplication:

$$(\lambda \mathbf{a}) \times \mathbf{b} = \mathbf{a} \times (\lambda \mathbf{b}) = \lambda (\mathbf{a} \times \mathbf{b})$$

$$\mathbf{a} \times (\mathbf{b} + \mathbf{c}) = \mathbf{a} \times \mathbf{b} + \mathbf{a} \times \mathbf{c}$$

$$(\mathbf{a} + \mathbf{b}) \times \mathbf{c} = \mathbf{a} \times \mathbf{c} + \mathbf{b} \times \mathbf{c}$$

$$\mathbf{b} \times \mathbf{a} = -\mathbf{a} \times \mathbf{b}. \qquad (1.10)$$

Exercise   Show that (a) $(\mathbf{a} \cdot \mathbf{b})^2 + (\mathbf{a} \times \mathbf{b})^2 = a^2 b^2$ and (b) $(\mathbf{a} \cdot \mathbf{b})^2 - (\mathbf{a} \times \mathbf{b})^2 = a^2 b^2 \cos 2\theta$ where θ is the angle between $\mathbf{a}$ and $\mathbf{b}$. Part (a) immediately leads to Cauchy–Schwartz inequality,

$$|\mathbf{a} \cdot \mathbf{b}| \le |\mathbf{a}| \, |\mathbf{b}|$$

with an additional piece of information that equality holds if and only if the vectors $\mathbf{a}$ and $\mathbf{b}$ are linearly dependent.   □

Exercise   If $\mathbf{a}_\perp$ and $\mathbf{b}_\perp$ are the components of $\mathbf{a}$ and $\mathbf{b}$ perpendicular to a vector $\mathbf{c}$ then show that (a) $\mathbf{a} \times \mathbf{c} = \mathbf{a}_\perp \times \mathbf{c}$ and (b) $(\mathbf{a} + \mathbf{b}) \times \mathbf{c} = (\mathbf{a}_\perp + \mathbf{b}_\perp) \times \mathbf{c}$.

Solution   Note that $\mathbf{c}, \mathbf{a}$ and $\mathbf{a}_\perp$ are coplanar with $\mathbf{a}$ and $\mathbf{a}_\perp$ on the same side of $\mathbf{c}$ (Draw a figure) and $\mathbf{a}_\perp \times \mathbf{c}$ and $\mathbf{a} \times \mathbf{c}$ have the same direction. Let θ be the angle between $\mathbf{a}$ and $\mathbf{c}$ and let the angle between $\mathbf{a}$ and $\mathbf{a}_\perp$ be ϕ. Note that $\theta + \phi = \frac{\pi}{2}$. Therefore, for the magnitudes, we get

$$a_\perp = a \cos \phi = a \sin \theta,$$

leading to $|\mathbf{a} \times \mathbf{c}| = |\mathbf{a}_\perp \times \mathbf{c}|$ so that (a) is proved. To get (b), note that $\mathbf{a}_\perp + \mathbf{b}_\perp$ is the component of $\mathbf{a} + \mathbf{b}$ perpendicular to $\mathbf{c}$ and apply (a). $\square$

Consider an orthonormal basis $\hat{\mathbf{i}}, \hat{\mathbf{j}}, \hat{\mathbf{k}}$ forming a right handed coordinate system. From the definitions of the vector product and a right handed coordinate system it immediately follows that

$$\hat{\mathbf{i}} \times \hat{\mathbf{i}} = \hat{\mathbf{j}} \times \hat{\mathbf{j}} = \hat{\mathbf{k}} \times \hat{\mathbf{k}} = 0$$

and

$$\hat{\mathbf{i}} \times \hat{\mathbf{j}} = -\hat{\mathbf{j}} \times \hat{\mathbf{i}} = \hat{\mathbf{k}}$$

$$\hat{\mathbf{j}} \times \hat{\mathbf{k}} = -\hat{\mathbf{k}} \times \hat{\mathbf{j}} = \hat{\mathbf{i}}$$

$$\hat{\mathbf{k}} \times \hat{\mathbf{i}} = -\hat{\mathbf{i}} \times \hat{\mathbf{k}} = \hat{\mathbf{j}}. \tag{1.11}$$

Note that we can obtain the second and the third equation above from the first by cyclically permuting the vectors $\hat{\mathbf{i}}, \hat{\mathbf{j}}, \hat{\mathbf{k}}$. i.e., by simultaneously changing $\hat{\mathbf{i}} \mapsto \hat{\mathbf{j}}, \hat{\mathbf{j}} \mapsto \hat{\mathbf{k}}, \hat{\mathbf{k}} \mapsto \hat{\mathbf{i}}$. This useful property holds for any vector relation involving an orthonormal basis.

For a left handed coordinate system the vectors $\hat{\mathbf{i}} \times \hat{\mathbf{j}}, \hat{\mathbf{j}} \times \hat{\mathbf{k}}, \hat{\mathbf{k}} \times \hat{\mathbf{i}}$ are in opposite direction to the basis vectors $\hat{\mathbf{k}}, \hat{\mathbf{i}}, \hat{\mathbf{j}}$ respectively. Therefore, Eq. (1.11) change to

$$\hat{\mathbf{i}} \times \hat{\mathbf{j}} = -\hat{\mathbf{k}}$$

$$\hat{\mathbf{j}} \times \hat{\mathbf{k}} = -\hat{\mathbf{i}}$$

$$\hat{\mathbf{k}} \times \hat{\mathbf{i}} = -\hat{\mathbf{j}}. \tag{1.12}$$

Equations (1.11) and (1.12) are often taken to be the definitions of the right handed and the left handed coordinate systems respectively.

Exercise   Prove that

$$\mathbf{a} \times \mathbf{b} = \begin{vmatrix} a_2 & b_2 \\ a_3 & b_3 \end{vmatrix} \hat{\sigma}_1 - \begin{vmatrix} a_1 & b_1 \\ a_3 & b_3 \end{vmatrix} \hat{\sigma}_2 + \begin{vmatrix} a_1 & b_1 \\ a_2 & b_2 \end{vmatrix} \hat{\sigma}_3,$$

$\{\hat{\sigma}_1, \hat{\sigma}_2, \hat{\sigma}_3\}$ is an orthonormal right handed basis and $a_k = \mathbf{a} \cdot \hat{\sigma}_k, b_k = \mathbf{b} \cdot \hat{\sigma}_k, k = 1, 2, 3$. $\square$

Exercise   Compute (a) $(\mathbf{a} + \mathbf{b}) \times (\mathbf{a} - \mathbf{b})$; (b) $(\mathbf{a} - \mathbf{b}) \times (\mathbf{b} - \mathbf{c})$. Give a geometrical interpretation of these.

Hint   Think of a tetrahedron. $\square$

Exercise   If $(\mathbf{a} \times \mathbf{b}) = (\mathbf{c} \times \mathbf{d})$ and $(\mathbf{a} \times \mathbf{c}) = (\mathbf{b} \times \mathbf{d})$ then show that $\mathbf{a} - \mathbf{d}$ is parallel to $\mathbf{b} - \mathbf{c}$.

Hint   Subtract these two equations. $\qquad\qquad\qquad\qquad\qquad\qquad\qquad\qquad\quad$ □

Using the distributive property of the vector product and Eq. (1.11) we can write the vector product of two vectors in terms of their Cartesian components with respect to a right handed coordinate system.

$$
\begin{aligned}
\mathbf{a} \times \mathbf{b} &= (a_x\hat{\mathbf{i}} + a_y\hat{\mathbf{j}} + a_z\hat{\mathbf{k}}) \times (b_x\hat{\mathbf{i}} + b_y\hat{\mathbf{j}} + b_z\hat{\mathbf{k}}) \\
&= (a_yb_z - b_ya_z)\hat{\mathbf{i}} + (a_zb_x - b_za_x)\hat{\mathbf{j}} + (a_xb_y - b_xa_y)\hat{\mathbf{k}}.
\end{aligned} \tag{1.13}
$$

This expression for the vector product in component form contains no easily accessible information about the magnitude and the direction of the vector product $\mathbf{a} \times \mathbf{b}$. Also, it depends on the coordinate system used as the components of the factors change if we use another orthonormal basis, (that is, another coordinate system). On the other hand, expressions involving vectors (and not their components) are invariant under the change of coordinate system and each term in them has the same value in all coordinate systems. Thus, if we can model a physical situation or a process using vectors and expressions involving vectors alone, we are free of the limitation of viewing the process with reference to a particular coordinate system and of extra baggage of transforming the expressions from one coordinate system to the other as and when required. The most important advantage of vectors is this coordinate-free approach they offer. In this book we will exclusively follow this coordinate-free approach, although we will spend some time with some of the important coordinate systems.

The components of $\mathbf{a} \times \mathbf{b}$ with respect to an orthonormal basis $\hat{\mathbf{i}}$, $\hat{\mathbf{j}}$, $\hat{\mathbf{k}}$ (and the corresponding coordinate system) can be expressed more conveniently in the form

$$
\begin{vmatrix}
\hat{\mathbf{i}} & \hat{\mathbf{j}} & \hat{\mathbf{k}} \\
a_x & a_y & a_z \\
b_x & b_y & b_z
\end{vmatrix}.
$$

Exercise   (Law of sines) Refer to the exercise where you are asked to prove law of cosines for a triangle ABC and Fig. 1.10. Prove Eq. (1.14).

Solution   Take the vector product of $\mathbf{c} = \mathbf{a} + \mathbf{b}$ successively with vectors $\mathbf{a}, \mathbf{b}, \mathbf{c}$ to get

$$
\mathbf{a} \times \mathbf{c} = \mathbf{a} \times \mathbf{b} = \mathbf{c} \times \mathbf{b}.
$$

Equating the magnitudes of these vectors and dividing by abc gives a relation true for any triangle,

$$
\frac{\sin A}{a} = \frac{\sin B}{b} = \frac{\sin C}{c}. \tag{1.14}
$$
$\qquad\qquad\qquad\qquad\qquad\qquad\qquad\qquad\qquad\qquad\qquad\qquad\qquad\qquad\qquad\quad$ □

If we reflect a vector in the origin, it is expected to change sign. A vector which changes sign under reflection in the origin (called inversion) is called a *polar* vector. However, this change of sign under inversion is not carried over to the vector product of two polar vectors. That is, if **a** and **b** are polar vectors then their vector product does not change sign under inversion of both **a** and **b**. Due to this property a vector product of two polar vectors is called a *pseudo* vector or an *axial* vector.

1.7.4   Generalizing the geometric interpretation of the vector product

Figure 1.23 tells us that $|\mathbf{a} \times \mathbf{b}|$ equals the area of the parallelogram spanned by **a** and **b**. From the relation $|\mathbf{a} \times \mathbf{b}| = ab\sin\theta$ we see that the factors a, b and $\sin\theta$ may be varied as long as the product $ab\sin\theta$ remains constant and equals $|\mathbf{a}\times\mathbf{b}|$. Thus, the geometric picture that $|\mathbf{a} \times \mathbf{b}|$ equals the area of a parallelogram with adjacent sides a and b, and **b** making angle θ with **a** can be relaxed and $ab\sin\theta$ can be taken to represent a plane area of any shape, numerically equal to $|\mathbf{a} \times \mathbf{b}|$ and with its normal in the direction of $\mathbf{a} \times \mathbf{b}$. To do this, we divide the original parallelogram into a number of similar parallelograms, all copies of one another and described in the counterclockwise sense just as the original parallelogram as in Fig. 1.24(a). If these parallelograms are displaced in any way by sliding them in the directions of the sides, a new figure of irregular shape is obtained such as that shown in Fig. 1.24(b). The area of this figure is the same as that of the original parallelogram.

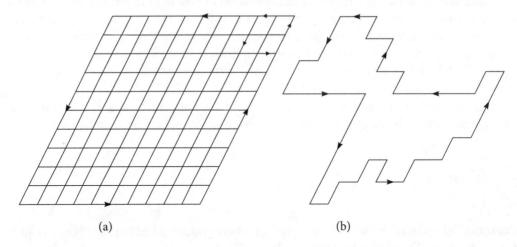

(a)   (b)

Fig. 1.24   Generalizing the geometric interpretation of vector product

If the number of constituent parallelograms is increased without limit, the contour of the figure becomes a curve enclosing an area equal to that of the original parallelogram. Note that the contours of Figs 1.24(a) and (b) are both traced in the same counterclockwise sense. This sense is preserved however small the constituent elementary parallelograms may be, so that in the limit an area equal to $|\mathbf{a} \times \mathbf{b}|$ results, with a curvilinear contour as its boundary, traced in the counterclockwise sense. Thus, we can say that this planar geometrical object is represented by $\mathbf{a}\times\mathbf{b}$, which is a vector of scalar magnitude numerically equal to the area of this planar figure and is at right angles to it on that side of the planar figure from which the description of its contour appears counterclockwise. This marks an important and useful generalization of the geometrical interpretation of a vector product.

Geometric interpretation of the coordinates of the vector product

Let $\mathbf{a} \equiv (a_1, a_2, a_3) \neq \mathbf{b} \equiv (b_1, b_2, b_3)$ be two non-zero vectors with a non-zero vector product. The individual Cartesian components of the vector product $(\mathbf{a} \times \mathbf{b}) \equiv (z_1, z_2, z_3)$ have a geometrical interpretation related to that of $(\mathbf{a} \times \mathbf{b})$ itself (see Fig. 1.25). We have,

$$z_3 = \begin{vmatrix} a_1 & b_1 \\ a_2 & b_2 \end{vmatrix} = a_1 b_2 - a_2 b_1. \tag{1.15}$$

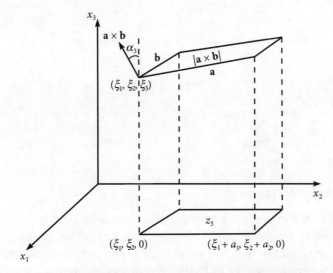

Fig. 1.25 Geometrical interpretation of coordinates of a vector product

However, the right side of this equation is the magnitude of the vector product of the vectors with Cartesian components $(a_1, a_2, 0)$ and $(b_1, b_2, 0)$, so that its absolute value $|z_3| = |a_1 b_2 - a_2 b_1|$ must equal the area of the parallelogram spanned by these vectors. The sign of z_3 is determined by the direction of the corresponding vector product: Whether it is in the positive or negative direction of the z-axis. Now the vectors $(a_1, a_2, 0)$ and $(b_1, b_2, 0)$ are simply the projections of the vectors $\mathbf{a}$ and $\mathbf{b}$ on the xy plane. Thus, $|z_3|$ is the area of the parallelogram obtained by projecting the parallelogram spanned by the vectors $\mathbf{a}$ and $\mathbf{b}$ on the xy plane. (see Fig. 1.25). Similarly, $|z_1|$ and $|z_2|$ are the areas of the projections of the parallelogram spanned by the vectors $\mathbf{a}, \mathbf{b}$ on the yz and xz planes respectively. If $\alpha_1, \alpha_2, \alpha_3$ are the angles made by the direction of the vector $\mathbf{a} \times \mathbf{b}$ with the positive directions of the x, y, z-axes respectively, then

$$|z_k| = |\mathbf{a} \times \mathbf{b}||\cos \alpha_k| \quad k = 1, 2, 3$$

as shown in Fig. 1.25.

1.7.5 Physical applications of the vector product

Consider a rigid body[3] which can rotate about an axis e.g., a door rotating about hinges. A force **F** in a plane perpendicular to the axis acts at a point away from the axis. Then, the *moment of this force* (or *torque*) is defined as the magnitude of the force multiplied by the perpendicular distance from the force to the axis. Referring to Fig. 1.26 we see that the moment **M** has a magnitude $|\mathbf{F}|s$ or $Fr\sin\theta$. The direction of **M** is along the axis in which a right handed screw will advance when rotated in the sense of rotation of the body (caused by the application of **F**). Thus, the direction of **M** in Fig. 1.26 is out of the paper. All this can be summarized in the vector equation

$$\mathbf{M} = \mathbf{r} \times \mathbf{F}.$$

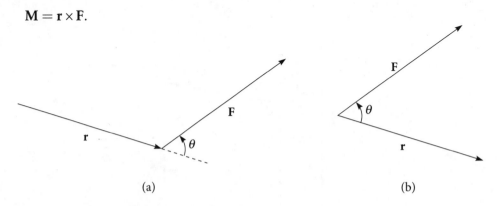

Fig. 1.26   Moment of a force

To get the direction of **M** from the vector product we must base **r** and **F** at the same point and take $\theta < \pi$. In fact, the definition of torque in terms of the vector product is completely general. The torque about any axis, not necessarily perpendicular to the plane containing **r** and **F** is given by the component of **M** in the direction of the axis.

The next important physical quantity defined by the vector product is *angular momentum*. A particle of mass m moving with velocity **v** has the angular momentum **L** about the origin given by

$$\mathbf{L} = m\mathbf{r} \times \mathbf{v} = \mathbf{r} \times \mathbf{p},$$

where $\mathbf{p} = m\mathbf{v}$ is the *linear momentum* of the particle. Angular momentum is an extremely important conserved quantity for the motion under a central force.

The force on a charge q moving with velocity **v** in a magnetic field **B** is given by

$$\mathbf{F} = q\mathbf{v} \times \mathbf{B}.$$

---

[3] A rigid body is the one for which the distance between every pair of particles in it remains invariant throughout its motion. Thus, there cannot be any relative motion between different parts of a rigid body and it cannot be deformed by applying external forces. The motion of a rigid body is composed solely of its translation and rotation as a whole. Of course, an ideal rigid body is a fiction, however, in many situations we can approximate the motion of a solid body by that of a perfect rigid body to get the required characteristics of the actual motion.

The torque on a electric dipole $\mathbf{p}$ in an electric field $\mathbf{E}$ is given by

$$\mathbf{T} = \mathbf{p} \times \mathbf{E}.$$

This can be easily understood by taking the dipole as two charges $+q$ and $-q$ separated by a small distance $2d$ as in Fig. 1.21. The force on each charge has a magnitude qE. The resulting torque is given by

$$\mathbf{M} = \mathbf{T} = 2\mathbf{d} \times (q\mathbf{E}) = 2q\mathbf{d} \times \mathbf{E}.$$

Since $\mathbf{p} = 2q\mathbf{d}$ this coincides with the previous expression of $\mathbf{T}$.

A similar result holds for the torque on a magnetic dipole in a magnetic field $\mathbf{B}$.

$$\mathbf{T} = \mathbf{\mu} \times \mathbf{B}.$$

1.8   Products of Three or More Vectors

A product is a binary operation defined on a set which combines two elements of a set and returns an element of the same set. We can say that both scalar and vector products are defined on the union of the set of vectors and the set of scalars. Then, the vector and the scalar products combine two vectors and return a vector and a scalar respectively. Any extension of these products to more than two vectors must involve successive evaluation of the vector and/or the scalar products of pairs of vectors drawn from a collection of more than two vectors. Since the vector product is not associative the order in which it is evaluated becomes important. Here, we learn about the scalar and vector triple products involving three vectors, which yield a scalar and a vector respectively. These products occur frequently in applications.

1.8.1   The scalar triple product

This is the scalar product of the vectors $\mathbf{a}$ and $\mathbf{b} \times \mathbf{c}$ given by $\mathbf{a} \cdot \mathbf{b} \times \mathbf{c}$. The scalar triple product has an elegant interpretation as the volume of the parallelepiped with edges $\mathbf{a}, \mathbf{b}$ and $\mathbf{c}$ based at the same origin (see Fig. 1.27). Area of the base is $A = |\mathbf{b} \times \mathbf{c}|$. The volume is $V = Ah$, where h is the height of the parallelepiped from the base. This height can be expressed as $h = \mathbf{a} \cdot \hat{\mathbf{n}}$, where $\hat{\mathbf{n}}$ is a unit vector normal to the base. Evidently, $\mathbf{b} \times \mathbf{c} = A\hat{\mathbf{n}}$ giving $V = A\mathbf{a} \cdot \hat{\mathbf{n}} = |\mathbf{a} \cdot \mathbf{b} \times \mathbf{c}|$. Since this volume does not depend on which face is chosen as the base, it follows that

$$\mathbf{a} \cdot \mathbf{b} \times \mathbf{c} = \mathbf{c} \cdot \mathbf{a} \times \mathbf{b} = \mathbf{b} \cdot \mathbf{c} \times \mathbf{a}.$$

Thus, the scalar triple product is invariant under the cyclic permutation of its factors given by $abc \leftrightarrow a \rightarrow b \rightarrow c \rightarrow a$. For example, note that

$$\mathbf{a} \cdot \mathbf{a} \times \mathbf{b} = \mathbf{b} \cdot \mathbf{a} \times \mathbf{a} = 0. \tag{1.16}$$

In fact, while keeping the cyclic order if we change the $\cdot$ and the $\times$ in the triple product, its value remains the same. For example,

$$\mathbf{a} \cdot \mathbf{b} \times \mathbf{c} = \mathbf{c} \cdot \mathbf{a} \times \mathbf{b} = \mathbf{a} \times \mathbf{b} \cdot \mathbf{c},$$

where the last equality follows because the scalar product of two vectors is independent of the order of the vectors. Thus, the scalar triple product depends only on the cyclic order abc and not on the position of $\cdot$ and $\times$ in the product. The sign of the scalar triple product is reversed if the cyclic order is broken by permuting two of the vectors.

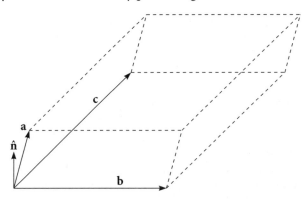

Fig. 1.27   Geometric interpretation of the scalar triple product (see text)

Exercise   Show that $\mathbf{a} \cdot \mathbf{b} \times \mathbf{c} = 0$ if and only if the vectors $\mathbf{a}, \mathbf{b}, \mathbf{c}$ are coplanar, that is, are linearly dependent.

Answer $\mathbf{a} \cdot \mathbf{b} \times \mathbf{c} = 0$ if and only if the volume of the corresponding parallelepiped is zero, if and only if $\mathbf{a}, \mathbf{b}, \mathbf{c}$ are coplanar.   □

Suppose that $\mathbf{a}, \mathbf{b}, \mathbf{c}$ are mutually orthogonal vectors forming a left handed system. Then, the signs of $\mathbf{a}$ and $\mathbf{b} \times \mathbf{c}$ will be opposite and the value of $\mathbf{a} \cdot \mathbf{b} \times \mathbf{c}$ will be negative. The same conclusion applies even if $\mathbf{a}, \mathbf{b}, \mathbf{c}$ are not mutually orthogonal however, $\mathbf{b} \times \mathbf{c}$ makes an obtuse angle with $\mathbf{a}$. In this case, the negative sign is interpreted as the *negative orientation of the volume* of the parallelepiped formed by the vectors $\mathbf{a}, \mathbf{b}, \mathbf{c}$ and their scalar triple product is said to equal the volume of their parallelepiped having negative orientation. Thus, in general, a scalar triple product is said to equal the *oriented volume* of the parallelepiped formed by its factors. The fact that the transition from a right handed to left handed system (or vice versa) changes the sign of the scalar triple product is expressed by saying that the scalar triple product is not a genuine scalar (whose value is invariant under any transformation of the basis) however, a *pseudo-scalar*. The right handed ↔ left handed transition can be carried out by reflecting all the basis vectors in origin. In fact a scalar triple product changes sign under the reflection of all of its factors (which form a basis unless its value is zero) in the origin: $-\mathbf{a} \cdot (-\mathbf{b} \times -\mathbf{c}) = -\mathbf{a} \cdot \mathbf{b} \times \mathbf{c}$.

Exercise   The scalar triple product can also be geometrically interpreted as the volume of a tetrahedron. Consider a tetrahedron $OABC$ with one of its vertices at the origin O

(see Fig. 1.28). Show that its volume is given by $\frac{1}{6}[\mathbf{a} \cdot (\mathbf{b} \times \mathbf{c})]$ where all the vectors are as defined in Fig. 1.28.

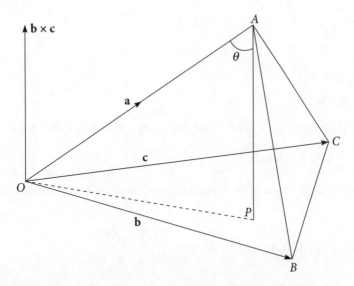

Fig. 1.28 The volume of a tetrahedron as the scalar triple product

Solution The required volume V is

$$V = \frac{1}{3} \cdot \text{area of } \triangle OBC \cdot AP$$

$$= \frac{1}{3} \cdot \frac{1}{2} |\mathbf{b} \times \mathbf{c}| \cdot |\mathbf{a}| \cos \theta$$

$$= \frac{1}{6}[\mathbf{a} \cdot (\mathbf{b} \times \mathbf{c})]. \qquad \square$$

Exercise Let $\mathbf{a}, \mathbf{b}, \mathbf{c}$ be non-coplanar. For an arbitrary non-zero vector $\mathbf{d}$ show that

$$\mathbf{d} = [(\mathbf{c} \cdot \mathbf{d})\mathbf{a} \times \mathbf{b} + (\mathbf{a} \cdot \mathbf{d})\mathbf{b} \times \mathbf{c} + (\mathbf{b} \cdot \mathbf{d})\mathbf{c} \times \mathbf{a}] / (\mathbf{a} \cdot \mathbf{b} \times \mathbf{c}).$$

Hint First note that the vectors $\mathbf{a} \times \mathbf{b}, \mathbf{b} \times \mathbf{c}, \mathbf{c} \times \mathbf{a}$ are non-coplanar because their scalar triple product is not zero. Therefore, these vectors form a basis in which an arbitrary vector $\mathbf{d}$ can be expanded. The coefficients in this expansion are determined by taking its scalar product successively with $\mathbf{c}, \mathbf{a}$ and $\mathbf{b}$. $\qquad \square$

Exercise Express the scalar triple product in its component form,

$$\mathbf{a} \cdot \mathbf{b} \times \mathbf{c} = a_x(b_y c_z - c_y b_z) + a_y(b_z c_x - c_z b_x) + a_z(b_x c_y - c_x b_y)$$

and write it in the determinant form

$$\mathbf{a} \cdot (\mathbf{b} \times \mathbf{c}) = \begin{vmatrix} a_x & a_y & a_z \\ b_x & b_y & b_z \\ c_x & c_y & c_z \end{vmatrix} = \det(\mathbf{a}, \mathbf{b}, \mathbf{c}),$$

which defines $\det(\mathbf{a}, \mathbf{b}, \mathbf{c})$.[4]

Hint   Use Eq. (1.13) for the vector product.   □

Exercise   Let θ be the angle between the directions of vectors $\mathbf{c}$ and $\mathbf{a} \times \mathbf{b}$. Show that

$$\det(\mathbf{a}, \mathbf{b}, \mathbf{c}) = |\mathbf{a} \times \mathbf{b}| \, |\mathbf{c}| \cos \theta.$$ □

Exercise   Show that the area of the parallelogram spanned by $\mathbf{a}, \mathbf{b}$, namely, $|\mathbf{a} \times \mathbf{b}|$, can be expressed by

$$|\mathbf{a} \times \mathbf{b}|^2 = (\mathbf{a} \cdot \mathbf{a})(\mathbf{b} \cdot \mathbf{b}) - (\mathbf{a} \cdot \mathbf{b})(\mathbf{b} \cdot \mathbf{a}) = \begin{vmatrix} \mathbf{a} \cdot \mathbf{a} & \mathbf{a} \cdot \mathbf{b} \\ \mathbf{b} \cdot \mathbf{a} & \mathbf{b} \cdot \mathbf{b} \end{vmatrix}. \tag{1.17}$$

This determinant is called *Gram determinant*. Since $|\mathbf{a} \times \mathbf{b}| = 0$ if and only if $\mathbf{a}, \mathbf{b}$ are dependent, we see that the gram determinant is zero if and only if $\mathbf{a}, \mathbf{b}$ are dependent.   □

Exercise   Show that the determinant form of $[\mathbf{a} \cdot (\mathbf{b} \times \mathbf{c})][\mathbf{d} \cdot (\mathbf{e} \times \mathbf{f})]$ is

$$[\mathbf{a} \cdot (\mathbf{b} \times \mathbf{c})][\mathbf{d} \cdot (\mathbf{e} \times \mathbf{f})] \equiv \begin{vmatrix} \mathbf{a} \cdot \mathbf{d} & \mathbf{a} \cdot \mathbf{e} & \mathbf{a} \cdot \mathbf{f} \\ \mathbf{b} \cdot \mathbf{d} & \mathbf{b} \cdot \mathbf{e} & \mathbf{b} \cdot \mathbf{f} \\ \mathbf{c} \cdot \mathbf{d} & \mathbf{c} \cdot \mathbf{e} & \mathbf{c} \cdot \mathbf{f} \end{vmatrix}.$$

Hint   Treat the rows and columns forming the determinants of factors as matrices, and find the determinant of the product of matrix of one factor and the transpose of the matrix of the other factor. This works because the determinant of the product of matrices is the product of their determinants and the determinant of a matrix is invariant under transpose of that matrix.   □

Let us now prove that the vector product is distributive. Let $\{\mathbf{a}, \mathbf{b}, \mathbf{c}\}$ be three arbitrary vectors and let $\hat{\mathbf{x}}$ be an arbitrary direction. Using the fact that the scalar triple product is invariant under the cyclic permutation of its factors, we can write

$$\begin{aligned} \hat{\mathbf{x}} \cdot \mathbf{a} \times (\mathbf{b} + \mathbf{c}) &= (\mathbf{b} + \mathbf{c}) \cdot (\hat{\mathbf{x}} \times \mathbf{a}) \\ &= \mathbf{b} \cdot (\hat{\mathbf{x}} \times \mathbf{a}) + \mathbf{c} \cdot (\hat{\mathbf{x}} \times \mathbf{a}) \\ &= \hat{\mathbf{x}} \cdot (\mathbf{a} \times \mathbf{b} + \mathbf{a} \times \mathbf{c}) \end{aligned}$$

---

[4]You are now advised to read the appendix on matrices and determinants, which will be used in the rest of the book.

Since $\hat{\mathbf{x}}$ is arbitrary, we get

$$\mathbf{a} \times (\mathbf{b} + \mathbf{c}) = \mathbf{a} \times \mathbf{b} + \mathbf{a} \times \mathbf{c},$$

which is the desired result.

The distributive law

$$(\mathbf{a} + \mathbf{b}) \times \mathbf{c} = \mathbf{a} \times \mathbf{c} + \mathbf{b} \times \mathbf{c}$$

can be proved similarly.

A powerful notation for the scalar triple product $\mathbf{a} \cdot (\mathbf{b} \times \mathbf{c})$ and all its cyclic permutations is $[\mathbf{abc}]$. This notation was first used by Grassmann. However, we will use this notation very rarely and prefer to write scalar triple product explicitly.

1.8.2 Physical applications of the scalar triple product

Reciprocal lattice of a crystal [4].

A single crystal is characterized by the periodic arrangement of atoms, ions or molecules. This periodic arrangement is modelled by a lattice of points in space, called a *Bravais lattice*. Since a crystal is a three dimensional object, we expect the lattice to have three independent periodic arrangements in three non-coplanar directions. We can imagine three basis vectors (called primitive vectors) say $\{\mathbf{a}_1, \mathbf{a}_2, \mathbf{a}_3\}$ along three non-coplanar directions forming the adjacent edges of a parallelepiped which is called a primitive cell of the Bravais lattice. The Bravais lattice can be constructed by translating this primitive cell integral number of times successively along the directions defined by the primitive vectors $\{\mathbf{a}_1, \mathbf{a}_2, \mathbf{a}_3\}$. Obviously, only those primitive cells are allowed which fill in all the space by such a translation. A vector joining the origin to any of the lattice points, say $\mathbf{R}$, is then given by

$$\mathbf{R} = n_1 \mathbf{a}_1 + n_2 \mathbf{a}_2 + n_3 \mathbf{a}_3$$

where $\{n_1, n_2, n_3\}$ are integers. The whole lattice is given by the set of vectors $\{\mathbf{R}\}$ generated by giving the triplet $\{n_1, n_2, n_3\}$ all possible integer values. Note that the volume of a primitive cell is given by the scalar triple product $\mathbf{a}_1 \cdot \mathbf{a}_2 \times \mathbf{a}_3$ or any of its cyclic permutations.

Consider a set of points $\{\mathbf{R}\}$ constituting the Bravais lattice of a crystal in which a plane wave $e^{i\mathbf{k}\cdot\mathbf{r}}$ is excited. Here, $\mathbf{k}$ is a wave vector and $\mathbf{r}$ is an arbitrary point in the crystal. We seek to find the set of wave vectors $\{\mathbf{K}\}$ for which the plane wave excitation has the same periodicity as the Bravais lattice of the crystal, that is,

$$e^{i\mathbf{K}\cdot(\mathbf{r}+\mathbf{R})} = e^{i\mathbf{K}\cdot\mathbf{r}},$$

which means

$$e^{i\mathbf{K}\cdot\mathbf{R}} = 1 \tag{1.18}$$

for all $\{\mathbf{R}\}$ in the Bravais lattice. The set of vectors $\{\mathbf{K}\}$ satisfying Eq. (1.18) is called the *reciprocal lattice* of the given Bravais lattice. The corresponding Bravais lattice is called the *direct lattice*.

If $\mathbf{K_1}, \mathbf{K_2}$ satisfy Eq. (1.18), then so do their sum and difference, which simply means that the set of reciprocal vectors form a Bravais lattice. We show that the primitive vectors of the reciprocal lattice are given by

$$\mathbf{b}_1 = 2\pi \frac{\mathbf{a}_2 \times \mathbf{a}_3}{\mathbf{a}_1 \cdot \mathbf{a}_2 \times \mathbf{a}_3},$$

$$\mathbf{b}_2 = 2\pi \frac{\mathbf{a}_3 \times \mathbf{a}_1}{\mathbf{a}_1 \cdot \mathbf{a}_2 \times \mathbf{a}_3},$$

$$\mathbf{b}_3 = 2\pi \frac{\mathbf{a}_1 \times \mathbf{a}_2}{\mathbf{a}_1 \cdot \mathbf{a}_2 \times \mathbf{a}_3}. \tag{1.19}$$

Exercise   Show that $\mathbf{a}_i \cdot \mathbf{b}_j = 2\pi \delta_{ij}$ where $\delta_{ij} = 0, 1 \, (i \neq j, i = j)$.   □

Exercise   Show that $\mathbf{b}_i$s are not all in one plane as long as $\mathbf{a}_i$s are not.   □

Since $\mathbf{b}_i$s are non-coplanar, any vector $\mathbf{k}$ can be written as a linear combination of $\{\mathbf{b}_i\}$,

$$\mathbf{k} = k_1 \mathbf{b}_1 + k_2 \mathbf{b}_2 + k_3 \mathbf{b}_3.$$

If $\mathbf{R}$ is any direct lattice vector, then

$$\mathbf{R} = n_1 \mathbf{a}_1 + n_2 \mathbf{a}_2 + n_3 \mathbf{a}_3$$

where $\{n_1, n_2, n_3\}$ are integers. Since $\mathbf{a}_i \cdot \mathbf{b}_j = 2\pi \delta_{ij}$ it follows that

$$\mathbf{k} \cdot \mathbf{R} = 2\pi (k_1 n_1 + k_2 n_2 + k_3 n_3).$$

We conclude from this equation that $e^{i\mathbf{k} \cdot \mathbf{R}}$ is unity for all $\mathbf{R}$, only when the coefficients $\{k_1, k_2, k_3\}$ are integers (i.e., when $\mathbf{k} \cdot \mathbf{R}$ is an integral multiple of 2π). Thus, we must have, for a reciprocal lattice vector $\mathbf{K}$,

$$\mathbf{K} = k_1 \mathbf{b}_1 + k_2 \mathbf{b}_2 + k_3 \mathbf{b}_3,$$

where $\{k_1, k_2, k_3\}$ are integers. Thus, reciprocal lattice is a Bravais lattice and $\mathbf{b}_i$s can be taken to be its primitive vectors. $\mathbf{b}_i$s form the adjacent sides of a parallelepiped which is the primitive cell of the reciprocal lattice.

Apart from, an enormous variety of situations in which the scalar triple product makes its appearance, it is an important tool for the development of the theory of vector operators, as we shall see in the next chapter. Also, the scalar triple product is the basis of a new and powerful notation for vector algebra and calculus, namely the Levi-Civita symbols (see section 1.11).

1.8.3 The vector triple product

This is the vector product of the vector $\mathbf{a}$ with the vector $\mathbf{b} \times \mathbf{c}$, that is, $\mathbf{a} \times (\mathbf{b} \times \mathbf{c})$. This vector is in the plane containing vectors $\mathbf{b}$ and $\mathbf{c}$ because $\mathbf{b} \times \mathbf{c}$ is perpendicular to this plane and $\mathbf{a} \times (\mathbf{b} \times \mathbf{c})$ is perpendicular to $\mathbf{b} \times \mathbf{c}$. Since the vector product is not associative the position of the brackets in $\mathbf{a} \times (\mathbf{b} \times \mathbf{c})$ is of vital importance. Generally, we do not have to directly evaluate a vector triple product as it can be transformed into a simpler expression via a vector identity (see section 1.12).

1.9 Homomorphism and Isomorphism

We need two algebraic concepts, namely, homomorphism and its special case isomorphism between two sets, which we now define. Consider two pairs $(S_1, \circ)$ and $(S_2, \times)$, where S_1, S_2 are sets and $\circ, \times$ are binary operations on S_1 and S_2 respectively. We assume that S_1, S_2 are closed under the corresponding binary operations. Let $\varphi : S_1 \mapsto S_2$ be a map from S_1 to S_2 such that for every $a \in S_1$ there is a $\varphi(a) \in S_2$. We say that φ is a *homomorphism* if, for every $a, b \in S_1$

$$\varphi(a \circ b) = \varphi(a) \times \varphi(b). \tag{1.20}$$

In other words, the image of the product of a and b in S_1 is the product of their images $\varphi(a)$ and $\varphi(b)$ in S_2.

Example   Consider $(\mathbb{Z}, +)$ and $((1,-1), \cdot)$ where $\mathbb{Z}$ is the set of integers and $+$ is the usual addition on it, while $\cdot$ is the usual multiplication on the two element set $(1,-1)$. Define a map φ by

$$\varphi(n) = (-1)^n,$$

that is,

$$(-1)^{a+b} = (-1)^a \cdot (-1)^b$$

which is clearly true.

If the map φ defining a homomorphism is also one to one and onto, then it is called *isomorphism*.

Exercise   Show that the set $\mathbb{Z}_2$ of integers modulo 2 and $((1,-1), \cdot)$ defined above, are isomorphic.   □

1.10 Isomorphism with $\mathbb{R}^3$

Until now we used $\mathbb{R}^3$ just as a name for the space we live in and in which all physical phenomena occur. In this section we give exact definition of $\mathbb{R}^3$ and justify using it as a name for our space.

Let us choose an orthonormal basis $\{\hat{\mathbf{i}}, \hat{\mathbf{j}}, \hat{\mathbf{k}}\}$ based at some origin O and the corresponding Cartesian coordinate system. We now use it to assign the Cartesian coordinates to all points in space. This procedure assigns a unique triplet of real numbers to every point in space. In fact the set of all triplets of real numbers can be identified with the set of all points in space. We call this set of triplets $\mathbb{R}^3$. Although, $\mathbb{R}^3$ stands for the set of all real number triplets, its one to one correspondence with the set of points in real space justifies naming real space by $\mathbb{R}^3$ as we have been doing until now.

We have already established a one to one correspondence between the set of vectors (representations of values of vector quantities in space) and $\mathbb{R}^3$, (for a given basis), using the fact that every vector can be written as a unique linear combination of the basis vectors (see sections 1.3 and 1.6). Here, we want to show something more. First, we define the addition in $\mathbb{R}^3$ as

$$(a_1, a_2, a_3) + (b_1, b_2, b_3) = (a_1 + b_1, a_2 + b_2, a_3 + b_3).$$

Consider two vectors $\mathbf{a}$ and $\mathbf{b}$ with coordinates $\{a_1, a_2, a_3\}$ and $\{b_1, b_2, b_3\}$ respectively. This means

$$\mathbf{a} = a_1 \hat{\mathbf{i}} + a_2 \hat{\mathbf{j}} + a_3 \hat{\mathbf{k}}$$

$$\mathbf{b} = b_1 \hat{\mathbf{i}} + b_2 \hat{\mathbf{j}} + b_3 \hat{\mathbf{k}}.$$

Using the distributive law for the multiplication of vectors by scalars and the commutativity and the associativity of the vector addition we can write

$$\mathbf{a} + \mathbf{b} = (a_1 + b_1)\hat{\mathbf{i}} + (a_2 + b_2)\hat{\mathbf{j}} + (a_3 + b_3)\hat{\mathbf{k}}.$$

Thus, the coordinates of $\mathbf{a} + \mathbf{b}$ are simply the addition of the coordinates of $\mathbf{a}$ and those of $\mathbf{b}$. Then, we have the following association.

$$\mathbf{a} \leftrightarrow (a_1, a_2, a_3),$$

$$\mathbf{b} \leftrightarrow (b_1, b_2, b_3),$$

$$\mathbf{a} + \mathbf{b} \leftrightarrow (a_1 + b_1, a_2 + b_2, a_3 + b_3). \tag{1.21}$$

Let us define the scalar product in $\mathbb{R}^3$ as the product of two 1×3 and 3×1 matrices (a row vector and a column vector),

$$[a_1 a_2 a_3][b_1 b_2 b_3]^T = \sum_i a_i b_i \tag{1.22}$$

where the superscript T denotes the transpose of a matrix. Thus, we see that the correspondence Eq. (1.21) preserves the scalar product of vectors.

Thus, we have a one to one map between the two sets: The set of vectors (whose elements are the 'values' of one or more vector quantities) and $\mathbb{R}^3$, (whose elements are the triplets of real numbers) which preserves the addition on individual sets in the sense of Eq. (1.20). Thus, the one to one map defined by Eq. (1.21) is an isomorphism between these two sets. Two isomorphic sets are algebraically identical and it is enough to study only one of them. Even the scalar and vector products can be expressed and processed in terms of the components of vectors, which are triplets of real numbers. So you may come up with the idea that we can just do away with the set of vectors and do everything using the set of triplets of real numbers, namely $\mathbb{R}^3$. This will free us from dealing with vectors altogether. A nice idea, but has the following problem. At the end of section 1.3 we saw that the one to one correspondence between vectors and $\mathbb{R}^3$ depends on the origin and the basis chosen. There is a different isomorphism for each possible origin and each possible basis because a change in the basis/origin changes the coordinates of every vector (see Fig. 1.4). Since there could be uncountably many origins and bases, there are uncountably many isomorphisms possible between the set of vectors and $\mathbb{R}^3$. It is then impossible to keep track of which isomorphism being used and to transform between these. On the other hand, the coordinate free approach, in which we directly deal with the set of vectors, frees us from this problem of keeping track of bases and transforming between them. It also enables us to reach conclusions that are independent of any particular basis or the coordinate system. Thus, coordinate free approach turns out to be more fruitful in many applications. On the other hand, an intelligent choice of the coordinate system, basically guided by the symmetry in the problem, can drastically reduce the algebra and can sharpen the understanding of the physics of the situation. Therefore, a judicious choice between these methods, depending on the problem, turns out to be rewarding.

A set V and the associated set of scalars S, with the operations of addition and scalar multiplication defined on V, which have all the properties of vector addition and scalar multiplication as listed in section 1.4, is called a *linear space*. If, in addition, we define a scalar product and the resulting metric (a distance function giving distance between every pair of elements), then it is called a *metric space*. Thus, a set of vectors is a metric space with a Euclidean metric. Let us call the 3-D space comprising all vectors (that is, all values of one or more vector quantities) $\mathcal{E}_3$. Both $\mathcal{E}_3$ and $\mathbb{R}^3$ are metric spaces with Euclidean metric (see Eq. (1.9) and the exercise following it). If a subset of a metric space is closed under addition, that is, the addition of every pair of vectors in the subset gives a vector in the same subset, then such a subset is a metric space in its own right and is called a subspace of the parent metric space. A basis in a subspace can always be extended to that of the whole space. The dimension of a subspace is always $\leq$ that of the whole space. Thus, for example, a set of planar vectors (a plane) and a set of vectors on a straight line (a straight line) are the 2-D and 1-D subspaces of $\mathcal{E}_3$ ($\mathbb{R}_3$) respectively.

Since $\mathbb{R}_3$ and $\mathcal{E}_3$ are isomorphic linear spaces, they can be used interchangeably in all contexts. However, we will basically refer to the space $\mathcal{E}_3$ as we intend to deal directly with the vectors, although we will make judicious use of $\mathbb{R}^3$ as well (when we operate by matrices on 3-D column vectors comprising the coordinates of vectors, see the next chapter).

Exercise   Any set on which addition and scalar multiplication operations (with all the properties stated in section 1.4) are defined, is a linear space. Show that (i) The set of real numbers forms a one dimensional linear space where addition of "vectors" is ordinary addition and multiplication by scalars is ordinary multiplication. (ii) The set of positive real numbers forms a linear space where addition of vectors is ordinary multiplication and scalar multiplication is appropriately defined.

Solution   (ii) The zero vector is the real number 1. "Multiplication" of the vector a by the scalar λ means raising a to power λ. Thus, if the addition is denoted by $\oplus$ and scalar multiplication by $\odot$ then

$$\lambda \odot (a \oplus b) = (ab)^\lambda = a^\lambda b^\lambda = (\lambda \odot a) \oplus (\lambda \odot b).$$ □

Exercise   Verify that the complex numbers form a two dimensional linear space where the addition is ordinary addition and scalars are real numbers. □

1.11   A New Notation: Levi-Civita Symbols

It is our common experience that something we want to say can be expressed in many different ways and each such expression is more or less effective depending on the context in which it is used. Mathematical modelling of physical systems and processes, being very much a human endeavor, is no exception. Here, this amounts to using different mathematical notations and expressions applied to the same physical situation. Depending on the context, that is, on the questions whose answers we are seeking, different notations and formulations are more or less effective. Using different notations and resulting formulations could be very effective, as this may throw light on various aspects of the process under study, which remain hidden while using other notations and formulations.

In this section we want to express various aspects of vectors we have learnt so far, in a new avatar, first used by Levi-Civita. We will find this notation very useful to deal with vectors in different contexts. To get to this formulation, we first invoke a *fixed* orthonormal basis giving a right handed system, say $\{\hat{\mathbf{1}}, \hat{\mathbf{2}}, \hat{\mathbf{3}}\}$. Let $\{\hat{\mathbf{i}}, \hat{\mathbf{j}}, \hat{\mathbf{k}}\}$ denote the unit vectors which are variables taking values in the set $\{\hat{\mathbf{1}}, \hat{\mathbf{2}}, \hat{\mathbf{3}}\}$. Let us now define the so called Levi-Civita symbols by

$$\varepsilon_{ijk} = \hat{\mathbf{i}} \cdot (\hat{\mathbf{j}} \times \hat{\mathbf{k}}).$$ (1.23)

Note the one to one correspondence between the index set $\{i, j, k\}$ and the unit vector variables $\{\hat{\mathbf{i}}, \hat{\mathbf{j}}, \hat{\mathbf{k}}\}$. Thus, different values for the index string ijk, drawn from the set $\{1, 2, 3\}$ uniquely decide the value of ε_{ijk} by giving the corresponding values to the vector variables $\hat{\mathbf{i}}, \hat{\mathbf{j}}, \hat{\mathbf{k}}$ in Eq. (1.23), drawn from the set $\{\hat{\mathbf{1}}, \hat{\mathbf{2}}, \hat{\mathbf{3}}\}$.

Exercise   Show that the number of strings of length n made up of symbols such that each symbol in the string is drawn from a set of m symbols, is m^n.

Solution   Each symbol can be chosen in m independent ways, so n symbols can be chosen in m^n independent ways.   □

In our case, we ask for the number of strings of length 3 made out of three symbols $\{123\}$. By the above exercise, there are totally $3^3 = 27$ of such strings, or, in other words, ε_{ijk} are totally 27 in number, which can be explicitly constructed by giving values from the set $\{\hat{1}, \hat{2}, \hat{3}\}$ to the variables $\hat{i}, \hat{j}, \hat{k}$ in Eq. (1.23). By Eqs (1.16) and (1.23), if any two or more variables $\hat{i}, \hat{j}, \hat{k}$ have the same value from the set $\{\hat{1}, \hat{2}, \hat{3}\}$ then $\varepsilon_{ijk} = 0$. In other words, $\varepsilon_{ijk} = 0$ whenever any two or more indices ijk have the same value.

Exercise   Show that exactly 21 ε_{ijk}s are zero.

Hint   The number of ε_{ijk}, with the indices $\{i, j, k\}$ all distinct, equals the number of permutations of $(123) = 3! = 6$.   □

When all of $\hat{i}, \hat{j}, \hat{k}$ have different values, $(\hat{i} \neq \hat{j} \neq \hat{k})$, using Eq. (1.23), $\varepsilon_{ijk} = \pm 1$ depending on whether $\{ijk\}$ is a cyclic permutation of $\{123\}$ or not. This follows from Eq. (1.11) and the fact that the scalar triple product changes sign if the cyclic order of its factors is changed (see subsection 1.8.1). Thus, $\varepsilon_{312} = \hat{3} \cdot (\hat{1} \times \hat{2}) = +1$ while $\varepsilon_{132} = \hat{1} \cdot (\hat{3} \times \hat{2}) = -1$. Further, ε_{ijk} is invariant under the cyclic permutation of its indices because the scalar triple product defining it is invariant under the cyclic permutation of its factors. ε_{ijk} can be viewed as a scalar valued function of three vector variables $\{\hat{i}, \hat{j}, \hat{k}\}$ defined on the set $\{\hat{1}, \hat{2}, \hat{3}\}$. When we write all 27 values of ε_{ijk} as a three dimensional ($3 \times 3 \times 3$) array, each element having three indices, we call it a tensor. ε_{ijk} is an antisymmetric tensor because all its non-zero elements change sign under the exchange of two of their indices.

Incidentally, any two of the vector variables say $\hat{i}, \hat{j}$ can be used to give an operative definition of the Kronecker delta symbol δ_{ij} as

$$\delta_{ij} = \hat{i} \cdot \hat{j}.$$

This is because whenever $\hat{i}$ and $\hat{j}$ pick up different values from the orthonormal set $\{\hat{1}, \hat{2}, \hat{3}\}$, $\hat{i} \cdot \hat{j}$ vanishes, while whenever $\hat{i}$ and $\hat{j}$ have the same value $\hat{i} \cdot \hat{j}$ is unity. Using this definition we immediately see that

$$\delta_{ji} = \delta_{ij}.$$

Also, we have,

$$\sum_{j=1}^{3} \delta_{ij}\delta_{jk} = \delta_{i1}\delta_{1k} + \delta_{i2}\delta_{2k} + \delta_{i3}\delta_{3k} = \delta_{ik} \tag{1.24}$$

The last equality follows because the sum in the middle is unity when i and k have the same value out of $\{1, 2, 3\}$, while it vanishes if i and k have different values.

We will now prove an identity involving Levi-Civita symbols and some of the special cases of this identity which turn out to be very useful in getting vector identities (see the next section) and also in the development of vector calculus. This is

$$\varepsilon_{ijk}\varepsilon_{lmn} = \begin{vmatrix} \delta_{il} & \delta_{im} & \delta_{in} \\ \delta_{jl} & \delta_{jm} & \delta_{jn} \\ \delta_{kl} & \delta_{km} & \delta_{kn} \end{vmatrix},$$

where the elements of the determinant on the right are the Kronecker deltas we already know. Here, the equality means that the action of the LHS on an expression depending on the indices $\{ijk\}$ and $\{lmn\}$, (taking values in $\{1, 2, 3\}$), is the same as that of the determinant expression involving Kronecker deltas on the RHS. This gives a powerful way to simplify the expressions involving the products of Levi-Civita symbols.

To prove this identity, we first note that the indices $\{ijk\}$ and $\{lmn\}$ correspond to two sets of vector variables $\{\hat{\mathbf{i}}, \hat{\mathbf{j}}, \hat{\mathbf{k}}\}$ and $\{\hat{\mathbf{l}}, \hat{\mathbf{m}}, \hat{\mathbf{n}}\}$ respectively, both taking values in the orthonormal basis set $\{\hat{\mathbf{1}}, \hat{\mathbf{2}}, \hat{\mathbf{3}}\}$. As shown in Fig. 1.29 we refer to another orthonormal basis $\{\hat{\sigma}_1, \hat{\sigma}_2, \hat{\sigma}_3\}$. By Eq. (1.23) and the determinant giving scalar triple product we can write

$$\varepsilon_{ijk} = \hat{\mathbf{i}} \cdot (\hat{\mathbf{j}} \times \hat{\mathbf{k}}) = \begin{vmatrix} \hat{\mathbf{i}} \cdot \hat{\sigma}_1 & \hat{\mathbf{i}} \cdot \hat{\sigma}_2 & \hat{\mathbf{i}} \cdot \hat{\sigma}_3 \\ \hat{\mathbf{j}} \cdot \hat{\sigma}_1 & \hat{\mathbf{j}} \cdot \hat{\sigma}_2 & \hat{\mathbf{j}} \cdot \hat{\sigma}_3 \\ \hat{\mathbf{k}} \cdot \hat{\sigma}_1 & \hat{\mathbf{k}} \cdot \hat{\sigma}_2 & \hat{\mathbf{k}} \cdot \hat{\sigma}_3 \end{vmatrix} = |A| \text{ say}$$

and

$$\varepsilon_{lmn} = \hat{\mathbf{l}} \cdot (\hat{\mathbf{m}} \times \hat{\mathbf{n}}) = \begin{vmatrix} \hat{\mathbf{l}} \cdot \hat{\sigma}_1 & \hat{\mathbf{l}} \cdot \hat{\sigma}_2 & \hat{\mathbf{l}} \cdot \hat{\sigma}_3 \\ \hat{\mathbf{m}} \cdot \hat{\sigma}_1 & \hat{\mathbf{m}} \cdot \hat{\sigma}_2 & \hat{\mathbf{m}} \cdot \hat{\sigma}_3 \\ \hat{\mathbf{n}} \cdot \hat{\sigma}_1 & \hat{\mathbf{n}} \cdot \hat{\sigma}_2 & \hat{\mathbf{n}} \cdot \hat{\sigma}_3 \end{vmatrix} = |B| \text{ say.}$$

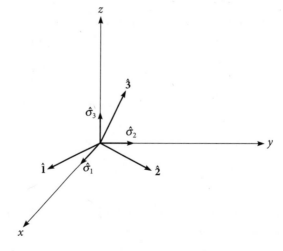

Fig. 1.29   See text

Here, $|A|$ and $|B|$ are the determinants of the corresponding matrices. Using the fact that the determinant of a matrix is the same as that of its transpose and that the product of the determinants of two matrices is the determinant of their product, (see Appendix A), we get,

$$\varepsilon_{ijk}\varepsilon_{lmn} = |A| \cdot |B| = |A| \cdot |B^{T}| = |AB^{T}| = \begin{vmatrix} \hat{\mathbf{i}}\cdot\hat{\mathbf{l}} & \hat{\mathbf{i}}\cdot\hat{\mathbf{m}} & \hat{\mathbf{i}}\cdot\hat{\mathbf{n}} \\ \hat{\mathbf{j}}\cdot\hat{\mathbf{l}} & \hat{\mathbf{j}}\cdot\hat{\mathbf{m}} & \hat{\mathbf{j}}\cdot\hat{\mathbf{n}} \\ \hat{\mathbf{k}}\cdot\hat{\mathbf{l}} & \hat{\mathbf{k}}\cdot\hat{\mathbf{m}} & \hat{\mathbf{k}}\cdot\hat{\mathbf{n}} \end{vmatrix}$$

To understand the last equality, note that a typical element of AB^{T} is (see Fig. 1.29)

$$(\hat{\mathbf{i}}\cdot\hat{\sigma}_{1})(\hat{\mathbf{l}}\cdot\hat{\sigma}_{1}) + (\hat{\mathbf{i}}\cdot\hat{\sigma}_{2})(\hat{\mathbf{l}}\cdot\hat{\sigma}_{2}) + (\hat{\mathbf{i}}\cdot\hat{\sigma}_{3})(\hat{\mathbf{l}}\cdot\hat{\sigma}_{3}) = \hat{\mathbf{i}}_{x}\hat{\mathbf{l}}_{x} + \hat{\mathbf{i}}_{y}\hat{\mathbf{l}}_{y} + \hat{\mathbf{i}}_{z}\hat{\mathbf{l}}_{z} = \hat{\mathbf{i}}\cdot\hat{\mathbf{l}}.$$

Since the variables $\{\hat{\mathbf{i}},\hat{\mathbf{j}},\hat{\mathbf{k}}\}$ and $\{\hat{\mathbf{l}},\hat{\mathbf{m}},\hat{\mathbf{n}}\}$ take values in the orthonormal basis set $\{\hat{\mathbf{1}},\hat{\mathbf{2}},\hat{\mathbf{3}}\}$, we have $\hat{\mathbf{i}}\cdot\hat{\mathbf{l}} = \delta_{il}$ etc, giving us the desired identity.

Before proceeding further, we need to introduce a convention, called Einstein summation convention, regarding the sum over a term in an expression whose terms depend on some index set, say $\{i,j,k\}$. As per this convention, a term in which an index say i is repeated is to be summed over that index. Thus, for example, $\varepsilon_{ijk}\varepsilon_{ilm} = \sum_{i=1}^{3}\varepsilon_{ijk}\varepsilon_{ilm}$, a sum in which at most one term survives. Also,

$$\delta_{kk} = \sum_{k=1}^{3}\delta_{kk} = \delta_{11} + \delta_{22} + \delta_{33} = 3.$$

Henceforth, in this book, whenever applicable, Einstein summation convention will always be assumed to apply, unless stated otherwise. So you will have to be alert about this.

We can now obtain some special cases of the result we just proved. Thus, the determinant for $\varepsilon_{ijk}\varepsilon_{ilm}$ can be obtained from that for $\varepsilon_{ijk}\varepsilon_{lmn}$ by replacing $\hat{\mathbf{l}}$ by $\hat{\mathbf{i}}$. Since all the indices $\{i,j,k\}$ must be different, (otherwise $\varepsilon_{ijk} = 0$), we must have $\hat{\mathbf{i}}\cdot\hat{\mathbf{i}} = 1$ and $\hat{\mathbf{j}}\cdot\hat{\mathbf{i}} = 0 = \hat{\mathbf{k}}\cdot\hat{\mathbf{i}}$. Substituting these values in the determinant and evaluating it we get

$$\varepsilon_{ijk}\varepsilon_{ilm} = \delta_{jl}\delta_{km} - \delta_{jm}\delta_{kl}.$$

Next, consider

$$\varepsilon_{ijk}\varepsilon_{ijl} = \delta_{jj}\delta_{kl} - \delta_{kj}\delta_{jl} = 3\delta_{kl} - \delta_{kl} = 2\delta_{kl}.$$

Here, we have used $\delta_{jj} = 3$ and $\delta_{kj}\delta_{jl} = \delta_{kl}$ which we proved above (see Eq. (1.24)).

Finally, we have,

$$\varepsilon_{ijk}\varepsilon_{ijk} = 2\delta_{kk} = 2\cdot 3 = 6.$$

Let us try and express the vector product in terms of the Levi-Civita symbols. Using Eqs (1.7) and (1.13) we can express the ith component of $\mathbf{a} \times \mathbf{b}$ as

$$(\mathbf{a} \times \mathbf{b})_i = \hat{\mathbf{i}} \cdot (\mathbf{a} \times \mathbf{b}) = a_j b_k - a_k b_j = \varepsilon_{ijk} a_j b_k. \tag{1.25}$$

In the last term, a sum over indices $j = 1, 2, 3$ and $k = 1, 2, 3$ is implied, which is a sum of nine terms. However, seven out of these nine terms vanish, because the corresponding ε_{ijk} vanish due to repeated indices, so that only two terms survive. Thus,

$$(\mathbf{a} \times \mathbf{b})_1 = \varepsilon_{123} a_2 b_3 + \varepsilon_{132} a_3 b_2 = a_2 b_3 - a_3 b_2.$$

Check that other terms in the implied sum vanish.

Subsequently, we will have many occasions to use these results.

1.12 Vector Identities

In this section, we equip our toolbox by acquiring some of the most penetrating tools of vector algebra and analysis. These are the so called vector identities. A vector identity is an equality involving vector variables which holds good for every possible (vector) value that these variables can take. From our school days, we are familiar with trigonometric identities like $\sin^2 \theta + \cos^2 \theta = 1$ or $\cos(A + B) = \cos(A)\cos(B) - \sin(A)\sin(B)$ which hold for all possible values of the angles involved. In this section, we deal with the identities involving the vector variables. We learn about the identities involving vector operators in a later section. All the vector identities can be proved using Levi-Civita notation.

We prove the vector identities one by one.

We first prove

$$\mathbf{a} \times (\mathbf{b} \times \mathbf{c}) = (\mathbf{a} \cdot \mathbf{c})\mathbf{b} - (\mathbf{a} \cdot \mathbf{b})\mathbf{c}. \tag{1.26}$$

We have,

$$\begin{aligned}
[\mathbf{a} \times (\mathbf{b} \times \mathbf{c})]_i &= \varepsilon_{ijk} a_j (\mathbf{b} \times \mathbf{c})_k \\[2mm]
&= \varepsilon_{kij} \varepsilon_{klm} a_j b_l c_m \\[2mm]
&= (\delta_{il}\delta_{jm} - \delta_{im}\delta_{jl}) a_j b_l c_m \\[2mm]
&= (a_j c_j) b_i - (a_j b_j) c_i \\[2mm]
&= (\mathbf{a} \cdot \mathbf{c}) b_i - (\mathbf{a} \cdot \mathbf{b}) c_i.
\end{aligned}$$

Thus, the ith components ($i = 1, 2, 3$) of both the sides are equal, which proves the identity. This identity tells us that the vector product of a polar and an axial vector equals the difference of two polar vectors and hence is itself a polar vector. By permuting $\mathbf{a}, \mathbf{b}, \mathbf{c}$ in cyclic order in the identity $\mathbf{a} \times (\mathbf{b} \times \mathbf{c}) = (\mathbf{a} \cdot \mathbf{c})\mathbf{b} - (\mathbf{a} \cdot \mathbf{b})\mathbf{c}$ we get two more identities,

$$\mathbf{b} \times (\mathbf{c} \times \mathbf{a}) = (\mathbf{a} \cdot \mathbf{b})\mathbf{c} - (\mathbf{b} \cdot \mathbf{c})\mathbf{a}$$

$$\mathbf{c} \times (\mathbf{a} \times \mathbf{b}) = (\mathbf{b} \cdot \mathbf{c})\mathbf{a} - (\mathbf{c} \cdot \mathbf{a})\mathbf{b}.$$

Adding these three identities we get

$$\mathbf{a} \times (\mathbf{b} \times \mathbf{c}) + \mathbf{c} \times (\mathbf{a} \times \mathbf{b}) + \mathbf{b} \times (\mathbf{c} \times \mathbf{a}) = 0.$$

The next identity is

$$(\mathbf{a} \times \mathbf{b}) \cdot (\mathbf{c} \times \mathbf{d}) = (\mathbf{a} \cdot \mathbf{c})(\mathbf{b} \cdot \mathbf{d}) - (\mathbf{a} \cdot \mathbf{d})(\mathbf{b} \cdot \mathbf{c}).$$

We have,

$$(\mathbf{a} \times \mathbf{b})_i (\mathbf{c} \times \mathbf{d})_i = \varepsilon_{ijk}\varepsilon_{ilm}a_j b_k c_l d_m$$

$$= (\delta_{jl}\delta_{km} - \delta_{jm}\delta_{kl})a_j b_k c_l d_m$$

$$= (a_j c_j)(b_k d_k) - (a_j d_j)(b_k c_k)$$

$$= (\mathbf{a} \cdot \mathbf{c})(\mathbf{b} \cdot \mathbf{d}) - (\mathbf{a} \cdot \mathbf{d})(\mathbf{b} \cdot \mathbf{c}).$$

Exercise   Prove the identity

$$(\mathbf{a} \times \mathbf{b}) \times (\mathbf{c} \times \mathbf{d}) = (\mathbf{a} \cdot \mathbf{c} \times \mathbf{d})\mathbf{b} - (\mathbf{b} \cdot \mathbf{c} \times \mathbf{d})\mathbf{a}$$

$$= (\mathbf{a} \cdot \mathbf{b} \times \mathbf{d})\mathbf{c} - (\mathbf{a} \cdot \mathbf{b} \times \mathbf{c})\mathbf{d}. \qquad \square$$

Throughout the remaining text, all these identities will be used very frequently. We recommend that you practice these identities by using them in as large variety of problems as possible. For future convenience we list these identities once again, separately. In the remaining part of the book we will refer to these identities by their Roman serial numbers in this list.

(I) $\mathbf{a} \times (\mathbf{b} \times \mathbf{c}) = (\mathbf{a} \cdot \mathbf{c})\mathbf{b} - (\mathbf{a} \cdot \mathbf{b})\mathbf{c}.$

(II) $(\mathbf{a} \times \mathbf{b}) \cdot (\mathbf{c} \times \mathbf{d}) = (\mathbf{a} \cdot \mathbf{c})(\mathbf{b} \cdot \mathbf{d}) - (\mathbf{a} \cdot \mathbf{d})(\mathbf{b} \cdot \mathbf{c}).$

(III) $\mathbf{a} \times (\mathbf{b} \times \mathbf{c}) + \mathbf{c} \times (\mathbf{a} \times \mathbf{b}) + \mathbf{b} \times (\mathbf{c} \times \mathbf{a}) = 0.$

(IV) $(\mathbf{a} \times \mathbf{b}) \times (\mathbf{c} \times \mathbf{d}) = (\mathbf{a} \cdot \mathbf{c} \times \mathbf{d})\mathbf{b} - (\mathbf{b} \cdot \mathbf{c} \times \mathbf{d})\mathbf{a} = (\mathbf{a} \cdot \mathbf{b} \times \mathbf{d})\mathbf{c} - (\mathbf{a} \cdot \mathbf{b} \times \mathbf{c})\mathbf{d}.$

Exercise   Show that

$$(\mathbf{a} \times \mathbf{b}) \cdot (\mathbf{c} \times \mathbf{d}) \times (\mathbf{e} \times \mathbf{f}) = [\mathbf{abd}][\mathbf{cef}] - [\mathbf{abc}][\mathbf{def}],$$

$$= [\mathbf{abc}][\mathbf{fcd}] - [\mathbf{abf}][\mathbf{ecd}],$$

$$= [\mathbf{cda}][\mathbf{bef}] - [\mathbf{cdb}][\mathbf{aef}],$$

where we have used Grassmann notation for the scalar triple product.   □

1.13   Vector Equations

An equation involving expressions of vectors and scalars is a (algebraic) vector equation. A vector equation can be solved either for an unknown vector or for an unknown scalar in it. The novel aspect of vector equations is that they can be transformed and solved using vector algebra. Here, we give some simple results regarding vector equations. We will have occasions to solve vector equations especially in the next chapter. In this section we use $\mathbf{x}, \mathbf{y}, \mathbf{z}, \ldots$ for vector variables (unknowns) and $\mathbf{a}, \mathbf{b}, \mathbf{c}, \ldots$ for known or constant vectors appearing in an equation. As usual, greek letters are used for scalars.

(i) A linear equation in one unknown vector may be solved similar to such a scalar equation. Thus, the equation

$$\lambda \mathbf{x} + \mu \mathbf{a} = \alpha \mathbf{x} + \beta \mathbf{b}$$

can be solved by shifting terms on either side of the equation giving

$$\mathbf{x} = \left(\frac{\beta}{\lambda - \alpha}\right)\mathbf{b} - \left(\frac{\mu}{\lambda - \alpha}\right)\mathbf{a}.$$

(ii) The vector equation $\lambda \mathbf{x} + \mu \mathbf{a} = \nu \mathbf{b}$ where $\lambda \neq 0, \mu, \nu$ are given constant scalars and $\mathbf{a}, \mathbf{b}$ are constant vectors has a unique solution $\mathbf{x} = \frac{1}{\lambda}(\nu \mathbf{b} - \mu \mathbf{a})$.

The fact that this equation admits a solution can be trivially checked. We have to subtract $\mu \mathbf{a}$ on both sides and then divide by λ on both sides to get the given solution. Properties of vector addition and scalar multiplication allow these operations. Next we can substitute the given solution for $\mathbf{x}$ in the equation and check that it satisfies the equation. Thus the given solution is a solution of the given equation. To see that this solution is unique, assume two solutions $\mathbf{x}_1$ and $\mathbf{x}_2$, substitute in the equation and equate the two resulting expressions to show that $\mathbf{x}_1 = \mathbf{x}_2$.

(iii) $\lambda \mathbf{a} + \mu \mathbf{b} = \mathbf{c}$ to be solved for two unknown scalars λ, μ where all the three vectors are given constant non-zero vectors.

Taking cross product by $\mathbf{b}$ on both sides of the equation from right we get

$$\lambda \mathbf{a} \times \mathbf{b} = \mathbf{c} \times \mathbf{b}.$$

Dotting both sides with $c \times b$ we get

$$\lambda = \frac{|c \times b|^2}{(a \times b) \cdot (c \times b)},$$

assuming that the pairs a, b and also b, c are not parallel to each other. If a and b are parallel, we have $a = \nu b$ and the equation reduces to $(\lambda \nu + \mu)b = c$. This shows that b and c are also parallel, hence there are infinite number of solutions of λ and μ. To get μ, we take cross product by a on both sides of the equation and proceed exactly as before. The result is

$$\mu = \frac{|c \times a|^2}{(b \times a) \cdot (c \times a)}.$$

(iv) The equation $x \cdot a = \lambda$ where λ is a known scalar and a is a known non-zero vector. We rewrite the equation as

$$x \cdot a = \lambda a^{-1} \cdot a, \quad \text{or} \quad (x - \lambda a^{-1}) \cdot a = 0,$$

which implies that the vector $x - \lambda a^{-1}$ is orthogonal to a so that

$$x - \lambda a^{-1} = a \times b,$$

where b is a non-zero arbitrary vector, not parallel to a. Thus,

$$x = \lambda a^{-1} + a \times b$$

is the general solution we are seeking.

(v) The equation $x \times a = b$ where $a \neq 0$ and b are known vectors admits a solution if and only if $a \cdot b = 0$.

To prove the necessity, assume that the equation admits a solution x. Hence, $a \cdot b = a \cdot (x \times a) = 0$, which establishes the necessity. Now assume $a \cdot b = 0$ and substitute the expansion of a vector x in terms of three non-coplanar vectors

$$x = \lambda a + \mu b + \nu (a \times b)$$

(with λ, μ, ν scalars), in the equation. We get, after some algebra and using $a \cdot b = 0$,

$$\mu (b \times a) + [\nu (a \cdot a) - 1]b = 0.$$

Since the vectors $b \times a$ and b are linearly independent, both the coefficients must vanish separately, giving

$$\mu = 0 \quad \text{and} \quad \nu |a|^2 - 1 = 0$$

which means $v = \frac{1}{|a|^2}$ and leads to

$$\mathbf{x} = \lambda \mathbf{a} + \frac{1}{|a|^2}(\mathbf{a} \times \mathbf{b}) = \lambda \mathbf{a} + (\mathbf{a}^{-1} \times \mathbf{b}),$$

which satisfies the given equation irrespective of the value of the scalar λ.

(vi) The equations $\mathbf{x} \cdot \mathbf{a} = \lambda$ and $\mathbf{x} \times \mathbf{b} = \mathbf{c}$ where $\mathbf{a}, \mathbf{b}, \mathbf{c}$ are given vectors with $\mathbf{a}, \mathbf{b}$ non-orthogonal ($\mathbf{a} \cdot \mathbf{b} \neq 0$,) uniquely determine vector $\mathbf{x}$.

Crossing the second equation on the left by $\mathbf{a}$ we get

$$\mathbf{a} \times (\mathbf{x} \times \mathbf{b}) = \mathbf{a} \times \mathbf{c},$$

or, using identity I,

$$(\mathbf{a} \cdot \mathbf{b})\mathbf{x} - (\mathbf{a} \cdot \mathbf{x})\mathbf{b} = \mathbf{a} \times \mathbf{c}$$

or,

$$\mathbf{x} = \frac{1}{\mathbf{a} \cdot \mathbf{b}}(\lambda \mathbf{b} + \mathbf{a} \times \mathbf{c})$$

which satisfies both the equations.

To get the uniqueness, suppose that two vectors $\mathbf{x}_1 \neq \mathbf{x}_2$ satisfy the given equations. This leads to

$$(\mathbf{x}_1 - \mathbf{x}_2) \cdot \mathbf{a} = 0 \text{ and } (\mathbf{x}_1 - \mathbf{x}_2) \times \mathbf{b} = \mathbf{0}.$$

Therefore, the vector $\mathbf{a}$ is perpendicular to and vector $\mathbf{b}$ is parallel to the vector $\mathbf{x}_1 - \mathbf{x}_2$. This makes vectors $\mathbf{a}$ and $\mathbf{b}$ mutually orthogonal, contradicting the assumption that they are not. Thus, we must require

$$\mathbf{x}_1 - \mathbf{x}_2 = \mathbf{0} \text{ or, } \mathbf{x}_1 = \mathbf{x}_2.$$

Exercise   Show that $\alpha \mathbf{a}^{-1}$ is a solution of

$$\mathbf{a} \cdot \mathbf{y} = \alpha, \ (\alpha \neq 0).$$

Show that there are infinitely many solutions.   □

Exercise   show that the necessary and sufficient condition for the equation

$$\mathbf{a} \times \mathbf{y} = \mathbf{b}$$

where $\mathbf{a}$ and $\mathbf{b}$ are known and $\mathbf{a} \neq \mathbf{0}$, posseses a solution is $\mathbf{a} \cdot \mathbf{b} = 0$.

Solution Since

$$\mathbf{a} \cdot \mathbf{b} = \mathbf{a} \cdot (\mathbf{a} \times \mathbf{y}) = 0,$$

the condition is necessary.

Now suppose $\mathbf{a} \cdot \mathbf{b} = 0$. Then,

$$\mathbf{a} \times (\mathbf{b} \times \mathbf{a}^{-1}) = \mathbf{b} - (\mathbf{a} \cdot \mathbf{b})\mathbf{a}^{-1} = \mathbf{b}.$$

Thus,

$$\mathbf{y} = \mathbf{b} \times \mathbf{a}^{-1}$$

satisfies $\mathbf{a} \times \mathbf{y} = \mathbf{b}$. The solution is not unique since

$$\mathbf{y} = \mathbf{b} \times \mathbf{a}^{-1} + \lambda \mathbf{a}$$

is also a solution. □

Exercise Show that a vector is uniquely determined if its dot product with three non-coplanar vectors are known.

Hint Expand the vector in the basis comprising the given three non-coplanar vectors. □

Exercise The resultant of two vectors is equal in magnitude to one of them and is perpendicular to it. Find the other vector.

Hint Let $\mathbf{a} + \mathbf{b} = \mathbf{c}$ with $|\mathbf{a}| = |\mathbf{c}| = \lambda$ say and let $|\mathbf{b}| = \mu$. Also, $\mathbf{a} \cdot \mathbf{c} = 0$. (Draw a figure). Take the unit vectors along $\mathbf{a}$ and $\mathbf{c}$ as the orthonormal basis. Express $\mathbf{a}, \mathbf{b}$ and $\mathbf{c}$ in terms of this basis and use the first equation. Find $\mathbf{b}$ in terms of the angle θ it makes with $\mathbf{c}$ and its magnitude λ.

Answer $\theta = \frac{\pi}{4}, \mu = \sqrt{2}\lambda$. You can get this answer just by drawing the figure. □

1.14 Coordinate Systems Revisited: Curvilinear Coordinates

As we go along any one of the coordinate axes, say x axis, only the corresponding coordinate changes while the other two remain unchanged. Let us *define* a coordinate line to be that curve in $\mathbb{R}^3$ along which only one of the coordinates changes, while other two remain the same. Now these coordinate lines need not be straight lines! The coordinate systems for which one or more coordinate lines are curves other than straight lines are called curvilinear coordinate systems. In fact we can set up coordinate systems in which the coordinate lines are circles!

1.14.1 Spherical polar coordinates

One such very useful coordinate system is the so called *spherical polar* coordinate system which we now set up (see Fig. 1.30). First, we fix a right handed rectangular Cartesian coordinate system at the origin O. Mark out a point P in space and draw the line joining points O and P. This line is the r axis and distance OP is the r coordinate of P. Note that r is always non-negative, $r \geq 0$. Let $\hat{\mathbf{r}}$ be the unit vector based at P and pointing away from O along the r coordinate line. Now draw the circle of radius r with center at O and lying in the plane defined by the unit vectors $\hat{\mathbf{r}}$ and $\hat{\mathbf{k}}$. As we go along this circle, only the polar angle θ, namely the angle between $\hat{\mathbf{r}}$ and $\hat{\mathbf{k}}$ (which defines the positive direction of the z axis), changes, while r and the third coordinate ϕ (see below) do not change. This is the θ coordinate line, which is actually a circle of radius r. Now, draw a circle in the plane parallel to the $x - y$ plane passing through P, with its center on the z axis and with radius $r \sin \theta$. (see Fig. 1.30 to check that this circle passes through P). We can measure the angular coordinate of a point on this circle, say ϕ, as the angle made by the radius of this circle passing through that point with $\hat{\mathbf{i}}$ which defines the positive direction of the x axis (the azimuthal angle). As we go along this circle, only the coordinate ϕ changes, while the other two, r and θ do not. This is the ϕ coordinate line, again a circle. Every point in $\mathbb{R}^3$ corresponds to a unique triplet of values of the (r, θ, ϕ) coordinates. Now draw the unit vectors, $\hat{\theta}$ and $\hat{\phi}$ tangent (at P) to the θ circle and ϕ circle respectively, so that the triplet $(\hat{\mathbf{r}},\hat{\theta},\hat{\phi})$ forms a right handed system. Note that different points in space have different triplet of vectors $(\hat{\mathbf{r}},\hat{\theta},\hat{\phi})$. We cannot express every vector as the linear combination of the vectors from the same triplet. A vector like $\alpha\hat{\theta}$, (α a scalar) which will appear in such a linear combination, is a vector of length α and tangent (at P) to the θ circle. However, the change in the θ coordinate corresponds to the angular advance of the vector $\mathbf{r} = \overrightarrow{OP}$ along the θ circle and not along a vector tangent at P to this circle. The vector $\mathbf{r} = \overrightarrow{OP}$ equals $r\hat{\mathbf{r}}$ where $\hat{\mathbf{r}}$ belongs to the triplet $(\hat{\mathbf{r}},\hat{\theta},\hat{\phi})$ defined at P and r is the magnitude of $\mathbf{r}$, or the length of the vector $\overrightarrow{OP}$.

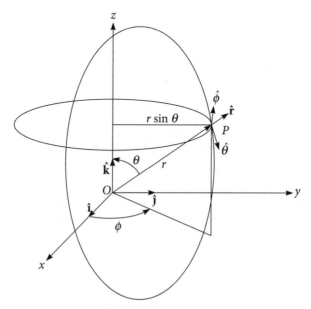

Fig. 1.30   Spherical polar coordinates

To find the relation between the Cartesian (x, y, z) and spherical polar (r, θ, ϕ) coordinates, replace $\mathbf{v}$ by $\hat{\mathbf{r}}$ (magnitude $r = 1$) in Eq. (1.8). We get,

$$\hat{\mathbf{r}} = \sin\theta\cos\phi\hat{\mathbf{i}} + \sin\theta\sin\phi\hat{\mathbf{j}} + \cos\theta\hat{\mathbf{k}}.$$

Since $\vec{OP} = r\hat{\mathbf{r}}$, we can identify the x, y, z coordinates of $\vec{OP} = \mathbf{r}$ to be

$$x = r\sin\theta\cos\phi,$$

$$y = r\sin\theta\sin\phi,$$

$$z = r\cos\theta. \tag{1.27}$$

Exercise   Convince yourself that the polar coordinates of all the vectors in $\mathbb{R}^3$ lie within $0 \le r < \infty$, $0 \le \theta \le \pi$ and $0 \le \phi < 2\pi$. (use Fig. 1.30)   □

Exercise   Show that

$$\hat{\theta} = \cos\theta\cos\phi\hat{\mathbf{i}} + \cos\theta\sin\phi\hat{\mathbf{j}} - \sin\theta\hat{\mathbf{k}}$$

and

$$\hat{\phi} = -\sin\phi\hat{\mathbf{i}} + \cos\phi\hat{\mathbf{j}}.$$

Hint   Note that $\hat{\theta} = \hat{\mathbf{r}}(\theta + \frac{\pi}{2}, \phi)$ and $\hat{\phi} = \hat{\mathbf{r}}(\theta = \frac{\pi}{2}, \phi + \frac{\pi}{2})$.   □

A coordinate line is a curve at all points of which two coordinates have constant values while the remaining coordinate takes all possible values as the coordinate line is scanned. We say that a coordinate line is parameterized by the corresponding coordinate. Thus, the (x, y) coordinates of every point on the ϕ coordinate line are completely specified by the corresponding value of ϕ, say $\phi = \phi_0$, as $x = r\sin\theta\cos\phi_0$, $y = r\sin\theta\sin\phi_0$ (remember that r and θ are constants for a ϕ coordinate line). Similarly, if we allow two of the three coordinates to vary through their all possible values, keeping the third coordinate fixed, we generate a coordinate surface, labelled by the coordinate which remains constant on that surface. For the spherical polar coordinates, the r-coordinate surface on which r remains constant say $r = R$ (R constant), is a sphere of radius R, For every $r = $ constant there is a r-surface, so we describe a family of r-surfaces as

$$x^2 + y^2 + z^2 = r^2 \text{ (spheres, } r = \text{constant).}$$

From Eq. (1.27) we see that θ-coordinate surface is generated by all points whose (x, y, z) coordinates satisfy

$$\tan\theta = (x^2 + y^2)^{1/2}/z$$

which are circular cones $\theta =$ constant. The ϕ coordinate surfaces are generated by all points whose (x, y, z) coordinates satisfy

$$\tan \phi = y/x$$

and z is arbitrary. These are half planes, that is, the planes which terminate at the z axis, because the other half plane, on the other side of the z axis corresponds to $\pi + \phi$. All these coordinate surfaces are depicted in Fig. 1.31.

Given any point in space, with coordinates R, θ_0, ϕ_0, the coordinate surfaces $r = R$, $\theta = \theta_0$ and $\phi = \phi_0$ pass through that point. The ϕ coordinate line is the intersection of the $r = R$, $\theta = \theta_0$ surfaces and lies in a plane parallel to xy plane while θ coordinate line is the intersection of $r = R$ and $\phi = \phi_0$ surfaces and lies in a plane normal to xy plane. Therefore, the vectors $\hat{\theta}, \hat{\phi}$ tangent to these curves must be mutually perpendicular. The plane containing these two vectors is tangent to the sphere $r = R$ at the given point, so that the unit vector $\hat{r}$ must be normal to both $\hat{\theta}, \hat{\phi}$. Thus, the vectors $\hat{r}, \hat{\theta}, \hat{\phi}$ form an orthonormal basis. Such a system is called an orthogonal curvilinear coordinate system.

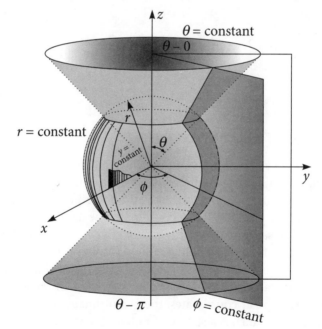

Fig. 1.31 Coordinate surfaces are $x^2 + y^2 + z^2 = r^2$ (spheres $r =$ constant) $\tan \theta = (x^2 + y^2)^{1/2}/z$ (circular cones, $\theta =$ constant) $\tan \phi = y/x$ (half planes $\phi =$ constant)

1.14.2 Parabolic coordinates

We shall learn about one more orthogonal curvilinear coordinate system, namely, the parabolic coordinate system. We first set up a right handed Cartesian coordinate system with orthonormal basis $(\hat{\mathbf{i}}, \hat{\mathbf{j}}, \hat{\mathbf{k}})$. A point in space having Cartesian coordinates (x, y, z)

has parabolic coordinates denoted by (μ, ν, ϕ), $(\mu, \nu \geq 0, 0 \leq \phi < 2\pi)$. These two sets of coordinates are related by

$$x = \mu \nu \cos \phi,$$

$$y = \mu \nu \sin \phi,$$

$$z = \frac{1}{2}\left(\mu^2 - \nu^2\right). \tag{1.28}$$

These equations have all the information regarding the geometry of the parabolic coordinate system. To get it, we first identify the coordinate ϕ with the azimuthal angle defined above in the context of polar coordinates. Then, the first two of Eq. (1.28) tell us that the ϕ coordinate line is a circle of radius $\mu \nu$, passing through the given point and the corresponding basis vector $\hat{\phi}$ must be tangent to this circle at the given point. The ϕ coordinate plane passes through the z axis, making an angle ϕ with the positive direction of the x axis.

To get the coordinate lines for μ and ν, we first fix the azimuthal angle $\phi = 0$. This mean we choose the xz or $y = 0$ plane to see the variations of μ and ν. We assume that the given point lies in the $y = 0$ plane. We now give some constant value to ν, say $\nu = \nu_0$. With $\phi = 0$ and $\nu = \nu_0$ the first of Eq. (1.28) gives $\mu = x/\nu_0$ and the third of Eq. (1.28) becomes

$$z = \frac{1}{2}\left(\frac{x^2}{\nu_0^2} - \nu_0^2\right). \tag{1.29}$$

This is a parabola flattened by dividing each value of x^2 by the constant $2\nu_0^2$ and shifted downwards from the origin by $\frac{1}{2}\nu_0^2$. By choosing the value of ν_0 properly, we can make this parabola pass through the given point giving ν_0 as the value of its ν coordinate. This parabola is the coordinate line for μ, because only μ varies on it, while both $\nu = \nu_0$ and $\phi = 0$ are constants. To get the coordinate line for ν, we make μ to be a constant $\mu = \mu_0$ so that the third of Eq. (1.28) becomes

$$z = \frac{1}{2}\left(\mu_0^2 - \frac{x^2}{\mu_0^2}\right). \tag{1.30}$$

This is an inverted parabola flattened by the division by the constant $2\mu_0^2$ and shifted upwards from the origin by $\frac{1}{2}\mu_0^2$. By suitably choosing μ_0, we can make this parabola pass through the given point, making chosen μ_0 to be the value of its μ coordinate. This parabola is the coordinate line for ν, on which only ν varies, while $\mu = \mu_0$ and $\phi = 0$ are constants.

Let us now show that these parabolas intersect normally at the given point. Let $d\mathbf{r}_1$ and $d\mathbf{r}_2$ be the differential displacements along the $\nu = \nu_0$ and $\mu = \mu_0$ parabolas respectively.

By differential displacement we mean the displacement ds of a point along the parabola, which is so small that the error incurred by replacing $|ds|$ by $|d\mathbf{r}|$, where $d\mathbf{r}$ is the difference between the position vectors at the endpoints, is utterly negligible (see Fig. 1.32). Let $d\mathbf{r}_1 = dx_1\hat{\mathbf{i}} + dz_1\hat{\mathbf{k}}$, and $d\mathbf{r}_2 = dx_2\hat{\mathbf{i}} + dz_2\hat{\mathbf{k}}$ define the corresponding components. We then have,

$$
\begin{aligned}
d\mathbf{r}_1 \cdot d\mathbf{r}_2 &= dx_1\,dx_2 + dz_1\,dz_2 \\
&= dx^2\left(1 - \frac{x_0^2}{\mu_0^2 v_0^2}\right) \\
&= 0
\end{aligned}
$$

(1.31)

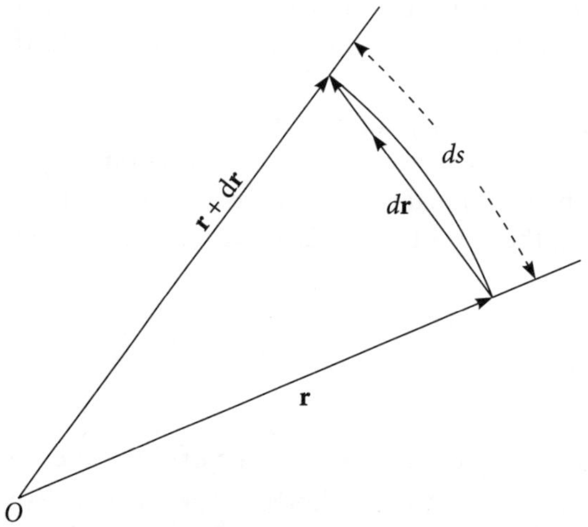

Fig. 1.32   Differential displacement corresponds to $|ds| = |d\mathbf{r}|$ (see text)

where we have taken $dx_1 = dx = dx_2$, differentiated Eqs (1.29) and (1.30) to get dz_1 and dz_2 and used the fact that by the first of Eq. (1.28) $x_0^2 = \mu_0^2 v_0^2$ for $\phi = 0$. Geometrically, this means that the tangent vectors to the two parabolas at the intersection point are orthogonal to each other. Since the tangent vector to the ϕ coordinate circle at the given point is normal to the $y = 0$ plane it is normal to the tangent vectors to the two parabolas. Thus, the basis vectors for the parabolic coordinate system form an orthonormal triad $(\hat{\mu}, \hat{v}, \hat{\phi})$ which are the tangent vectors to the three coordinate lines at the given point such that they form a right handed system (Fig. 1.33).

If we change the azimuthal angle ϕ from zero, the $y = 0$ plane rotates through the same angle, without changing the μ and v parabolas in any way. This completes the construction of the parabolic coordinate system.

Note, again, that the basis triad $(\hat{\mu}, \hat{v}, \hat{\phi})$ changes from point to point. Therefore, for the same reasons as explained in the case of polar coordinates, every vector cannot be expanded in terms of the same basis triad. To get the coordinate surfaces say for constant μ ($\mu = \mu_0$) we note that for an arbitrary value of ϕ say $\phi = \phi_0$, the first two of Eq. (1.28) give $x^2 + y^2 = \mu^2 v^2$ and hence the equation for the parabola with $\mu = \mu_0$ in the plane corresponding to $\phi = \phi_0$ is obtained by replacing x^2 in Eq. (1.29) by $x^2 + y^2$. This equation is independent of ϕ and hence applies to every value of ϕ. Thus, all the points (x, y, z) satisfying

$$z = \frac{1}{2}\left(\mu_0^2 - \frac{x^2 + y^2}{\mu_0^2}\right)$$

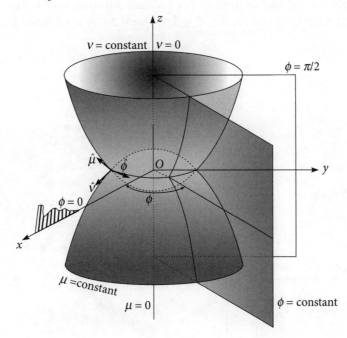

Fig. 1.33   Parabolic coordinates (μ, ν, ϕ). Coordinate surfaces are paraboloids of revolution ($\mu =$ constant, $\nu =$ constant) and half-planes ($\phi =$ constant)

or,

$$x^2 + y^2 = \mu_0^2\left(\mu_0^2 - 2z\right)$$

for constant $\mu = \mu_0$ lie on the paraboloid of revolution revolving the parabola (that is, covering all values of ϕ) about the z axis. On this surface $\mu = \mu_0$ and (ν, ϕ) can take all possible values. The surface for constant $\phi = \phi_0$ is a half plane, that is, the plane terminating at the z axis, because the half plane on the other side of the z axis corresponds to $\phi = \pi + \phi_0$. Thus, the families of coordinate surfaces are given by

$$x^2 + y^2 = \mu_0^2\left(\mu_0^2 - 2z\right) \tag{1.32}$$

(paraboloids of revolution, $\mu = $ constant),

$$x^2 + y^2 = \mu_0^2 \left(\mu_0^2 + 2z \right) \tag{1.33}$$

(paraboloids of revolution, $\nu = $ constant),

$$\tan \phi = y/x \tag{1.34}$$

(half planes $\phi = $ constant).

Exercise Justify the coordinate lines and coordinate surfaces, shown in Fig. 1.34, for the cylindrical coordinates $(0 \leq \rho < \infty, 0 \leq \phi < 2\pi, -\infty < z < +\infty)$ defined by

$$x = \rho \cos \phi,$$

$$y = \rho \sin \phi,$$

$$z = z, \tag{1.35}$$

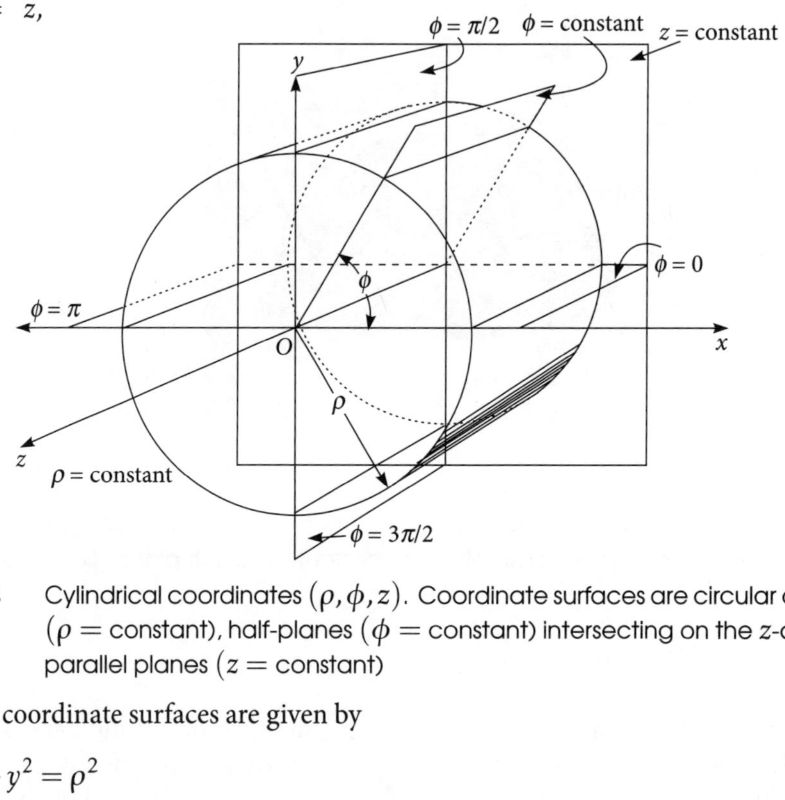

Fig. 1.34   Cylindrical coordinates (ρ, ϕ, z). Coordinate surfaces are circular cylinders $(\rho = $ constant), half-planes $(\phi = $ constant) intersecting on the z-axis, and parallel planes $(z = $ constant)

where the coordinate surfaces are given by

$$x^2 + y^2 = \rho^2$$

(circular cylinders, $\rho = $ constant),

$$\tan \phi = y/x$$

(half planes, $\phi = $ constant),

$$z = \text{constant}$$

(planes).   □

Exercise   Find the coordinate lines and the coordinate surfaces for the prolate spheroidal coordinates ($0 \leq \eta < \infty$, $0 \leq \theta \leq \pi$, $0 \leq \phi < 2\pi$) given by (see Fig. 1.35)

$$x = a \sinh \eta \sin \theta \cos \phi,$$

$$y = a \sinh \eta \sin \theta \sin \phi,$$

$$z = a \cosh \eta \cos \theta, \tag{1.36}$$

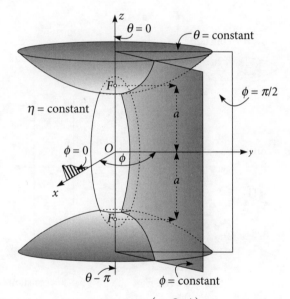

Fig. 1.35   Prolate spheroidal coordinates (η, θ, ϕ). Coordinate surfaces are prolate spheroids ($\eta = $ constant), hyperboloids ($\theta = $ constant), and half-planes ($\phi = $ constant)

where the coordinate surfaces are

$$\frac{x^2}{a^2 \sinh^2 \eta} + \frac{y^2}{a^2 \sinh^2 \eta} + \frac{z^2}{a^2 \cosh^2 \eta} = 1$$

(prolate spheroids, $\eta = $ constant),

$$\frac{-x^2}{a^2 \sin^2 \theta} - \frac{y^2}{a^2 \sin^2 \theta} + \frac{z^2}{a^2 \cos^2 \theta} = 1$$

(hyperboloids of two sheets, $\theta = $ constant),

$\tan \phi = y/x$

(half planes, $\phi = $ constant). □

Exercise Find the coordinate lines and the coordinate surfaces for the oblate spheroidal coordinates $(0 \le \eta < \infty, 0 \le \theta \le \pi, 0 \le \phi < 2\pi)$ given by (see Fig. 1.36)

$$x = a \cosh \eta \sin \theta \cos \phi,$$

$$y = a \cosh \eta \sin \theta \sin \phi,$$

$$z = a \sinh \eta \cos \theta, \tag{1.37}$$

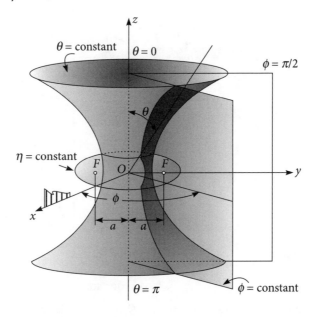

Fig. 1.36 Oblate spheroidal coordinates (η, θ, ϕ). Coordinate surfaces are oblate spheroids ($\eta = $ constant), hyperboloids ($\theta = $ constant), and half-planes ($\phi = $ constant)

where the coordinate surfaces are

$$\frac{x^2}{a^2 \cosh^2 \eta} + \frac{y^2}{a^2 \cosh^2 \eta} + \frac{z^2}{a^2 \sinh^2 \eta} = 1$$

(oblate spheroids, $\eta = $ constant),

$$\frac{x^2}{a^2 \sin^2 \theta} + \frac{y^2}{a^2 \sin^2 \theta} - \frac{z^2}{a^2 \cos^2 \theta} = 1$$

(hyperboloids of one sheet, $\theta = $ constant),

$$\tan\phi = y/x$$

(half planes, $\phi = $ constant).   □

1.15   Vector Fields

We want to understand the concept of a vector field. The best way for us is to understand it operatively first, which will then lead to its mathematical meaning. To get to the physical meaning of a field, we must apply the principle of relativity by Einstein, however, we will not attempt that in this book. We first choose a point in space to be the origin O. We then obtain the position vector of a point P in space based at the origin O. Thereafter, we base a vector giving the value of some physical quantity at P. We now imagine that we base some vector giving a value of this physical quantity at every point in space, or in some region of space. This association, of the set of vectors giving values of a physical quantity with the set of position vectors or points in space (including the origin) is called a vector field. To give this procedure a meaning, we must seek the rule by which the vector values of a vector quantity are associated with the points in space. This rule can be either a one to one or many to one correspondence between the points in space and the vector values of a vector quantity (that is, the vectors assigned to different points in space could be different or equal). In other words, this rule is a function taking in a position vector and returning the vector value of a vector quantity corresponding to that position vector or the point. Thus, the vector field is the vector valued function of the position vectors. A function taking in a position vector specifying a point in space and returning a scalar is said to generate a scalar field. A function generating a vector field or a scalar field can be viewed as the function of the coordinates, that is, a function which takes in a triplet of real numbers (components of the position vector or coordinates specifying a point in space) and returns another triplet of real numbers (components of the vector to be assigned to that point) or a scalar. When viewed as a function of coordinates, a function generating a field is required to be a 'point function' that is, the value of the function at any point must remain invariant even if we switch over to another coordinate system changing the coordinates of that point. A coordinate transformation will yield a new function of new coordinates, which, when evaluated at the new coordinates of the same point, must give the same value of the field at that point. A field value at a point cannot depend on which coordinate system we use to refer to that point. Suppose a function of the latitude and longitude returns the temperature at a place on earth with the given latitude and longitude. If we specify the coordinates of the points on earth using a rotated mesh of latitude-longitude and use the corresponding transformation to get a new function of new coordinates for this scalar field, then this new function, when evaluated at the new coordinates of the same place, must give the same temperature. Temperature at a place cannot depend on which coordinate system we choose to refer to that place.

Physically, a vector field is produced by its sources and the problem is to relate this field to the characteristic properties of its sources. These relations are often expressed as differential equations. Thus, the electromagnetic field produced by a given source of charges and currents is the solution of Maxwell's equations which relate the fields with the charge and current densities of the source. Since the Maxwell's equations are linear, the fields produced by the multiple sources can simply be added (superposed) to get the total field at a point. Another example is the velocity field of a fluid, which is the assignment of the fluid velocity vector at every point in the region of space occupied by the fluid. For a general fluid, this field has to solve the Navier–Stokes equation, whose analytical solution still eludes us. Further, Navier–Stokes equation is non-linear and gives rise to phenomena like turbulence, which is another unsolved problem. Solving Maxwell's equations and special cases of the Navier–Stokes equation in various circumstances forms the content of Electrodynamics and Fluid Mechanics. We will not make any attempt to learn about these differential equations as they are far away lands where we have no intentions of trading.

1.16 Orientation of a Triplet of Non-coplanar Vectors

We have seen how an ordered triplet forming an orthonormal basis can be given an orientation when we defined the right handed and left handed coordinate systems. Generally, any ordered triple of linearly independent (non-coplanar) vectors $(\mathbf{a}, \mathbf{b}, \mathbf{c})$ (based at a common point O say) defines a certain *sense* or *orientation*. We may, for example, rotate the direction of $\mathbf{a}$ into that of $\mathbf{b}$ in the $(\mathbf{a}, \mathbf{b})$ plane, by an angle between 0 and π, and try and relate a vector whose direction depends on such a rotation with that of $\mathbf{c}$. Thus, we call the triplet $(\mathbf{a}, \mathbf{b}, \mathbf{c})$ *positively oriented* if the rotation of the direction of $\mathbf{a}$ into that of $\mathbf{b}$ by an angle between 0 and π in the $(\mathbf{a}, \mathbf{b})$ plane advances a right handed screw toward that side of the $(\mathbf{a}, \mathbf{b})$ plane to which the vector $\mathbf{c}$ points. The triplet $(\mathbf{a}, \mathbf{b}, \mathbf{c})$ is *negatively oriented* if the advance of the right handed screw under the above rotation is toward the opposite side. Equivalently, the sense or orientation of the triplet $(\mathbf{a}, \mathbf{b}, \mathbf{c})$ is defined by the sense (counterclockwise or clockwise) that the above rotation appears to have, when viewed from that side of the $(\mathbf{a}, \mathbf{b})$ plane to which the vector $\mathbf{c}$ points. Thus for example, the triplets $(\mathbf{a}, \mathbf{b}, \mathbf{c})$ and $(\mathbf{b}, \mathbf{a}, \mathbf{c})$ have opposite orientations (see Fig. 1.37).

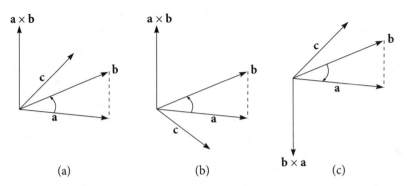

Fig. 1.37 (a) Positively and (b) negatively oriented triplets $(\mathbf{a}, \mathbf{b}, \mathbf{c})$, (c) Triplet $(\mathbf{b}, \mathbf{a}, \mathbf{c})$ has orientation opposite to that of $(\mathbf{a}, \mathbf{b}, \mathbf{c})$ in (a)

We shall now show that the necessary and sufficient condition for a triplet $(\mathbf{a}, \mathbf{b}, \mathbf{c})$ to be positively oriented is that $\mathbf{c} \cdot (\mathbf{a} \times \mathbf{b})$ or any of its cyclic permutations exceeds zero.

Suppose $(\mathbf{a}, \mathbf{b}, \mathbf{c})$ are positively oriented. Then from the definitions of the positive orientation and the vector product we see that both $(\mathbf{a} \times \mathbf{b})$ and $\mathbf{c}$ are on the same side of the $(\mathbf{a}, \mathbf{b})$ plane. This implies that the angle between $(\mathbf{a} \times \mathbf{b})$ and $\mathbf{c}$ is less than $\pi/2$ which means $\mathbf{c} \cdot (\mathbf{a} \times \mathbf{b}) > 0$.

Suppose $\mathbf{c} \cdot (\mathbf{a} \times \mathbf{b}) > 0$. This means the angle between $(\mathbf{a} \times \mathbf{b})$ and $\mathbf{c}$ is less than $\pi/2$, or, $(\mathbf{a} \times \mathbf{b})$ and $\mathbf{c}$ are on the same side of the $(\mathbf{a}, \mathbf{b})$ plane, or the rotation from $\mathbf{a}$ toward $\mathbf{b}$ advances a right handed screw on the same side of the $(\mathbf{a}, \mathbf{b})$ plane to which $\mathbf{c}$ points. In other words, $(\mathbf{a}, \mathbf{b}, \mathbf{c})$ are positively oriented.

Since the scalar triple product is invariant under cyclic permutations of factors, above proof applies to all cyclic permutations of $\mathbf{c} \cdot (\mathbf{a} \times \mathbf{b})$. Thus, we can conclude that the orientation of $(\mathbf{a}, \mathbf{b}, \mathbf{c})$ is invariant under the cyclic permutation of $(\mathbf{a}, \mathbf{b}, \mathbf{c})$.

Triplets $(\mathbf{a}, \mathbf{b}, \mathbf{c})$ and $(\mathbf{d}, \mathbf{e}, \mathbf{f})$ are oriented (mutually) positively (negatively) with respect to each other if they have the same (opposite) orientations. In particular, $(\mathbf{a}, \mathbf{b}, \mathbf{c})$ is oriented positively (negatively) with respect to an orthonormal basis $(\hat{\mathbf{e}}_1, \hat{\mathbf{e}}_2, \hat{\mathbf{e}}_3)$ or the corresponding coordinate axes (x, y, z) if $(\mathbf{a}, \mathbf{b}, \mathbf{c})$ and $(\hat{\mathbf{e}}_1, \hat{\mathbf{e}}_2, \hat{\mathbf{e}}_3)$ have the same (opposite) orientations. Whether a given triplet $(\mathbf{a}, \mathbf{b}, \mathbf{c})$ is oriented positively or negatively with respect to an orthonormal basis $(\hat{\mathbf{e}}_1, \hat{\mathbf{e}}_2, \hat{\mathbf{e}}_3)$ is decided, respectively, by the positive or negative sign of

$$\det(\mathbf{a}, \mathbf{b}, \mathbf{c}) = \begin{vmatrix} a_1 & a_2 & a_3 \\ b_1 & b_2 & b_3 \\ c_1 & c_2 & c_3 \end{vmatrix}, \tag{1.38}$$

where each row consists of the components of the corresponding vector with respect to the orthonormal basis $(\hat{\mathbf{e}}_1, \hat{\mathbf{e}}_2, \hat{\mathbf{e}}_3)$ (see the second exercise on page 39). Exchanging the first two columns of this determinant amounts to exchanging x, y axes or changing over to a coordinate system with different handedness. This changes the sign of the determinant, so that orientation of $(\mathbf{a}, \mathbf{b}, \mathbf{c})$ with respect to the new coordinate system becomes opposite to that with respect to the previous one. Thus, the sign of the determinant comprising the components of a given triplet of vectors $(\mathbf{a}, \mathbf{b}, \mathbf{c})$ decides the orientation of $(\mathbf{a}, \mathbf{b}, \mathbf{c})$ with respect to the corresponding orthonormal basis $(\hat{\mathbf{e}}_1, \hat{\mathbf{e}}_2, \hat{\mathbf{e}}_3)$, or, as sometimes said, with respect to the (x, y, z) coordinates or axes. Thus, the sign of the determinant in Eq. (1.38) does not have a geometrical meaning independent of a coordinate system. However, a statement like 'two non-coplanar ordered triplets have the same or the opposite orientation' has a coordinate free geometrical meaning.

Consider two ordered triplets of non-coplanar vectors $\mathbf{a}_1, \mathbf{a}_2, \mathbf{a}_3$ and $\mathbf{b}_1, \mathbf{b}_2, \mathbf{b}_3$. The two sets have the same orientation, that is, are both positively or both negatively oriented with respect to a common coordinate system (x_1, x_2, x_3) if and only if the condition

$$\det(\mathbf{a}_1, \mathbf{a}_2, \mathbf{a}_3) \cdot \det(\mathbf{b}_1, \mathbf{b}_2, \mathbf{b}_3) > 0$$

is satisfied. Using identity (A.31), we can write this condition in the form

$$[\mathbf{a}_1, \mathbf{a}_2, \mathbf{a}_3; \mathbf{b}_1, \mathbf{b}_2, \mathbf{b}_3] > 0 \tag{1.39}$$

where the symbol on the left denotes a function of six vector variables defined by

$$[\mathbf{a}_1, \mathbf{a}_2, \mathbf{a}_3; \mathbf{b}_1, \mathbf{b}_2, \mathbf{b}_3] = \begin{vmatrix} \mathbf{a}_1 \cdot \mathbf{b}_1 & \mathbf{a}_1 \cdot \mathbf{b}_2 & \mathbf{a}_1 \cdot \mathbf{b}_3 \\ \mathbf{a}_2 \cdot \mathbf{b}_1 & \mathbf{a}_2 \cdot \mathbf{b}_2 & \mathbf{a}_2 \cdot \mathbf{b}_3 \\ \mathbf{a}_3 \cdot \mathbf{b}_1 & \mathbf{a}_3 \cdot \mathbf{b}_2 & \mathbf{a}_3 \cdot \mathbf{b}_3 \end{vmatrix}. \tag{1.40}$$

Note that for $\mathbf{b}_1 = \mathbf{a}_1, \mathbf{b}_2 = \mathbf{a}_2, \mathbf{b}_3 = \mathbf{a}_3$ Eq. (1.40) reduces to the definition of the Gram determinant $\Gamma(\mathbf{a}_1, \mathbf{a}_2, \mathbf{a}_3)$ (see Appendix A). Equations (1.39) and (1.40) show that, for two ordered triplets having the same orientation (relative to a coordinate system) is a geometric property independent of any particular Cartesian coordinate system used. We denote this property symbolically by

$$\Omega(\mathbf{a}_1, \mathbf{a}_2, \mathbf{a}_3) = \Omega(\mathbf{b}_1, \mathbf{b}_2, \mathbf{b}_3) \tag{1.41}$$

and the property of having opposite orientation by

$$\Omega(\mathbf{a}_1, \mathbf{a}_2, \mathbf{a}_3) = -\Omega(\mathbf{b}_1, \mathbf{b}_2, \mathbf{b}_3). \tag{1.42}$$

We can combine these two equations in a single one:

$$\Omega(\mathbf{a}_1, \mathbf{a}_2, \mathbf{a}_3) = sgn[\mathbf{a}_1, \mathbf{a}_2, \mathbf{a}_3; \mathbf{b}_1, \mathbf{b}_2, \mathbf{b}_3]\Omega(\mathbf{b}_1, \mathbf{b}_2, \mathbf{b}_3). \tag{1.43}$$

The last three equations are meaningful even if we do not assign a numeric value to the individual orientation Ω. Equation (1.43) associates a value ± 1 to the *ratio* of two orientations, while Eqs (1.41) and (1.42) express equality or inequality of orientations. It is possible to specify two possible orientations of triplets of vectors completely by assigning numerical values say $\Omega = \pm 1$ to these orientations by arbitrarily choosing the standard value $+1$ for the orientation of the basis vectors $(\hat{\mathbf{e}}_1, \hat{\mathbf{e}}_2, \hat{\mathbf{e}}_3)$ defining the coordinate system. Such a situation arises in science and engineering in the context of every measurable quantity. For example, equality of distances between points in space or even the ratio of distances have meaning even if no numerical values are assigned to the individual distances. It is of course possible to assign numerical values to individual distances such that the ratio of distances equals the ratio of the corresponding real numbers. This requires an arbitrary selection of a "standard distance" or a unit of distance to which all other distances are referred. Thus Eq. (1.41) is analogus to saying that distances between two pairs of points are equal without giving them specific values.

The triplet $\mathbf{a}_1, \mathbf{a}_2, \mathbf{a}_3$ is oriented positively or negatively with respect to (x_1, x_2, x_3) coordinates according to whether they are oriented positively or negatively with respect to the corresponding orthonormal basis $(\hat{\mathbf{e}}_1, \hat{\mathbf{e}}_2, \hat{\mathbf{e}}_3)$, that is, whether

$$\Omega(\mathbf{a}_1, \mathbf{a}_2, \mathbf{a}_3) = \Omega(\hat{\mathbf{e}}_1, \hat{\mathbf{e}}_2, \hat{\mathbf{e}}_3) \tag{1.44}$$

or

$$\Omega(\mathbf{a}_1,\mathbf{a}_2,\mathbf{a}_3) = -\Omega(\hat{\mathbf{e}}_1,\hat{\mathbf{e}}_2,\hat{\mathbf{e}}_3). \tag{1.45}$$

Sometimes, we denote the orientation of the coordinate system $\Omega(\hat{\mathbf{e}}_1,\hat{\mathbf{e}}_2,\hat{\mathbf{e}}_3)$ by $\Omega(x_1,x_2,x_3)$. Since the value of the determinant in Eq. (1.38) gives the signed volume of the parallelepiped spanned by a triplet of linearly independent vectors, for two such triplets of vectors we have,

$$[\mathbf{a}_1,\mathbf{a}_2,\mathbf{a}_3;\mathbf{b}_1,\mathbf{b}_2,\mathbf{b}_3] = \epsilon_1\epsilon_2 V_1 V_2 \tag{1.46}$$

where V_1 and V_2 are, respectively the volumes of the parallelepipeds spanned by the two triplets and the factors ϵ_1,ϵ_2 depend on their orientations with respect to the basis $(\hat{\mathbf{e}}_1,\hat{\mathbf{e}}_2,\hat{\mathbf{e}}_3)$ defining the coordinate system:

$$\epsilon_1 = sgn[\mathbf{a}_1,\mathbf{a}_2,\mathbf{a}_3;\hat{\mathbf{e}}_1,\hat{\mathbf{e}}_2,\hat{\mathbf{e}}_3]$$

$$\epsilon_2 = sgn[\mathbf{b}_1,\mathbf{b}_2,\mathbf{b}_3;\hat{\mathbf{e}}_1,\hat{\mathbf{e}}_2,\hat{\mathbf{e}}_3] \tag{1.47}$$

and the relative orientation of the two triplets

$$\epsilon_1\epsilon_2 = sgn[\mathbf{a}_1,\mathbf{a}_2,\mathbf{a}_3;\mathbf{b}_1,\mathbf{b}_2,\mathbf{b}_3] \tag{1.48}$$

is independent of the choice of the coordinate system and has the value $+1$ if the parallelepipeds have the same orientation but -1 if they have the opposite orientations. If the two triplets refer to two different coordinate systems with the orthonormal bases $(\hat{\mathbf{e}}_1,\hat{\mathbf{e}}_2,\hat{\mathbf{e}}_3)$ and $(\hat{\mathbf{h}}_1,\hat{\mathbf{h}}_2,\hat{\mathbf{h}}_3)$ then,

$$\epsilon_1 = sgn[\mathbf{a}_1,\mathbf{a}_2,\mathbf{a}_3;\hat{\mathbf{e}}_1,\hat{\mathbf{e}}_2,\hat{\mathbf{e}}_3]$$

$$\epsilon_2 = sgn[\mathbf{b}_1,\mathbf{b}_2,\mathbf{b}_3;\hat{\mathbf{h}}_1,\hat{\mathbf{h}}_2,\hat{\mathbf{h}}_3]$$

$$\mu = sgn[\mathbf{e}_1,\mathbf{e}_2,\mathbf{e}_3;\hat{\mathbf{h}}_1,\hat{\mathbf{h}}_2,\hat{\mathbf{h}}_3] \tag{1.49}$$

and the relative orientation of the two triplets, independent of the coordinate systems is given by

$$\epsilon_1\epsilon_2\mu = sgn[\mathbf{a}_1,\mathbf{a}_2,\mathbf{a}_3;\mathbf{b}_1,\mathbf{b}_2,\mathbf{b}_3] \tag{1.50}$$

and

$$[\mathbf{a}_1,\mathbf{a}_2,\mathbf{a}_3;\mathbf{b}_1,\mathbf{b}_2,\mathbf{b}_3] = \epsilon_1\epsilon_2\mu V_1 V_2 \tag{1.51}$$

where $\epsilon_1,\epsilon_2,\mu$ equal ±1 according to whether the corresponding triplets are oriented positively or negatively. These equations are useful while dealing with triplets of vectors (generally based in different regions of space) which refer to different coordinate systems.

However, if it is possible to choose the two coordinate systems which are positively oriented with respect to each other, so as to ensure $\mu = +1$, then Eq. (1.48) applies, which decides the relative orientation of the two triplets.

Our method of deciding the orientation of ordered sets of vectors by the sign of their determinants can be applied to the doublets of non-collinear vectors spanning a plane. We just have to find out

$$[\mathbf{a}_1,\mathbf{a}_2;\mathbf{b}_1,\mathbf{b}_2] = \begin{vmatrix} \mathbf{a}_1 \cdot \mathbf{b}_1 & \mathbf{a}_1 \cdot \mathbf{b}_2 \\ \mathbf{a}_2 \cdot \mathbf{b}_1 & \mathbf{a}_2 \cdot \mathbf{b}_2 \end{vmatrix}. \tag{1.52}$$

so that the equation

$$\Omega(\mathbf{a}_1,\mathbf{a}_2) = sgn[\mathbf{a}_1,\mathbf{a}_2;\mathbf{b}_1,\mathbf{b}_2]\Omega(\mathbf{b}_1,\mathbf{b}_2) \tag{1.53}$$

decides whether the two doublets $(\mathbf{a}_1,\mathbf{a}_2)$ and $(\mathbf{b}_1,\mathbf{b}_2)$ have the same or opposite orientations.

Exercise Let $\hat{\mathbf{e}}_1,\hat{\mathbf{e}}_2$ be an orthonormal basis in a plane. Show that the doublets $\hat{\mathbf{e}}_1,\hat{\mathbf{e}}_2$ and $\hat{\mathbf{e}}_2,\hat{\mathbf{e}}_1$ have opposite orientations.

Solution We have

$$[\hat{\mathbf{e}}_1,\hat{\mathbf{e}}_2;\hat{\mathbf{e}}_2,\hat{\mathbf{e}}_1] = \begin{vmatrix} \hat{\mathbf{e}}_1 \cdot \hat{\mathbf{e}}_2 & \hat{\mathbf{e}}_1 \cdot \hat{\mathbf{e}}_1 \\ \hat{\mathbf{e}}_2 \cdot \hat{\mathbf{e}}_2 & \hat{\mathbf{e}}_2 \cdot \hat{\mathbf{e}}_1 \end{vmatrix} = -1, \tag{1.54}$$

so that,

$$\Omega(\hat{\mathbf{e}}_2,\hat{\mathbf{e}}_1) = -\Omega(\hat{\mathbf{e}}_1,\hat{\mathbf{e}}_2). \qquad \square$$

1.16.1 Orientation of a plane

To orient a plane π we set up a 2-D coordinate system given by a pair of orthonormal vectors $\hat{\mathbf{e}}_1,\hat{\mathbf{e}}_2$ and define the orientation of the oriented plane π^* by

$$\Omega(\pi^*) = \Omega(\hat{\mathbf{e}}_1,\hat{\mathbf{e}}_2). \tag{1.55}$$

Any two linearly independent vectors $(\mathbf{a}_1,\mathbf{a}_2)$ in the plane are oriented positively if

$$\Omega(\mathbf{a}_1,\mathbf{a}_2) = \Omega(\pi^*) = \Omega(\hat{\mathbf{e}}_1,\hat{\mathbf{e}}_2).$$

Thus, all doublets positively oriented with respect to the basis $(\hat{\mathbf{e}}_1,\hat{\mathbf{e}}_2)$ are positively oriented with respect to π^*.

An oriented plane π^* can be characterized by a distinguished *positive sense of rotation*. If a pair of vectors $\mathbf{a}, \mathbf{b}$ is oriented positively with respect to π^*, the positive sense of rotation of π^* is the sense of rotation by an angle less than π radians that takes the direction of $\mathbf{a}$ into that of $\mathbf{b}$.

Just as we can orient a plane, we can orient a 3-D region σ by specifying an orthonormal basis $(\hat{\mathbf{h}}_1, \hat{\mathbf{h}}_2, \hat{\mathbf{h}}_3)$ and defining the orientation of the oriented region σ^* by

$$\Omega(\sigma^*) = \Omega(\hat{\mathbf{h}}_1, \hat{\mathbf{h}}_2, \hat{\mathbf{h}}_3).$$

All triplets which are positively oriented with respect to this basis are positively oriented with respect to σ^*. When an oriented plane π^* lies in an oriented 3-D region σ^*, we can define the positive and negative sides of π^*. We take two independent vectors $\mathbf{b}$ and $\mathbf{c}$ in π^* that are positively oriented:

$$\Omega(\mathbf{b}, \mathbf{c}) = \Omega(\pi^*).$$

A third vector $\mathbf{a}$, independent of $\mathbf{b}, \mathbf{c}$ is said to point to the *positive side* of π^* if

$$\Omega(\mathbf{a}, \mathbf{b}, \mathbf{c}) = \Omega(\sigma^*).$$

Since σ^* is oriented positively with respect to a Cartesian coordinate system, we can replace this condition by

$$\det(\mathbf{a}, \mathbf{b}, \mathbf{c}) > 0.$$

If σ^* is oriented positively with respect to a right handed coordinate system, then the positive side of an oriented plane π^* is the one from which the positive sense of rotation in π^* appears counterclockwise.

2

Vectors and Analytic Geometry

Analytic geometry is the representation of curves and surfaces by algebraic equations. If this representation is in $\mathbb{R}^3$, where each point in space and hence each position vector is represented by an ordered triplet of scalars, (that is, by coordinates), the corresponding equations representing geometrical objects involve coordinates of points on these objects. In such a case, analytic geometry is aptly called coordinate geometry. In this section, we try and work with $\mathscr{E}_3$, in a coordinate free way to obtain equations for various geometrical curves and surfaces. Since we axiomatize that both $\mathbb{R}^3$ and $\mathscr{E}_3$ are faithful representations of real space in which objects move, the equations we derive are supposed to represent the paths of moving particles or the surfaces confining their motions. In reality we do not deal with point particles, therefore, the mathematical curves and surfaces described by these equations are approximations to the actual motions.

2.1 Straight Lines

Geometry, as we practice it today, is based on straight lines and planes as the basic elements to be used to build other forms of curves and surfaces. Therefore, we start by finding out equations for the straight lines and planes. From the definition of the vector product, given a fixed vector $\mathbf{u} \neq \mathbf{0}$, all the points with position vectors $\mathbf{x}$ satisfying

$$\mathbf{x} \times \mathbf{u} = \mathbf{0} \tag{2.1}$$

lie on the straight line on which $\mathbf{u}$ lies. Since $\mathbf{x} = \mathbf{0}$ satisfies this equation, this line passes through the origin. Replacement of $\mathbf{x}$ by $(\mathbf{x} - \mathbf{a})$ in Eq. (2.1) for fixed vector $\mathbf{a}$, rigidly displaces each point on the line given by Eq. (2.1) by the same vector $\mathbf{a}$. The resulting line is in the direction $\hat{\mathbf{u}}$ and passing through the point $\mathbf{a}$, given by the equation

$$(\mathbf{x} - \mathbf{a}) \times \mathbf{u} = \mathbf{0}. \tag{2.2}$$

Each possible straight line in space is described by Eq. (2.2) for some $\mathbf{a}$ and $\mathbf{u}$. We denote the set of all points on the line by $\mathscr{L}$, that is, $\mathscr{L} = \{\mathbf{x}\}$.

Exercise From Eq. (2.2) derive the following equations for the line $\mathscr{L}$ in terms of rectangular coordinates in $\mathscr{E}_3$:

$$\frac{x_1 - a_1}{u_1} = \frac{x_2 - a_2}{u_2} = \frac{x_3 - a_3}{u_3},$$

where $x_k = \mathbf{x} \cdot \hat{\sigma}_k, a_k = \mathbf{a} \cdot \hat{\sigma}_k, u_k = \mathbf{u} \cdot \hat{\sigma}_k, k = 1, 2, 3$ and $\hat{\sigma}_1, \hat{\sigma}_2, \hat{\sigma}_3$ an orthonormal basis.

Hint $[(\mathbf{x} - \mathbf{a}) \times \mathbf{u}] \cdot \hat{\sigma}_3 = (x_1 - a_1)u_2 - (x_2 - a_2)u_1$ etc. ☐

Exercise
(a) Show that Eq. (2.2) is equivalent to the parametric equation

$$\mathbf{x} = \mathbf{a} + \lambda\hat{\mathbf{u}}.$$

(b) Describe the solution set $\{\mathbf{x} = \mathbf{x}(t)\}$ of the parametric equation

$$\mathbf{x} = \mathbf{a} + t^2\mathbf{u}$$

for all scalar values of the parameter t.

Hint
(a) Equation (2.2) implies $(\mathbf{x} - \mathbf{a}) \cdot \hat{\mathbf{u}} \equiv \lambda$.
(b) $\{\mathbf{x}\} =$ half line with the direction $\mathbf{u}$ and endpoint $\mathbf{a}$. ☐

Dividing Eq. (2.2) by $|\mathbf{u}|$ and taking the constant term on the right, we get,

$$\mathbf{x} \times \hat{\mathbf{u}} = \mathbf{a} \times \hat{\mathbf{u}}.$$

We take the vector product on both sides from the left with $\hat{\mathbf{u}}$ and use identity I to get

$$\begin{aligned} \mathbf{x} &= \mathbf{a} - (\hat{\mathbf{u}} \cdot \mathbf{a})\hat{\mathbf{u}} + (\hat{\mathbf{u}} \cdot \mathbf{x})\hat{\mathbf{u}} \\ &= \mathbf{d} + (\hat{\mathbf{u}} \cdot \mathbf{x})\hat{\mathbf{u}}, \end{aligned} \tag{2.3}$$

which we take to be the definition of the vector $\mathbf{d}$. Noting that $\mathbf{d} \cdot \hat{\mathbf{u}} = 0$ we get, for the length of vector $\mathbf{x}$,

$$x^2 = d^2 + (\hat{\mathbf{u}} \cdot \mathbf{x})^2.$$

This distance is minimum for $\mathbf{x} = \mathbf{d}$ or $\hat{\mathbf{u}} \cdot \mathbf{x} = 0$. This minimum distance is simply the distance of the line from the origin and is given by $d = |\mathbf{d}|$ (see Fig. 2.1). We call $\mathbf{d}$ the *directance* [10] (the directed distance) from the origin $\mathbf{0}$ to the line $\mathscr{L}$. Its magnitude is called the *distance* from the origin to the line $\mathscr{L}$. Note that $\mathbf{d}$ can be obtained from any point $\mathbf{x}$ on the line by subtracting the component of $\mathbf{x}$ along $\hat{\mathbf{u}}$ from $\mathbf{x}$ (Eq. 2.3).

The vector

$$\mathbf{m} = \mathbf{x} \times \hat{\mathbf{u}}$$

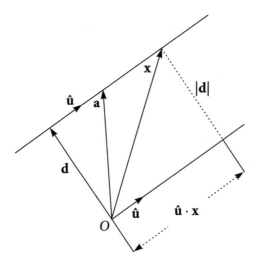

Fig. 2.1   Line $\mathscr{L}$ with directance $\mathbf{d} = \mathbf{x} - (\hat{\mathbf{u}} \cdot \mathbf{x})\hat{\mathbf{u}}$

is called the *moment* of the line $\mathscr{L}$. Figure 2.2 shows that the magnitude $|\mathbf{m}|$, which is the area of the parallelogram spanned by $\mathbf{x}$ and $\hat{\mathbf{u}}$, is the same for all points $\mathbf{x}$ on the line and equals the distance $d = |\mathbf{d}|$ of the line from the origin $\mathbf{O}$. Thus, any oriented line $\mathscr{L}$ is uniquely determined by specifying the direction $\hat{\mathbf{u}}$ and its moment $\mathbf{m}$, or by specifying a single quantity $\mathbf{L} = \hat{\mathbf{u}} + \mathbf{d} \times \hat{\mathbf{u}}$.

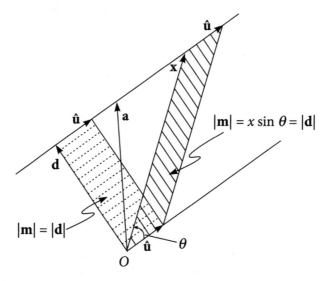

Fig. 2.2 $|\mathbf{m}| = |\mathbf{x} \times \hat{\mathbf{u}}| = |\mathbf{d}|$ for all $\mathbf{x}$ on the line $\mathscr{L}$

The equation to a line can be expressed in terms of a pair of points on it, which determines the relations between such pairs of points. In order to get such an equation, we note that Eq. (2.2) is equivalent to the statement that the segment $\mathbf{x} - \mathbf{a}$ is collinear with the vector $\mathbf{u}$. Since $\mathbf{x}$ and $\mathbf{a}$ are any two points on the line, it follows that all segments of the line are collinear. If $\mathbf{x}$, $\mathbf{a}$, $\mathbf{b}$ are any three points on the line, the collinearity of the segments $\mathbf{x} - \mathbf{a}$ and $\mathbf{b} - \mathbf{a}$ is expressed by the equation

$$(\mathbf{x} - \mathbf{a}) \times (\mathbf{b} - \mathbf{a}) = \mathbf{0}. \tag{2.4}$$

This differs from Eq. (2.2) in that $\mathbf{u}$ is replaced by the segment $\mathbf{b} - \mathbf{a}$ which is proportional to $\mathbf{u}$. Thus, Eqs (2.2) and (2.4) are equivalent provided $\mathbf{a}$ and $\mathbf{b}$ are distinct points on the line.

Exercise   Find the directance to the line through points $\mathbf{a}$ and $\mathbf{b}$ (a) from the origin and (b) from an arbitrary point $\mathbf{c}$.

Answer

(a) $\dfrac{((\mathbf{b} - \mathbf{a}) \cdot \mathbf{a})\mathbf{b} - ((\mathbf{b} - \mathbf{a}) \cdot \mathbf{b})\mathbf{a}}{|\mathbf{b} - \mathbf{a}|^2}.$

(b) Shift the origin to $\mathbf{c}$. We get, $\dfrac{(\mathbf{b} - \mathbf{a}) \cdot (\mathbf{a} - \mathbf{c})(\mathbf{b} - \mathbf{c}) - (\mathbf{b} - \mathbf{a})^2(\mathbf{a} - \mathbf{c})}{|\mathbf{b} - \mathbf{a}|^2}.$ □

Exercise   Show that the distance from an arbitrary point A to the line BC is

$$\frac{|\mathbf{a} \times \mathbf{b} + \mathbf{b} \times \mathbf{c} + \mathbf{c} \times \mathbf{a}|}{|\mathbf{b} - \mathbf{c}|}$$

where $\mathbf{a}, \mathbf{b}, \mathbf{c}$ are the position vectors of points A, B, C respectively, with respect to some origin O, (see Fig. 2.3).

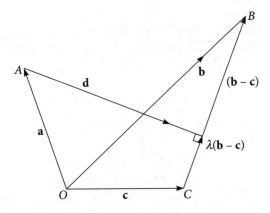

Fig. 2.3   See text

Solution   Let $\mathbf{d}$ be the vector from A perpendicular to $\mathbf{b} - \mathbf{c}$ (see Fig. 2.3). We want to find $|\mathbf{d}|$. We can write

$$|\mathbf{d}| = \frac{|\mathbf{d} \times (\mathbf{c} - \mathbf{b})|}{|\mathbf{b} - \mathbf{c}|}$$

as $\mathbf{d}$ and $\mathbf{c} - \mathbf{b}$ are orthogonal. Next, check that

$$\mathbf{d} = -\mathbf{a} + \mathbf{c} + \lambda(\mathbf{b} - \mathbf{c}), \quad \lambda \text{ a scalar,}$$

$$\mathbf{d} \times \mathbf{c} = -\mathbf{a} \times \mathbf{c} + \lambda(\mathbf{b} \times \mathbf{c}),$$

$$\mathbf{d} \times \mathbf{b} = -\mathbf{a} \times \mathbf{b} + \mathbf{c} \times \mathbf{b} - \lambda(\mathbf{c} \times \mathbf{b}).$$

Thus,

$$\mathbf{d} \times (\mathbf{c} - \mathbf{b}) = \mathbf{c} \times \mathbf{a} + \mathbf{a} \times \mathbf{b} + \mathbf{b} \times \mathbf{c}$$

and substituting in the equation for $|\mathbf{d}|$ above, the result follows.   □

Exercise   Let $\hat{\mathbf{u}}, \hat{\mathbf{v}}, \hat{\mathbf{w}}$ be the directions of three coplanar lines. The relative directions of lines are then specified by $\alpha = \hat{\mathbf{v}} \cdot \hat{\mathbf{w}}$, $\beta = \hat{\mathbf{u}} \cdot \hat{\mathbf{w}}$, $\gamma = \hat{\mathbf{u}} \cdot \hat{\mathbf{v}}$. Show that $2\alpha\beta\gamma = \alpha^2 + \beta^2 + \gamma^2 - 1$.

Solution   Since $\hat{\mathbf{u}}, \hat{\mathbf{v}}, \hat{\mathbf{w}}$ are coplanar, they are linearly dependent, so that their Gram determinant must vanish (see Appendix A). Thus we have,

$$\Gamma(\hat{\mathbf{u}}, \hat{\mathbf{v}}, \hat{\mathbf{w}}) = \begin{vmatrix} 1 & \gamma & \beta \\ \gamma & 1 & \alpha \\ \beta & \alpha & 1 \end{vmatrix} = 0$$

Expanding the determinant, we get the result.   □

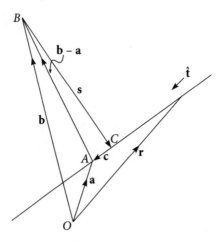

Fig. 2.4   See text

Exercise   Find the parametric values λ_1, λ_2 for which the line $\mathbf{x} = \mathbf{x}(\lambda) = \mathbf{a} + \lambda\hat{\mathbf{u}}$ intersects the circle whose equation is $\mathbf{x}^2 = r^2$ and show that $\lambda_1\lambda_2 = a^2 - r^2$ for every line through $\mathbf{a}$ which intersects the circle.

Solution At the points of intersection $r^2 = (\mathbf{a} + \lambda\hat{\mathbf{u}})^2$. Thus, the corresponding values of λ satisfy $\lambda^2 + 2\lambda\mathbf{a}\cdot\hat{\mathbf{u}} + (a^2 - r^2) = 0$, or, $\lambda_{1,2} = -\mathbf{a}\cdot\hat{\mathbf{u}} \pm \sqrt{r^2 + (a\cdot u)^2 - a^2}$. We know that the product of the roots of the quadratic $ax^2 + bx + c$ is c/a so that the above quadratic in λ gives $\lambda_1\lambda_2 = a^2 - r^2$. If the line is a tangent to the circle, $r^2 + (a\cdot u)^2 = a^2$ and $\lambda_1 = \lambda_2$. These results are valid for any line intersecting the circle. □

Exercise Show that the vector $\mathbf{s}$ (vector $\overrightarrow{BC}$ in Fig. 2.4) along the perpendicular dropped on the line $(\mathbf{x} - \mathbf{a}) \times \hat{\mathbf{t}} = \mathbf{0}$ from the point B with position vector $\mathbf{b}$ (see Fig. 2.4) is given by

$$\mathbf{s} = \hat{\mathbf{t}} \times [\hat{\mathbf{t}} \times (\mathbf{b} - \mathbf{a})].$$

Solution $-\mathbf{s} = \mathbf{b} - \mathbf{a} + \mathbf{c}$ where $\mathbf{c}$ is given by the projection of $\mathbf{b} - \mathbf{a}$ on the line Fig. 2.4. Now $\mathbf{c} = -[(\mathbf{b} - \mathbf{a}) \cdot \hat{\mathbf{t}}]\hat{\mathbf{t}}$ so that, using identity I we get,

$$\begin{aligned} -\mathbf{s} &= \mathbf{b} - \mathbf{a} - [(\mathbf{b} - \mathbf{a}) \cdot \hat{\mathbf{t}}]\hat{\mathbf{t}} \\ &= (\hat{\mathbf{t}}\cdot\hat{\mathbf{t}})(\mathbf{b} - \mathbf{a}) - [(\mathbf{b} - \mathbf{a}) \cdot \hat{\mathbf{t}}]\hat{\mathbf{t}} \\ &= \hat{\mathbf{t}} \times [(\mathbf{b} - \mathbf{a}) \times \hat{\mathbf{t}}], \end{aligned} \tag{2.5}$$

which is what we wanted to prove. □

If we expand the the vector product in Eq. (2.4) using the distributive rule and multiply each term by $\frac{1}{2}$ we get

$$\frac{1}{2}(\mathbf{a} \times \mathbf{b}) = \frac{1}{2}(\mathbf{a} \times \mathbf{x}) + \frac{1}{2}(\mathbf{x} \times \mathbf{b}). \tag{2.6}$$

Now $\frac{1}{2}(\mathbf{a} \times \mathbf{b})$ is the directed area of a triangle with vertices $\mathbf{a}$, $\mathbf{0}$, $\mathbf{b}$ and sides given by $\mathbf{a}$, $\mathbf{b}$, $\mathbf{b} - \mathbf{a}$. The other two terms in Eq. (2.6) can be interpreted similarly. We note that any two of these three triangles have one side in common. Thus, Eq. (2.6) expresses the area of a triangle as the sum of the areas of two triangles into which it can be decomposed. This is depicted in Fig. 2.5(a) when $\mathbf{x}$ lies between $\mathbf{a}$ and $\mathbf{b}$ and in Fig. 2.5(b) when it does not. From Eq. (2.6)

$$(\mathbf{a} \times \mathbf{b}) \cdot \mathbf{x} = 0 \tag{2.7}$$

which means that all three vectors and the three triangles they determine are in the same plane. We define the vectors

$$\mathbf{B} \equiv \frac{1}{2}(\mathbf{a} \times \mathbf{x})$$

$$\mathbf{A} \equiv \frac{1}{2}(\mathbf{x} \times \mathbf{b}), \tag{2.8}$$

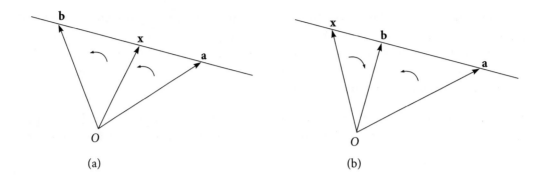

Fig. 2.5   With **A** and **B** defined in Eq. (2.8) (a) $|\mathbf{a} \times \mathbf{b}| = |\mathbf{A}| + |\mathbf{B}|$ and (b) $|\mathbf{a} \times \mathbf{b}| = |\mathbf{B}| - |\mathbf{A}|$. These equations can be written in terms of the areas of the corresponding triangles

whose magnitudes equal the areas of the corresponding triangles. These areas are depicted in Figs 2.5(a) and 2.5(b). Note that the orientation of **A** and hence, the sign of A is opposite in the two figures.

Since the segments of a line are all collinear, we can write

$$\mathbf{a} - \mathbf{x} = \lambda(\mathbf{x} - \mathbf{b}) \tag{2.9}$$

where λ is a scalar. Taking absolute values on both sides,

$$|\lambda| = \frac{|\mathbf{a} - \mathbf{x}|}{|\mathbf{x} - \mathbf{b}|} \quad \text{or,} \quad \lambda = \pm \frac{|\mathbf{a} - \mathbf{x}|}{|\mathbf{x} - \mathbf{b}|}.$$

Again, the vector product of Eq. (2.9) with **x** gives

$$\mathbf{a} \times \mathbf{x} = \lambda(\mathbf{x} \times \mathbf{b}).$$

Absolute values on both sides yield

$$\lambda = \pm \frac{|\mathbf{a} \times \mathbf{x}|}{|\mathbf{x} \times \mathbf{b}|} = \pm \frac{|\mathbf{B}|}{|\mathbf{A}|} = \pm \frac{B}{A}.$$

We thus get,

$$\lambda = \pm \frac{|\mathbf{a} - \mathbf{x}|}{|\mathbf{x} - \mathbf{b}|} = \pm \frac{|\mathbf{B}|}{|\mathbf{A}|} = \pm \frac{B}{A}, \tag{2.10}$$

where the positive sign applies if **x** is between **a** and **b** and the negative sign applies if it is not. The point **x** is called the *point of division* for the oriented line segment $[\mathbf{a}, \mathbf{b}]$ and as per Eq. (2.10), **x** is said to divide $[\mathbf{a}, \mathbf{b}]$ *in the ratio* B/A. The *division ratio* λ parameterizes the segment from **a** to **b** to give

$$\mathbf{x} = \frac{\mathbf{a} + \lambda \mathbf{b}}{1 + \lambda}, \tag{2.11}$$

as can be obtained by solving Eq. (2.9). Thus, the *midpoint* of the segment $[\mathbf{a}, \mathbf{b}]$ is defined by $\lambda = 1$ and is given by $\frac{1}{2}(\mathbf{a} + \mathbf{b})$.

Equation (2.11) can be written as

$$\mathbf{x} = \frac{A\mathbf{a} + B\mathbf{b}}{A + B}. \tag{2.12}$$

The scalars A and B in Eq. (2.12) are called *homogeneous* (line) *coordinates* for the point $\mathbf{x}$. They are also called *barycentric coordinates* because of the similarity of Eq. (2.12) to the formula for center of mass of a rigid body. Unlike mass, however, the scalars A and B can be negative and can be interpreted geometrically as oriented areas.

Exercise Prove that three points $\mathbf{a}, \mathbf{b}, \mathbf{c}$ lie on a line if and only if there are non-zero scalars α, β, γ such that $\alpha \mathbf{a} + \beta \mathbf{b} + \gamma \mathbf{c} = 0$ and $\alpha + \beta + \gamma = 0$.

Hint This is an immediate consequence of Eq. (2.12). □

The parameter λ is invariant under the shift in origin from $\mathbf{O}$ to $\mathbf{O}'$ by a vector $\mathbf{c}$ as depicted in Fig. 2.6. We have, with respect to the new origin,

$$\lambda = \pm \frac{|\mathbf{a} - \mathbf{c} - \mathbf{x} + \mathbf{c}|}{|\mathbf{x} - \mathbf{c} - \mathbf{b} + \mathbf{c}|} = \pm \frac{|\mathbf{a} - \mathbf{x}|}{|\mathbf{x} - \mathbf{b}|}.$$

This means (see Fig. 2.6)

$$\lambda = \frac{B}{A} = \frac{B'}{A'} = \frac{B \pm B'}{A \pm A'}. \tag{2.13}$$

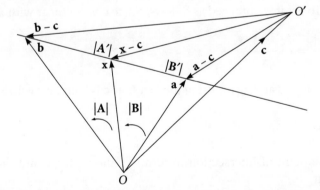

Fig. 2.6 $A' = (\mathbf{x} - \mathbf{c}) \times (\mathbf{b} - \mathbf{c})$ and $B' = (\mathbf{a} - \mathbf{c}) \times (\mathbf{x} - \mathbf{c})$ (see text)

For the special case when $\mathbf{c}$ is collinear with $\mathbf{x}$, we have one of the three cases depicted in Figs 2.7(a),(b),(c). All the three cases validate Eq. (2.13). The point $\mathbf{x}$ also divides the segment $[\mathbf{c}, 0]$ in a ratio λ' given by

$$\lambda' = \pm \frac{|\mathbf{c} - \mathbf{x}|}{|\mathbf{x}|} = \frac{B}{B'} = \frac{A}{A'} = \frac{A \pm B}{A' \pm B'}. \tag{2.14}$$

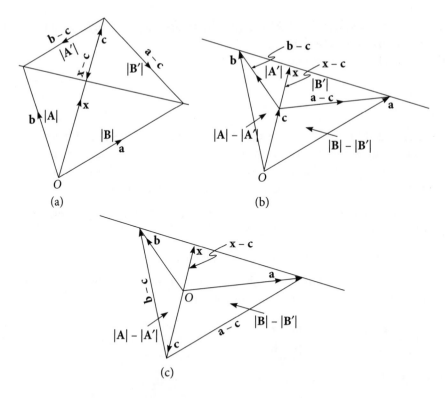

Fig. 2.7 Case of **c** parallel to **x**

The point **x** is the *point of intersection* of the line through points $[\mathbf{c}, \mathbf{0}]$ with the line through the points $[\mathbf{a}, \mathbf{b}]$. To get it we proceed as follows. Since **c** is collinear with **x**, we have,

$$\lambda' = \pm \frac{|\mathbf{c} - \mathbf{x}|}{|\mathbf{x}|} = \frac{(\mathbf{c} - \mathbf{x}) \cdot \hat{\mathbf{x}}}{x},$$

or, rearranging the terms and again using the fact that **c** is collinear with **x**,

$$\mathbf{x} = \frac{\mathbf{c}}{1 + \lambda'}, \tag{2.15}$$

which gives us the point of intersection in terms of the vector **c** and the ratio λ'. From Fig. 2.8 we see that

$$A + B = \frac{1}{2}|\mathbf{a} \times \mathbf{b}|$$

and

$$A' + B' = \frac{1}{2}|(\mathbf{a} - \mathbf{c}) \times (\mathbf{b} - \mathbf{c})|.$$

These equations, when coupled with Eq. (2.14) give

$$\lambda' = \frac{|\mathbf{a} \times \mathbf{b}|}{|(\mathbf{a} - \mathbf{c}) \times (\mathbf{b} - \mathbf{c})|}. \tag{2.16}$$

Equations (2.15) and (2.16) determine $\mathbf{x}$ in terms of vectors $\mathbf{a}, \mathbf{b}, \mathbf{c}$. They determine point $\mathbf{x}$ in Fig. 2.8 and by interchanging $\mathbf{a}$ and $\mathbf{c}$, they determine the point $\mathbf{y}$ in the same figure.

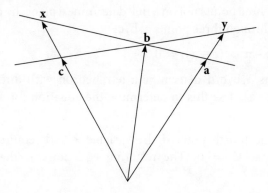

Fig. 2.8   See text

2.2 Planes

The algebraic description of a plane is similar to that of a line.

We set up an orthonormal basis in the plane, say $\hat{\sigma}_1, \hat{\sigma}_2$. We call such a plane $\hat{\sigma}_1, \hat{\sigma}_2$ *plane*. Let $\mathbf{a}$ denote a fixed point on the plane. Then, every point $\mathbf{x}$ on the plane must satisfy (see Fig. 2.9)

$$(\mathbf{x} - \mathbf{a}) \cdot (\hat{\sigma}_1 \times \hat{\sigma}_2) = 0. \tag{2.17}$$

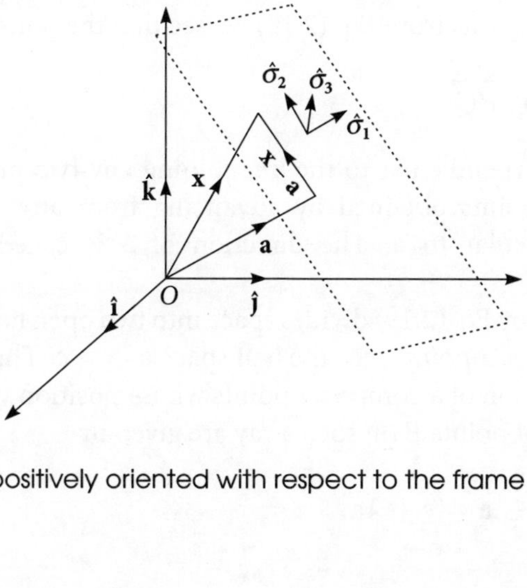

Fig. 2.9   A plane positively oriented with respect to the frame $(\hat{\mathbf{i}}, \hat{\mathbf{j}}, \hat{\mathbf{k}})$

If we put $\hat{\sigma}_3 = \hat{\sigma}_1 \times \hat{\sigma}_2$ then $\hat{\sigma}_1, \hat{\sigma}_2, \hat{\sigma}_3$ form an orthonormal basis in 3-D space. $\hat{\sigma}_3$ defines the orientation of the plane which is positive if the triplet $\hat{\sigma}_1, \hat{\sigma}_2, \hat{\sigma}_3$ is oriented positively with respect to the orthonormal coordinate system based at the origin O (see Fig. 2.9).

Exercise Show that the distance of the plane from the origin is given by $|\mathbf{d}| = |\mathbf{a} \cdot \hat{\sigma}_3|$. The directance is given by the vector $\mathbf{d}$ along the line perpendicular to the plane and passing through the origin, directed away from the origin. □

Exercise Show that three points not on a line determine a plane, by obtaining an equation for the plane passing through three points $\mathbf{a}, \mathbf{b}, \mathbf{c}$.

Answer $(\mathbf{x} - \mathbf{a}) \cdot [(\mathbf{b} - \mathbf{a}) \times (\mathbf{c} - \mathbf{a})] = 0.$ □

Exercise Four points $\mathbf{a}, \mathbf{b}, \mathbf{c}, \mathbf{d}$ determine a tetrahedron with directed volume $V = \frac{1}{6}$ $(\mathbf{b} - \mathbf{a}) \times (\mathbf{c} - \mathbf{a}) \cdot (\mathbf{d} - \mathbf{a})$. Use this to determine the equation for a plane through three distinct points $\mathbf{a}, \mathbf{b}, \mathbf{c}$.

Answer We make the fourth point $\mathbf{d}$ the variable $\mathbf{x}$ and require that $\mathbf{a}, \mathbf{b}, \mathbf{c}, \mathbf{x}$ lie on the same plane so that $V = 0$. The resulting equation for the plane is $(\mathbf{b} - \mathbf{a}) \times (\mathbf{c} - \mathbf{a}) \cdot (\mathbf{x} - \mathbf{a}) = 0.$ □

Algebraically, a plane is defined as the locus of points $P(x_1, x_2, x_3)$ in the three dimensional space $\mathbb{R}^3$ satisfying a linear equation of the form

$$a_1 x_1 + a_2 x_2 + a_3 x_3 = c, \tag{2.18}$$

where a_1, a_2, a_3 do not all vanish. Introducing the vector $\mathbf{a} \equiv (a_1, a_2, a_3)$, $(\mathbf{a} \neq \mathbf{0})$ and the position vector $\mathbf{x} = \overrightarrow{OP} \equiv (x_1, x_2, x_3)$ of the point P, we can write Eq. (2.18) as a vector equation:

$$\mathbf{a} \cdot \mathbf{x} = c \tag{2.19}$$

Let $\mathbf{y} = \overrightarrow{OQ} \equiv (y_1, y_2, y_3)$ be the position vector of a particular point Q on the plane so that $\mathbf{a} \cdot \mathbf{y} = c$. Subtracting this from Eq. (2.19) we see that the points P of the plane satisfy

$$0 = \mathbf{a} \cdot (\mathbf{x} - \mathbf{y}) = \mathbf{a} \cdot \overrightarrow{PQ}. \tag{2.20}$$

Thus, the vector $\mathbf{a}$ is perpendicular to the line joining any two points on the plane. The plane consists of the points obtained by advancing from any one of its points Q in all directions perpendicular to $\mathbf{a}$. The direction of $\mathbf{a}$ is called *normal* to the plane (see Fig. 2.10).

The plane described by Eq. (2.19) divides space into two open half-spaces given by $\mathbf{a} \cdot \mathbf{x} < c$ and $\mathbf{a} \cdot \mathbf{x} > c$. The vector $\mathbf{a}$ *points into* the half space $\mathbf{a} \cdot \mathbf{x} > c$. Thus, a ray from a point Q of the plane in the direction of $\mathbf{a}$ comprises points whose position vectors $\mathbf{x}$ satisfy $\mathbf{a} \cdot \mathbf{x} > c$. The position vectors $\mathbf{x}$ of points P on such a ray are given by

$$\mathbf{x} = \overrightarrow{OP} = \overrightarrow{OQ} + \lambda \mathbf{a} = \mathbf{y} + \lambda \mathbf{a}$$

where **y** is the position vector of Q and λ is a positive number. Dotting this equation by **a** gives,

$$\mathbf{a} \cdot \mathbf{x} = c + \lambda |\mathbf{a}|^2 > c.$$

In general, any vector **b** forming an acute angle with **a** points into the half space $\mathbf{a} \cdot \mathbf{x} > c$, since $\mathbf{a} \cdot \mathbf{b} > 0$ means

$$\mathbf{a} \cdot \mathbf{x} = \mathbf{a} \cdot \mathbf{y} + \lambda \mathbf{a} \cdot \mathbf{b} > c.$$

If $c > 0$, the half-space $\mathbf{a} \cdot \mathbf{x} < c$ contains the origin as $\mathbf{a} \cdot \mathbf{0} = 0 < c$. Then the direction of **a** or the direction of the normal is away from the origin.

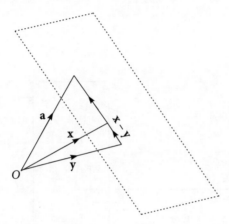

Fig. 2.10   Every line in the plane is normal to **a**

Equation (2.19) describing a given plane is not unique. It can be replaced by $(\lambda \mathbf{a}) \cdot \mathbf{x} = \lambda c$, $\lambda \neq 0$. We can choose λ to be $\lambda = \frac{sgn\,c}{|\mathbf{a}|}$ to cast the equation to the given plane in the *normal form*

$$\hat{\mathbf{a}} \cdot \mathbf{x} = d$$

where $d > 0$ is a constant and $\hat{\mathbf{a}}$ is the unit normal vector pointing away from the origin. The constant d is the distance of the plane from the origin. To see this, note that the distance of an arbitrary point on the plane with position vector **x** is $|\mathbf{x}| \geq \hat{\mathbf{a}} \cdot \mathbf{x} = d$, where equality holds for $\mathbf{x} = d\hat{\mathbf{a}}$. The distance $d(Q)$ of a point Q in space with position vector **y** from the plane is then $|\hat{\mathbf{a}} \cdot \mathbf{y} - d|$. As an example, consider a plane wave with wave vector **k** propagating in the direction $\hat{\mathbf{k}}$. The phase of a plane wave is given by $\mathbf{k} \cdot \mathbf{r}$ where **r** is the position vector of a point on the wave. For a plane wave a surface of constant phase is a plane, because the equation to such a surface must be $\hat{\mathbf{k}} \cdot \mathbf{r} = c$. Such a plane is perpendicular to $\hat{\mathbf{k}}$ as shown in Fig. 2.11.

Exercise   Find the equation to the plane passing through $(4, -1, 2)$ and perpendicular to the planes $2x - 3y + z = 4$ and $x + 2y + 3z = 5$.

Solution   The equation to the plane can be written in the form

$$\mathbf{x} \cdot \hat{\mathbf{n}} = d,$$

where $\mathbf{x}$ is the position vector of a point on the plane, $\hat{\mathbf{n}}$ is unit vector normal to the plane and pointing into the region $\mathbf{x} \cdot \hat{\mathbf{n}} > d$ and d is the distance of the plane from the origin. $\hat{\mathbf{n}}$ is given to be perpendicular to the vectors $2\hat{\mathbf{i}} - 3\hat{\mathbf{j}} + \hat{\mathbf{k}}$ and $\hat{\mathbf{i}} + 2\hat{\mathbf{j}} + 3\hat{\mathbf{k}}$, so that its dot product with these vectors must vanish, which means

$$2n_1 - 3n_2 + n_3 = 0,$$

$$n_1 + 2n_2 + 3n_3 = 0$$

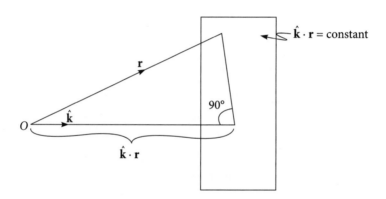

Fig. 2.11   As seen from the figure, for every point on the plane $\hat{\mathbf{k}} \cdot \mathbf{r} = $ constant

and $\hat{\mathbf{n}}$ being a unit vector, $n_1^2 + n_2^2 + n_3^2 = 1$. Solving this system we get,

$$n_1 = \frac{\pm 11}{\sqrt{195}}, \quad n_2 = \frac{\pm 5}{\sqrt{195}}, \quad n_3 = \frac{\mp 7}{\sqrt{195}}.$$

Thus, the required equation becomes

$$\mathbf{x} \cdot \hat{\mathbf{n}} = \left(\frac{11x + 5y - 7z}{\sqrt{195}} \right) = d.$$

Since the point $(4, -1, 2)$ lies on the plane,

$$d = \pm \frac{39 - 5 - 14}{\sqrt{195}} = \pm \frac{25}{\sqrt{195}}.$$

Regardless of which sign is used we get the required equation

$$11x + 5y - 7z = 25. \qquad \Box$$

Exercise   Find the equation to a plane which passes through the line of intersection of two planes which are equidistant from the origin.

Solution   The equations to the given planes are $\mathbf{x} \cdot \hat{\mathbf{n}}_1 = d = \mathbf{x} \cdot \hat{\mathbf{n}}_2$ since both are equidistant from the origin. The points lying on both these planes satisfy the linear combination of their equations

$$\mathbf{x} \cdot (\hat{\mathbf{n}}_1 + \mu \hat{\mathbf{n}}_2) = d + \mu d = (1 + \mu)d$$

where μ is a parameter. However, each term on the LHS of this equation can be taken to equal $\pm d$. Choosing both to equal $+d$ makes $\mu = +1$ and one $+d$ and the other $-d$ makes $\mu = -1$. In the first case the required equation becomes $\mathbf{x} \cdot (\hat{\mathbf{n}}_1 + \hat{\mathbf{n}}_2) = 2d$ while in the second case the equation is $\mathbf{x} \cdot (\hat{\mathbf{n}}_1 + \hat{\mathbf{n}}_2) = 0$ which is a plane passing through the origin. $\qquad \Box$

Exercise   Find an expression for the angle between two planes given by $\mathbf{x} \cdot \hat{\mathbf{n}}_1 = d_1$ and $\mathbf{x} \cdot \hat{\mathbf{n}}_2 = d_2$.

Solution   The angle between two planes is the angle θ between their unit normals and is given by $\cos \theta = \hat{\mathbf{n}}_1 \cdot \hat{\mathbf{n}}_2 = \lambda_1 \lambda_2 + \mu_1 \mu_2 + \nu_1 \nu_2$, where $(\lambda_1, \mu_1, \nu_1)$ and $(\lambda_2, \mu_2, \nu_2)$ are the direction cosines of $\hat{\mathbf{n}}_1$ and $\hat{\mathbf{n}}_2$ respectively. $\qquad \Box$

Exercise   Find the equation to a plane containing a line and parallel to a vector.

Solution   Let the plane contain a line $\mathbf{x} = \mathbf{u} + \lambda \mathbf{v}$, λ being a parameter and parallel to a given vector ω. Thus, the plane passes through a point with position vector $\mathbf{u}$ and is perpendicular to $\mathbf{v} \times \omega$. Its equation is

$$(\mathbf{x} - \mathbf{u}) \cdot (\mathbf{v} \times \omega) = 0 \quad \text{or} \quad \mathbf{x} \cdot \mathbf{v} \times \omega = \mathbf{u} \cdot \mathbf{v} \times \omega. \qquad \Box$$

Exercise   Find the shortest distance between two skew lines as well as the equation to the corresponding line.

Solution   Skew lines is a pair of lines which are neither parallel nor intersecting. Let $\mathscr{L}_1$ and $\mathscr{L}_2$ be two skew lines with equations

$$\mathscr{L}_1 : \mathbf{x} = \mathbf{u} + \lambda \mathbf{s} \quad \text{and} \quad \mathscr{L}_2 : \mathbf{x} = \mathbf{v} + \mu \mathbf{t},$$

λ, μ being parameters. Thus, $\mathscr{L}_1$ passes through the point A with position vector $\mathbf{u}$ and is parallel to vector $\mathbf{s}$ and $\mathscr{L}_2$ passes through the point B with position vector $\mathbf{v}$ and is parallel to vector $\mathbf{t}$ (see Fig. 2.12). Let the segment PQ, joining points P and Q on the lines $\mathscr{L}_1$ and $\mathscr{L}_2$ respectively, give the shortest distance between them. Then PQ is perpendicular to both the lines and hence, it is parallel to the cross product of the vectors $\mathbf{s}$ and $\mathbf{t}$. The segment PQ perpendicular to both the lines is unique, because if there was another such segment, it would be parallel to PQ, making $\mathscr{L}_1$ and $\mathscr{L}_2$ parallel. The shortest distance is the projection of AB specified by the vector $\mathbf{v} - \mathbf{u}$ on PQ that is, on the unit vector $\frac{\mathbf{s} \times \mathbf{t}}{|\mathbf{s} \times \mathbf{t}|}$. Therefore, we have,

$$d(P, Q) = \left| (\mathbf{v} - \mathbf{u}) \cdot \frac{\mathbf{s} \times \mathbf{t}}{|\mathbf{s} \times \mathbf{t}|} \right|.$$

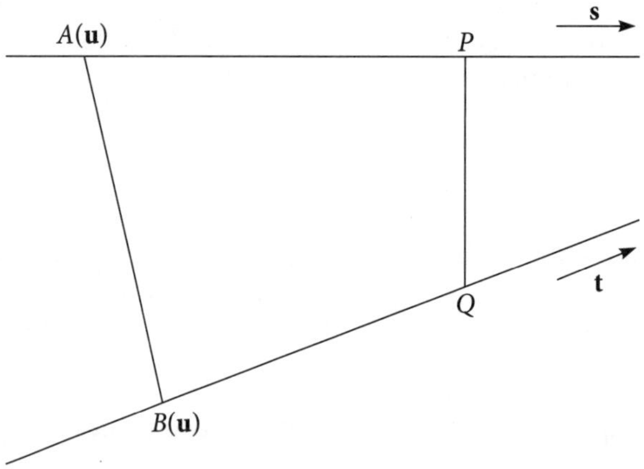

Fig. 2.12 Shortest distance between two skew lines

Note that when $d(P, Q) = 0$ we get

$$(\mathbf{v} - \mathbf{u}) \cdot (\mathbf{s} \times \mathbf{t}) = 0, \ \text{ or } \ \mathbf{v} \cdot (\mathbf{s} \times \mathbf{t}) = \mathbf{u} \cdot (\mathbf{s} \times \mathbf{t}),$$

which is the condition of intersection of two lines.

To find the equation to the line of shortest distance we note that the vector $\mathbf{p}$ joining PQ is

$$\mathbf{p} = \frac{[(\mathbf{v} - \mathbf{u}) \cdot \mathbf{s} \times \mathbf{t}]\mathbf{s} \times \mathbf{t}}{|\mathbf{s} \times \mathbf{t}|^2}.$$

Thus, the line passing through $\mathbf{u}$ and parallel to $\mathbf{p}$ is given by

$$(\mathbf{x} - \mathbf{u}) \times \hat{\mathbf{p}} = \mathbf{0},$$

where $\hat{\mathbf{p}}$ is the unit vector along $\mathbf{p}$. □

Exercise Find the equation to the line of intersection of the two planes $(\mathbf{x} - \mathbf{a}) \cdot \hat{\mathbf{n}}_1 = 0$ and $(\mathbf{x} - \mathbf{b}) \cdot \hat{\mathbf{n}}_2 = 0$ where $\hat{\mathbf{n}}_1, \hat{\mathbf{n}}_2$ are unit vectors normal to the respective planes.

Answer $(\mathbf{x} - \mathbf{c}) \times (\hat{\mathbf{n}}_2 - \hat{\mathbf{n}}_1) = \mathbf{0}$, where

$$\mathbf{c} = \frac{1}{|\hat{\mathbf{n}}_1 \times \hat{\mathbf{n}}_2|^2} [(\mathbf{a} \cdot \hat{\mathbf{n}}_2)\hat{\mathbf{n}}_1 \times (\hat{\mathbf{n}}_2 \times \hat{\mathbf{n}}_1) + (\mathbf{b} \cdot \hat{\mathbf{n}}_1)\hat{\mathbf{n}}_2 \times (\hat{\mathbf{n}}_1 \times \hat{\mathbf{n}}_2)]. \quad □$$

Exercise Find the radius vector **s** of the point of intersection of three planes $(\mathbf{x}-\mathbf{a})\cdot\hat{\mathbf{n}} = 0$, $(\mathbf{x}-\mathbf{b})\cdot\hat{\mathbf{m}} = 0$ and $(\mathbf{x}-\mathbf{c})\cdot\hat{\mathbf{p}} = 0$, where $\hat{\mathbf{n}}, \hat{\mathbf{m}}, \hat{\mathbf{p}}$ are the unit vectors normal to the respective planes and $\hat{\mathbf{n}} \cdot (\hat{\mathbf{m}} \times \hat{\mathbf{p}}) \neq 0$.

Answer $s = \dfrac{1}{\hat{\mathbf{n}} \cdot (\hat{\mathbf{m}} \times \hat{\mathbf{p}})}[(\mathbf{a} \cdot \hat{\mathbf{n}})\hat{\mathbf{m}} \times \hat{\mathbf{p}} + (\mathbf{b} \cdot \hat{\mathbf{m}})\hat{\mathbf{p}} \times \hat{\mathbf{n}} + (\mathbf{c} \cdot \hat{\mathbf{p}})\hat{\mathbf{n}} \times \hat{\mathbf{m}}].$ □

2.3 Spheres

Spheres form another instance of elementary geometrical figures. A sphere with radius r and center **c** is the set of all points $\mathbf{x} \in \mathscr{E}_3$ satisfying the equation

$$|\mathbf{x} - \mathbf{c}| = r \ \text{ or } \ (\mathbf{x} - \mathbf{c})^2 = r^2. \tag{2.21}$$

The vectors $\{\mathbf{x} - \mathbf{c}\}$ satisfying Eq. (2.21) and also the constraint $\hat{\mathbf{r}} \cdot (\mathbf{x} - \mathbf{c}) = $ constant, where $\hat{\mathbf{r}}$ is a unit vector based at the center, trace out a circle on the sphere and can be taken to be the defining equation for the circle.

As an example of applying vectors to sphere, we derive a basic result in spherical trigonometry. For simplicity we deal with a unit sphere S with its center at the origin O given by $r^2 = 1$. If A, B, C are any three points on S, then we call the intersection of the planes OAB, OAC, OBC with S a *spherical triangle* (see Fig. 2.13).

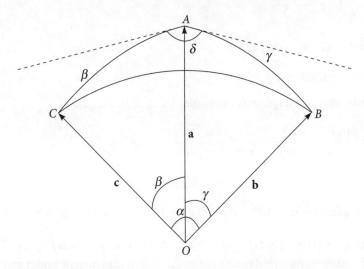

Fig. 2.13 A spherical triangle

The metric we adopt on S is that of the Euclidean space embedding S, so that the 'length' of the side AB is determined by the angle $AOB = \gamma$. In fact, these angles α, β, γ, which are subtended by the sides BC, CA and AB at O give precisely the desired lengths if they are expressed in *radians* that is, as a fraction of 2π (see section 1.2). We define the angle A at the vertex A of the spherical triangle ABC to be that between the tangents AD and AE to the great circles AB and AC. Note that the complementary parts of the great circles passing through AB, BC and CA also form a spherical triangle ABC. We can specify the triangle in Fig. 2.13 by requiring that *every angle of the triangle ABC has to be less than* π.

We wish to prove the identity

$$\cos \alpha = \cos \gamma \cos \beta + \sin \gamma \sin \beta \cos A.$$

To this end we use identity II by replacing $\mathbf{c}$ by $\mathbf{a}$ and $\mathbf{d}$ by $\mathbf{c}$. We get, remembering that all vectors are unit vectors,

$$(\hat{\mathbf{a}} \times \hat{\mathbf{b}}) \cdot (\hat{\mathbf{a}} \times \hat{\mathbf{c}}) = (\hat{\mathbf{b}} \cdot \hat{\mathbf{c}}) - (\hat{\mathbf{a}} \cdot \hat{\mathbf{c}})(\hat{\mathbf{b}} \cdot \hat{\mathbf{a}}).$$

The angle between $(\hat{\mathbf{a}} \times \hat{\mathbf{b}})$ and $(\hat{\mathbf{a}} \times \hat{\mathbf{c}})$ is the dihedral angle between the planes OAC and OAB, that is, angle A. Further,

$$|\hat{\mathbf{a}} \times \hat{\mathbf{b}}| = \sin \gamma,$$

$$|\hat{\mathbf{a}} \times \hat{\mathbf{c}}| = \sin \beta,$$

$$(\hat{\mathbf{a}} \times \hat{\mathbf{b}}) \cdot (\hat{\mathbf{a}} \times \hat{\mathbf{c}}) = \sin \gamma \sin \beta \cos A,$$

$$\hat{\mathbf{b}} \cdot \hat{\mathbf{c}} = \cos \alpha,$$

$$(\hat{\mathbf{a}} \cdot \hat{\mathbf{b}})(\hat{\mathbf{a}} \cdot \hat{\mathbf{c}}) = \cos \gamma \cos \beta.$$

which gives the required result.

Exercise Show that, for a spherical triangle ABC, as in Fig. 2.13.,

$$\frac{\sin A}{\sin \alpha} = \frac{\sin B}{\sin \beta} = \frac{\sin C}{\sin \gamma} = \frac{\sigma}{\sin \alpha \sin \beta \sin \gamma},$$

where

$$\sigma = 2[\sin s \sin(s - \alpha) \sin(s - \alpha) \sin(s - \alpha)]^{1/2} \; ; \; s = \alpha + \beta + \gamma.$$

Hint First get $|(\hat{\mathbf{a}} \times \hat{\mathbf{b}}) \times (\hat{\mathbf{a}} \times \hat{\mathbf{c}})| = |\hat{\mathbf{a}} \times \hat{\mathbf{b}}||\hat{\mathbf{a}} \times \hat{\mathbf{c}}| \sin A = \sin \gamma \sin \beta \sin A$. Then evaluate $|(\hat{\mathbf{a}} \times \hat{\mathbf{b}}) \times (\hat{\mathbf{a}} \times \hat{\mathbf{c}})|$ differently to obtain a quantity σ which is invarient under any permutation of vectors $\hat{\mathbf{a}}, \hat{\mathbf{b}}, \hat{\mathbf{c}}$. □

2.4 Conic Sections

Next we consider an important set of planar curves called conic sections because each one of them can be obtained as an intersection of a cone with a plane.

We prefer the following alternative definition because it leads to the generic parametric equation which applies to all the conic sections. A *conic* is the set of all points in the Euclidean plane $\mathscr{E}_2$ with the following property: The distance of each point from a fixed point (the *focus*) is in fixed ratio (the *eccentricity*) to the distance of that point from a fixed line (the *directrix*). This definition can be expressed as the equation defining the conic in the following way. Denote the eccentricity by e, the directance from the focus to the directrix by $\mathbf{d} = d\hat{\mathbf{e}}$ ($\hat{\mathbf{e}}^2 = 1$) and the directance from the focus to any point on the conic by $\mathbf{r}$ (see Fig. 2.14). The defining condition for the conic can then be written

$$e = \frac{|\mathbf{r}|}{d - \mathbf{r} \cdot \hat{\mathbf{e}}}.$$

Solving this for $r = |\mathbf{r}|$ and introducing the *eccentricity vector* $\mathbf{e} = e\hat{\mathbf{e}}$ along with the so called *semi-latus rectum* $l = ed$, we get the equation

$$r = \frac{l}{1 + \mathbf{e} \cdot \hat{\mathbf{r}}}. \tag{2.22}$$

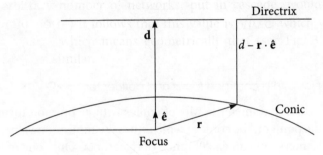

Directrix

$d - \mathbf{r} \cdot \hat{\mathbf{e}}$

Conic

$\mathbf{d}$

$\hat{\mathbf{e}}$

$\mathbf{r}$

Focus

Fig. 2.14   Depicting Eq. (2.22)

This expresses the distance r from the focus to a point on the conic as a function of the direction $\hat{\mathbf{r}}$ to that point. Equation (2.22) can also be expressed as a parametric equation for r as a function of the angle θ between $\mathbf{e}$ and $\hat{\mathbf{r}}$. This equation is obtained by substituting $\mathbf{e} \cdot \hat{\mathbf{r}} = e \cos \theta$ into Eq. (2.22). We get

$$r = \frac{l}{1 + e \cos \theta}. \tag{2.23}$$

This is the standard equation for conics however, we usually prefer Eq. (2.22) as it is an explicit function of vectors and their scalar product, so that it shows the dependence of r on the directions $\hat{\mathbf{e}}$ and $\hat{\mathbf{r}}$ explicitly.

Equation (2.22) traces a curve when r is restricted to the directions in a plane however, if r is allowed to range over all directions in $\mathscr{E}_3$ then Eq. (2.22) describes a two dimensional surface called *conicoid*. Our definition of a conic can be used for a conicoid by redefining the directrix as a plane instead of a line. Different ranges of values of eccentricity correspond to different conics or conicoid as shown in Table 2.1.

Table 2.1   Classification of Conics and Conicoids

Eccentricity	Conic	Conicoid
$e > 1$	Hyperbola	hyperboloid
$e = 1$	parabola	paraboloid
$0 < e < 1$	ellipse	ellipsoid
$e = 0$	circle	sphere

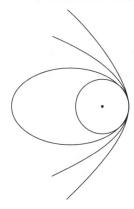

Fig. 2.15   Conics with a common focus and pericenter

Figure 2.15 shows the 1-parameter family of conics with a common focus and pericenter. The pericenter is the point on the conic at which r has the minimum value. For a hyperbola, there are two pericenters, one on each branch of hyperbola. Only one of these is shown in Fig. 2.15. If the conics in Fig. 2.15 are rotated about the *axis* joining the focus and the pericenter, they "sweep out" corresponding conicoids.

Exercise   Parametric curves $\mathbf{x} = \mathbf{x}(\lambda)$ of the second order are defined by equation

$$\mathbf{x} = \frac{\mathbf{a}_0 + \mathbf{a}_1 \lambda + \mathbf{a}_2 \lambda^2}{\alpha_0 + \alpha_1 \lambda + \alpha_2 \lambda^2}.$$

Note that this generalizes Eq. (2.11) for a line. By the change of parameters $\lambda \to \lambda - \alpha_1 / 2\alpha_2$, this can be reduced to the form

$$\mathbf{x} = \frac{\mathbf{a}_0 + \mathbf{a}_1 \lambda + \mathbf{a}_2 \lambda^2}{\alpha + \lambda^2}.$$

Show that

(a) For $\alpha = 1$, the change of parameters $\lambda = \tan \frac{1}{2}\phi$ can be used to put this equation in the form

$$\mathbf{x} = \mathbf{a}\cos\phi + \mathbf{b}\sin\phi + \mathbf{c}$$

which is the general equation for an ellipse.

(b) For $\alpha = -1$, $\lambda = \tanh \frac{1}{2}\phi$ gives

$$\mathbf{x} = \mathbf{a}\cosh\phi + \mathbf{b}\sinh\phi + \mathbf{c}.$$

which is the general equation for a hyperbola.

Actually ultimate conclusion you can draw turns out to be true: All conics are second order curves and conversely.

Hint   (a) $mf a_0 = \mathbf{a} + \mathbf{c}$, $\mathbf{a}_1 = 2\mathbf{b}$, $\mathbf{a}_2 = \mathbf{c} - \mathbf{a}$ $\cos\phi = \frac{1-\lambda^2}{1+\lambda^2}$, $\sin\phi = \frac{2\lambda}{1+\lambda^2}$.   □

Conics and conicoids can be described in many different ways which disclose a variety of their remarkable properties. However, any discussion of these issues will take us far away from the main theme of this book. These are discussed at length in various books on mechanics and geometry [9, 18].

3

Planar Vectors and Complex Numbers

The purpose of this chapter is to demonstrate how the geometry on a plane can be effectively described using the set of complex numbers in place of planar vectors. We choose the circle as the planar curve to be analysed for this purpose.

3.1 Planar Curves on the Complex Plane

Instead of vectors, the complex numbers and their algebra [1][1] can be used to describe curves on a complex plane $\mathbb{Z}$. Basically, we have to use the trivial isomorphism between $\mathscr{E}_2$ and $\mathbb{Z}$ (see Fig. 3.1):

$$z = x + iy \leftrightarrow x\hat{\mathbf{x}} + y\hat{\mathbf{y}} = \mathbf{r}$$

or,

$$z = re^{i\theta}; \; -\pi < \theta < \pi, \, r \geq 0, \; \leftrightarrow r(e^{i\theta}\hat{\mathbf{x}}) = \mathbf{r}$$

where $e^{i\theta}\hat{\mathbf{x}}$ is the direction obtained by rotating vector $\hat{\mathbf{x}}$ by θ *counterclockwise* if $\theta > 0$ and *clockwise* if $\theta < 0$ and $e^{\pm i\pi}\hat{\mathbf{x}} = -\hat{\mathbf{x}}$.

Exercise Show that the above map is both one to one and onto. □

The required isomorphism is easily established by

$$z_1 + z_2 = (x_1 + x_2) + i(y_1 + y_2) \leftrightarrow (x_1 + x_2)\hat{\mathbf{x}} + (y_1 + y_2)\hat{\mathbf{y}}$$

$$= (x_1\hat{\mathbf{x}} + y_1\hat{\mathbf{y}}) + (x_2\hat{\mathbf{x}} + y_2\hat{\mathbf{y}}) = \mathbf{r}_1 + \mathbf{r}_2$$

---

[1]We assume that the reader is familiar with the algebra of complex numbers.

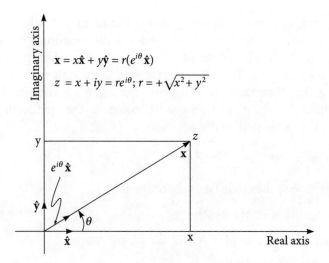

Fig. 3.1   Isomorphism between the complex plane $\mathbb{Z}$ and $\mathscr{E}_2$

and

$$az \leftrightarrow a\mathbf{r},$$

where a is a scalar (real number) and $\mathbf{r}$ and z are the images of each other under the isomorphism.

Thus, the set of vectors on a plane can be replaced by the set of complex numbers having richer algebraic structure, as each complex number has a multiplicative inverse and there is a unique identity element with respect to their product ($z_1 z_2 = 1$ implies $z_2 = 1/z_1$ and $z_1 = 1/z_2$). Due to this isomorphism, we may use the same symbol z to denote a complex number as well as a planar vector.

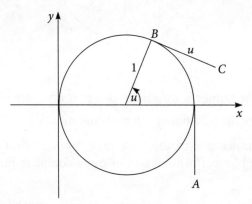

Fig. 3.2   Finding evolute of a unit circle

The product of two complex numbers $z_1 = r_1 e^{i\theta_1}$ and $z_2 = r_2 e^{i\theta_2}$ is $z = z_1 z_2 = r_1 r_2 e^{i(\theta_1 + \theta_2)}$. Thus, the absolute value of the product is the product of the absolute values of the factors, while the argument of the product is the sum of the arguments of the factors. In particular, squaring a vector z doubles the argument, while taking the square root halfs the argument. As an example we multiply the function $f(z) = 1 - iu$ by the function $\exp(iu)$ (u real). The graph of $1 - iu$ is a straight line parallel to the y-axis passing through the point $z = 1$. This line is tangent to the unit circle at the point $z = 1$, as depicted in Fig. 3.2. By rotating this line over the angle u it remains a tangent moving the point A in Fig. 3.2 to the point C. Since BC equals u, the arc length of the circle, the locus of the point C represented by the equation

$$z = (1 - iu)\exp(iu)$$

is evidently the evolute of the circle (see subsection 9.2.5).

Exercise   Show that $i^i = \exp(-\pi/2)$.

Hint   Raise the equation $i = \exp(i\pi/2)$ to the ith power.   □

Exercise   Show that $\log i = i\pi/2$.

Hint   Take logarithms on both sides of $i^i = \exp(-\pi/2)$.   □

Exercise   Show that $\sqrt{i} = \pm\frac{1}{\sqrt{2}}(1 + i)$ and $\sqrt{-i} = \pm\frac{1}{\sqrt{2}}(1 - i)$.

Hint   see Fig. 3.3.   □

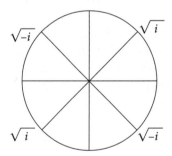

Fig. 3.3   Finding $\sqrt{i}$

Exercise   Show that the numbers whose nth power is unity are given by $z = \exp\left(i\frac{2\pi k}{n}\right)$ ($k = 1,\dots,n$). These are the n values of nth roots of unity, $\sqrt[n]{1}$.

Hint   Divide the circumference of the unit circle by n to find the points whose nth power is unity, obtained by performing one or more complete turns over the unit circle (see Fig. 3.4).   □

The complex conjugate of a complex number $z = x + iy = r\exp(i\theta)$ is given by $z^* = x - iy = r\exp(-i\theta)$. The point z^* is obtained by reflecting the point z in the x axis, as shown in Fig. 3.5. We easily check that the real and imaginary parts of z are $x = \mathcal{R}(z) = \frac{1}{2}(z + z^*)$ and $y = \mathcal{I}(z) = -i\frac{1}{2}(z - z^*)$.

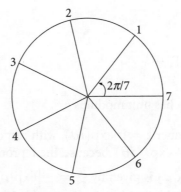

Fig. 3.4   Finding nth roots of unity

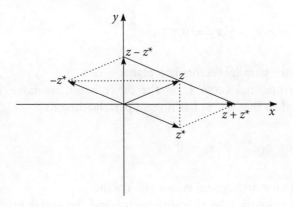

Fig. 3.5 $z, z^*, z \pm z^*$

Exercise   Find the real and imaginary parts of $z = (1 - iu)\exp(iu)$.

Answer

$$x = \cos u + u \sin u,$$

$$y = \sin u - u \cos u. \qquad \qquad \qquad \square$$

The sum of any two conjugate numbers or functions is real while their difference is imaginary. For any complex valued function $f(u)$, $z = \exp[f(u) - f^*(u)]$ and $z = \exp[i(f(u) + f^*(u))]$ are points on the unit circle.

Again, we easily find that the modulus or the absolute value of a complex number $z = |z|\exp(i\theta)$ is given by $|z| = \sqrt{zz^*}$ and its argument is obtained from $\exp(i\theta) = \sqrt{\frac{z}{z^*}}$. Note that any function which is the quotient of two conjugate functions must have unit modulus : $\left|\frac{z}{z^*}\right| = 1$, because $\frac{z}{z^*}\frac{z^*}{z} = 1$.

Exercise   Show that for the function $(1 - iu)\exp(iu)$

$$|z|^2 = 1 + u^2$$

and

$$\exp(i\theta) = \sqrt{\frac{1-iu}{1+iu}} \exp(iu).$$

Note that the function $\sqrt{\frac{1-iu}{1+iu}}$ has unit modulus.   □

The inverse of a complex number $z = |z|\exp(i\theta)$, with respect to the product of complex numbers, is given by $\frac{1}{z} = \frac{1}{|z|}\exp(-i\theta)$ because their product is $z(\frac{1}{z}) = 1$. Thus, the quotient of two vectors z_1 and z_2 is given by $\frac{z_1}{z_2} = \frac{|z_1|}{|z_2|}\exp\{i(\theta_1 - \theta_2)\}$. If the two vectors are parallel, $\theta_1 - \theta_2 = 0$ and the quotient is purely real. The imaginary part vanishes in this case, so that

$$\frac{z_1}{z_2} - \frac{z_1^*}{z_2^*} = 0 \text{ or } z_1 z_2^* - z_1^* z_2 = 0. \tag{3.1}$$

This is the *criterion for parallel vectors* in a plane.

For a pair of orthogonal vectors, on the other hand, we have, $\theta_1 - \theta_2 = \pm\pi/2$, $\exp\{i(\theta_1 - \theta_2)\} = \pm i$ so that z_1/z_2 has no real part, leading to

$$\frac{z_1}{z_2} + \frac{z_1^*}{z_2^*} = 0 \text{ or } z_1 z_2^* + z_1^* z_2 = 0 \tag{3.2}$$

which is the *criterion for orthogonal vectors* in a plane.

These criteria are closely related to the vector and the scalar products of two planar vectors. The magnitude of the vector product of two vectors z_1 and z_2 is the area of the parallelogram formed by them. This is

$$A = |z_1|\,|z_2|\sin(\theta_1 - \theta_2).$$

However,

$$z_1 z_2^* - z_1^* z_2 = 2i|z_1|\,|z_2|\sin(\theta_1 - \theta_2),$$

so that the area of the parallelogram is

$$A = \frac{1}{2i}(z_1 z_2^* - z_1^* z_2) = \mathcal{I}(z_1 z_2^*).$$

Similarly, we get for the scalar product B:

$$B = |z_1|\,|z_2|\cos(\theta_1 - \theta_2) = \frac{1}{2}(z_1 z_2^* + z_1^* z_2) = \mathcal{R}(z_1 z_2^*).$$

Thus, the scalar and the vector products turn out to be the real and imaginary parts of the complex vector product $z_1 z_2^*$:

$$z_1 z_2^* = B + iA.$$

Expressed in terms of x and y,

$$A = x_1 y_2 - x_2 y_1,$$

$$B = x_1 x_2 + y_1 y_2.$$

3.2   Comparison of Angles Between Vectors

Proportionality of four vectors (see Fig. 3.6)

$$\frac{z_1}{z_2} = \frac{z_3}{z_4} \tag{3.3}$$

implies that moduli are proportional:

$$\frac{|z_1|}{|z_2|} = \frac{|z_3|}{|z_4|}$$

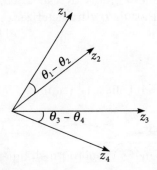

Fig. 3.6   Depicting Eq. (3.3)

and that the enclosed angles are equal: $\theta_1 - \theta_2 = \theta_3 - \theta_4$. The two triangles constructed on z_1, z_2 and z_3, z_4 are similar. For equality of angles, it is enough to require

$$\frac{z_1}{z_2} \propto \frac{z_3}{z_4},$$

or

$$z_1 z_4 \propto z_2 z_3$$

with a real constant of proportionality. In the special case of $z_2 = z_3$ the two remaining vectors make equal angles with the middle vector if

$$z_1 z_2 \propto z_2^2$$

with a real constant of proportionality. These rules are always employed to prove the equality of angles in geometrical figures. Thus, for example, $z_2 = \sqrt{f(u)}$ bisects the angle between $z_1 = f(u)$ and the real axis $z_3 = 1$. Similarly, $z_2 = \sqrt{if(u)}$ bisects the angle between $z_1 = f(u)$ and the imaginary axis $z_3 = i$.

3.3 Anharmonic Ratio: Parametric Equation to a Circle

By the *anharmonic ratio, cross ratio* or *double quotient* D of four vectors we mean the expression:

$$D = \frac{z_1 - z_3}{z_1 - z_4} \div \frac{z_2 - z_3}{z_2 - z_4}. \tag{3.4}$$

D is in general complex and its argument is the difference of the arguments of $\frac{z_1 - z_3}{z_1 - z_4}$ and $\frac{z_2 - z_3}{z_2 - z_4}$. If this difference is zero, that is, (see Fig. 3.7) if $\angle z_3 z_1 z_4 = \angle z_3 z_2 z_4$, D is real. In this case, the four points will be situated on a circle and the criterion for the concentric configuration of four points is the reality of the cross ratio. Let three of the four points be fixed on the circle and let z_4 move over it. Then, D assumes all the positive and negative real values. The circle is then parameterized by D and the formula for the circle passing through z_1, z_2, z_3 is

$$D = \frac{z_1 - z_3}{z_1 - z} \div \frac{z_2 - z_3}{z_2 - z}. \tag{3.5}$$

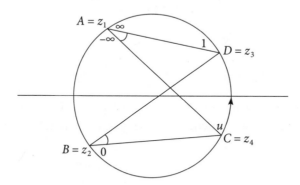

Fig. 3.7 If D is real, z_1, z_2, z_3, z_4 lie on a circle

The value of the cross ratio depends on the order in which we take the four points. We denote the sequence by writing $D(1234)$ for the sequence chosen in the definition. We see that interchanging 1 and 2 or 3 and 4 inverts the value. Interchanging 2 and 3 or 1 and 4 changes D into 1-D as can be checked by calculation. This leads to the rules named after Mobius:

(i) $D(1234) = D(3412) = D(2143) = D(4321) = \delta$

(ii) $D(2134) = D(1243) = 1/\delta$

(iii) $D(1324) = D(4231) = 1 - D(1234) = 1 - \delta$ (3.6)

and by further permutation of indices, the values $1 - 1/\delta$, $\frac{1}{1-\delta}$ and $\frac{\delta}{\delta-1}$ can be obtained.

In case D is real, it represents the cross ratio of the lengths of the four vectors $z_1 - z_3$, $z_1 - z_4$, $z_2 - z_3$ and $z_2 - z_4$.

Mobius' third rule gives us the following famous result (see Fig. 3.7),

$$D(1234) = \frac{z_1 - z_3}{z_1 - z_4} \div \frac{z_2 - z_3}{z_2 - z_4} = \frac{AD \cdot BC}{AC \cdot BD} = \delta$$

$$D(1324) = \frac{z_1 - z_2}{z_1 - z_4} \div \frac{z_3 - z_2}{z_3 - z_4} = \frac{AB \cdot CD}{AC \cdot BD} = 1 - \delta.$$ (3.7)

Since the sum is 1 we get

$$AD \cdot BC + AB \cdot CD = AC \cdot BD.$$ (3.8)

In words: The product of the diagonals of a quadrilateral inscribed in a circle equals the sum of the products of the opposite sides.

3.4 Conformal Transforms, Inversion

A transformation $\omega = f(z)$, ω, z complex, makes one or more points of the complex ω plane correspond to one or more points to the complex z plane. We assume that the derivative $d\omega/dz$ is a single valued function of z, that is, it is independent of the direction of dz. In this case $d\omega$ makes a constant angle with dz, this angle being the argument of $d\omega/dz$. Two lines passing through z and making a certain angle with each other, will be transformed into two lines passing through ω and making the same angle with each other as the original ones. This is the defining property of the so called *conformal transformations*. Conformality means that infinitely small polygons do not change their shape under this transformation.

In general, $d\omega/dz$ may vanish at finite number of z values (zeros of $d\omega/dz$) and may blow up, or become infinite, at some other finite number of z values (poles of $d\omega/dz$). At neither of these two sets of points the argument of $d\omega/dz$ is well defined so that at these points we may find deviations from conformality of the transforms. Since these exceptional points are finite in number, we call the corresponding transformation conformal. Thus, for the transformation $\omega = \sqrt{z}$, $\frac{d\omega}{dz} = \frac{1}{2\sqrt{z}}$ has a pole at $z = 0$ and a zero at $z = \infty$ so that the whole of z plane is transformed conformally except at $z = 0$ and $z = \infty$.

We consider here the transformation

$$\omega = \frac{z - z_0}{z + z_0} \tag{3.9}$$

where z_0 is a complex constant. This transformation plays a role in the problem of the reflection of a plane wave travelling in a medium of wave-resistance z_0, against a wall of impedance z. The number ω is the complex reflection factor whose modulus is the ratio of the amplitudes of the reflected and incident waves and the argument is the phase shift at reflection.

The argument Δ of ω is constructed in Fig. 3.8.

Exercise   Show that the argument Δ of ω is constant along a circle passing through the points $-z_0$ and $+z_0$ of the z plane.

Hint   Make use of the constant angle property of the circle (see below) and Fig. 3.8.   □

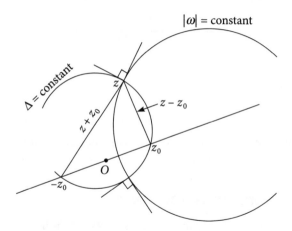

Fig. 3.8   The argument Δ of ω defined by Eq. (3.9)

The modulus of ω is the ratio of the lengths of the vectors $z - z_0$ and $z + z_0$ and we know from elementary geometry that this ratio is constant along a circle (*Circle of Apollonius*) with its center on the straight line through $-z_0$ and $+z_0$.

As in the ω plane the lines $|\omega| = $ constant (circles around the origin) and the lines $\Delta = $ constant (radii) are two orthogonal sets of curves, the two sets of circles in the z plane for $|\omega| = $ constant and $\Delta = $ constant must be orthogonal by the property of conformal transformations.

This example leads to the following two geometrical conclusions:

(a) The circle passing through the points z_1 and z_2 such that the chord $z_1 z_2$ subtends at any point of the arc $z_1 z_2$ of the circle constant angle Δ is given by the equation:

$$u \exp(i\Delta) = \frac{z - z_1}{z - z_2}.$$

(b) The circle of Apollonius, for which the ratio of the distances of any point of the circle to the two fixed points z_1 and z_2 is constant say a, is given by the equation

$$a \exp(iu) = \frac{z - z_1}{z - z_2}.$$

One of the most important transformations is the *inversion*:

$$\omega = \frac{1}{z^*},$$

which leaves the argument the same while inverting the modulus.

Exercise Show that the inversion of the vertical straight line $z = 1 + iu$ is a circle passing through the origin.

Solution The real and imaginary parts of the inversion $\frac{1}{1-iu}$ are given by

$$x = \frac{1}{1 + u^2}; \, y = \frac{u}{1 + u^2},$$

which are seen to satisfy the equation $(x - \frac{1}{2})^2 + y^2 = \frac{1}{4}$ which is the Cartesian equation of the circle with center at $(0, \frac{1}{2})$ and radius $\frac{1}{2}$. We call this an O-circle.   □

Exercise Show that all straight lines in the complex z plane $(z = u + i(mu + c), u, m, c$ real) can be converted to O-circles and conversely, the angle between two of these straight lines being equal to the angle at the intersection of the two corresponding O-circles.   □

Under inversion the cross ratio of four points goes over to

$$D(\omega) = \frac{\omega_1 - \omega_3}{\omega_1 - \omega_4} \div \frac{\omega_2 - \omega_3}{\omega_2 - \omega_4} = \frac{z_1^* - z_3^*}{z_1^* - z_4^*} \div \frac{z_2^* - z_3^*}{z_2^* - z_4^*}$$

which is the conjugate value of the original $D(z)$. The cross ratio is, in general, changed by inversion, it will remain the same, if it is real. In other words, if the four points are on a circle, before the transformation, they will still be on a circle after the transformation, straight line being included as the circles of infinite radius.

There are pairs of curves which are mutual inversions, e.g., parabola and cardioid, orthogonal hyperbola and lemniscate. All the properties concerning angles between straight lines related to one member of a pair can immediately be converted to the properties of angles between O-circles related to the second one. Concyclical location of four or more points will be invariant with respect to inversion.

3.5   Circle: Constant Angle and Constant Power Theorems

Let A, B and P be points on the circle $z = r \exp(iu)$; B situated on the real axis $(u = 0)$, A is fixed $(u = \phi)$ and P is arbitrary (see Fig. 3.9).

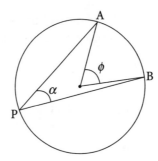

Fig. 3.9   Constant angle property of the circle

Vector $\overrightarrow{AP}$ is given by $r \exp(iu) - r \exp(i\phi)$. Vector $\overrightarrow{BP}$ is $r \exp(iu) - r$. The quotient of these two vectors contains the factor $\exp(i\alpha)$:

$$(\text{Real function})\exp(i\alpha) = \frac{r \exp(iu) - r \exp(i\phi)}{r \exp(iu) - r}.$$

Dividing this by the conjugate equation we get $\exp(2i\alpha) = \exp(i\phi)$ implying $\alpha = \phi/2$ which is the constant angle property of the circle.

Next consider a circle with center at origin O and choose point A on the negative real axis at a distance A from O (see Fig. 3.10). Draw a secant through A whose formula is

$$z = -a + s \exp(i\phi).$$

It cuts the circle $z = r \exp(iu)$ at

$$-a + s\exp(i\phi) = r \exp(iu).$$

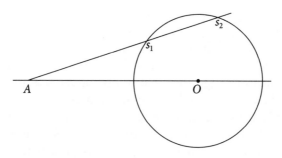

Fig. 3.10   Constant power property of the circle

Multiplying this equation by its conjugate, we find

$$a^2 - 2 \, as \cos \phi + s^2 = r^2.$$

This equation has two roots s_1 and s_2, the product of which equals $a^2 - r^2$, independent of the choice of ϕ which proves the constant power property of the circle.

3.6   General Circle Formula

We prove that a curve represented by the equation

$$z = \frac{z_1 + z_2 u}{z_3 + z_4 u} \tag{3.10}$$

is a circle.

The curve passes through point $A = z_1/z_3$ ($u = 0$) and point $B = z_2/z_4$ ($u = \infty$) (see Fig. 3.11). Let P be a point on the curve, represented by Eq. (3.10). The vector $\overrightarrow{PA}$ is

$$\frac{z_1 + z_2 u}{z_3 + z_4 u} - \frac{z_1}{z_3} = \frac{u}{z_3} \frac{z_2 z_3 - z_1 z_4}{z_3 + z_4 u}.$$

The vector $\overrightarrow{PB}$ is

$$\frac{z_1 + z_2 u}{z_3 + z_4 u} - \frac{z_2}{z_4} = -\frac{1}{z_4} \frac{z_2 z_3 - z_1 z_4}{z_3 + z_4 u},$$

so that the quotient $\frac{PA}{PB} = -\frac{z_4}{z_3} u$. As z_3 and z_4 are constant and u is real, the argument of this quotient is constant. Therefore, the angle α in Fig. 3.11 is independent of u. Therefore, we may conclude that P describes a circle.

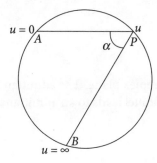

Fig. 3.11   Illustrating Eq. (3.10)

In order to get the radius r and the center z_c of the circle represented by Eq. (3.10), we solve this equation for u:

$$-u = \frac{z_1 - z z_3}{z_2 - z z_4}.$$

As u is real, it must equal the conjugate of the right side so that the circle is represented by the equation:

$$(z_1 - z z_3)(z_2^* - z^* z_4^*) = (z_1^* - z^* z_3^*)(z_2 - z z_4).$$

Comparison with the equation

$$(z - z_c)(z^* - z_c^*) = r^2$$

yields

$$z_c = \frac{z_1 z_4^* - z_2 z_3^*}{z_3 z_4^* - z_3^* z_4} \text{ and } |z_c|^2 - r^2 = \frac{z_1 z_2^* - z_1^* z_2}{z_3 z_4^* - z_3^* z_4}.$$

Exercise   Interpret the last expression in terms of the power of the circle (see above and Fig. 3.11).   □

3.7   Circuit Impedance and Admittance

The impedance of an electrical circuit containing a resistance R, inductance L and capacity C in series, with applied electromotive force of angular frequency ω is

$$z = i\omega L + R + \frac{1}{i\omega C}.$$

With the new parameter

$$u = \omega L - \frac{1}{\omega C},$$

the impedance becomes

$$z = f(u) = R + iu,$$

which is a straight line in the complex plane. The admittance, $\frac{1}{z} = \frac{1}{R+iu}$ is then a circle.

Connecting R, C and L in parallel leads to an admittance

$$\frac{1}{z} = f(u) = \frac{1}{R} + iu$$

where $u = \omega C - \frac{1}{\omega L}$ and represents a straight line in the complex plane. However, the impedance z will now be a circle.

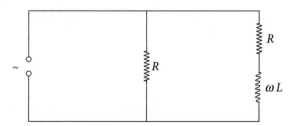

Fig. 3.12   Both impedance and admittance of this circuit are circles

There are circuits for which both impedance and admittance are circles. For the circuit in Fig. 3.12 the admittance is

$$\frac{1}{R_1} + \frac{1}{R_2 + i\omega L} = \frac{R_1 + R_2 + i\omega L}{R_1 R_2 + i\omega L R_1}$$

and this as well as its inversion represent a circle.

There are circuits for which the variable parameter is not the frequency however, some other quantity pertaining to the circuit. In Boucherot's circuit (see Fig. 3.13) we find the variable resistance u. The impedance is

$$z = \frac{a^2}{i(b-a) + u}$$

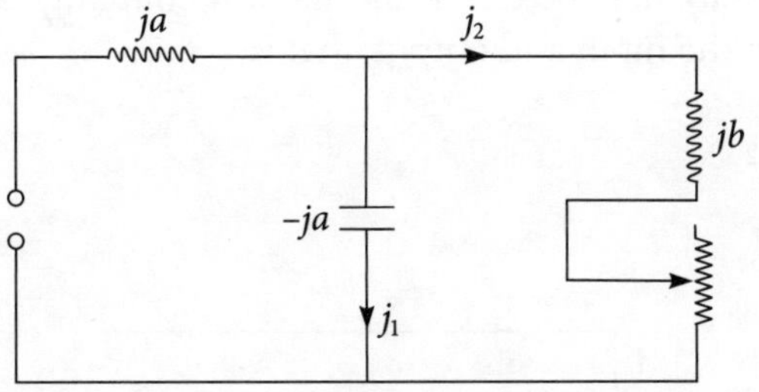

Fig. 3.13   Boucherot's circuit

and this is again represented by a circle. We may observe that j_2 is independent of u:

$$e = ia(j_1 + j_2) + v_2; \quad v_2 = -iaj_1; \quad \therefore \quad e = iaj_2.$$

As another example, the circle diagram named after Heyland is obtained by plotting the admittance of a motor as a function of load.

The reason why circle diagrams occur so often in electrical engineering is the linear character of the fundamental equations. As the mechanical vibrations follow similar equations, the field of application includes mechanics and acoustics.

3.8   The Circle Transformation

The transformation

$$\omega = \frac{az + b}{cz + d} \quad a,b,c,d \text{ complex} \tag{3.11}$$

transforms the circle

$$z = \frac{z_1 + z_2 u}{z_3 + z_4 u}$$

into other circle:

$$\omega = \frac{az_1 + bz_3 + (az_2 + bz_4)u}{cz_1 + dz_3 + (cz_2 + dz_4)u}.$$

Therefore, the transformation in Eq. (3.11) is called the *circle transformation*. Straight lines are considered to be the special cases of circles, as the straight line

$$z = \frac{z_1 + z_2 u}{m + nu}$$

is also transformed into a circle and can turn out to be the transform of a circle.

A prominent example of the application of the circle transformation is the four terminal network (see Fig. 3.14). Four terminal networks can be of electrical, mechanical, acoustic or optical character. They may be electromechanical couplings and so on. We assume a linear relation between the input and output, that is,

$$v_1 = av_2 + bj_2$$

$$j_1 = cv_2 + dj_2. \tag{3.12}$$

Fig. 3.14 Four terminal network

Dividing these equations we get $v_1 / j_1 = \frac{a(v_2/j_2)+b}{c(v_2/j_2)+d}$, which reduces to the transformation in Eq. (3.11) if we identify $\omega = v_1 / j_1$ and $z = v_2 / j_2$. Thus, if z is a circle impedance, ω will also have circular character.

Symmetrical networks are the ones which remain invariant under the maps $(v_1, v_2) \mapsto (v_2, v_1)$ and $(j_1, j_2) \mapsto (-j_2, -j_1)$. Note that applying this map twice reduces to identity. Thus, in addition to Eq. (3.12) the equations

$$v_2 = av_1 - bj_1$$

$$-j_2 = cv_1 + dj_1 \tag{3.13}$$

must hold. Eliminate v_1 from the first of Eq. (3.12) and the first of Eq. (3.13) to get

$$j_1 = \frac{a^2 - 1}{b} v_2 + aj_2$$

and identify this with the second of Eq. (3.12). Comparing the corresponding coefficients we see that for a symmetrical network the coefficients must satisfy

$$a = d \text{ and } a^2 - bc = 1.$$

Imposing these conditions on Eq. (3.11) we see that, for a symmetrical network, the transformation is

$$\omega = \frac{az + b}{cz + a}. \tag{3.14}$$

The characteristic value $z = \infty$ corresponds to the open output ($j_2 = 0$) condition, while $z = 0$ corresponds to the shorted output terminals. The corresponding values of ω, denoted ω_∞ and ω_0 respectively, are

$$\omega_\infty = a/c \; ; \; \omega_0 = b/a.$$

The case where $\omega = z$ is of importance. The corresponding value of z is called the wave impedance. An arbitrary number of networks, put in cascade, would not change this impedance. From Eq. (3.14) it follows that this value is $\sqrt{b/c}$, which we denote by ω_z. Note that $\omega_z^2 = \omega_0 \omega_\infty$, which means geometrically that (see Fig. 3.15) the triangles $\omega_\infty O \omega_z$ and $\omega_z O \omega_0$ are similar.

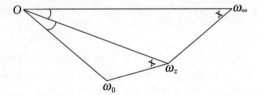

Fig. 3.15   Geometrical meaning of $\omega_z^2 = \omega_0 \omega_\infty$

The transformation in Eq. (3.14) can be written as

$$\left(\omega - \frac{a}{c}\right)\left(z + \frac{a}{c}\right) = \frac{b}{c} - \frac{a^2}{c^2}$$

or,

$$(\omega - \omega_\infty)(z + \omega_\infty) = \omega_z^2 - \omega_\infty^2$$

or,

$$\frac{\omega - \omega_\infty}{\omega_z - \omega_\infty} = \frac{\omega_z + \omega_\infty}{z + \omega_\infty}$$

which means the triangles $\omega, -\omega_\infty, \omega_z$ and ω, ω_∞, z are similar (see Fig. 3.16).

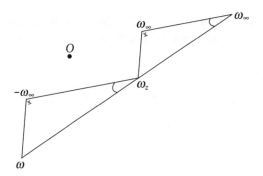

Fig. 3.16   Point by point implementation of transformation Eq. (3.14)

As $\omega_\infty, -\omega_\infty, \omega_z$ are fixed points in the plane, this offers us a method to construct point ω for any given value of z, thus performing the transformation point by point.

Exercise   Let x and y be the rectangular coordinates of a point $\mathbf{x}$. Show that the equations to an ellipse and a hyperbola, in terms of these coordinates, are

$$\frac{x^2}{a^2} + \frac{y^2}{b^2} = 1, \quad \frac{x^2}{a^2} - \frac{y^2}{b^2} = 1$$

respectively. These parameters are related to those in Eq. (2.23) by

$$a = \frac{l}{|1 - e^2|}, \quad b^2 = al, \quad \mathbf{x} = \mathbf{r} + a\mathbf{e}.$$

The curves and related parameters are shown in Figs 3.17(a),(b). Use the equations in terms of coordinates to show that an ellipse has a parametric equation $\mathbf{x} = \mathbf{x}(\phi)$:

$$\mathbf{x} = \mathbf{a}\cos\phi + \mathbf{b}\sin\phi,$$

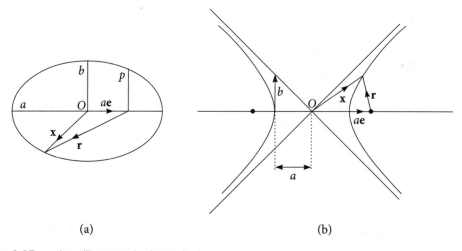

(a)   (b)

Fig. 3.17   An ellipse and a hyperbola

while a hyperbola has the parametric equation:

$$\mathbf{x} = \mathbf{a} \cosh\phi + \mathbf{b} \sinh\phi,$$

where $\mathbf{a}^2 = a^2$, $\mathbf{b}^2 = b^2$, and $\mathbf{a} \cdot \mathbf{b} = 0$.

Hint   Treat these as the curves on a complex plane and use complex algebra. Write the equations to ellipse and hyperbola as $z = a\cos\phi + ib\sin\phi$ and $z = a\cosh\phi + ib\sinh\phi$ respectively.   □

Theory of plane curves is a subject in itself and we recommend reference [26] for further study.

Part II

Vector Operators

"My Lord! Please make me a cat!" prayed the mouse.
— from a Panchatantra story

4

Linear Operators

4.1 Linear Operators on $\mathscr{E}_3$

We have seen that the fields are functions defined over the domain of position vectors or points in space and are either vector valued or scalar valued. We now consider functions (either vector valued or scalar valued) defined over some domain of vectors (not necessarily position vectors) with the additional requirement that the function be linear, that is,

$$f(\alpha \mathbf{x} + \beta \mathbf{y}) = \alpha f(\mathbf{x}) + \beta f(\mathbf{y}),$$

where α and β are scalars. Such a function is called a linear operator, or operator for brevity. In different contexts, such a function is also called a linear transformation or a tensor. The term 'tensor' is used for describing certain properties of a physical system. Thus, the 'inertia tensor' is a property of a rigid body or the 'strain tensor' is a property of an elastic body. These are never called an 'inertia or strain linear transformation'. On the other hand, the term 'transformation' suggests a change of state of a physical system or an equivalence of one state with another. The term 'linear operator' is generally used when the emphasis is on the mathematical structure. Finally, we note that an operator is essentially a mapping or association between the elements of two sets or between the elements of the same set. Henceforth, in this book, whenever we refer to an operator, we mean it to be a linear operator, unless otherwise specified.

Two simple examples of linear operators are $\alpha(\mathbf{x}) = \alpha \mathbf{x}$ (the scalar multiplication operator) and $f(\mathbf{x}) = \mathbf{a} \cdot \mathbf{x}$. In the first example, α is a fixed scalar and the operator maps a vector $\mathbf{x}$ to a vector $\alpha \mathbf{x}$. Also, here the symbol α is used as the operator as well as a scalar. In the second example, $\mathbf{a}$ is a fixed vector and the operator maps a vector $\mathbf{x}$ to the scalar $\mathbf{a} \cdot \mathbf{x}$. Note that if we change the fixed vector $\mathbf{a}$ in the second operator, we get a new operator giving a new value for every vector $\mathbf{x}$. This is often expressed by saying that the operator parametrically depends on $\mathbf{a}$. Similarly, the first operator parametrically depends on α.

Exercise   Check that the operators in these examples are linear operators.   ☐

The set of vectors on which a given operator f acts is called its *domain*. The set of vectors or scalars generated by the action of f on its domain is called its *range*. All the operators we deal with act on $\mathscr{E}_3$. For a real life application, $\mathscr{E}_3$ consists of vector values of one or more vector quantities e.g., electric and magnetic fields. When a linear operator f acts on a vector $\mathbf{x} \in \mathscr{E}_3$, it either returns a vector $\mathbf{y} \in \mathscr{E}_3$, or a scalar $\alpha \in \mathbb{R}$. $\mathbf{y}$ (or α) is called the image of $\mathbf{x}$ under f. In the first case, we denote $f : \mathscr{E}_3 \mapsto \mathscr{E}_3$ and in the second case $f : \mathscr{E}_3 \mapsto \mathbb{R}$. We assume that the domain of an operator we deal with is whole of $\mathscr{E}_3$ and its range is either a subset of $\mathscr{E}_3$ or a subset of $\mathbb{R}$. Two operators $f : \mathscr{E}_3 \mapsto \mathscr{E}_3$ or $\mathbb{R}$ and $g : \mathscr{E}_3 \mapsto \mathscr{E}_3$ or $\mathbb{R}$ are *equal* if they have common domain ($\mathscr{E}_3$) and range (a subset of $\mathscr{E}_3$ or $\mathbb{R}$) and if $f(\mathbf{x}) = g(\mathbf{x})$ for all $\mathbf{x} \in \mathscr{E}_3$.

The product of two linear operators, in a given order, is a linear operator in itself and is defined as an operator obtained by successively applying the two operators in the given order. Thus, in order to get the action of the product fg on vector $\mathbf{x}$ we have to act first by the operator g on $\mathbf{x}$ to get the vector $g(\mathbf{x})$ and then act by the operator f on the vector $g(\mathbf{x})$ to get the vector $fg(\mathbf{x})$. In general, the product of two linear operators is not commutative.[1] Such a product is written in many different ways like

$$g(f(\mathbf{x})) = g(f\mathbf{x}) = gf(\mathbf{x}) = gf\mathbf{x}.$$

Note that the product of operators $f : \mathscr{E}_3 \mapsto \mathbb{R}$ and $g : \mathscr{E}_3 \mapsto \mathscr{E}_3$ is defined only in the order $fg : \mathscr{E}_3 \mapsto \mathbb{R}$. The general condition for the existence of the product of the two operators, fg, is that the range of g must be a subset of the domain of f. Note that, two commuting operators must be defined on a common set of vectors, forming the domain as well as the range for both.

Exercise   Show that the product of two linear operators is a linear operator. Check this for the two operators defined in the above examples. Also check that two operators defined via scalar multiplication as in the first example above, commute. In fact, check that the operator of scalar multiplication $\alpha(\mathbf{x}) = \alpha\mathbf{x}$ commutes with all linear operators.   ☐

The addition of two linear operators is defined by

$$(f + g)(\mathbf{x}) = f(\mathbf{x}) + g(\mathbf{x})$$

for all $\mathbf{x} \in \mathscr{E}_3$ and is itself a linear operator (check this). The operators being added must be either $\mathscr{E}_3 \mapsto \mathscr{E}_3$ or $\mathscr{E}_3 \mapsto \mathbb{R}$. Both the product and the addition of linear operators are associative. That is, for three linear operators f, g and h we have

$$h(gf) = hgf = (hg)f \quad \text{and} \quad (h + g) + f = h + (g + f).$$

---

[1] Two operators f and g are said to commute if $fg(\mathbf{x}) = gf(\mathbf{x})$ for all $\mathbf{x} \in \mathscr{E}_3$.

This follows easily from the definitions of the product and the addition of operators. Using the linearity of operators and the definition of their product we can show that the product of operators is distributive with respect to addition, that is,

$$h(g+f) = hg + hf.$$

Identity operator

The identity operator I is defined via

$$I(\mathbf{x}) = \mathbf{x}$$

for all $\mathbf{x} \in \mathscr{E}_3$. The scalar multiplication operator we saw above can also be defined as $(\alpha I)(\mathbf{x}) = \alpha I(\mathbf{x}) = \alpha \mathbf{x}$. It is trivial to check that for every operator f

$$If = f = fI,$$

that is, I commutes with every operator[2].

4.1.1 Adjoint operators

To every linear operator $f : \mathscr{E}_3 \mapsto \mathscr{E}_3$ there corresponds another linear operator $f^{\dagger} : \mathscr{E}_3 \mapsto \mathscr{E}_3$ uniquely defined by

$$\mathbf{y} \cdot f(\mathbf{x}) = f^{\dagger}(\mathbf{y}) \cdot \mathbf{x}$$

for all vectors $\mathbf{x}$ and $\mathbf{y}$ in $\mathscr{E}_3$. The operator $f^{\dagger}$ is called the adjoint of f. You will know its utility after we use it in the sequel.

Exercise   Show that $(f^{\dagger})^{\dagger} = f$. □

Consider two operators f and g and their product fg. Given any two vectors $\mathbf{x}, \mathbf{y} \in \mathscr{E}_3$ we can write,

$$fg\mathbf{x} \cdot \mathbf{y} = \mathbf{x} \cdot (fg)^{\dagger} \mathbf{y} \tag{4.1}$$

and

$$fg\mathbf{x} \cdot \mathbf{y} = g\mathbf{x} \cdot (f)^{\dagger} \mathbf{y} = \mathbf{x} \cdot (g)^{\dagger} (f)^{\dagger} \mathbf{y}. \tag{4.2}$$

Since the LHS of Eqs (4.1) and (4.2) are the same, their RHS must also be equal. Since $\mathbf{x}, \mathbf{y} \in \mathscr{E}_3$ are arbitrary, this leads to the operator equality

$$(fg)^{\dagger} = (g)^{\dagger} (f)^{\dagger}.$$

4.1.2 Inverse of an operator

Consider an operator $f : \mathscr{E}_3 \mapsto \mathscr{E}_3$ or $\mathbb{R}$ acting on all vectors in $\mathscr{E}_3$. The set containing the images of all vectors in $\mathscr{E}_3$ under f (the range of f, also called the image set of f) need not

---

[2]Note that if $f : \mathscr{E}_3 \mapsto \mathscr{E}_3$ then $I : \mathscr{E}_3 \mapsto \mathscr{E}_3$, but if $f : \mathscr{E}_3 \mapsto \mathbb{R}$ then on LHS $I : \mathscr{E}_3 \mapsto \mathscr{E}_3$ while on RHS $I : \mathbb{R} \mapsto \mathbb{R}$. Henceforth keep track of the mapping corresponding to operators occurring in an expression.

equal $\mathscr{E}_3$ (or $\mathbb{R}$) however, can be a proper subset of $\mathscr{E}_3$ (or of $\mathbb{R}$). This can happen when two or more elements of $\mathscr{E}_3$ have the same image under f. However, when this image set equals $\mathscr{E}_3$, (or $\mathbb{R}$), that is, for every $\mathbf{y} \in \mathscr{E}_3$ (or $y \in \mathbb{R}$) there is a $\mathbf{x} \in \mathscr{E}_3$ such that $f(\mathbf{x}) = \mathbf{y}$ (or $f(\mathbf{x}) = y$), we call the operator 'onto'. If two different elements of $\mathscr{E}_3$ always have different images under f then the operator f is said to make a one to one mapping (or one to one correspondence) between $\mathscr{E}_3$ and its image set under f. If f is both onto and one to one, then we can define its inverse operator $f^{-1} : \mathscr{E}_3(\text{or } \mathbb{R}) \mapsto \mathscr{E}_3$ as follows. For each $\mathbf{y} \in \mathscr{E}_3$ or $y \in \mathbb{R}$ we find that unique element $\mathbf{x} \in \mathscr{E}_3$ such that $f(\mathbf{x}) = \mathbf{y}$ or y ($\mathbf{x}$ exists and is unique since f is onto and one to one). We then define $\mathbf{x} = f^{-1}(\mathbf{y} \text{ or } y)$. This equation is the result of solving $\mathbf{y} = f(\mathbf{x})$ (or $y = f(\mathbf{x})$) for $\mathbf{x}$ in just the same way as $x = \log(y)$ is the result of solving $y = e^x$ for x. Below we give two examples to illustrate this. Figure 4.1 illustrates the concept of the inverse of a mapping.

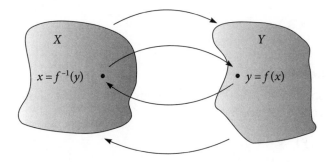

Fig. 4.1   Inverse of a mapping. A one to one and onto map $f : X \mapsto Y$ has the unique inverse $f^{-1} : Y \mapsto X$

If f^{-1} exists, we call the operator f invertible. It follows directly from its definition based on f being a one to one correspondence that f^{-1}, if it exists, is unique.

Using the definition of the inverse, we can write,

$$(f^{-1}f)(\mathbf{x}) = f^{-1}(f(\mathbf{x})) = f^{-1}(\mathbf{y}) = \mathbf{x}$$

for all $\mathbf{x} \in \mathscr{E}_3$ and similarly for $f f^{-1}(\mathbf{y})$, for all $\mathbf{y} \in \mathscr{E}_3$. This gives us the operator equation

$$f^{-1}f = I \text{ and } f f^{-1} = I. \tag{4.3}$$

The identity operators in Eq. (4.3) may act on different spaces. Thus, if $f : \mathscr{E}_3 \mapsto \mathbb{R}$ is invertible with $f^{-1} : \mathbb{R} \mapsto \mathscr{E}_3$ then the product $f^{-1}f : \mathscr{E}_3 \mapsto \mathscr{E}_3$ is an operator on $\mathscr{E}_3$ while $f f^{-1} : \mathbb{R} \mapsto \mathbb{R}$ is an operator on $\mathbb{R}$. Both are identity operators on respective spaces.

We now check whether the inverse of a linear operator is linear. The answer is yes. We have,

$$f^{-1}(\mathbf{y}_1 + \mathbf{y}_2) = f^{-1}(f(\mathbf{x}_1) + f(\mathbf{x}_2)) = f^{-1}f(\mathbf{x}_1 + \mathbf{x}_2)$$

$$= I(\mathbf{x}_1 + \mathbf{x}_2) = \mathbf{x}_1 + \mathbf{x}_2 = f^{-1}\mathbf{y}_1 + f^{-1}\mathbf{y}_2$$

and

$$f^{-1}(\alpha \mathbf{y}) = f^{-1}(\alpha f(\mathbf{x})) = f^{-1} f(\alpha \mathbf{x}) = \alpha \mathbf{x} = \alpha f^{-1}(\mathbf{y}),$$

which proves the linearity of f^{-1}.

For any linear operator f we show that $f(\mathbf{0}) = \mathbf{0}$. We have

$$f(\mathbf{0}) = f(\mathbf{x} - \mathbf{x}) = f(\mathbf{x}) - f(\mathbf{x}) = \mathbf{0}.$$

For an invertible operator, $f(\mathbf{a}) = \mathbf{0}$ implies $\mathbf{a} = \mathbf{0}$ as can be seen from

$$\mathbf{0} = f^{-1}(\mathbf{0}) = f^{-1}(f(\mathbf{a})) = \mathbf{a},$$

where the first equality follows because f^{-1} is a linear operator, so that $f^{-1}(\mathbf{0}) = \mathbf{0}$.

Next we show that for an invertible operator f the set $\{f(\mathbf{x}), f(\mathbf{y}), f(\mathbf{z})\}$ is linearly independent (non-coplanar) provided the set $\{\mathbf{x}, \mathbf{y}, \mathbf{z}\}$ is linearly independent (non-coplanar). We see that the equation

$$\mathbf{0} = \alpha f(\mathbf{x}) + \beta f(\mathbf{y}) + \gamma f(\mathbf{z}) = f(\alpha \mathbf{x} + \beta \mathbf{y} + \gamma \mathbf{z})$$

implies that all the coefficients α, β, γ vanish, because $\mathbf{x}, \mathbf{y}, \mathbf{z}$ are linearly independent. Here, we have used $f(\mathbf{a}) = \mathbf{0}$ implies $\mathbf{a} = \mathbf{0}$ for an invertible operator. The same argument shows that if $\mathbf{x}, \mathbf{y}, \mathbf{z}$ are linearly dependent, then so are $f(\mathbf{x}), f(\mathbf{y}), f(\mathbf{z})$.

For arbitrary $\mathbf{x} \in \mathscr{E}_3$, let $fg\mathbf{x} = \mathbf{y}$, so that $\mathbf{x} = (fg)^{-1}\mathbf{y}$. Successively multiplying both sides by $(f)^{-1}$ and $(g)^{-1}$ we get $\mathbf{x} = (g)^{-1}(f)^{-1}\mathbf{y}$. This leads to the operator equality

$$(fg)^{-1} = (g)^{-1}(f)^{-1}.$$

4.1.3   Determinant of an invertible linear operator

Consider an orthonormal basis $\{\hat{\sigma}_1, \hat{\sigma}_2, \hat{\sigma}_3\}$ forming a right handed system. The parallelepiped with adjacent sides $\hat{\sigma}_1, \hat{\sigma}_2, \hat{\sigma}_3$ is a cube with volume unity (unit cube). That is, $\hat{\sigma}_1 \cdot \hat{\sigma}_2 \times \hat{\sigma}_3 = 1$. Under the action of an invertible linear operator $f : \mathscr{E}_3 \mapsto \mathscr{E}_3$ this unit cube goes over to a parallelepiped with adjacent sides $f(\hat{\sigma}_1), f(\hat{\sigma}_2), f(\hat{\sigma}_3)$ and with volume proportional to that of the unit cube $\hat{\sigma}_1 \cdot \hat{\sigma}_2 \times \hat{\sigma}_3 = 1$. We write

$$f(\hat{\sigma}_1) \cdot f(\hat{\sigma}_2) \times f(\hat{\sigma}_3) = \det f \; \hat{\sigma}_1 \cdot \hat{\sigma}_2 \times \hat{\sigma}_3 = \det f.$$

This equation defines the proportionality factor $\det f$ which depends exclusively on the operator f and is an important characteristic of f. $\det f$ is called the *determinant* of the operator f. Note that for an invertible operator f, $\det f \neq 0$ because the vectors $f(\hat{\sigma}_1), f(\hat{\sigma}_2), f(\hat{\sigma}_3)$ are linearly independent, that is non-coplanar. Given any set $\{\mathbf{x}, \mathbf{y}, \mathbf{z}\}$ of linearly independent (non-coplanar) vectors, the number of unit cubes that can be accommodated in the parallelepiped with adjacent sides $\mathbf{x}, \mathbf{y}, \mathbf{z}$ is given by its volume

$\mathbf{x} \cdot \mathbf{y} \times \mathbf{z}$. Under the action of f, a unit cube is transformed to a parallelepiped with volume $\det f$. Therefore, the volume of the parallelepiped transformed under the action of f is

$$f(\mathbf{x}) \cdot f(\mathbf{y}) \times f(\mathbf{z}) = \det f \, \mathbf{x} \cdot \mathbf{y} \times \mathbf{z},$$

or,

$$\det f = \frac{f(\mathbf{x}) \cdot f(\mathbf{y}) \times f(\mathbf{z})}{\mathbf{x} \cdot \mathbf{y} \times \mathbf{z}}. \tag{4.4}$$

The determinant $\det f$ of an invertible linear operator is invariant under the change of orthonormal basis. We shall see later that any two triads of orthonormal unit vectors can be made to coincide by three successive independent rotations called Euler rotations (see section 6.5). Under these rotations the volume of the unit cube scanned by one orthonormal triad does not change. Since the determinant of f is simply the volume of the deformed unit cube under the action of f, we see that $\det f$ is invariant under the change of basis, which amounts to the rotation of one orthonormal triad of vectors to the other.

If f is invertible, then we know that any non-coplanar triad $(\mathbf{x}, \mathbf{y}, \mathbf{z})$ is mapped to another non-coplanar triad $(f(\mathbf{x}), f(\mathbf{y}), f(\mathbf{z}))$. This makes both the numerator and the denominator on the RHS of Eq. (4.4) non-zero, that is, $\det f \neq 0$. Thus, if f is invertible, then $\det f \neq 0$.

If f is not invertible, then there exist two vectors $\mathbf{x}, \mathbf{y} \in \mathcal{E}_3$, $\mathbf{x} \neq \mathbf{y}$ such that $f(\mathbf{x}) = f(\mathbf{y})$. We can make a linearly independent triad $(\mathbf{x}, \mathbf{y}, \mathbf{z})$ by adding a non-coplanar vector $\mathbf{z}$ to the set $\{\mathbf{x}, \mathbf{y}\}$, $\mathbf{x} \neq \mathbf{y}$ satisfying $f(\mathbf{x}) = f(\mathbf{y})$. Using this triad in Eq. (4.4), we see that $\det f = 0$. This proves that $\det f \neq 0$ implies f is invertible.

The last two paragraphs together imply that a linear operator f is invertible if and only if $\det f \neq 0$.

Many simple properties of the determinant $\det f$ now follow. First, it is trivial to check that $\det I = 1$. Next, consider the product gf of two linear invertible operators g and f. We have, using an orthonormal basis $\{\hat{\sigma}_1, \hat{\sigma}_2, \hat{\sigma}_3\}$,

$$\begin{aligned}
\det gf &= gf(\hat{\sigma}_1) \cdot gf(\hat{\sigma}_2) \times gf(\hat{\sigma}_3) \\
&= g(f(\hat{\sigma}_1)) \cdot g(f(\hat{\sigma}_2)) \times g(f(\hat{\sigma}_3)) \\
&= \left(\frac{g(f(\hat{\sigma}_1)) \cdot g(f(\hat{\sigma}_2)) \times g(f(\hat{\sigma}_3))}{f(\hat{\sigma}_1) \cdot f(\hat{\sigma}_2) \times f(\hat{\sigma}_3)} \right) (f(\hat{\sigma}_1) \cdot f(\hat{\sigma}_2) \times f(\hat{\sigma}_3)) \\
&= \det g \cdot \det f.
\end{aligned}$$

Thus, the determinant of the product is the product of determinants. This result can be used to write

$$1 = \det I = \det ff^{-1} = (\det f)(\det f^{-1}), \quad \text{or,} \quad \det f^{-1} = (\det f)^{-1}.$$

If det $f < 0$, the operator f not only scales the volume of the parallelepiped formed by $(\mathbf{x}, \mathbf{y}, \mathbf{z})$ however, also changes its orientation. That is, f changes a right handed system formed by $(\mathbf{x}, \mathbf{y}, \mathbf{z})$ to a left handed one or the acute angle between $\mathbf{x}$ and $\mathbf{y} \times \mathbf{z}$ to an obtuse angle between them. (see the interpretation of the scalar triple product in subsection 1.8.1). Further, det f is defined via a scalar triple product, so that interchange of any two factors changes its sign. This is not surprising, because interchanging any two of the three linearly independent vectors changes them from a right handed to a left handed system and vice-versa (see section 1.16).

4.1.4 Non-singular operators

An operator f with det $f = 0$ is called singular. If det $f \neq 0$ then f is called non-singular. We can now prove that the following three statements are equivalent. We have proved some parts of it in the last two sections however, it is worth putting everything at one place.

(a) f is non-singular.

(b) $f(\mathbf{x}) = 0$ implies $\mathbf{x} = 0$.

(c) f is invertible.

We first prove (a) $\Rightarrow$ (b). Let $\{\hat{\sigma}_k\}$, $k = 1, 2, 3$ be an orthonormal basis. Assume that $f(\mathbf{x}) = 0$ for some $\mathbf{x} \neq 0$. This means

$$f(\mathbf{x}) = \sum_k x_k f(\hat{\sigma}_k) = 0.$$

Since $\mathbf{x} \neq 0$, not all x_ks can be zero. Therefore, the above equation means that the vectors $f(\hat{\sigma}_k)$ $k = 1, 2, 3$ are linearly dependent (coplanar). Therefore, det $f = 0$ which contradicts the assumption that f is non-singular.

(b) $\Rightarrow$ (c): Suppose that f is not invertible, that is, it is not a one to one correspondence between $\mathbf{x}$ and $f(\mathbf{x})$ so that there are two different non-zero vectors $\mathbf{x}_1$ and $\mathbf{x}_2$ ($\mathbf{x}_1 \neq \mathbf{x}_2$) satisfying

$$f(\mathbf{x}_1) = \mathbf{y} = f(\mathbf{x}_2),$$

which gives

$$\mathbf{0} = f(\mathbf{x}_1) - f(\mathbf{x}_2) = f(\mathbf{x}_1 - \mathbf{x}_2)$$

which means that there is a non-zero vector $\mathbf{z} = \mathbf{x}_1 - \mathbf{x}_2$ with $f(\mathbf{z}) = 0$. This contradicts assumption (b).

(c) $\Rightarrow$ (a) That f is invertible implies it is non-singular is proved in subsection 4.1.3.

4.1.5 Examples

We find the inverses of the following linear operators.

(a) $f(\mathbf{x}) = \alpha \mathbf{x} + \mathbf{a}(\mathbf{b} \cdot \mathbf{x})$.

(b) $g(\mathbf{x}) = \alpha\mathbf{x} + \mathbf{b} \times \mathbf{x}.$

(a) Let

$$\mathbf{y} = f(\mathbf{x}) = \alpha\mathbf{x} + \mathbf{a}(\mathbf{b} \cdot \mathbf{x}). \tag{4.5}$$

Dotting both sides with $\mathbf{b}$ we get,

$$\mathbf{y} \cdot \mathbf{b} = \alpha\mathbf{x} \cdot \mathbf{b} + (\mathbf{a} \cdot \mathbf{b})(\mathbf{x} \cdot \mathbf{b}),$$

or,

$$\mathbf{x} \cdot \mathbf{b} = \frac{\mathbf{y} \cdot \mathbf{b}}{\alpha + \mathbf{a} \cdot \mathbf{b}}.$$

Multiply both sides by $\mathbf{a}$ to get

$$\mathbf{a}(\mathbf{x} \cdot \mathbf{b}) = \frac{\mathbf{a}(\mathbf{y} \cdot \mathbf{b})}{\alpha + \mathbf{a} \cdot \mathbf{b}}.$$

Using Eq. (4.5) we get,

$$\mathbf{y} - \alpha\mathbf{x} = \frac{\mathbf{a}(\mathbf{y} \cdot \mathbf{b})}{\alpha + \mathbf{a} \cdot \mathbf{b}},$$

or,

$$\mathbf{x} = \frac{\mathbf{y}}{\alpha} - \frac{\mathbf{a}(\mathbf{y} \cdot \mathbf{b})}{\alpha(\alpha + \mathbf{a} \cdot \mathbf{b})} = f^{-1}(\mathbf{y}).$$

(b)

$$\mathbf{y} = g(\mathbf{x}) = \alpha\mathbf{x} + \mathbf{b} \times \mathbf{x}. \tag{4.6}$$

Dot with $\mathbf{b}$ to get

$$\mathbf{b} \cdot \mathbf{y} = \alpha\mathbf{b} \cdot \mathbf{x}. \tag{4.7}$$

Cross with $\mathbf{b}$ to get

$$\mathbf{b} \times \mathbf{y} = \alpha\mathbf{b} \times \mathbf{x} + \mathbf{b} \times (\mathbf{b} \times \mathbf{x}). \tag{4.8}$$

Using Eqs (4.6), (4.7) in Eq. (4.8) and identity I, we get,

$$\mathbf{b} \times \mathbf{y} = \alpha(\mathbf{y} - \alpha\mathbf{x}) + (\mathbf{b} \cdot \mathbf{x})\mathbf{b} - b^2\mathbf{x}$$

$$= \alpha\mathbf{y} - (\alpha^2 + b^2)\mathbf{x} + \alpha^{-1}(\mathbf{b} \cdot \mathbf{y})\mathbf{b},$$

or,

$$\mathbf{x} = \frac{\alpha\mathbf{y} + \alpha^{-1}(\mathbf{b}\cdot\mathbf{y})\mathbf{b} - (\mathbf{b}\times\mathbf{y})}{\alpha^2 + b^2} = g^{-1}(\mathbf{y}).$$

Exercise In these two examples, check that $f^{-1}f(\mathbf{x}) = \mathbf{x}$ and $ff^{-1}(\mathbf{y}) = \mathbf{y}$. Also, check whether both these operators are non-singular. □

(c) We solve the vector equation

$$\alpha_1\mathbf{a}_1 + \alpha_2\mathbf{a}_2 + \alpha_3\mathbf{a}_3 = \mathbf{c} \tag{4.9}$$

for α_is; $\{\mathbf{a}_i\}$, $i = 1, 2, 3$ and $\mathbf{c}$ being given, using vector methods. We then compare our solution with that obtained by Cramer's rule for solving simultaneous equations.

Cross the given equation with $\mathbf{a}_3$ to get

$$\alpha_1(\mathbf{a}_3\times\mathbf{a}_1) + \alpha_2(\mathbf{a}_3\times\mathbf{a}_2) = \mathbf{a}_3\times\mathbf{c}$$

Dotting with $\mathbf{a}_2$ and solving for α_1 we get

$$\alpha_1 = \frac{\mathbf{a}_2\cdot(\mathbf{a}_3\times\mathbf{c})}{\mathbf{a}_2\cdot(\mathbf{a}_3\times\mathbf{a}_1)}.$$

Similarly,

$$\alpha_2 = \frac{\mathbf{a}_3\cdot(\mathbf{a}_1\times\mathbf{c})}{\mathbf{a}_3\cdot(\mathbf{a}_1\times\mathbf{a}_2)}$$

and

$$\alpha_3 = \frac{\mathbf{a}_1\cdot(\mathbf{a}_2\times\mathbf{c})}{\mathbf{a}_1\cdot(\mathbf{a}_2\times\mathbf{a}_3)}.$$

The given vector equation is equivalent to

$$\alpha_1 a_{11} + \alpha_2 a_{12} + \alpha_3 a_{13} = c_1$$

$$\alpha_1 a_{21} + \alpha_2 a_{22} + \alpha_3 a_{23} = c_2$$

$$\alpha_1 a_{31} + \alpha_2 a_{32} + \alpha_3 a_{33} = c_3$$

where a_{ij} is the ith component of $\mathbf{a}_j$ and c_i is the ith component of $\mathbf{c}$ with respect to some orthonormal basis. By Cramer's rule, its solution is

$$\alpha_1 = \frac{\begin{vmatrix} c_1 & a_{12} & a_{13} \\ c_2 & a_{22} & a_{23} \\ c_3 & a_{32} & a_{33} \end{vmatrix}}{\begin{vmatrix} a_{11} & a_{12} & a_{13} \\ a_{21} & a_{22} & a_{23} \\ a_{31} & a_{32} & a_{33} \end{vmatrix}},$$

where in the upper determinant the 1st column in $[a_{ij}]$ is replaced by $[c_1, c_2, c_3]^T$ and similarly for α_2 and α_3. It is straightforward to check that the two solutions are equivalent.

If we try to apply the vector method given above to the equation with more than three variables, (α_i $i = 1, \dots, 4$ say), it fails. We can make one of the four terms vanish by taking a suitable cross product and treat the resulting equation in three unknowns by the method given above. However, the vectors in the three term equation are all coplanar making the scalar triple product like $\mathbf{a}_1 \cdot (\mathbf{a}_2 \times \mathbf{a}_3)$ vanish. Thus, a generalization of our method needs a more general kind of algebraic setting, than the vector compositions based on dot and cross products. Geometric algebra is such an algebra in which the above method can be generalized. We refer to references [10, 7, 11] for a comprehensive treatment of geometric algebra.

4.2   Frames and Reciprocal Frames

In this section we deal with the problem of expressing arbitrary vectors in terms of a *non-orthonormal* basis. Let $\{\mathbf{e}_k\}$, $k = 1, 2, 3$ be a basis in $\mathcal{E}_3$, *not necessarily orthonormal*. We call it a frame and associate a pseudoscalar $e = \hat{\mathbf{e}}_1 \cdot (\hat{\mathbf{e}}_2 \times \hat{\mathbf{e}}_3)$ with this frame. $e > 0(< 0)$ means the frame is positively (negatively) oriented. For an orthonormal frame (basis) $e = +1$ or $e = -1$ depending on whether it is right or left handed. The reciprocal frame $\{\mathbf{e}^k\}$, $k = 1, 2, 3$ is determined by the set of equations

$$\mathbf{e}^k \cdot \mathbf{e}_j = \delta_j^k; \ j, k = 1, 2, 3,$$

where $\delta_j^k = 1$ if $j = k$ and zero otherwise. To solve for $\mathbf{e}^k$ we note that it is a vector normal to both the vectors $\mathbf{e}_j$ $j \neq k$ and its scalar product with $\mathbf{e}_k$ must be $+1$. Such a vector is uniquely given by the vector product of $\mathbf{e}_j$ $j \neq k$ in the cyclic order of $\{123\}$. Thus, the unique solution to these equations are given by

$$\mathbf{e}^1 = \frac{\mathbf{e}_2 \times \mathbf{e}_3}{e},$$

$$\mathbf{e}^2 = \frac{\mathbf{e}_3 \times \mathbf{e}_1}{e},$$

$$\mathbf{e}^3 = \frac{\mathbf{e}_1 \times \mathbf{e}_2}{e}.$$

Exercise   Check that an orthonormal frame is reciprocal to itself.   □

Any vector **a** can be expressed as a linear combination

$$\mathbf{a} = a^1\mathbf{e}_1 + a^2\mathbf{e}_2 + a^3\mathbf{e}_3 = a^k\mathbf{e}_k, \tag{4.10}$$

where the summation convention is used on the right. The coefficients a^k are called contravarient components of vector **a** (with respect to frame $\{\mathbf{e}_k\}$). We note that the Eq. (4.10) is the same as Eq. (4.9) with $\alpha_{1,2,3}$ replaced by $a^{1,2,3}$ and $\mathbf{a}_{1,2,3}$ replaced by $\mathbf{e}_{1,2,3}$ and **c** replaced by **a**. Making these substitutions, we get the following solutions for Eq. (4.10).

$$a^1 = \frac{\mathbf{a}\cdot(\mathbf{e}_2\times\mathbf{e}_3)}{\mathbf{e}_1\cdot(\mathbf{e}_2\times\mathbf{e}_3)},$$

$$a^2 = \frac{\mathbf{a}\cdot(\mathbf{e}_3\times\mathbf{e}_1)}{\mathbf{e}_1\cdot(\mathbf{e}_2\times\mathbf{e}_3)},$$

$$a^3 = \frac{\mathbf{a}\cdot(\mathbf{e}_1\times\mathbf{e}_2)}{\mathbf{e}_1\cdot(\mathbf{e}_2\times\mathbf{e}_3)}. \tag{4.11}$$

Exercise   Show that these solutions reduce to

$$a^k = \mathbf{e}^k\cdot\mathbf{a}; \ k = 1,2,3.$$

(Remember that $\mathbf{e}_k$, $k = 1,2,3$ are *not* mutually orthogonal!)

If we expand a vector **a** in terms of the $\mathbf{e}^k$ basis, we get

$$\mathbf{a} = a_1\mathbf{e}^1 + a_2\mathbf{e}^2 + a_3\mathbf{e}^3 = a_k\mathbf{e}^k,$$

where the coefficients a_k are called covariant components of vector **a** (with respect to frame $\{\mathbf{e}^k\}$).

Exercise   Show that the contravariant components a_k are given by

$$a_k = \mathbf{e}_k\cdot\mathbf{a}.$$ □

Exercise   Let $\hat{\mathbf{i}}, \hat{\mathbf{j}}, \hat{\mathbf{k}}$ be an orthonormal basis and define a non-orthonormal frame by $\mathbf{e}_1 = \hat{\mathbf{i}} + 3\hat{\mathbf{j}}$, $\mathbf{e}_2 = 4\hat{\mathbf{j}}$ and $\mathbf{e}_3 = \hat{\mathbf{k}}$. Find the corresponding reciprocal frame. Find the contravariant and covariant components of $\mathbf{a} = 7\hat{\mathbf{i}} + 2\hat{\mathbf{j}} + \hat{\mathbf{k}}$ with respect to these frames. Draw figures to depict both the frames and the contravariant and covariant components of **a**.   □

Exercise   Show that primitive bases of the Bravis lattice of a crystal and its reciprocal lattice form reciprocal frames.   □

4.3   Symmetric and Skewsymmetric Operators

We have already defined the adjoint of a linear operator. We now define two important types of linear operators, namely symmetric and skewsymmetric operators.

A linear operator S is said to be symmetric (or self adjoint) if $S = S^\dagger$ that is, if it is equivalent to its adjoint. Similarly, a linear operator $\mathscr{A}$ is said to be skewsymmetric (or antisymmetric) if $\mathscr{A}^\dagger = -\mathscr{A}$. A very simple but important observation is the following identity. For any operator f we can write,

$$f = \frac{1}{2}\left(f + f^\dagger\right) + \frac{1}{2}\left(f - f^\dagger\right) = f_+ + f_-.$$

Obviously, the first term (f_+) is a symmetric operator, while the second (f_-) is a skewsymmetric operator. Thus, any operator can be written as the sum of a symmetric and a skewsymmetric operator.

We now show that any skewsymmetric operator $\mathscr{A}$ can be put in a canonical (or standard) form

$$\mathscr{A}\mathbf{x} = \mathbf{x} \times (\mathbf{a} \times \mathbf{b}), \tag{4.12}$$

where $(\mathbf{a} \times \mathbf{b})$ is a unique pseudo vector.

We first check whether this operator is indeed a skewsymmetric operator. We have,

$$
\begin{aligned}
\mathbf{y} \cdot (\mathbf{x} \times (\mathbf{a} \times \mathbf{b})) &= \mathbf{y} \cdot ((\mathbf{b} \cdot \mathbf{x})\mathbf{a} - (\mathbf{a} \cdot \mathbf{x})\mathbf{b}), \\
&= (\mathbf{b} \cdot \mathbf{x})(\mathbf{a} \cdot \mathbf{y}) - (\mathbf{a} \cdot \mathbf{x})(\mathbf{b} \cdot \mathbf{y}) \\
&= -\mathbf{x} \cdot (\mathbf{y} \times (\mathbf{a} \times \mathbf{b})),
\end{aligned}
\tag{4.13}
$$

giving

$$\mathscr{A}^\dagger = -\mathscr{A}.$$

Here, we have used identity I.

We note that it is enough to prove Eq. (4.12) for a standard basis $\{\hat{\sigma}_k\}$, $k = 1, 2, 3$, for then the result is generally true by the linearity of $\mathscr{A}$. We know that the vectors $\mathscr{A}\hat{\sigma}_k$ and $\mathscr{A}^\dagger \hat{\sigma}_j$ can be written as

$$\mathbf{a}_k = \mathscr{A}\hat{\sigma}_k = \sum_j \hat{\sigma}_j A_{jk},$$

where $A_{jk} = \hat{\sigma}_j \cdot \mathscr{A}\hat{\sigma}_k$ and

$$\mathscr{A}^\dagger \hat{\sigma}_j = \sum_k \hat{\sigma}_k A_{jk},$$

where we have used the definition of the adjoint of an operator. Now we choose

$$\mathbf{a} \times \mathbf{b} = \frac{1}{2} \sum_k \mathbf{a}_k \times \hat{\sigma}_k$$

and consider

$$
\begin{aligned}
\hat{\sigma}_j \times (\mathbf{a} \times \mathbf{b}) &= \frac{1}{2} \sum_k \hat{\sigma}_j \times (\mathbf{a}_k \times \hat{\sigma}_k) \\
&= \frac{1}{2} \sum_k \left[\left(\hat{\sigma}_j \cdot \hat{\sigma}_k \right) \mathbf{a}_k - \hat{\sigma}_k \left(\hat{\sigma}_j \cdot \mathbf{a}_k \right) \right] \\
&= \frac{1}{2} \sum_k \left[\delta_{jk} \left(\mathscr{A} \hat{\sigma}_k \right) - \hat{\sigma}_k A_{jk} \right] \\
&= \frac{1}{2} \left(\mathscr{A} \hat{\sigma}_j - \mathscr{A}^\dagger \hat{\sigma}_j \right) = \mathscr{A} \hat{\sigma}_j.
\end{aligned}
\tag{4.14}
$$

Here, we have used identity I and the orthonormality of the $\{\sigma_k\}$ basis. As an example, the magnetic force due to magnetic field on a charged particle is a skewsymmetric linear operator on the particle velocity given by $\mathbf{F} = \mathscr{B} \mathbf{v} = \frac{q}{c} \mathbf{v} \times \mathbf{B}$ acting via the psuedovector $\mathbf{B}$.[3]

Example

We find the adjoint as well as the symmetric and the skewsymmetric parts of the operator

$$f\mathbf{x} = \alpha \mathbf{x} + \mathbf{a}(\mathbf{b} \cdot \mathbf{x}) + \mathbf{x} \times (\mathbf{c} \times \mathbf{d}). \tag{4.15}$$

We find

$$f^\dagger \mathbf{x} = \alpha \mathbf{x} + \mathbf{b}(\mathbf{a} \cdot \mathbf{x}) + (\mathbf{c} \times \mathbf{d}) \times \mathbf{x},$$

$$f_+ \mathbf{x} = \alpha \mathbf{x} + \frac{1}{2} [\mathbf{a}(\mathbf{b} \cdot \mathbf{x}) + \mathbf{b}(\mathbf{a} \cdot \mathbf{x})],$$

and

$$
\begin{aligned}
f_- \mathbf{x} &= \frac{1}{2} [\mathbf{a}(\mathbf{b} \cdot \mathbf{x}) - \mathbf{b}(\mathbf{a} \cdot \mathbf{x})] + \mathbf{x} \times (\mathbf{c} \times \mathbf{d}) \\
&= \frac{1}{2} \mathbf{x} \times (\mathbf{a} \times \mathbf{b}) + \mathbf{x} \times (\mathbf{c} \times \mathbf{d}).
\end{aligned}
\tag{4.16}
$$

where f_+ and f_- are the symmetric and skewsymmetric parts of f respectively.

---

[3] Since $\mathbf{F}$ and $\mathbf{v}$ are polar vectors, $\mathbf{B}$ has to be a pseudovector.

Exercise Obtain these expressions for the adjoint, the symmetric and the skewsymmetric parts of f given in Eq. (4.15). □

4.3.1 Vector product as a skewsymmetric operator

For a fixed vector $\mathbf{a} \neq \mathbf{0}$, the map $\mathbf{x} \mapsto \mathbf{a} \times \mathbf{x}$ defines an operator f on $\mathscr{E}_3$. This operator is linear by virtue of the distributive property of the vector product, that is,

$$f(\alpha\mathbf{x} + \beta\mathbf{y}) = \mathbf{a} \times (\alpha\mathbf{x} + \beta\mathbf{y}) = \alpha\mathbf{a} \times \mathbf{x} + \beta\mathbf{a} \times \mathbf{y} = \alpha f(\mathbf{x}) + \beta f(\mathbf{y}).$$

This operator is skewsymmetric, because

$$\mathbf{y} \cdot f^\dagger(\mathbf{x}) = \mathbf{x} \cdot f(\mathbf{y}) = \mathbf{x} \cdot (\mathbf{a} \times \mathbf{y}) = \mathbf{y} \cdot (\mathbf{x} \times \mathbf{a}),$$

which means

$$f^\dagger(\mathbf{x}) = (\mathbf{x} \times \mathbf{a}) = -(\mathbf{a} \times \mathbf{x}) = -f(\mathbf{x}).$$

Note that this operator maps to $\mathbf{0}$ all (non-zero) vectors $\mathbf{x}$ which are parallel or antiparallel to $\mathbf{a}$, so that it is not invertible.

Let $\{a_1, a_2, a_3\}$ $\{x_1, x_2, x_3\}$ and $\{f_1, f_2, f_3\}$ be the components of the vectors $\mathbf{a}$, $\mathbf{x}$ and $f(\mathbf{x})$ with respect to some orthonormal basis. Then expressing the vector product in terms of the Levi-Civita symbols we get

$$f_i = \varepsilon_{ijk} a_j x_k,$$

where we have used the summation convention. Using the values of the antisymmetric tensor ε_{ijk} we can write this equation in the matrix form

$$\begin{bmatrix} f_1 \\ f_2 \\ f_3 \end{bmatrix} = \begin{bmatrix} 0 & -a_3 & a_2 \\ a_3 & 0 & -a_1 \\ -a_2 & a_1 & 0 \end{bmatrix} \begin{bmatrix} x_1 \\ x_2 \\ x_3 \end{bmatrix}.$$

Thus, the action of the skewsymmetric operator $f(\mathbf{x}) = \mathbf{a} \times \mathbf{x}$ on a vector $\mathbf{x}$ is obtained by multiplying the column vector $[x_1, x_2, x_3]^T$ by the skewsymmetric matrix

$$f \equiv \mathbf{a} \times \;\leftrightarrow\; [\varepsilon_{ijk} a_j] \equiv \begin{bmatrix} 0 & -a_3 & a_2 \\ a_3 & 0 & -a_1 \\ -a_2 & a_1 & 0 \end{bmatrix}.$$

4.4   Linear Operators and Matrices

Let f be a linear operator and $\{\hat{\sigma}_k\}$ $k = 1, 2, 3$ be an orthonormal basis in $\mathscr{E}_3$. Using the fact that $\{\hat{\sigma}_k\}$ is a basis and the linearity of f, we can write

$$f(\mathbf{x}) = f\left(\sum_k (\hat{\sigma}_k \cdot \mathbf{x})\hat{\sigma}_k\right) = \sum_k (\hat{\sigma}_k \cdot \mathbf{x}) f(\hat{\sigma}_k),$$

where $x_k = \hat{\sigma}_k \cdot \mathbf{x}$ $k = 1, 2, 3$ are the components of $\mathbf{x}$ in the basis $\{\hat{\sigma}_k\}$. We can expand the vectors $\mathbf{f}_k = f(\hat{\sigma}_k)$ in the basis $\{\hat{\sigma}_k\}$ to get

$$\mathbf{f}_k = f(\hat{\sigma}_k) = \sum_j \hat{\sigma}_j (\hat{\sigma}_j \cdot \mathbf{f}_k) = \sum_j \hat{\sigma}_j f_{jk}.$$

There are three coefficients f_{jk} for each value of k (that is, each $\mathbf{f}_k$) so that for $k = 1, 2, 3$ there are nine coefficients f_{jk}. We arrange them in a 3×3 matrix with j running over rows and k over columns. We have,

$$[f] = [f_{jk}] = \begin{bmatrix} f_{11} & f_{12} & f_{13} \\ f_{21} & f_{22} & f_{23} \\ f_{31} & f_{32} & f_{33} \end{bmatrix}.$$

The coefficients

$$f_{jk} = \hat{\sigma}_j \cdot f(\hat{\sigma}_k) = \hat{\sigma}_j \cdot \mathbf{f}_k$$

which form a 3×3 matrix as above, are called the matrix elements of the linear operator f. The matrix formed by f_{jk} is called the matrix representing f in the basis $\{\hat{\sigma}_k\}$. If we change over to some other orthonormal basis say $\{\hat{\mathbf{e}}_k\}$, the matrix representing f in the basis $\{\hat{\mathbf{e}}_k\}$ is in general different than that representing f in the basis $\{\hat{\sigma}_k\}$. Later in this discussion, we shall relate these two matrix representatives of the same operator f. By $[f]_{\{\cdot\}}$ we denote the matrix representing operator f using the basis $\{\cdot\}$. Whenever the basis is fixed, we shall drop the suffix $\{\cdot\}$.

A linear operator is completely determined by its matrix in a given basis. To see this, consider the action of f on an arbitrary vector $\mathbf{x} \in \mathscr{E}_3$. We have,

$$f(\mathbf{x}) = \sum_k f(\hat{\sigma}_k) x_k = \sum_j \sum_k \hat{\sigma}_j f_{jk} x_k.$$

Thus, the vector $f(\mathbf{x})$ has the following components along $\hat{\sigma}_j$.

$$(f(\mathbf{x}))_j = \sum_k f_{jk} x_k.$$

Therefore, jth component of the vector equation

$$f(\mathbf{x}) = \mathbf{y}$$

is

$$(f(\mathbf{x}))_j = \sum_k f_{jk} x_k = y_j.$$

There is one such equation for each value of $j = 1, 2, 3$ so that the vector equation $f(\mathbf{x}) = \mathbf{y}$ is equivalent to the set of three simultaneous equations

$$\sum_k f_{jk} x_k = y_j \ j = 1, 2, 3$$

completely determined by the matrix $[f_{jk}]$. Written in matrix form, these equations read

$$
\begin{bmatrix} f_{11} & f_{12} & f_{13} \\ f_{21} & f_{22} & f_{23} \\ f_{31} & f_{32} & f_{33} \end{bmatrix}
\begin{bmatrix} x_1 \\ x_2 \\ x_3 \end{bmatrix}
=
\begin{bmatrix} y_1 \\ y_2 \\ y_3 \end{bmatrix}.
$$

Thus, the action of a linear operator f on a vector $\mathbf{x} \in \mathscr{E}_3$ is completely determined by the matrix of f in a given orthonormal basis. Note that the determinant of the matrix $[f_{jk}]$ representing the linear operator f in the basis $\{\hat{\sigma}_k\}$ is the same as the determinant of f, namely, $\det f = f(\hat{\sigma}_1) \cdot f(\hat{\sigma}_2) \times f(\hat{\sigma}_3)$ as can be seen by expressing this scalar triple product in its determinant form (see the exercise in subsection 1.8.1). A student will do better by explicitly working out the matrix elements f_{jk} for different values of the indices j, k.

4.5 An Equivalence Between Algebras

The algebra of 3×3 matrices is equivalent to the algebra of linear operators on $\mathscr{E}_3$. To see this, we first note that the operator sum $f + g$ corresponds to the matrix sum

$$(f + g)_{jk} = \hat{\sigma}_j \cdot (f(\hat{\sigma}_k) + g(\hat{\sigma}_k)) = \hat{\sigma}_j \cdot f(\hat{\sigma}_k) + \hat{\sigma}_j \cdot g(\hat{\sigma}_k) = f_{jk} + g_{jk},$$

where the first equality follows from the definition of the matrix element of an operator. Thus, the matrix element of the addition of two operators equals the addition of the matrix elements of the operators, or,

$$[f + g] = [f] + [g].$$

For the product of two linear operators say gf consider (work this out),

$$gf(\hat{\sigma}_k) = \sum_j (g(\hat{\sigma}_j)) f_{jk} = \sum_i \hat{\sigma}_i \left(\sum_j g_{ij} f_{jk} \right).$$

Compare with

$$gf(\hat{\sigma}_k) = \sum_i \hat{\sigma}_i (\hat{\sigma}_i \cdot gf(\hat{\sigma}_k))$$

to get

$$\sum_j g_{ij} f_{jk} = \hat{\sigma}_i \cdot gf(\hat{\sigma}_k).$$

The RHS of this equation is the ikth element of the matrix of the operator gf, while the LHS is the ikth element of the product of the matrices of the operators g and f in that order. Thus, we see that

$$[gf] = [g][f]. \tag{4.17}$$

The ikth element of the identity operator is,

$$\hat{\sigma}_i \cdot I(\hat{\sigma}_k) = \hat{\sigma}_i \cdot \hat{\sigma}_k = \delta_{ik}$$

because the basis $\{\hat{\sigma}_k\}$ is orthonormal. Thus, the matrix representing the identity operator, (which is the identity with respect to operator multiplication), is the unit matrix I, (which is the identity with respect to matrix multiplication).

For an invertible operator f, using Eq. (4.17), we have,

$$I = [f^{-1}f] = [f^{-1}][f] \tag{4.18}$$

which simply means that the matrix representing f^{-1} is the inverse of the matrix representing f. Since f^{-1} is assumed to exist det $f \neq 0$. Since det f is the same as that of the matrix representing f, its determinant is non-zero and Eq. (4.18) is meaningful. We have already seen that det f is invariant under the change of orthonormal basis so that Eq. (4.18) holds irrespective of the orthonormal basis used. In fact we shall independently prove that the determinant of $[f]$ is invariant under the change of basis. In particular, the determinant of the operator f can be alternatively defined as the determinant of its matrix in any orthonormal basis.

Thus, we have shown that the set of linear operators on $\mathcal{E}_3$ and the set of matrices representing them (with respect to a fixed orthonormal basis) are isomorphic under the binary operations of addition and multiplication defined on these sets. This fact is expressed by saying that the algebra of linear operators on $\mathcal{E}_3$ and that of their matrix representatives are equivalent[4].

---

[4]To establish this equivalence both sets must have the algebraic structure called ring with respect to the multiplications defined on them, which is known to be true. We shall not discuss this point any further.

We establish the relation between the matrix representing an operator and that representing its adjoint. We have,

$$f^\dagger_{jk} = \hat{\sigma}_j \cdot f^\dagger \hat{\sigma}_k = f\hat{\sigma}_j \cdot \hat{\sigma}_k = \hat{\sigma}_k \cdot f\hat{\sigma}_j = f_{kj},$$

which means

$$[f^\dagger] = [f]^T \tag{4.19}$$

where the superscript T denotes the transpose of the matrix.

4.6 Change of Basis

We get the relation between the matrices of a linear operator f in two different orthonormal bases. We denote these bases by $\{\hat{\sigma}_k\}$ and $\{\hat{e}_k\}$. We write equation $f(\mathbf{x}) = \mathbf{y}$ for basis $\{\hat{\sigma}_k\}$ as

$$FX = Y \tag{4.20}$$

where F is the matrix of operator f in $\{\hat{\sigma}_k\}$ and X and Y are the column (3×1) matrices comprising coordinates of vectors $\mathbf{x}$ and $\mathbf{y}$ in the basis $\{\hat{\sigma}_k\}$ (see the last equation in section 4.4). We write $f(\mathbf{x}) = \mathbf{y}$ for the corresponding matrices in the basis $\{\hat{e}_k\}$ as

$$F'X' = Y'. \tag{4.21}$$

It is straightforward to check, by expanding the basis $\{\hat{e}_k\}$ using the basis $\{\hat{\sigma}_k\}$, that for a vector $\mathbf{x} \in \mathscr{E}_3$,

$$X' = QX$$

with

$$Q_{ij} = \hat{e}_i \cdot \hat{\sigma}_j \tag{4.22}$$

Apply Eq. (4.22) to X' and Y' in Eq. (4.21) to get

$$F'QX = QY$$

or,

$$(Q^{-1}F'Q)X = Y \tag{4.23}$$

Comparing Eq. (4.20) with Eq. (4.23) we have,

$$F = Q^{-1}F'Q$$

$$F' = QFQ^{-1}$$

The transformations induced by Q are called *similarity transformations*. Thus, the matrices of a linear operator in different bases are related by a similarity transformation, via Q defined in Eq. (4.22).

It is now trivial to check that the determinant of a matrix of a linear operator f is invariant under the change of basis. We have,

$$\det(F') = \det(QFQ^{-1})$$

$$= \det(Q)\det(F)\det(Q^{-1})$$

$$= \det(QQ^{-1})\det(F) = \det(F).$$

Exercise   Let g, f be linear operators on $\mathscr{E}_3$. Prove that

$$\det[gf] = \det[g]\det[f]$$

and

$$\det[f^{-1}] = (\det[f])^{-1},$$

where $\det[\cdot]$ is the determinant of the matrix representative of the corresponding operator.   □

Eigenvalues and Eigenvectors

5.1 Eigenvalues and Eigenvectors of a Linear Operator

Suppose a non-zero vector $\mathbf{u}$ is transformed into a scalar multiple of itself by a linear operator f, that is,

$$f\mathbf{u} = \lambda\mathbf{u}, \tag{5.1}$$

where λ is a scalar. Then, we say that $\mathbf{u}$ is an eigenvector of f corresponding to the eigenvalue λ. Equation (5.1) is called the eigenvalue equation for the operator f. Equation (5.1) remains valid if we multiply it by a non-zero scalar. Therefore, any scalar multiple of $\mathbf{u}$ is also an eigenvector of f corresponding to the eigenvalue λ. However, these two eigenvectors are linearly dependent. If $n \geq 2$ *linearly independent*[1] eigenvectors correspond to the same eigenvalue, we call this eigenvalue n-fold degenerate. This happens when the eigenvalue equation is satisfied by $n \geq 2$ linearly independent eigenvectors for the same eigenvalue. We will deal with the degenerate eigenvalues later. The problem of finding the eigenvalues and the corresponding eigenvectors of a given linear operator is called the eigenvalue problem for that operator. If we list out all the linearly independent eigenvectors and the corresponding eigenvalues (if there is a m-fold degenerate eigenvalue, it will repeat m times in this list) it is called the spectrum of the corresponding operator. This list of linearly independent eigenvectors obviously cannot exceed the dimension of the space on which the operator acts, as the number of linearly independent vectors cannot exceed the dimension. Thus, the maximum number of linearly independent eigenvectors of a linear operator f acting on $\mathscr{E}_3$ is three.

If all the eigenvectors of an operator can form a basis of the space on which it acts, that is, if the maximum number of linearly independent eigenvectors can be found, it is called *diagonalizable*. In our case the operator f on $\mathscr{E}_3$ is diagonalizable if all of the three linearly independent eigenvectors can be obtained. If all the eigenvalues of an operator are real and

---

[1] That is, two non-collinear vectors, or three non-coplanar vectors. There cannot be more than three linearly independent vectors in $\mathscr{E}_3$.

distinct (no degeneracy) then the operator can be proved to be diagonalizable. Even if degeneracy is present, we can find the maximal set of linearly independent eigenvectors, that is, the corresponding operator can be diagonalized. All the information of a diagonalizable operator is contained in its eigenvalues and eigenvectors because its action on any vector, (by virtue of its linearity and by the fact that its eigenvectors form a basis), can be expressed in terms of these quantities in the simplest possible way. The differential or integral equations, which are the principal mathematical models in physics and engineering, are often expressed or related to the eigenvalue problem of operators on different kinds of spaces called function spaces. These are some of the reasons why the eigenvalue problem is of such a paramount importance in mathematical modeling of real life processes. Here, we shall confine ourselves to the case of operators on $\mathscr{E}_3$ with real eigenvalues. As we shall see later, these are symmetric operators. We shall touch upon the case of complex eigenvalues later.

The basis formed by the eigenvectors of an operator on $\mathscr{E}_3$ gives a coordinate frame in $\mathscr{E}_3$. Its coordinate axes are called *principal axes* and the frame is called the *principal axes system*.

Typically, the operator is given in its matrix form $[f_{jk}]$, that is, we are given the vectors

$$\mathbf{f}_k = f(\hat{\boldsymbol{\sigma}}_k) = \sum_{j=1}^{3} \hat{\boldsymbol{\sigma}}_j f_{jk},$$

where $\{\hat{\boldsymbol{\sigma}}_j\}$ is a suitable orthonormal basis.

To develop a general method for solving the eigenvalue problem from this information, we re-write the eigenvalue equation (Eq. (5.1)) as

$$(f - \lambda I)\mathbf{u} = \mathbf{0}. \tag{5.2}$$

Equation (5.2) tells us that the operator $(f - \lambda I)$ must be singular because it maps a non-zero vector $\mathbf{u} \neq \mathbf{0}$ to the zero vector, so that its determinant must vanish.

$$\det (f - \lambda I) = (\mathbf{f}_1 - \lambda\hat{\boldsymbol{\sigma}}_1) \cdot [(\mathbf{f}_2 - \lambda\hat{\boldsymbol{\sigma}}_2) \times (\mathbf{f}_3 - \lambda\hat{\boldsymbol{\sigma}}_3)] = 0. \tag{5.3}$$

If we expand the LHS of Eq. (5.3), successively applying the distributive law for the scalar and the vector products, we can transform it to

$$\lambda^3 - \alpha_1\lambda^2 + \alpha_2\lambda - \alpha_3 = 0, \tag{5.4}$$

where,

$$\alpha_1 = \sum_k \hat{\boldsymbol{\sigma}}_k \cdot \mathbf{f}_k = f_{11} + f_{22} + f_{33}$$

$$\alpha_2 = \hat{\boldsymbol{\sigma}}_1 \cdot (\mathbf{f}_2 \times \mathbf{f}_3) + \hat{\boldsymbol{\sigma}}_2 \cdot (\mathbf{f}_3 \times \mathbf{f}_1) + \hat{\boldsymbol{\sigma}}_3 \cdot (\mathbf{f}_1 \times \mathbf{f}_2)$$

$$\alpha_3 = \det f = \mathbf{f}_1 \cdot (\mathbf{f}_2 \times \mathbf{f}_3) \tag{5.5}$$

Exercise   Establish Eqs (5.4) and (5.5).   □

Equation (5.3) or Eq. (5.4) are commonly called the secular equation for f. It is an algebraic equation of third degree in λ. From the fundamental theorem of algebra we know that a third degree polynomial has exactly three roots, or, has at most three distinct roots, a pair of which could be complex. Even if you are a junior college student, you are expected to know this, may be without proof. These roots are the eigenvalues of f, because $\det(f - \lambda I) = 0$ only when λ equals one of the roots or, the eigenvalue equation (Eq. (5.2)) is satisfied only when λ equals one of the roots. We assume that this cubic polynomial in λ has three real roots, that is, all the eigenvalues of f are real. (That is, we assume the operator f to be a symmetric operator, to be defined in the next section).

Once the eigenvalues are known, the corresponding eigenvectors are found from Eq. (5.2). We expand $\mathbf{u}$ in Eq. (5.2) in terms of the basis $\{\hat{\sigma}_k\}$ and write Eq. (5.2) in the form

$$\mathbf{g}_1 u_1 + \mathbf{g}_2 u_2 + \mathbf{g}_3 u_3 = 0, \tag{5.6}$$

where the vectors

$$\mathbf{g}_k = \mathbf{f}_k - \lambda \hat{\sigma}_k \quad k = 1, 2, 3 \tag{5.7}$$

are known for each eigenvalue λ and the scalar components $u_k = \mathbf{u} \cdot \hat{\sigma}_k$ of the eigenvector are to be determined[2] for one eigenvalue λ. We can solve Eq. (5.6) for the ratios of u_k as follows. Cross Eq. (5.6) with $\mathbf{g}_3$ to get

$$(\mathbf{g}_3 \times \mathbf{g}_1) u_1 + (\mathbf{g}_3 \times \mathbf{g}_2) u_2 = 0. \tag{5.8}$$

Dotting this with $(\mathbf{g}_3 \times \mathbf{g}_2)/|\mathbf{g}_3 \times \mathbf{g}_2|^2$ we get

$$\frac{u_2}{u_1} = \frac{(\mathbf{g}_3 \times \mathbf{g}_1) \cdot (\mathbf{g}_2 \times \mathbf{g}_3)}{|\mathbf{g}_3 \times \mathbf{g}_1|^2}. \tag{5.9}$$

Similarly,

$$\frac{u_3}{u_1} = \frac{(\mathbf{g}_1 \times \mathbf{g}_2) \cdot (\mathbf{g}_2 \times \mathbf{g}_3)}{|\mathbf{g}_2 \times \mathbf{g}_3|^2}. \tag{5.10}$$

We have already seen that if $\mathbf{u}$ satisfies Eq. (5.2), so does any of its scalar multiples. This means that the length or the sense (orientation) of $\mathbf{u}$ is not determined by the eigenvector equation (Eq. (5.2)). Therefore, it is not a surprise that Eq. (5.6) fixes only the ratios of the components of $\mathbf{u}$ and we are free to fix the sign and magnitude of $\mathbf{u}$ by assigning any convenient value to the component u_1. After u_1 is assigned a value, Eq. (5.9) and Eq. (5.10) determine u_2 and u_3 uniquely. Here, we have assumed that every pair of vectors

---

[2]Note that the vectors $(\mathbf{g}_1, \mathbf{g}_2, \mathbf{g}_3)$ must be coplanar, otherwise they form a linearly independent set of vectors and Eq. (5.6) has only the trivial solution $u_i = 0$, $i = 1, 2, 3$.

formed out of $(\mathbf{g}_1,\mathbf{g}_2,\mathbf{g}_3)$ is linearly independent, if not, all of them will be proportional to each other[3], in which case the ratios u_2/u_1 and u_3/u_1 obtained via Eq. (5.9) or Eq. (5.10) will become indeterminate and Eqs (5.9), (5.10) do not apply. In such a case we can proceed as follows. Since $\mathbf{g}_k$s are proportional to each other, we can put $\mathbf{g}_2 = c\mathbf{g}_1$ and $\mathbf{g}_3 = d\mathbf{g}_1$ in Eq. (5.6) to get

$$(u_1 + cu_2 + du_3)\mathbf{g}_1 = 0,$$

or, since $\mathbf{g}_1 \neq 0$,

$$u_1 + cu_2 + du_3 = 0. \tag{5.11}$$

Thus, we can give arbitrary values to any two of the components of $\mathbf{u}$ and the remaining component is fixed via Eq. (5.11). We can choose two sets of u_i values in such a way that the resulting eigenvectors (via Eq. (5.6) or Eq. (5.11)) are linearly independent. Setting $u_1 = u_2 = 1$ in Eq. (5.6) for example, gives,

$$\mathbf{g}_1 + \mathbf{g}_2 + u_3\mathbf{g}_3 = 0. \tag{5.12}$$

Alternatively, choose $u_1 = 1$ and $u_3 = 0$ so Eq. (5.6) reduces to

$$\mathbf{g}_1 + u_2\mathbf{g}_2 = 0. \tag{5.13}$$

To get the respective eigenvectors, we have to solve Eq. (5.12) for u_3 and Eq. (5.13) for u_2 respectively, which is trivially done using known $\mathbf{g}_1 \propto \mathbf{g}_2 \propto \mathbf{g}_3$. These eigenvectors are trivially seen to be linearly independent. Any eigenvector corresponding to a different choice of components will be a linear combination of these two eigenvectors. Thus, linearly dependent pairs of $\mathbf{g}_k$s (so that they are mutually proportional) imply that the eigenvectors belonging to the corresponding eigenvalue span a 2-D space i.e., a plane. This is to be contrasted with the fact that when every pair of the $\mathbf{g}_k$s is linearly independent, the eigenvectors belonging to the corresponding eigenvalue span a 1-D space.

It turns out that if λ is a simple root of the secular equation (for a symmetric linear operator f), then every two of the three vectors $\mathbf{g}_k = \mathbf{f}_k - \lambda\hat{\sigma}_k$ are necessarily linearly independent. Thus, the eigenvectors belonging to a simple root λ span a 1-D space i.e., a real line in $\mathcal{E}_3$. If λ is a double root, every pair of $\mathbf{g}_k$s is linearly dependent so that the eigenvectors belonging to a double root λ span a 2-D space, i.e., a plane in $\mathcal{E}_3$. Note that any two linearly independent (i.e., non-collinear) vectors in this plane can be the eigenvectors.

A multiple root of a secular equation is said to be k-fold degenerate if the root has multiplicity k. To an eigenvalue with multiplicity k there correspond exactly k linearly independent eigenvectors (in $\mathcal{E}_3$, provided f is symmetric).

Eigenvalues of a symmetric operator are real. To get a flavor of the complex eigenvalues, (i.e., complex roots of the secular equation) consider the skewsymmetric operator

$$f\mathbf{x} = \mathbf{x} \times (\hat{\sigma}_1 \times \hat{\sigma}_2)$$

---

[3]This is because $(\mathbf{g}_1,\mathbf{g}_2,\mathbf{g}_3)$ have to satisfy Eq. (5.6) with one or more $u_i \neq 0$.

where $\{\hat{\sigma}_k\}$ is some orthonormal basis. Operating on this basis we get

$$f(\hat{\sigma}_1) = \hat{\sigma}_1 \times (\hat{\sigma}_1 \times \hat{\sigma}_2) = -\hat{\sigma}_2 = -i\hat{\sigma}_1$$

$$f(\hat{\sigma}_2) = \hat{\sigma}_2 \times (\hat{\sigma}_1 \times \hat{\sigma}_2) = \hat{\sigma}_1 = -i\hat{\sigma}_2$$

$$f(\hat{\sigma}_3) = \mathbf{0} = 0\hat{\sigma}_3 \tag{5.14}$$

Exercise   Show that the secular equation for f is

$$\lambda(\lambda^2 + 1) = 0 \qquad \qquad \square$$

The root $\lambda = 0$ corresponds to the eigenvector $\hat{\sigma}_3$ in Eq. (5.14). The eigenvalue equations for the eigenvalue $-i$ the first two of Eq. (5.14). The last equalities in these equations derive from the fact that multiplication of a vector in the complex plane by $-i$ results in the clockwise rotation of that vector through $\pi/2$. In general, multiplication by $e^{i\theta}$ results in the counterclockwise rotation through θ. Thus, we see that complex eigenvalues result in the rotation of the eigenvectors.

5.1.1   Examples

We obtain the eigenvalues and eigenvectors of the operator f represented by the matrix

$$[f] = \begin{bmatrix} 4 & -1 & -1 \\ -1 & 4 & -1 \\ -1 & -1 & 4 \end{bmatrix}$$

in an orthonormal basis $\{\hat{\sigma}_1, \hat{\sigma}_2, \hat{\sigma}_3\}$.

Operating on the basis by f we get

$$f(\hat{\sigma}_1) = 4\hat{\sigma}_1 - \hat{\sigma}_2 - \hat{\sigma}_3 = \mathbf{f}_1$$

$$f(\hat{\sigma}_2) = -\hat{\sigma}_1 + 4\hat{\sigma}_2 - \hat{\sigma}_3 = \mathbf{f}_2$$

$$f(\hat{\sigma}_3) = -\hat{\sigma}_1 - \hat{\sigma}_2 + 4\hat{\sigma}_3 = \mathbf{f}_3 \tag{5.15}$$

From these vectors we find

$$\mathbf{f}_1 \times \mathbf{f}_2 = 15(\hat{\sigma}_1 \times \hat{\sigma}_2) + 5(\hat{\sigma}_2 \times \hat{\sigma}_3) + 5(\hat{\sigma}_3 \times \hat{\sigma}_1)$$

$$\mathbf{f}_2 \times \mathbf{f}_3 = 5(\hat{\sigma}_1 \times \hat{\sigma}_2) + 15(\hat{\sigma}_2 \times \hat{\sigma}_3) + 5(\hat{\sigma}_3 \times \hat{\sigma}_1)$$

$$\mathbf{f}_3 \times \mathbf{f}_1 = 5(\hat{\sigma}_1 \times \hat{\sigma}_2) + 5(\hat{\sigma}_2 \times \hat{\sigma}_3) + 15(\hat{\sigma}_3 \times \hat{\sigma}_1) \tag{5.16}$$

Using Eqs (5.15) and (5.16) we get the values of the coefficients in the secular equation,

$$\alpha_1 = 4 + 4 + 4 = 12$$

$$\alpha_2 = 15 + 15 + 15 = 45$$

$$\alpha_3 = \mathbf{f}_1 \cdot (\mathbf{f}_2 \times \mathbf{f}_3) = 50 \tag{5.17}$$

Hence, the secular equation is

$$\lambda^3 - 12\lambda^2 + 45\lambda - 50 = 0$$

which can be factored into

$$(\lambda - 2)(\lambda - 5)^2 = 0.$$

So the eigenvalues are 2 (simple) and 5 (doubly degenerate).

To get the eigenvectors for $\lambda = 2$ we prepare the vectors $\mathbf{g}_k$ defined in Eq. (5.7) using Eq. (5.15). We have,

$$\mathbf{g}_1 = \mathbf{f}_1 - 2\hat{\boldsymbol{\sigma}}_1 = 2\hat{\boldsymbol{\sigma}}_1 - \hat{\boldsymbol{\sigma}}_2 - \hat{\boldsymbol{\sigma}}_3$$

$$\mathbf{g}_2 = \mathbf{f}_2 - 2\hat{\boldsymbol{\sigma}}_2 = -\hat{\boldsymbol{\sigma}}_1 + 2\hat{\boldsymbol{\sigma}}_2 - \hat{\boldsymbol{\sigma}}_3$$

$$\mathbf{g}_3 = \mathbf{f}_3 - 2\hat{\boldsymbol{\sigma}}_3 = -\hat{\boldsymbol{\sigma}}_1 - \hat{\boldsymbol{\sigma}}_2 + 2\hat{\boldsymbol{\sigma}}_3 \tag{5.18}$$

From this we find

$$\mathbf{g}_1 \times \mathbf{g}_2 = 3(\hat{\boldsymbol{\sigma}}_1 \times \hat{\boldsymbol{\sigma}}_2 + \hat{\boldsymbol{\sigma}}_2 \times \hat{\boldsymbol{\sigma}}_3 + \hat{\boldsymbol{\sigma}}_3 \times \hat{\boldsymbol{\sigma}}_1) = \mathbf{g}_2 \times \mathbf{g}_3 = \mathbf{g}_3 \times \mathbf{g}_1$$

Using this in Eqs (5.9) and (5.10) with $u_1 = 1$ we get $u_2 = u_3 = 1$. Hence,

$$\mathbf{u}_1 = \hat{\boldsymbol{\sigma}}_1 + \hat{\boldsymbol{\sigma}}_2 + \hat{\boldsymbol{\sigma}}_3 \tag{5.19}$$

is the eigenvector belonging to the eigenvalue 2.

To get the eigenvectors corresponding to $\lambda = 5$, we evaluate $\mathbf{g}_k = \mathbf{f}_k - 5\hat{\boldsymbol{\sigma}}_k$ to find

$$\mathbf{g}_1 = \mathbf{g}_2 = \mathbf{g}_3 = -(\hat{\boldsymbol{\sigma}}_1 + \hat{\boldsymbol{\sigma}}_2 + \hat{\boldsymbol{\sigma}}_3)$$

Using this in Eq. (5.12) we find $u_3 = -2$ when $u_1 = u_2 = 1$ so that

$$\mathbf{u}_2 = \hat{\boldsymbol{\sigma}}_1 + \hat{\boldsymbol{\sigma}}_2 - 2\hat{\boldsymbol{\sigma}}_3 \tag{5.20}$$

is an eigenvector for $\lambda = 5$. To get the other linearly independent eigenvector, we find, from Eq. (5.13), that $u_2 = -1$ when $u_1 = 1$ and $u_3 = 0$. Hence,

$$\mathbf{u}_3 = \hat{\sigma}_1 - \hat{\sigma}_2 \tag{5.21}$$

is the other eigenvector. Therefore, every vector in the plane defined by $\mathbf{u}_2$ and $\mathbf{u}_3$ is an eigenvector with eigenvalue $\lambda = 5$. (Operate by f on any linear combination of $\mathbf{u}_2$ and $\mathbf{u}_3$).

Although, our method to find the eigenvalues and eigenvectors is sufficiently general, it may cost us more work than necessary in special cases. Often, an eigenvector is known in advance. Then, the corresponding eigenvalue is easily obtained via

$$(f(\mathbf{u}) \cdot \mathbf{u}) / |\mathbf{u}|^2$$

instead of using the secular equation. More often than not, an eigenvector can be identified easily from the symmetries in the given problem. Thus, perusal of Eq. (5.15) shows that adding these three equations we get

$$f(\hat{\sigma}_1 + \hat{\sigma}_2 + \hat{\sigma}_3) = 2(\hat{\sigma}_1 + \hat{\sigma}_2 + \hat{\sigma}_3),$$

so we know that 2 is the eigenvalue corresponding to eigenvector $\mathbf{u} = \hat{\sigma}_1 + \hat{\sigma}_2 + \hat{\sigma}_3$, in agreement with the result of the general method, obtained after a lot of effort. In order to get the other two eigenvectors $\mathbf{u}_1$ and $\mathbf{u}_2$ we use the fact that any two vectors in the $(\mathbf{u}_1, \mathbf{u}_2)$ plane will do. As we shall see in the next section, $(\mathbf{u}_1, \mathbf{u}_2)$ plane is perpendicular to $\mathbf{u}_1$. So we can write $\mathbf{u}_2 = \hat{\sigma}_1 + \hat{\sigma}_2 + u_3\hat{\sigma}_3$ and choose u_3 such that

$$\mathbf{u}_1 \cdot \mathbf{u}_2 = (\hat{\sigma}_1 + \hat{\sigma}_2 + \hat{\sigma}_3) \cdot (\hat{\sigma}_1 + \hat{\sigma}_2 + u_3\hat{\sigma}_3) = 2 + u_3 = 0$$

This gives $u_3 = -2$, so $\mathbf{u}_2 = \hat{\sigma}_1 + \hat{\sigma}_2 - 2\hat{\sigma}_3$ which coincides with Eq. (5.20). From Eq. (5.15) we now find $f(\mathbf{u}_2) = 5\mathbf{u}_2$ so the eigenvalue is 5. The vector $\mathbf{u}_1 \times \mathbf{u}_2 = -3(\hat{\sigma}_1 - \hat{\sigma}_2)$ is orthogonal to both $\mathbf{u}_1$ and $\mathbf{u}_2$ and is proportional to the eigenvector $\mathbf{u}_3$ in Eq. (5.21).

Exercise   Obtain the eigenvectors and eigenvalues of the operators represented by the following matrices in an orthonormal basis.

(i) $[f] = \begin{bmatrix} 1 & 0 & 5 \\ 0 & -2 & 0 \\ 5 & 0 & 1 \end{bmatrix}$.

(ii) $[f] = \begin{bmatrix} 7 & \sqrt{6} & -\sqrt{3} \\ \sqrt{6} & 2 & -5\sqrt{2} \\ -\sqrt{3} & -5\sqrt{2} & -3 \end{bmatrix}$.

$$(iii) \quad [f] = \begin{bmatrix} 1 & 2 & 0 \\ 2 & 6 & -2 \\ 0 & -2 & 5 \end{bmatrix}. \qquad \square$$

Exercise Let **u** be an eigenvector of an invertible operator with eigenvalue λ. Show that **u** is an eigenvector of f^{-1} with eigenvalue $\frac{1}{\lambda}$.

Hint Multiply the eigenvalue equation $f\mathbf{u} = \lambda\mathbf{u}$ by f^{-1} and use the definition and the linearity of f^{-1}. $\qquad \square$

5.2 Spectrum of a Symmetric Operator

We have already stated that the eigenvalues of a symmetric linear operator are real. We shall now prove this statement. We will also score a bonus point by proving that the eigenvectors of a symmetric operator corresponding to different eigenvalues are orthogonal.

We have seen that the eigenvalues of a linear operator f on $\mathscr{E}_3$ can, in general, be complex. This makes it necessary for us to give a meaning to the multiplication of vectors in $\mathscr{E}_3$ by complex numbers. Note that such a multiplication cannot be taken to be a multiplication by a scalar, because $\mathscr{E}_3$ is a real linear space with a Euclidean metric, so that scalars comprise only real numbers. A multiplication by a complex number $\lambda = re^{i\theta}$ involves multiplication by the real number r which will simply multiply the magnitude of the vector by r. Thus, we have to worry about the interpretation of the multiplication by $e^{i\theta}$. Such a multiplication can be given a meaning by noting that multiplication by a complex number of unit magnitude $(e^{i\theta})$ is equivalent to the rotation of the vector through angle θ in a suitable plane. We have already seen this in section 3.1, (where we proved the spaces $\mathscr{E}_2$ and $\mathbb{Z}$ to be isomorphic), only difference being the space we consider there was $\mathscr{E}_2$ rather than $\mathscr{E}_3$. To make this interpretation precise for $\mathscr{E}_3$, we consider the scalar product of two linearly independent (non-collinear) vectors in $\mathscr{E}_3$ such as $\mathbf{u} \cdot (e^{i\theta}\mathbf{v})$. To evaluate this scalar product, we have to rotate **v**, in the plane spanned by **u** and **v**, *counterclockwise* through angle θ and then dot the resulting vector with **u**. Equivalently, we could have rotated **u** *clockwise* through angle θ and dotted the resulting vector with **v**. This is depicted in Fig. 5.1.

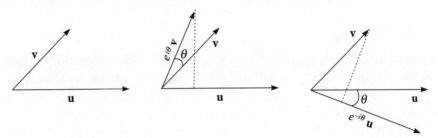

Fig. 5.1 $\mathbf{u} \cdot \left(e^{i\theta}\mathbf{v}\right) = \left(e^{-i\theta}\mathbf{u}\right) \cdot \mathbf{v}$

However, the alternative scalar product is just $\left(e^{-i\theta}\mathbf{u}\right) \cdot \mathbf{v}$. Thus, we have the general result

$$\mathbf{u} \cdot (\lambda \mathbf{v}) = (\lambda^* \mathbf{u}) \cdot \mathbf{v}$$

where $\lambda = re^{i\theta}$ is any complex number and λ^* its complex conjugate.

Now consider a symmetric linear operator S and its eigenvectors $\mathbf{u}$ and $\mathbf{v}$ belonging to the eigenvalues λ_1 and λ_2 respectively, presumably complex. We have,

$$(\lambda_1 \mathbf{u}) \cdot \mathbf{v} = S(\mathbf{u}) \cdot \mathbf{v} = \mathbf{u} \cdot S(\mathbf{v}) = \mathbf{u} \cdot (\lambda_2 \mathbf{v}) = (\lambda_2^* \mathbf{u}) \cdot \mathbf{v} \tag{5.22}$$

where we have used the fact that S is symmetric. Remember that when λ is complex, the vectors $\mathbf{u}$ and $\lambda \mathbf{u}$ are not collinear. Equation (5.22) gives

$$(\lambda_1 - \lambda_2^*)\mathbf{u} \cdot \mathbf{v} = 0. \tag{5.23}$$

Two cases arise. In the first case, $\lambda_1 = \lambda_2 = \lambda$ and the scalar product in Eq. (5.23) is non-zero. This gives $\lambda = \lambda^*$. This proves that the eigenvalues of a symmetric operator are real. In the second case, $\lambda_1 \neq \lambda_2$ so that the scalar product of the two eigenvectors $\mathbf{u}$ and $\mathbf{v}$ must vanish. This simply means that the eigenvectors belonging to two different eigenvalues of a symmetric operator are orthogonal.

We now show that for every symmetric operator on $\mathscr{E}_3$, there exists a set of eigenvectors which are mutually orthogonal. The axes of the resulting frame are called the principal axes. If all the three eigenvalues of the given symmetric operator are distinct, then this statement follows from the fact that the eigenvectors belonging to different eigenvalues of a symmetric operator must be orthogonal. Further, in this case, the eigenvectors are unique upto multiplication by a scalar (there is no degeneracy) so that all the principal axes are unique.

Now suppose $\lambda_1 \neq \lambda_2$, $\lambda_1 \neq \lambda_3$ but $\lambda_2 = \lambda_3 = \lambda$ say. Since λ_1 is distinct from λ_2 and λ_3, the eigenvector $\mathbf{u}_1$ belonging to λ_1 must be orthogonal to both the eigenvectors belonging to the degenerate eigenvalue λ. Further, we know that the eigenvectors belonging to λ are linearly independent (non-collinear) and every vector in the plane spanned by two linearly independent eigenvectors for λ is also an eigenvector. Thus, we can take any vector in the plane normal to $\mathbf{u}_1$ as one of the eigenvectors, say $\mathbf{u}_2$ of the eigenvalue λ and the third eigenvector $\mathbf{u}_3$ can be obtained from

$$\mathbf{u}_3 = \mathbf{u}_1 \times \mathbf{u}_2.$$

If all the three eigenvalues are equal to say λ, three linearly independent eigenvectors belong to this common eigenvalue λ and every linear combination of them is also an eigenvector. In other words, every vector in $\mathscr{E}_3$ is an eigenvector belonging to λ. Obviously, any orthonormal triad of vectors $(\mathbf{u}_1, \mathbf{u}_2, \mathbf{u}_3)$ gives a principal axes system.

The fact that a symmetric operator S has three orthogonal principal axes is expressed by the equations

$$S\mathbf{u}_k = \lambda_k \mathbf{u}_k \quad k = 1, 2, 3$$

and

$$\mathbf{u}_j \cdot \mathbf{u}_k = 0 \text{ if } j \neq k.$$

Thus, a symmetric operator is not only diagonalizable, but its eigenvectors naturally form an orthogonal basis.

Thus, we see that the eigenvectors of a symmetric operator form an orthogonal basis of $\mathscr{E}_3$. This basis is called the eigenbasis of the symmetric operator and the corresponding eigenvectors are called principal vectors and eigenvalues are called the principal values. If we denote this basis by $(\mathbf{u}_1, \mathbf{u}_2, \mathbf{u}_3)$ we can write an arbitrary vector $\mathbf{x} \in \mathscr{E}_3$ as a linear combination of the eigenvectors as

$$\mathbf{x} = \alpha_1 \mathbf{u}_1 + \alpha_2 \mathbf{u}_2 + \alpha_3 \mathbf{u}_3.$$

Dotting both sides by $\mathbf{u}_k$ $k = 1, 2, 3$, using the orthogonality of the eigenvector basis and dividing both sides by $|\mathbf{u}_k|^2$ we get

$$\alpha_k = (\mathbf{u}_k \cdot \mathbf{x}) / |\mathbf{u}_k|^2.$$

Thus, the result of operating by a symmetric operator S on a vector $\mathbf{x} \in \mathscr{E}_3$ can be expressed as

$$S\mathbf{x} = \sum_{k=1}^{3} \lambda_k \mathbf{u}_k \left[\frac{\mathbf{u}_k \cdot \mathbf{x}}{|\mathbf{u}_k|^2} \right] = \sum_{k=1}^{3} \lambda_k \hat{\mathbf{u}}_k (\hat{\mathbf{u}}_k \cdot \mathbf{x}) \tag{5.24}$$

where $\hat{\mathbf{u}}_k$ is a unit vector in the direction of $\mathbf{u}_k$. Equation (5.24) is often written in terms of the so called projection operators. Thus,

$$S\mathbf{x} = \left(\sum_{k=1}^{3} \lambda_k \mathscr{P}_k \right) \mathbf{x},$$

where the projection operator $\mathscr{P}_k$ which projects any vector $\mathbf{x} \in \mathscr{E}_3$ onto the kth principal axis along $\mathbf{u}_k$ is given by

$$\mathscr{P}_k \mathbf{x} = \hat{\mathbf{u}}_k (\hat{\mathbf{u}}_k \cdot \mathbf{x}). \tag{5.25}$$

In terms of the projection operators, Eq. (5.24) can be re-expressed as

$$S\mathbf{x} = \left(\sum_{k} \lambda_k \mathscr{P}_k \right). \tag{5.26}$$

The canonical form Eq. (5.24) or Eq. (5.26) is called the *spectral decomposition* (or the *spectral form*) of the symmetric operator S. Note that if we use an eigenvector $\mathbf{u}_k$ in place of $\mathbf{x}$ in the spectral decomposition, the eigenvalue equation for $\mathbf{u}_k$ emerges trivially.

As we have already seen, an eigenvector multiplied by a scalar continues to be the eigenvector for the same eigenvalue. Thus, we can divide each of the eigenvectors by its magnitude to get the unit vector in its direction and this unit vector continues to be the eigenvector for the same eigenvalue. In this way, we can convert the orthogonal basis comprising eigenvectors to the orthonormal basis comprising unit eigenvectors given by $\{\hat{\mathbf{u}}_1, \hat{\mathbf{u}}_2, \hat{\mathbf{u}}_3\}$. We have used this orthonormal eigenbasis of the symmetric operator S while obtaining Eqs (5.24), (5.26). We will always set up the matrix of a symmetric operator with respect to its orthonormal eigenbasis.

Exercise Using its definition, establish the following properties of projection operators.

(a) Orthogonality: $\mathscr{P}_j \mathscr{P}_k = 0$ if $j \neq k$

(b) Idempotence: $\mathscr{P}_k^2 = \mathscr{P}_k$

(c) Completeness: $\mathscr{P}_1 + \mathscr{P}_2 + \mathscr{P}_3 = I$ □

Exercise Show that the matrix for a symmetric operator in its orthonormal eigenbasis is diagonal, with its eigenvalues appearing on the diagonal. □

Since the determinant of a diagonal matrix is the product of its diagonal elements, the determinant of a symmetric operator is the product of its eigenvalues. Thus, if one or more of the eigenvalues of a symmetric operator are zero, its determinant is zero. Such a symmetric operator is singular, and hence non-invertible.

The matrix $[S]$ representing a symmetric operator in an orthonormal basis $\{\hat{\sigma}_k\}$ $k = 1, 2, 3$ is symmetric. We have, for the ijth element of such a matrix,

$$S_{ij} = \hat{\sigma}_i \cdot S(\hat{\sigma}_j) = S(\hat{\sigma}_i) \cdot \hat{\sigma}_j = \hat{\sigma}_j \cdot S(\hat{\sigma}_i) = S_{ji}$$

where we have used the fact that S is symmetric. On the other hand, the matrix $[\mathscr{A}]$ representing a skewsymmetric operator $\mathscr{A}$ in an orthonormal basis is skewsymmetric. We have, for the ijth element of the matrix $[\mathscr{A}]$,

$$\mathscr{A}_{ij} = \hat{\sigma}_i \cdot \mathscr{A}(\hat{\sigma}_j) = -\mathscr{A}(\hat{\sigma}_i) \cdot \hat{\sigma}_j = -\hat{\sigma}_j \cdot \mathscr{A}(\hat{\sigma}_i) = -\mathscr{A}_{ji}$$

where we have used the fact that $\mathscr{A}$ is skewsymmetric. Obviously, a matrix representing a skewsymmetric operator has vanishing diagonal elements because they have to satisfy $\mathscr{A}_{ii} = -\mathscr{A}_{ii}$. That means, the pairs $(\hat{\sigma}_i, \mathscr{A}\hat{\sigma}_i), i = 1, 2, 3$ are orthogonal.

As you may have noticed, all the matrices given in the exercise at the end of the last section are symmetric.

From the spectral decomposition for a non-singular symmetric operator S, we can write, for the inverse operator,

$$S^{-1} = \sum_k \frac{1}{\lambda_k} \mathscr{P}_k. \tag{5.27}$$

Exercise   Using the spectral decomposition of S (Eq. (5.26)) and that of S^{-1} (Eq. (5.28)) verify explicitly $S^{-1}S = I = SS^{-1}$.   □

We can show that the inverse of a symmetric operator is also symmetric. We have, for all $\mathbf{x} \in \mathscr{E}_3$ $(SS^{-1})^{\dagger}\mathbf{x} = I\mathbf{x} = \mathbf{x}$ implies $(S^{-1})^{\dagger}S\mathbf{x} = \mathbf{x} = S^{-1}S\mathbf{x}$ which means $(S^{-1})^{\dagger} = S^{-1}$ because the inverse is unique.

A symmetric operator S is called positive, if all its eigenvalues $\lambda_k > 0$, $k = 1, 2, 3$ and non-negative if $\lambda_k \geq 0$, $k = 1, 2, 3$. A positive symmetric operator S is also non-negative, however, the converse is not true. A general linear operator f is called positive (non-negative) if $f(\mathbf{x}) \cdot \mathbf{x} > 0, (\geq 0)$ for every $\mathbf{x} \neq \mathbf{0}$.

Exercise   Show that a non-negative symmetric operator S has a unique square root

$$S^{1/2} = \sum_k \lambda_k^{1/2} \mathscr{P}_k$$

in the sense that $S^{1/2}(S^{1/2}\mathbf{x}) = S\mathbf{x}$ for all $\mathbf{x} \in \mathscr{E}_3$.   □

The square root of a non-negative symmetric operator is a non-negative symmetric operator which is obvious from its definition.

Remark   A positive symmetric operator, say S_+, acting on any of its eigenvectors, changes its length by multiplying it by a positive number, namely by its eigenvalue. Since the eigenvectors form an orthogonal basis, the effect of the action of a positive symmetric operator on an arbitrary vector can be completely accounted by the change in length of the eigenvectors due to the action of the positive symmetric operator on them.

This leads to some interesting geometric consequences. Thus, S_+ stretches a circle drawn in a principal plane (containing two principal vectors) into an ellipse. In particular, S_+ stretches a unit circle drawn in a principal plane into an ellipse for which the lengths of the semiaxes are the principal values of S_+. We see from Fig. 5.2 that S_+ stretches the points on a square to points on a parallelogram.

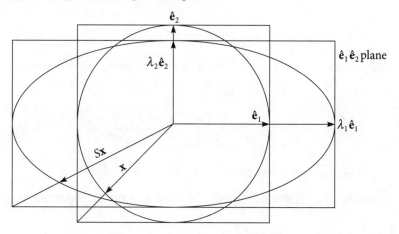

Fig. 5.2   Symmetric transformation with principal values $\lambda_1 > 1$ and $\lambda_2 < 1$

A positive symmetric operator S_+ on $\mathscr{E}_3$ transforms the unit sphere into ellipsoid. The transformation is,

$$\mathbf{x} = S_+\hat{\mathbf{n}} \tag{5.28}$$

where $\hat{\mathbf{n}}$ is any unit vector. This is a parametric equation for the ellipsoid with vector parameter $\hat{\mathbf{n}}$. A non-parametric equation can be obtained by eliminating $\hat{\mathbf{n}}$ as follows.

$$\left(S_+^{-1}\mathbf{x}\right)^2 = \hat{\mathbf{n}}^2 = 1.$$

Since S_+^{-1} is symmetric, we have,

$$\left(S_+^{-1}\mathbf{x}\right)^2 = S_+^{-1}\mathbf{x} \cdot S_+^{-1}\mathbf{x} = \mathbf{x} \cdot \left(S_+^{-1}\right)^2 \mathbf{x} = 1. \tag{5.29}$$

Now using the spectral decomposition of S_+^{-1} (Eq. (5.28)) and the properties of the projection operator we can write Eq. (5.29) in the form

$$\frac{x_1^2}{\lambda_1^2} + \frac{x_2^2}{\lambda_2^2} + \frac{x_3^2}{\lambda_3^2} = 1, \tag{5.30}$$

where $x_k = \mathbf{x}_k \cdot \mathbf{u}_k$. Equation (5.30) is the standard equation for an ellipsoid with semiaxes $\lambda_1, \lambda_2, \lambda_3$ (see Fig. 5.3).

In some situations, eigenvalues and eigenvectors are supplied as the initial information, so that the corresponding symmetric operator can be constructed directly from its spectral decomposition. Some variants of the spectral form are more convenient in certain applications. All these variants are, of course, constructed from the eigenvectors and eigenvalues.

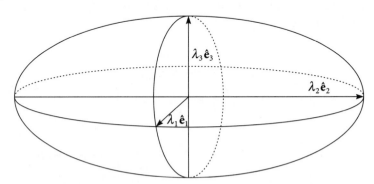

Fig. 5.3   An ellipsoid with semi-axes $\lambda_1, \lambda_2, \lambda_3$

Exercise   Describe the eigenvalue spectrum of a symmetric operator S so that the equation

$$\mathbf{x} \cdot (S\mathbf{x}) = 1 \tag{5.31}$$

is equivalent to the standard coordinate forms for each of the following quadratic surfaces.

(a) Ellipsoid:

$$\frac{x_1^2}{a^2} + \frac{x_2^2}{b^2} + \frac{x_3^2}{c^2} = 1,$$

(b) Hyperboloid of one sheet:

$$\frac{x_1^2}{a^2} + \frac{x_2^2}{b^2} - \frac{x_3^2}{c^2} = 1,$$

(c) Hyperboloid of two sheets:

$$\frac{x_1^2}{a^2} - \frac{x_2^2}{b^2} - \frac{x_3^2}{c^2} = 1.$$

Answer   (a) All positive, (b) One negative, (c) Two negative eigenvalues.   □

Exercise   Obtain the solution set $\{\mathbf{x}\}$ of the equation

$$[f(\mathbf{x} - \mathbf{a})]^2 = 1$$

where f is any linear operator.

Solution   The given equation is

$$f(\mathbf{x} - \mathbf{a}) \cdot f(\mathbf{x} - \mathbf{a}) = 1$$

or,

$$(\mathbf{x} - \mathbf{a}) \cdot f^\dagger f(\mathbf{x} - \mathbf{a}) = 1.$$

$f^\dagger f$ is obviously a symmetric operator. Call it S. Therefore, the above equation becomes,

$$(\mathbf{x} - \mathbf{a}) \cdot S(\mathbf{x} - \mathbf{a}) = 1. \tag{5.32}$$

We know from the previous exercise that Eq. (5.32) corresponds to that for an ellipsoid if all the eigenvalues of S are positive, hyperboloid of one sheet if one eigenvalue is negative and hyperboloid of two sheets if two of the eigenvalues are negative. Obviously, there is no solution for all negative eigenvalues of S. Note that, for Eq. (5.32), all the quadratic surfaces are centered at $\mathbf{a}$.   □

5.3   Mohr's Algorithm

We have developed a general method of finding the spectrum of a linear operator acting on $\mathcal{E}_3$. Many a time we have to deal with the problem of finding the spectrum of a (typically symmetric) operator acting on a plane, which is a 2-D subspace of $\mathcal{E}_3$. Another situation we may face is when one of the three eigenvectors of a symmetric operator is known and the other two are to be found. The remaining eigenvectors lie in the plane normal to the known eigenvector, so the problem reduces to that of finding the spectrum of an operator acting on a plane. Although, we can employ the general method to do this job, for a positive symmetric operator S_+ an efficient algorithm called Mohr's algorithm is available. We first state the algorithm and then justify it.[4]

The algorithm comprises the following.

Choose any convenient unit vector $\hat{\mathbf{b}}$ in the plane and compute the two vectors

$$\mathbf{b}_\pm = S_+ \hat{\mathbf{b}} \mp i S_+(-i\hat{\mathbf{b}})$$

where multiplication by $e^{i\theta}$ rotates a vector counterclockwise through angle θ in the plane on which the operator S_+ acts. Then for $\mathbf{b}_+ \times \mathbf{b}_- \neq \mathbf{0}$, the vectors

$$\mathbf{u}_\pm = \alpha(\mathbf{b}_+ \pm \mathbf{b}_-)$$

are the principal vectors of S_+ with principal values

$$\lambda_\pm = \frac{1}{2}(|\mathbf{b}_+| \pm |\mathbf{b}_-|).$$

We will discuss the case $\mathbf{b}_+ \times \mathbf{b}_- = \mathbf{0}$ which we have omitted from the algorithm. Obviously, we assume that[5] $\lambda_+ \neq \lambda_-$. This algorithm is called Mohr's algorithm.

To understand the algorithm, we proceed as follows.

For a positive symmetric operator S_+ acting on a plane, the eigenvalue equation can be written,

$$S_+ \mathbf{u}_\pm = \lambda_\pm \mathbf{u}_\pm$$

where $\mathbf{u}_+$ and $\mathbf{u}_-$ are the principal vectors corresponding to the principal values λ_+ and λ_- respectively.

Since S_+ is a given operator, the vector $S_+ \hat{\mathbf{b}}$, resulting due to its action on any given unit vector $\hat{\mathbf{b}}$ in the plane is known. We write $\mathbf{u} = \hat{\mathbf{u}}_+$ and decompose $\hat{\mathbf{b}}$ into components $\mathbf{b}_\parallel$ and $\mathbf{b}_\perp$ parallel and orthogonal to $\mathbf{u}$ respectively. We have,

$$S_+ \hat{\mathbf{b}} = S_+(\mathbf{b}_\parallel + \mathbf{b}_\perp) = \lambda_+ \mathbf{b}_\parallel + \lambda_- \mathbf{b}_\perp,$$

Exercise   Justify the second equality in this equation.   □

Or,

$$S_+ \hat{\mathbf{b}} = \lambda_+ \mathbf{u}(\mathbf{u} \cdot \hat{\mathbf{b}}) + \lambda_-(\mathbf{u} \times \hat{\mathbf{b}}) \times \mathbf{u}. \tag{5.33}$$

---

[4]Mohr's algorithm is discussed using geometric algebra in [10].
[5]Otherwise, if S_+ has a single doubly degenerate eigenvalue, every vector in the plane is an eigenvector and the other linearly independent eigenvector is simply the one in the same plane and normal to it.

Introducing the vector

$$\hat{\mathbf{x}} = 2(\mathbf{u} \cdot \hat{\mathbf{b}})\mathbf{u} - \hat{\mathbf{b}}$$

we can re-write Eq. (5.33) (Exercise) as,

$$S_+\hat{\mathbf{b}} = \frac{1}{2}(\lambda_+ + \lambda_-)\hat{\mathbf{b}} + \frac{1}{2}(\lambda_+ - \lambda_-)\hat{\mathbf{x}}. \tag{5.34}$$

Exercise   Show that the vector $\hat{\mathbf{x}}$ defined above is a unit vector.   □

Let ϕ denote the angle through which $\hat{\mathbf{b}}$ has to be counterclockwise rotated to meet $\mathbf{u}$. Then

$$\mathbf{u} = e^{i\phi}\hat{\mathbf{b}}. \tag{5.35}$$

Thus, Eq. (5.34) involves three unknowns λ_+, λ_- and ϕ (through $\hat{\mathbf{x}}$) so we need another equation to solve for these unknowns. We have (Exercise)

$$-iS_+(i\hat{\mathbf{b}}) = \frac{1}{2}(\lambda_+ + \lambda_-)\hat{\mathbf{b}} - \frac{1}{2}(\lambda_+ - \lambda_-)\hat{\mathbf{x}}. \tag{5.36}$$

Combining Eqs (5.35) and (5.36) we get

$$\mathbf{b}_+ = S_+\hat{\mathbf{b}} - iS_+(i\hat{\mathbf{b}}) = (\lambda_+ + \lambda_-)\hat{\mathbf{b}} \tag{5.37}$$

$$\mathbf{b}_- = S_+\hat{\mathbf{b}} + iS_+(i\hat{\mathbf{b}}) = (\lambda_+ - \lambda_-)\hat{\mathbf{x}}. \tag{5.38}$$

Without losing generality, we assume $\lambda_+ \geq \lambda_-$, so Eq. (5.37) show that the principal values are determined by the magnitudes $|\mathbf{b}_\pm| = \lambda_+ \pm \lambda_-$ of the known vectors $\mathbf{b}_+$ and $\mathbf{b}_-$, produced by the known action of S_+ on the vectors $\hat{\mathbf{b}}$ and $i\hat{\mathbf{b}}$. Dotting the unit vector equation $\hat{\mathbf{b}}_- = \hat{\mathbf{x}}$ with $\mathbf{u}$ we have,

$$\mathbf{u} \cdot \hat{\mathbf{b}}_- = \mathbf{u} \cdot \hat{\mathbf{b}} = \cos\phi. \tag{5.39}$$

Equation (5.39) tells us that direction of $\mathbf{u}$ is half way between the directions $\hat{\mathbf{b}}_-$, (or $\hat{\mathbf{x}}$) and $\hat{\mathbf{b}} = \hat{\mathbf{b}}_+$. Therefore,

$$\mathbf{u}_+ = \alpha(\hat{\mathbf{b}}_+ + \hat{\mathbf{b}}_-) \tag{5.40}$$

is an eigenvector of S_+ for any non-zero scalar α. If $\hat{\mathbf{b}}_+ \times \hat{\mathbf{b}}_- \neq \mathbf{0}$ then

$$\mathbf{u}_- = \alpha(\hat{\mathbf{b}}_+ - \hat{\mathbf{b}}_-) \tag{5.41}$$

is the other eigenvector, because $\mathbf{u}_+ \cdot \mathbf{u}_- = 0$. Thus,

$$\mathbf{u}_\pm = \alpha(\hat{\mathbf{b}}_+ \pm \hat{\mathbf{b}}_-). \tag{5.42}$$

If $\hat{\mathbf{b}}_+ \times \hat{\mathbf{b}}_- = 0$ then $\hat{\mathbf{b}}$ is parallel or antiparallel to one of the principal vectors. Then $\hat{\mathbf{x}} = \pm \alpha \hat{\mathbf{b}}$ and Eq. (5.42) yields only that vector. The other eigenvector is perpendicular to the one found.

This completes the proof of Mohr's algorithm. Figure 5.4 depicts the parameters in Mohr's algorithm.

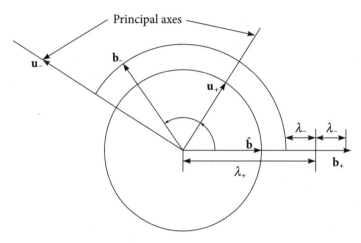

Fig. 5.4   Parameters in Mohr's algorithm

Exercise   Show that

$$\tan 2\phi = \frac{|\hat{\mathbf{b}}_+ \times \hat{\mathbf{b}}_-|}{\hat{\mathbf{b}}_+ \cdot \hat{\mathbf{b}}_-}, \tag{5.43}$$

so that the principal vectors $\mathbf{u}_\pm$ can be obtained via Eq. (5.35).

Mohr's algorithm is routinely used by engineers to solve eigenvalue problem on a plane by graphical means. Here, the key construction is the Mohr's circle (Fig. 5.5). The parametric equation for the Mohr's circle can be obtained from Eqs (5.34) and (5.35) as

$$Z(\phi) = \hat{\mathbf{b}} \cdot S_+ \hat{\mathbf{b}} = \frac{1}{2}(\lambda_+ + \lambda_-) + \frac{1}{2}(\lambda_+ - \lambda_-)\cos 2\phi. \tag{5.44}$$

To see it as an equation to a circle, replace $\cos 2\phi$ by $e^{i2\phi}$. It is then clear that this circle has radius $\frac{1}{2}(\lambda_+ - \lambda_-)$ and its center is at a distance $\frac{1}{2}(\lambda_+ + \lambda_-)$ from the origin along the x axis. To solve for two unknowns (λ_+, λ_-), Z must be known for two values of ϕ. The choice corresponding to Eq. (5.36) is

$$Z_\perp(\phi) = Z(\phi + \frac{\pi}{2}) = \frac{1}{2}(\lambda_+ + \lambda_-) - \frac{1}{2}(\lambda_+ - \lambda_-)\cos 2\phi. \tag{5.45}$$

Solution of Eqs (5.44) and (5.45) is, of course, equivalent to Mohr's algorithm.

The graphical solution to Eqs (5.44) and (5.45) is obtained as follows. First, we choose a value of ϕ and choose positive direction of x axis along the vector $\hat{\mathbf{b}}$ defined by Eq. (5.35).

This fixes $\hat{\mathbf{b}}$. Knowing the action of S_+ on $\hat{\mathbf{b}}$, we can find the value of $Z(\phi) = \hat{\mathbf{b}} \cdot S_+ \hat{\mathbf{b}}$. We can calculate the value of $Z_\perp(\phi) = Z(\phi + \frac{\pi}{2})$ in the same way, by noting that the corresponding $\hat{\mathbf{b}}$ vector is orthogonal to the x axis. Now, we draw a straight line making an angle 2ϕ with the positive direction of x axis, intersecting it at a point O. Then, we mark out two points S_1 and S_2 on this line, which are equidistant from O and are at distances $Z(\phi)$ and $Z_\perp(\phi)$ from the origin respectively. While doing this, we may have to slide this line parallel to itself along the x axis. Finally, we draw a circle (Mohr's circle) with its center at O and radius $OS_{1,2}$. This circle cuts the x axis at two points at distance λ_- (closer) and λ_+ (farther) from the origin, giving us the required eigenvalues. All this is depicted in Fig. 5.5. One eigenvector is along the bisector of the angle 2ϕ made with the positive direction of x axis and the second eigenvector is orthogonal to it.

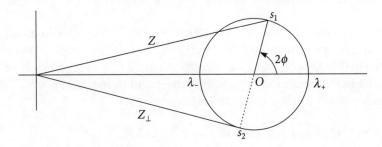

Fig. 5.5   Mohr's Circle

Exercise   Where exactly would Mohr's algorithm fail if the operator S_+ was not positive?   □

5.3.1 Examples

(a) Using Mohr's algorithm, we solve the eigenvalue problem for the operator

$$S_+(\mathbf{b}) = (\mathbf{a} \times \mathbf{b}) \times \mathbf{a} + (\mathbf{c} \times \mathbf{b}) \times \mathbf{c}, \tag{5.46}$$

where $\mathbf{a}$ and $\mathbf{c}$ are not collinear.

Exercise   Show that $S_+(\mathbf{b})$ in Eq. (5.46) is both symmetric and positive.   □

The operator in Eq. (5.46) is the general form of the moment of inertia operator of a plane lamina. Note that

$$S_+ \hat{\mathbf{a}} = (\mathbf{c} \times \hat{\mathbf{a}}) \times \mathbf{c} = c^2 \hat{\mathbf{a}} - (\hat{\mathbf{a}} \cdot \mathbf{c})\mathbf{c}, \tag{5.47}$$

where we have used identity I involving vector triple product and

$$-iS_+(i\hat{\mathbf{a}}) = a^2 \hat{\mathbf{a}} + (\mathbf{c} \cdot \hat{\mathbf{a}})\mathbf{c}. \tag{5.48}$$

To understand Eq. (5.48), make use of Fig. 5.6 and construct the vector

$$-iS_+(i\hat{\mathbf{a}}) = -i[(\mathbf{a} \times i\hat{\mathbf{a}}) \times \mathbf{a} + (\mathbf{c} \times i\hat{\mathbf{a}}) \times \mathbf{c}] \tag{5.49}$$

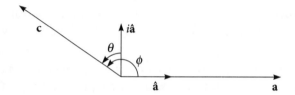

Fig. 5.6   Verification of Eq. (5.48)

on this figure. Convince yourself that the result holds arbitrary **a** and **c**. Otherwise, using the standard identity for the vector triple product and noting that $\hat{\mathbf{a}} \cdot i\hat{\mathbf{a}} = 0$ we have, from Eq. (5.49),

$$-iS_+(i\hat{\mathbf{a}}) = -i\left[a^2(i\hat{\mathbf{a}}) + c^2(i\hat{\mathbf{a}}) - c^2(i\hat{\mathbf{a}} \cdot \hat{\mathbf{c}}) \cdot \hat{\mathbf{c}}\right]. \tag{5.50}$$

The vector formed by the last two terms in Eq. (5.50) is orthogonal to **c** in the direction $-i\hat{\mathbf{c}}$ with magnitude $c^2 \sin\theta$ where θ is the angle between $i\hat{\mathbf{a}}$ and **c**. Writing $\sin\theta = \sin(\phi - \pi/2) = -\cos\phi = -(\hat{\mathbf{c}} \cdot \hat{\mathbf{a}})$ (see Fig. 2.7) we see that the last two terms in the bracket in Eq. (5.50) correspond to the vector $-c^2(\hat{\mathbf{c}} \cdot \hat{\mathbf{a}})(-i\hat{\mathbf{c}})$. We now multiply by $-i$ in Eq. (5.50) to get

$$-iS_+(i\hat{\mathbf{a}}) = a^2\hat{\mathbf{a}} + c^2(\hat{\mathbf{c}} \cdot \hat{\mathbf{a}})\hat{\mathbf{c}} = a^2\hat{\mathbf{a}} + (\mathbf{c} \cdot \hat{\mathbf{a}})\mathbf{c}. \tag{5.51}$$

As the next step we obtain

$$\mathbf{a}_+ = S_+\hat{\mathbf{a}} - iS_+(i\hat{\mathbf{a}}) = (a^2 + c^2)\hat{\mathbf{a}},$$

$$\mathbf{a}_+ = (c^2 - a^2)\hat{\mathbf{a}} - 2(\mathbf{c} \cdot \hat{\mathbf{a}})\mathbf{c}. \tag{5.52}$$

It is trivial to check that

$$|\mathbf{a}_-| = \left[\left(c^2 - a^2\right)^2 + 4(\mathbf{c} \cdot \hat{\mathbf{a}})^2\right]^{1/2}$$

and $|\mathbf{a}_+| = (a^2 + c^2)$ so that we get for the principal values

$$\lambda_\pm = \frac{1}{2}(|\mathbf{a}_+| + |\mathbf{a}_-|)$$

$$= \frac{1}{2}(a^2 + b^2) \pm \frac{1}{2}\left[\left(c^2 - a^2\right)^2 + 4(\mathbf{c} \cdot \hat{\mathbf{a}})^2\right]^{1/2}. \tag{5.53}$$

By Eq. (5.42) the corresponding principal vectors are

$$\hat{\mathbf{u}} = \hat{\mathbf{a}} \pm \frac{\left(c^2 - a^2\right)\hat{\mathbf{a}} - 2(\mathbf{c} \cdot \hat{\mathbf{a}})\mathbf{c}}{\left[(c^2 - a^2)^2 + 4(\mathbf{c} \cdot \hat{\mathbf{a}})^2\right]^{1/2}}. \tag{5.54}$$

We note that a free choice of the argument $\mathbf{b}$ in Mohr's algorithm enabled us to simplify the computation by taking the special structure of the operator S_+ into account.

(b) We find the eigenvalues and eigenvectors of the operator

$$S_+(\mathbf{b}) = \mathbf{a}(\mathbf{a} \cdot \mathbf{b}) + \mathbf{c}(\mathbf{c} \cdot \mathbf{b}).$$

Exercise Show that $S_+(\mathbf{b})$ is symmetric as well as positive. $\square$

As in the previous example, we evaluate S_+ at the defining unit vector $\hat{\mathbf{a}}$. We have,

$$S_+\hat{\mathbf{a}} = a^2\hat{\mathbf{a}} + (\mathbf{c} \cdot \hat{\mathbf{a}})$$

and

$$-iS_+(i\hat{\mathbf{a}}) = -i(\mathbf{c} \cdot i\hat{\mathbf{a}}).$$

These can be written, by resolving $\mathbf{c}$ along $\hat{\mathbf{a}}$ and $i\hat{\mathbf{a}}$ as

$$S_+\hat{\mathbf{a}} = a^2\hat{\mathbf{a}} + (\cdot\hat{\mathbf{a}})^2\hat{\mathbf{a}} + (\mathbf{c} \cdot \hat{\mathbf{a}})(\mathbf{c} \cdot i\hat{\mathbf{a}})i\hat{\mathbf{a}},$$

$$-iS_+(i\hat{\mathbf{a}}) = (\mathbf{c} \cdot i\hat{\mathbf{a}})^2\hat{\mathbf{a}} + (\mathbf{c} \cdot \hat{\mathbf{a}})(\mathbf{c} \cdot i\hat{\mathbf{a}})i\hat{\mathbf{a}}.$$

This gives

$$\mathbf{a}_+ = S_+\hat{\mathbf{a}} - iS_+(i\hat{\mathbf{a}}) = (1 + a^2)\hat{\mathbf{a}} + 2(\mathbf{c} \cdot \hat{\mathbf{a}})(\mathbf{c} \cdot i\hat{\mathbf{a}})i\hat{\mathbf{a}}$$

$$\mathbf{a}_- = S_+\hat{\mathbf{a}} + iS_+(i\hat{\mathbf{a}}) = [a^2 + (\mathbf{c} \cdot \hat{\mathbf{a}})^2 - (\mathbf{c} \cdot i\hat{\mathbf{a}})^2]\hat{\mathbf{a}} \tag{5.55}$$

or,

$$|\mathbf{a}_-| = a^2 + (\mathbf{c} \cdot \hat{\mathbf{a}})^2 - |\mathbf{c} \times \hat{\mathbf{a}}|^2$$

$$|\mathbf{a}_+| = [(1 + a^2)^2 + 4(\mathbf{c} \cdot \hat{\mathbf{a}})^2|\mathbf{c} \times \hat{\mathbf{a}}|^2]^{1/2}. \tag{5.56}$$

Therefore,

$$\lambda_\pm = \frac{1}{2}(|\mathbf{a}_+| + |\mathbf{a}_-|)$$

$$= \frac{1}{2}\left[(1 + a^2)^2 + 4(\mathbf{c} \cdot \hat{\mathbf{a}})^2|\mathbf{c} \times \hat{\mathbf{a}}|^2\right]^{1/2}$$

$$\pm \frac{1}{2}\left[a^2 + (\mathbf{c} \cdot \hat{\mathbf{a}})^2 - |\mathbf{c} \times \hat{\mathbf{a}}|^2\right]. \tag{5.57}$$

Exercise Show that an eigenvector $\hat{\mathbf{u}}$ of S_+ is obtained by rotating $\hat{\mathbf{a}}$ counterclockwise by an angle ϕ satisfying

$$\tan 2\phi = \left(\frac{c^2}{1+a^2}\right)\sin 2\theta$$

where θ is the angle between $\mathbf{a}$ and $\mathbf{c}$. $\square$

(c) We find the eigenvalues and the eigenvectors of the operator

$$S_+(\mathbf{e}) = (\mathbf{a}\times\mathbf{e})\times\mathbf{a} + (\mathbf{b}\times\mathbf{e})\times\mathbf{b} + (\mathbf{c}\times\mathbf{e})\times\mathbf{c}, \tag{5.58}$$

where

$$\mathbf{a}+\mathbf{b}+\mathbf{c} = 0.$$

Note that the condition $\mathbf{a}+\mathbf{b}+\mathbf{c}=0$ makes the vectors $\mathbf{a},\mathbf{b},\mathbf{c}$ coplanar and the given operator then acts on the plane containing $\mathbf{a},\mathbf{b},\mathbf{c}$.

Exercise Show that S_+ in Eq. (5.58) is both, symmetric and positive.

Hint Use identity I. $\square$

Thus, Mohr's algorithm applies. We proceed on the same line as the previous examples. We get,

$$S_+(\hat{\mathbf{a}}) = (b^2+c^2)\hat{\mathbf{a}} - (\hat{\mathbf{a}}\cdot\mathbf{b})\mathbf{b} - (\hat{\mathbf{a}}\cdot\mathbf{c})\mathbf{c} \tag{5.59}$$

$$-iS_+(i\hat{\mathbf{a}}) = a^2\hat{\mathbf{a}} + (\hat{\mathbf{a}}\cdot\mathbf{b})\mathbf{b} + (\hat{\mathbf{a}}\cdot\mathbf{c})\mathbf{c}. \tag{5.60}$$

This gives,

$$\mathbf{a}_+ = S_+(\hat{\mathbf{a}}) - iS_+(i\hat{\mathbf{a}}) = (a^2+b^2+c^2)\hat{\mathbf{a}}, \tag{5.61}$$

$$\mathbf{a}_- = S_+(\hat{\mathbf{a}}) - iS_+(i\hat{\mathbf{a}}) = (b^2+c^2-a^2)\hat{\mathbf{a}} - 2(\hat{\mathbf{a}}\cdot\mathbf{b})\mathbf{b} - 2(\hat{\mathbf{a}}\cdot\mathbf{c})\mathbf{c}. \tag{5.62}$$

We now make use of the condition $\mathbf{a}+\mathbf{b}+\mathbf{c}=0$ and simplify Eq. (5.61) to

$$\mathbf{a}_+ = 2(a^2+b^2+\mathbf{a}\cdot\mathbf{b})\hat{\mathbf{a}} \tag{5.63}$$

$$\mathbf{a}_- = 2(b^2-a^2)\hat{\mathbf{a}} - 4(\hat{\mathbf{a}}\cdot\mathbf{b})\mathbf{b}. \tag{5.64}$$

We have,

$$|\mathbf{a}_-| = 2[(b^2-a^2)^2 + 4(\mathbf{a}\cdot\mathbf{b})^2]^{1/2}.$$

Therefore, the principal values are

$$\lambda_{\pm} = \frac{1}{2}(|\mathbf{a}_+| \pm |\mathbf{a}_-|) = (a^2 + b^2 + \mathbf{a} \cdot \mathbf{b}) \pm [(b^2 - a^2)^2 + 4(\mathbf{a} \cdot \mathbf{b})^2]^{1/2}$$

and the corresponding eigenvectors are

$$\mathbf{u}_{\pm} = \hat{\mathbf{a}} \pm \frac{(b^2 - a^2)\hat{\mathbf{a}} - 2(\hat{\mathbf{a}} \cdot \mathbf{b})\mathbf{b}}{[(b^2 - a^2)^2 + 4(\mathbf{a} \cdot \mathbf{b})^2]^{1/2}}.$$

Exercise Find the eigenvalues and the eigenvectors of the positive symmetric operator

$$S_+(\mathbf{b}) = \mathbf{a}(\mathbf{c} \cdot \mathbf{b}) + \mathbf{c}(\mathbf{a} \cdot \mathbf{b}). \qquad \Box$$

Unfortunately, no generalization of Mohr's algorithm to the eigenvalue problem of a positive symmetric operator acting on 3-D space is available. However, as mentioned before, knowledge of one eigenvector enables us to use Mohr's algorithm to find the remaining two eigenvectors in the plane orthogonal to the known eigenvector. For example, any operator constructed out of two vectors $\mathbf{a}$ and $\mathbf{c}$ necessarily has $\mathbf{a} \times \mathbf{c}$ as an eigenvector. Thus, for the operator in Eq. (5.46) we find

$$S_+(\mathbf{a} \times \mathbf{c}) = (a^2 + c^2)(\mathbf{a} \times \mathbf{c}).$$

5.4 Spectrum of a 2 × 2 Symmetric Matrix

We find the eigenvalues and the eigenvectors of an operator f acting on a plane, given by a symmetric matrix

$$[S] = \begin{bmatrix} S_{11} & S_{12} \\ S_{12} & S_{22} \end{bmatrix},$$

with respect to an orthonormal basis $(\hat{\sigma}_1, \hat{\sigma}_2)$.

The roots of the characteristic polynomial of a 2×2 matrix A is easily seen to be

$$\lambda_{\pm} = \frac{1}{2}[Tr(A) \pm \sqrt{(Tr(A))^2 - 4\det(A)}]$$

where $Tr(A)$ and $\det(A)$ mean the trace and the determinant of A respectively. This immediately gives, for the eigenvalues of the symmetric matrix $[S]$ above,

$$\lambda_{\pm} = \frac{1}{2}(S_{11} + S_{22}) \pm \frac{1}{2}[(S_{11} - S_{22})^2 + 4S_{12}^2]^{1/2}.$$

To get the eigenvectors, we assume the plane to be the complex plane and identify the orthonormal basis $(\hat{\sigma}_1, \hat{\sigma}_2)$ with $(\hat{\sigma}_1, i\hat{\sigma}_1)$. In this basis, $\hat{\sigma}_1$ has coordinates $(1,0)$ and $\hat{\sigma}_2 = i\hat{\sigma}_1$ has coordinates $(0,1)$. Therefore,

$$S(\hat{\sigma}_1) = \begin{bmatrix} S_{11} & S_{12} \\ S_{12} & S_{22} \end{bmatrix} \begin{bmatrix} 1 \\ 0 \end{bmatrix} = \begin{bmatrix} S_{11} \\ S_{12} \end{bmatrix}$$

and

$$S(i\hat{\sigma}_1) = S(\hat{\sigma}_2) = \begin{bmatrix} S_{11} & S_{12} \\ S_{12} & S_{22} \end{bmatrix} \begin{bmatrix} 0 \\ 1 \end{bmatrix} = \begin{bmatrix} S_{12} \\ S_{22} \end{bmatrix}.$$

The vector $-iS(i\hat{\sigma}_1)$ is obtained by rotating $S(i\hat{\sigma}_1)$ clockwise through $\pi/2$. This will interchange its coordinates so that

$$-iS(i\hat{\sigma}_1) = \begin{bmatrix} S_{22} \\ S_{12} \end{bmatrix}$$

and we get,

$$\mathbf{b}_+ = S(\hat{\sigma}_1) - iS(i\hat{\sigma}_1) = \begin{bmatrix} S_{11} + S_{22} \\ 2S_{12} \end{bmatrix},$$

and

$$\mathbf{b}_- = S(\hat{\sigma}_1) + iS(i\hat{\sigma}_1) = \begin{bmatrix} S_{11} - S_{22} \\ 0 \end{bmatrix}.$$

We immediately see that $\mathbf{b}_-$ is in the direction of $\hat{\sigma}_1$. So the angle χ between $\hat{\sigma}_1$ and $\mathbf{b}_+$ is

$$\tan \chi = \frac{2S_{12}}{S_{11} + S_{22}}.$$

However, we have seen before that the eigenvector $\mathbf{u}$ bisects the angle between $\mathbf{b}_+$ and $\mathbf{b}_-$ or $\hat{\sigma}_1$. Denoting the angle between $\mathbf{u}$ and $\hat{\sigma}_1$ to be ϕ, we get

$$\tan(2\phi) = \frac{2S_{12}}{S_{11} + S_{22}}.$$

5.5   Spectrum of S^n

We define $S^n = S \circ S \circ S \cdots \circ S$ (n times), where $S \circ S(\mathbf{x}) = S(S(\mathbf{x}))$. Let S be a symmetric operator on $\mathscr{E}_3$ with eigenvalues $\{\lambda_k\}$. We show that S^n is symmetric with eigenvalues λ_k^n and S^n has the same eigenvectors as S.

We prove the first claim by induction on n. Assume that for $n = l$,

$$S^l = \sum_k (\lambda_k)^l \mathscr{P}_k. \tag{5.65}$$

is the spectral representation of S^l given by the projection operators $\mathscr{P}_k$ defined by Eq. (5.25). Consider,

$$
\begin{aligned}
S^{l+1} &= \left(\sum_k (\lambda_k)^l \mathscr{P}_k \right) \left(\sum_j (\lambda_j) \mathscr{P}_j \right) \\
&= \sum_{k,j} (\lambda_k)^l \lambda_j \mathscr{P}_j \mathscr{P}_k = \sum_{k,j} (\lambda_k)^l \lambda_j \delta_{jk} \mathscr{P}_k \\
&= \sum_k (\lambda_k)^{l+1} \mathscr{P}_k,
\end{aligned} \tag{5.66}
$$

where we have used the property $\mathscr{P}_j \mathscr{P}_k = \delta_{jk} \mathscr{P}_k$ of the projection operators. Thus, we have shown that if S^l is a symmetric operator (because of its spectral representation in terms of projectors) with eigenvalues $(\lambda_k)^l$ then S^{l+1} is a symmetric operator with eigenvalues $(\lambda_k)^{l+1}$. However, we know that Eq. (5.65) is true for $l = 1$ which is simply the spectral representation of the symmetric operator S. Therefore, by induction, Eq. (5.65) must be true for any value $l = n$.

To show that S^n and S share the same set of eigenvectors, consider an eigenvector $\mathbf{u}$ of S with eigenvalue λ. We have,

$$S^n(\mathbf{u}) = S^{n-1}(S\mathbf{u}) = S^{n-1}(\lambda \mathbf{u}) = S^{n-2}(\lambda S \mathbf{u}) = S^{n-2}(\lambda^2 \mathbf{u}) = \cdots = \lambda^n \mathbf{u}.$$

Thus, we see that if $\mathbf{u}$ is an eigenvector of a symmetric operator S with an eigenvalue λ then it is the eigenvector of the operator S^n with the eigenvalue λ^n. Thus, all the eigenvalues of S^n are real (because λ are real) so that S^n is also symmetric. Note that this proof goes through even if S were not symmetric and admitted complex eigenvalues. Therefore, the result that S and S^n have common set of eigenvectors and eigenvalues of S^n are given by the nth power of the eigenvalues of S is valid for a general linear operator.

Exercise If $\mathbf{a}, \mathbf{b}, \mathbf{c}$ are mutually orthogonal and S is a symmetric operator show that the three vectors $\mathbf{a} \times S(\mathbf{a})$, $\mathbf{b} \times S(\mathbf{b})$ and $\mathbf{c} \times S(\mathbf{c})$ are coplanar.

Hint If $\mathbf{a}, \mathbf{b}, \mathbf{c}$ were the principal vectors of S then each of the products $\mathbf{a} \times S(\mathbf{a})$ etc, vanish. Therefore, let $\{\mathbf{u}_k\}$ denote the orthogonal principal vectors of S. We have to show

$$(\mathbf{a} \times S(\mathbf{a})) \cdot [(\mathbf{b} \times S(\mathbf{b})) \times (\mathbf{c} \times S(\mathbf{c}))] = 0.$$

This can be done by using the spectral representation of S and the expansion of $\mathbf{a}, \mathbf{b}, \mathbf{c}$ in the eigenbasis $\{\mathbf{u}_k\}$ of S. $\qquad\square$

Rotations and Reflections

6.1 Orthogonal Transformations: Rotations and Reflections

In this section, we try and understand an extremely important class of linear operators called orthogonal operators. These operators are frequently called transformations because they correspond to rotations or reflections of points in space, which can be physical operations of rotating (about some axis) or reflecting (with respect to a point or a plane) a point particle or a system of particles. An orthogonal operator preserves the length of a vector in $\mathscr{E}_3$ as well as the orthogonality of vectors, say those forming an orthogonal basis.

An operator f is said to be orthogonal if it satisfies

$$f(\mathbf{x}) \cdot f(\mathbf{y}) = \mathbf{x} \cdot \mathbf{y} \tag{6.1}$$

for all vectors $\mathbf{x}, \mathbf{y} \in \mathscr{E}_3$.

A fixed point of an operator is the vector satisfying $f(\mathbf{x}) = \mathbf{x}$, that is, the vector left invariant under the action of f. We know that the origin (the zero vector) is a fixed point of f by virtue of its linearity. However, for an orthogonal operator acting on $\mathscr{E}_3$, no non-zero vector $\mathbf{x}^* \neq \mathbf{0}$ can be a fixed point, because for such a vector $\mathbf{x}^*$ the orthogonality condition

$$\mathbf{x}^* \cdot f(\mathbf{y}) = \mathbf{x}^* \cdot \mathbf{y} \tag{6.2}$$

is satisfied only by the vectors $\mathbf{y}$ whose projection along $\mathbf{x}^*$ equals that of $f(\mathbf{y})$ along $\mathbf{x}^*$ and not by all vectors in $\mathscr{E}_3$. All vectors $\mathbf{y}$ and $f(\mathbf{y})$ satisfying Eq. (6.2) for any given $\mathbf{x}$, correspond to points which lie on a plane normal to $\mathbf{x}$, so that an orthogonal operator restricted to act on a plane will leave invariant all vectors on a line normal to this plane which is a 2-D subspace of $\mathscr{E}_3$ and we call it $\mathscr{E}_2$. To see this in another way, consider an orthogonal operator f on a plane. It has one fixed point on the plane namely the origin on the plane. As a subspace of $\mathscr{E}_3$, this plane can be translated parallel to itself so that the origin traces a line normal to the plane, all points on which are invariant under the action of this f. Thus, an orthogonal operator acting on $\mathscr{E}_3$ leaves only one vector, namely the origin or the zero vector, invariant, while an orthogonal operator acting on a plane leaves invariant all points on a line normal to this plane. If we club this observation with the fact that an orthogonal operator preserves the length of a vector as well as the angle between vectors we see that an orthogonal operator corresponds to rotation (either about a point or an axis) or reflection in the origin or in a plane as we shall see below.

We now prove different properties of an orthogonal operator.

Equation (6.1) can be rewritten

$$f(\mathbf{x}) \cdot f(\mathbf{y}) = \mathbf{x} \cdot f^\dagger f(\mathbf{y}) = \mathbf{x} \cdot \mathbf{y}$$

which implies (in order to be consistent with Eq. (6.1)) that

$$f^\dagger = f^{-1}. \tag{6.3}$$

Thus, an orthogonal operator is a non-singular operator for which the inverse equals its adjoint. The same property holds for the matrix representing an orthogonal operator. To see this, consider the jkth element of the matrix for the operator $f^\dagger f$,

$$(f^\dagger f)_{jk} = \hat{\boldsymbol{\sigma}}_j \cdot f^\dagger f \hat{\boldsymbol{\sigma}}_k = f \hat{\boldsymbol{\sigma}}_j \cdot f \hat{\boldsymbol{\sigma}}_k = \hat{\boldsymbol{\sigma}}_j \cdot \hat{\boldsymbol{\sigma}}_k = \delta_{jk}, \tag{6.4}$$

which means

$$[f^\dagger f] = [f^\dagger][f] = I \tag{6.5}$$

where I is the 3×3 unit matrix, giving

$$[f^\dagger] = [f]^{-1}. \tag{6.6}$$

Written explicitly in elemental form, Eq. (6.5) becomes

$$\sum_i f_{ji}^\dagger f_{ik} = \delta_{jk},$$

or,

$$\sum_i f_{ij} f_{ik} = \delta_{jk}, \quad (1 \leq j \leq k \leq 3), \tag{6.7}$$

where we have used $[f^\dagger] = [f]^T$ (Eq. (4.19)). The matrix satisfying Eq. (6.7) consists of columns which are mutually orthogonal and individually normalized. Such a matrix is called orthogonal. Thus, an orthogonal operator is represented by an orthogonal matrix.

Exercise Show that the inverse of an orthogonal operator (matrix) is an orthogonal operator (matrix).   □

Replacing **y** by **x** in Eq. (6.1) it follows that

$$(f(\mathbf{x}))^2 = (\mathbf{x})^2 = |\mathbf{x}|^2. \tag{6.8}$$

Thus, the magnitude of every vector in $\mathscr{E}_3$ is invariant under an orthogonal transformation. This immediately tells us that an orthogonal operator preserves Euclidean distance between every pair of vectors in $\mathscr{E}_3$, because Euclidean distance between **x**, **y** is simply the length of the vector $\mathbf{x} - \mathbf{y}$.

We get immediately from Eq. (6.1) that

$$|f(\mathbf{x})||f(\mathbf{y})|\cos\theta_2 = |\mathbf{x}||\mathbf{y}|\cos\theta_1$$

which, when coupled with Eq. (6.8) implies,

$$\cos\theta_2 = \cos\theta_1, \text{ or, } \theta_2 = \theta_1$$

where $0 \le \theta_1, \theta_2 < 2\pi$ are the angles between **x** and **y** and $f(\mathbf{x}), f(\mathbf{y})$ respectively. Thus, an orthogonal transformation preserves angle between vectors. For $\mathbf{f}_k = f\hat{\sigma}_k$, Eq. (6.1) implies

$$\mathbf{f}_j \cdot \mathbf{f}_k = \hat{\sigma}_j \cdot \hat{\sigma}_k = \delta_{jk}.$$

Thus, an orthogonal f preserves the orthogonality of vectors in a standard basis.

Exercise Show that, if an operator f preserves length of all vectors, then it preserves angle between every pair of vectors. That is, a length preserving operator is orthogonal.

Solution We are given $f\mathbf{x} \cdot f\mathbf{x} = \mathbf{x} \cdot \mathbf{x}$ for all $\mathbf{x} \in \mathscr{E}_3$. We have to show that $f\mathbf{x} \cdot f\mathbf{y} = \mathbf{x} \cdot \mathbf{y}$ for all $\mathbf{x}, \mathbf{y} \in \mathscr{E}_3$. This follows from

$$\mathbf{x} \cdot \mathbf{y} = \frac{1}{4}(\mathbf{x} + \mathbf{y}) \cdot (\mathbf{x} + \mathbf{y}) - \frac{1}{4}(\mathbf{x} - \mathbf{y}) \cdot (\mathbf{x} - \mathbf{y}). \qquad \square$$

Thus, the action of an orthogonal f on a right handed orthonormal basis $\hat{\sigma}_1, \hat{\sigma}_2, \hat{\sigma}_3$ results in an orthonormal basis given by $f(\hat{\sigma}_1), f(\hat{\sigma}_2), f(\hat{\sigma}_3)$, either right handed or left handed. We can therefore write

$$(\hat{\sigma}_1 \cdot [\hat{\sigma}_2 \times \hat{\sigma}_3])^2 = (f(\hat{\sigma}_1) \cdot [f(\hat{\sigma}_2) \times f(\hat{\sigma}_3)])^2 = 1,$$

or,

$$\det f = f(\hat{\sigma}_1) \cdot [f(\hat{\sigma}_2) \times f(\hat{\sigma}_3)] = \pm 1. \tag{6.9}$$

Condition Eq. (6.9) tells apart two kinds of orthogonal transformations. An orthogonal transformation is said to be proper if $\det f = +1$ and improper if $\det f = -1$. The proper orthogonal transformations preserve the handedness of a orthonormal basis triad, while the improper orthogonal transformations change the handedness of an orthonormal basis triad. The handedness of a basis triad is changed if all the basis vectors are reflected in the origin. If we replace the basis in a given linear combination for a vector **x** by the basis reflected in the origin, the resulting linear combination gives the vector −**x** obtained by reflecting **x** in the origin. If we reflect one of the basis vectors in the plane normal to it, the handedness of the basis is changed and a general vector **x** gets reflected in that plane. Thus, we see that the improper orthogonal transformation corresponds to reflection either in the origin or in a plane. In fact, inversion of a vector **x** in the origin is the product of reflections of **x** in the orthogonal planes as we shall see below. Since a transformation leaving only the origin invariant has to be either a reflection or a rotation, a proper orthogonal transformation must correspond to a rotation. The fact that it preserves the handedness of the orthonormal basis is consistent with this conclusion.

6.1.1   The canonical form of the orthogonal operator for reflection

Given a unit vector $\hat{\mathbf{n}}$, we obtain an orthogonal operator $\mathscr{U}$ which reflects a vector **x** in the plane normal to $\hat{\mathbf{n}}$. We show that for a particle rebounding elastically from a fixed plane (with normal $\hat{\mathbf{n}}$), the final momentum $\mathbf{p}'$ is related to the initial momentum $\mathbf{p}$ by

$$\mathbf{p}' = \mathscr{U}(\mathbf{p}). \tag{6.10}$$

The required operator is

$$\mathscr{U}(\mathbf{x}) = (\hat{\mathbf{n}} \times \mathbf{x}) \times \hat{\mathbf{n}} - (\mathbf{x} \cdot \hat{\mathbf{n}})\hat{\mathbf{n}}. \tag{6.11}$$

Note that the parenthesis in the cross product term is necessary, because cross product is not associative. Comparing with Fig. 6.1, we see that the first term is the projection of **x** in the plane normal to $\hat{\mathbf{n}}$ (say $\mathbf{x}_\perp$) and the second term is the projection of **x** along $\hat{\mathbf{n}}$ (say $\mathbf{x}_\parallel$). Thus we have,

$$\mathscr{U}(\mathbf{x}) = \mathbf{x}_\perp - \mathbf{x}_\parallel,$$

which is simply the vector we get by reflecting **x** in the plane normal to $\hat{\mathbf{n}}$.

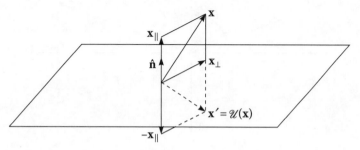

Fig. 6.1   Reflection of a vector in a plane

To show that $\mathscr{U}(\mathbf{x})$ is an orthogonal operator, we must test whether

$$\mathscr{U}(\mathbf{x}) \cdot \mathscr{U}(\mathbf{y}) = \mathbf{x} \cdot \mathbf{y}.$$

This can simply be done by evaluating the LHS using the definition of $\mathscr{U}(\mathbf{x})$ in Eq. (6.11). (Hint: use identity II.)

To show that $\det \mathscr{U} = -1$, we take a right handed orthonormal triad $\{\hat{\sigma}_1, \hat{\sigma}_2, \hat{\sigma}_3\}$ with $\hat{\sigma}_1 = \hat{\mathbf{n}}$. Then, it is trivial to see that

$$\mathscr{U}\hat{\sigma}_1 = -\hat{\sigma}_1, \; \mathscr{U}\hat{\sigma}_2 = \hat{\sigma}_2, \; \mathscr{U}\hat{\sigma}_3 = \hat{\sigma}_3.$$

Therefore,

$$\begin{aligned}
\det \mathscr{U} &= \mathscr{U}(\hat{\sigma}_1) \cdot (\mathscr{U}(\hat{\sigma}_2) \times \mathscr{U}(\hat{\sigma}_3)) \\[2mm]
&= -\hat{\sigma}_1 \cdot (\hat{\sigma}_2 \times \hat{\sigma}_3) \\[2mm]
&= -1 \times (+1) = -1
\end{aligned} \tag{6.12}$$

To endorse Eq. (6.10), we make following observations. Equation (6.10), in conjunction with Eq. (6.11), implies $|\mathbf{p}'|^2 = |\mathbf{p}|^2$, (Hint: use identity I) which is consistent with kinetic energy conservation valid for an elastic scattering event. Dotting Eq. (6.10) with $\hat{\mathbf{n}}$ and using Eq. (6.11) we get,

$$\hat{\mathbf{n}} \cdot \mathbf{p}' = -\hat{\mathbf{n}} \cdot \mathbf{p} = (-\hat{\mathbf{n}}) \cdot \mathbf{p}. \tag{6.13}$$

From Fig. 6.2 we see that Eq. (6.13) means $\theta = \theta'$ or the angle of reflection equals the angle of incidence. Crossing Eq. (6.10) with $\hat{\mathbf{n}}$ we get

$$\hat{\mathbf{n}} \times \mathbf{p}' = \hat{\mathbf{n}} \times \mathbf{p},$$

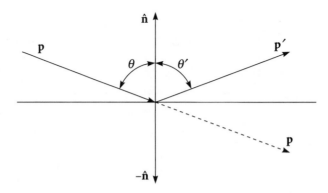

Fig. 6.2   Reflection of a particle with momentum **p** by an unmovable plane

which simply means that $\mathbf{p}$, $\hat{\mathbf{n}}$ and $\mathbf{p}'$ lie in the same plane, determined by $\hat{\mathbf{n}}$ and $\mathbf{p}$. Thus, Eq. (6.10) is the full description of reflection, or the complete statement of the law of reflection.

To find the inverse of $\mathscr{U}$ we note that $\mathbf{y} = \mathscr{U}(\mathbf{x})$ implies $\mathbf{x} = \mathscr{U}(\mathbf{y})$, that is, $\mathbf{x}$ and $\mathbf{y}$ are mutual images under reflection. (This establishes the operator equation $\mathscr{U}^2 = I$.) Therefore, we have

$$\mathscr{U}^{-1} = \mathscr{U}. \tag{6.14}$$

As a corollary, we can show that the reflection $\mathscr{U}$ is a symmetric operator. Orthogonality of $\mathscr{U}$ coupled with Eq. (6.14) gives

$$\mathscr{U}^{\dagger} = \mathscr{U}^{-1} = \mathscr{U} \tag{6.15}$$

Exercise   Prove that the product of three elementary reflections in orthogonal planes is an inversion, the linear transformation that reverses the direction of every vector.

Solution   We denote by $\mathscr{U}_{\hat{\mathbf{n}}}(\mathbf{x})$ the operator for reflection of $\mathbf{x}$ in the plane normal to $\hat{\mathbf{n}}$. Let $\{\hat{\sigma}_1, \hat{\sigma}_2, \hat{\sigma}_3\}$ be an orthonormal triad of vectors. Note that

$$\mathscr{U}_{\hat{\sigma}_j}(\hat{\sigma}_k) = -\delta_{jk}\hat{\sigma}_k + (1 - \delta_{jk})\hat{\sigma}_k \tag{6.16}$$

Now let

$$\mathbf{x} = \hat{\sigma}_1 x_1 + \hat{\sigma}_2 x_2 + \hat{\sigma}_3 x_3$$

be a vector in $\mathscr{E}_3$. We have, by virtue of Eq. (6.16),

$$\mathscr{U}_{\hat{\sigma}_3}\mathscr{U}_{\hat{\sigma}_2}\mathscr{U}_{\hat{\sigma}_1}(\mathbf{x}) = -\hat{\sigma}_1 x_1 - \hat{\sigma}_2 x_2 - \hat{\sigma}_3 x_3 = -\mathbf{x} \tag{6.17}$$

which is what we wanted to prove.   □

If we successively reflect a vector in two different planes in different order, we get, in general, two different vectors. This fact is expressed by saying that reflections, in general, do not commute. Thus, if $\mathscr{U}_1$, $\mathscr{U}_2$ denote the reflection operators for two planes then

$$\mathscr{U}_1\mathscr{U}_2(\mathbf{x}) \neq \mathscr{U}_2\mathscr{U}_1(\mathbf{x}).$$

Exercise   Show that the reflections defined via Eq. (6.16) commute.   □

Now consider two reflections which commute, that is, the corresponding reflection operators satisfy

$$\mathscr{U}_1\mathscr{U}_2(\mathbf{x}) = \mathscr{U}_2\mathscr{U}_1(\mathbf{x})$$

for all $\mathbf{x} \in \mathscr{E}_3$. Setting $\mathscr{U} = \mathscr{U}_1\mathscr{U}_2$ we get

$$\mathscr{U}^{\dagger} = (\mathscr{U}_1\mathscr{U}_2)^{\dagger} = \mathscr{U}_2^{\dagger}\mathscr{U}_1^{\dagger} = \mathscr{U}_2\mathscr{U}_1 = \mathscr{U}_1\mathscr{U}_2 = \mathscr{U}$$

where we have used that $\mathcal{U}_1$ and $\mathcal{U}_2$ are symmetric and that they commute. Thus, if two reflections commute, their product is a symmetric operator. Physically, this means that the effect of two successive reflections can be obtained via a single reflection.

6.1.2 Hamilton's theorem

Hamilton's theorem states that every rotation can be expressed as the product of two elementary (in a single plane) reflections.

To prove this theorem we refer to Fig. 6.3. Let a vector $\mathbf{x}$ be rotated about the direction implied by a unit vector $\hat{\mathbf{n}}$ through an angle θ to reach vector $\mathbf{x}'$. Without losing generality we assume $\theta < \pi$. Let $\mathbf{x}_{\parallel}$ and $\mathbf{x}'_{\parallel}$ be the projections of $\mathbf{x}$ and $\mathbf{x}'$ on the plane normal to $\hat{\mathbf{n}}$ and $\hat{\mathbf{u}}$ and $\hat{\mathbf{v}}$ be unit vectors along $\mathbf{x}_{\parallel}$ and $\mathbf{x}'_{\parallel}$ respectively. Rotation of $\mathbf{x}$ to $\mathbf{x}'$ is equivalent to that of $\mathbf{x}_{\parallel}$ to $\mathbf{x}'_{\parallel}$. To show that this rotation is equivalent to two elementary reflections, we first reflect $\mathbf{x}_{\parallel}$ in the plane normal to $\hat{\mathbf{u}} + \hat{\mathbf{v}}$. By construction the angle between $\mathbf{x}_{\parallel}$ and this plane is $(\pi/2 - \theta/2)$ so the reflected vector is along $-\hat{\mathbf{v}}$. Now we reflect this vector in the plane normal to $\hat{\mathbf{v}}$ to get $\mathbf{x}'_{\parallel}$. We thus have

$$\mathcal{R}(\theta) = \mathcal{U}_{\hat{\mathbf{v}}}\mathcal{U}_{\hat{\mathbf{u}}+\hat{\mathbf{v}}}$$

which proves the theorem. Here, $\mathcal{R}(\theta)$ is the orthogonal operator for rotation about $\hat{\mathbf{n}}$ through angle θ.

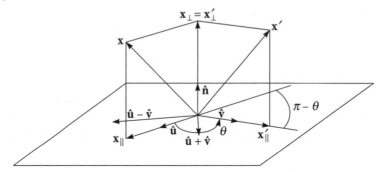

Fig. 6.3   See text

Hamilton's theorem expresses the operation of rotation in terms of that of reflection. It is trivial to see that, given any reflection (in a plane or in the origin) of a vector $\mathbf{x}$ to produce a vector $\mathbf{x}'$ it is always possible to choose a rotation (that is, the axis and the angle of rotation) which rotates $\mathbf{x}$ to $\mathbf{x}'$. This establishes the equivalence of rotations and reflections. However, it is physically easier to implement rotations than reflections. Many a time, rotation and reflection operations are implemented in natural systems like two molecules which are reflections of each other in a plane. Most important are the structures of physical systems that are invariant under certain rotations and reflections. These operations are called the symmetry operations of the system and play a crucial role in the dynamical and physical properties of the system. We shall say something about the symmetries in section 6.4.

6.2   Canonical Form for Linear Operators

Of all the linear operators, the symmetric, positive and orthogonal operators are the most important in modeling the physical world. The symmetric operators are diagonalizable, have real eigenvalues and their eigenvectors can form an orthonormal basis of $\mathscr{E}_3$. Since the magnitudes of all vector quantities are real, only real eigenvalues can correspond to the values of any measurable physical quantity. Further, the action of a symmetric operator on an arbitrary vector can be obtained via its action on its eigenvectors. This is possible only because a symmetric operator has real eigenvalues and its eigenvectors form a basis. A positive symmetric operator has positive eigenvalues having simple geometric interpretation and are required to express many physical quantities that are positive, e.g., the kinetic energy of a rotating rigid body expressed using the moment of inertia operator. Finally, orthogonal operators are required to incorporate elementary physical operations like reflection and rotation of a system. All this motivates a question whether a given linear operator can be expressed in terms of these operators. If this is possible, the action of such an operator on an arbitrary vector can be completely understood and carried out. In this section, we try and answer this question.

We start by proving that every symmetric transformation can be expressed as the product of a symmetric orthogonal transformation and a positive symmetric transformation. We proceed as follows.

Let S be a symmetric operator and let $\{\mathbf{e}_k\}$ $k = 1, 2, 3$ be its eigenvectors forming an orthonormal frame. Define the reflections

$$\mathscr{U}_{\mathbf{e}_j}(\mathbf{e}_k) = -\delta_{jk}\mathbf{e}_k + (1 - \delta_{jk})\mathbf{e}_k$$

as in Eq. (6.16). We know that $\mathscr{U}_{\mathbf{e}_j}$ reverse the direction of $\mathbf{e}_j$ and that their products are orthogonal and symmetric. Now consider the spectral representation of S,

$$S = \sum_k \lambda_k \mathscr{P}_k$$

and define a positive symmetric operator

$$S_+ = \sum_k |\lambda_k| \mathscr{P}_k.$$

We consider four cases.

(i) All $\lambda_k \geq 0$. We write

$$S = IS_+.$$

(ii) One eigenvalue (say jth) < 0. ($\lambda_j < 0$). We write

$$S = \mathscr{U}_{\mathbf{e}_j} S_+.$$

(iii) Two eigenvalues (say ith and jth < 0. ($\lambda_i < 0, \lambda_j < 0$). We write

$$S = \mathscr{U}_{\mathbf{e}_i} \mathscr{U}_{\mathbf{e}_j} S_+.$$

(iv) All the eigenvalues < 0. We write

$$S = \mathscr{U}_{\mathbf{e}_1} \mathscr{U}_{\mathbf{e}_2} \mathscr{U}_{\mathbf{e}_3} S_+.$$

There are no other cases and in each of the above case we have shown that the symmetric operator S can be written as the product of a symmetric orthogonal operator and a positive symmetric operator.

Next, we obtain a unique rotation $\mathscr{R}$ for an arbitrary improper orthogonal operator $\mathscr{I}$ satisfying

$$\mathscr{I} = \mathscr{R}\mathscr{U},$$

where $\mathscr{U}$ is a simple reflection in the plane normal to any direction $\hat{\mathbf{u}}$ as expressed by its canonical form Eq. (6.11).

We use the fact that $\mathscr{U}^2 = I$ to write

$$\mathscr{I} = (\mathscr{I}\mathscr{U})\mathscr{U}$$

and define $\mathscr{R} = \mathscr{I}\mathscr{U}$. The fact that $\mathscr{R}$ is a rotation follows from

$$\det \mathscr{R} = (\det \mathscr{I})(\det \mathscr{U})$$

$$= (-1)(-1) = 1.$$

Next, we prove the *Polar Decomposition Theorem* which states that every non-singular operator f has a unique decomposition in the form

$$f = \mathscr{R}S = \mathscr{I}\mathscr{R}, \tag{6.18}$$

where $\mathscr{R}$ is a rotation and S and $\mathscr{I}$ are positive symmetric operators given by

$$S = (f^\dagger f)^{1/2}$$

$$\mathscr{I} = (f f^\dagger)^{1/2}. \tag{6.19}$$

A canonical form for f is therefore obtained from that for $\mathscr{R}$ and S.

To prove Eq. (6.18) we note that

$$\mathbf{y} \cdot (f^\dagger f \mathbf{x}) = f(\mathbf{y}) \cdot f(\mathbf{x}) = \mathbf{x} \cdot (f^\dagger f \mathbf{y}),$$

so that the operator S' defined by

$$S' = f^\dagger f$$

is symmetric. Further,

$$\mathbf{x} \cdot (f^\dagger f \mathbf{x}) = (f\mathbf{x})^2 > 0 \text{ if } \mathbf{x} \neq 0$$

which makes S' positive. Therefore, the square root of $S' = f^\dagger f$ is well defined and unique

$$S = (f^\dagger f)^{1/2}.$$

Since S is non-singular, we solve Eq. (6.18) for the rotation $\mathscr{R}$,

$$\mathscr{R} = f^{-1} = f(f^\dagger f)^{-1/2}. \tag{6.20}$$

We have,

$$\det f^\dagger = \det f,$$

or,

$$\det(f^\dagger f) = (\det f)^2,$$

or,

$$\det S^{-1} = \det(f^\dagger f)^{-1/2} = (\det f)^{-1},$$

or,

$$\det \mathscr{R} = (\det f)(\det S^{-1}) = 1,$$

which shows that $\mathscr{R}$ is a rotation. The other part of Eq. (6.18) namely,

$$f = \mathscr{S}\mathscr{R}$$

is proved similarly.

The eigenvalues and eigenvectors of S decide the basic structural properties of f (see below for a geometric interpretation), because the other factor is just a rotation. They are sometimes called *principal vectors* and *principal values* of f to distinguish them from eigenvectors and eigenvalues of f which may, in general, be complex and are not related in a simple way with the principal values which are always real. Of course, there is no distinction if f itself is symmetric. Equation (6.18) clearly tells us that complex eigenvalues correspond to rotations as we have seen before (see section 5.2).

The polar decomposition, Eq. (6.18), provides a simple geometrical interpretation for any linear operator f. Consider the action of f on points $\mathbf{x}$ of a 3-D body or a geometrical figure. According to Eq. (6.18), the body is first stretched and/or reflected along the principal directions of f. Then, the deformed body is rotated about the axis through the angle both specified by $\mathscr{R}$.

6.2.1   Examples

(a) We find the polar decomposition of the skewsymmetric transformation

$$f(\mathbf{x}) = \mathbf{x} \times (\mathbf{a} \times \mathbf{b}). \tag{6.21}$$

Using the skew symmetry of $f\,(f^\dagger = -f)$ we can write

$$f^\dagger f = (\mathbf{a} \times \mathbf{b}) \times (\mathbf{x} \times (\mathbf{a} \times \mathbf{b}))$$

$$= (\mathbf{a} \times \mathbf{b})^2 \mathbf{x} - [(\mathbf{a} \times \mathbf{b}) \cdot \mathbf{x}](\mathbf{a} \times \mathbf{b}) \tag{6.22}$$

where we have used identity I. Note that

$$\mathbf{y} \cdot f^\dagger f \mathbf{x} = (\mathbf{a} \times \mathbf{b})^2 \mathbf{x} \cdot \mathbf{y} - [(\mathbf{a} \times \mathbf{b}) \cdot \mathbf{x}][(\mathbf{a} \times \mathbf{b}) \cdot \mathbf{y}]$$

$$= \mathbf{x} \cdot f^\dagger f \mathbf{y} \tag{6.23}$$

which means that $f^\dagger f$ is a symmetric operator. Further, $\mathbf{x} \cdot f^\dagger f \mathbf{x} > 0$ for $\mathbf{x} \neq 0$ making $f^\dagger f$ a positive operator. It is easily verified that the square root operator is given by

$$S = (f^\dagger f)^{1/2} = |\mathbf{a} \times \mathbf{b}|\mathbf{x} - (\mathbf{a} \times \mathbf{b}) \cdot \mathbf{x} \widehat{\mathbf{a} \times \mathbf{b}} \tag{6.24}$$

where $\widehat{\mathbf{a} \times \mathbf{b}}$ is the unit vector in the direction of $\mathbf{a} \times \mathbf{b}$.

We now find the rotation $\mathscr{R}$ in Eq. (6.18) with f given by Eq. (6.21). We have already found S. We note that $(\mathbf{a} \times \mathbf{b}) \cdot S(\mathbf{x}) = 0$ so that $S\mathbf{x}$ lies in the plane normal to $\mathbf{a} \times \mathbf{b}$. Thus, we need to rotate $S\mathbf{x}$ about $\widehat{\mathbf{a} \times \mathbf{b}}$ through $\pi/2$, so $\mathscr{R} = \mathscr{R}_{\widehat{\mathbf{a} \times \mathbf{b}}}(\pi/2)$. Taking this plane to be the complex plane, and real and imaginary axes along $S\mathbf{x}$ and $f\mathbf{x}$ respectively, this rotation amounts to multiplication by $e^{i\pi/2} = i$.[1]

(b) The linear transformation

$$f\mathbf{x} = \mathbf{x} + 2\alpha\hat{\sigma}_1(\hat{\sigma}_2 \cdot \mathbf{x}) \tag{6.25}$$

is called a shear. Figure 6.4 shows the effect of f on a unit square in the $\hat{\sigma}_1\hat{\sigma}_2$ plane. We find the eigenvectors, eigenvalues, principal vectors and principal values of f in this plane. We also find the angle of rotation in the polar decomposition of f.

It is easily seen that the only eigenvector of f in Eq. (6.25) is $\hat{\sigma}_1$ satisfying

$$f(\hat{\sigma}_1) = \hat{\sigma}_1 \tag{6.26}$$

---

[1]Note that $f(\mathbf{x})$ is perpendicular to both, $\mathbf{a} \times \mathbf{b}$ and $S(\mathbf{x})$.

Every other vector (linearly independent with $\hat{\sigma}_1$) gets transformed to a distinct vector (having different direction) under f. Thus, f is not diagonalizable.

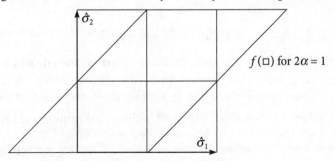

Fig. 6.4   Shear of a unit square

To get the principal vectors and principal values of f we must find the operator $f^\dagger f$. Note that

$$f^\dagger(\mathbf{y}) = \mathbf{y} + 2\alpha\hat{\sigma}_2(\hat{\sigma}_1 \cdot \mathbf{y}) \tag{6.27}$$

as can be seen from $\mathbf{y} \cdot f\mathbf{x} = \mathbf{x} \cdot f^\dagger(\mathbf{y})$ with f and $f^\dagger$ as in Eqs (6.25) and (6.27) respectively. We operate by $f^\dagger f$ on the basis vectors $(\hat{\sigma}_1, \hat{\sigma}_2)$ to get

$$f^\dagger f \hat{\sigma}_1 = \hat{\sigma}_1 + 2\alpha\hat{\sigma}_2$$

$$f^\dagger f \hat{\sigma}_2 = 2\alpha\hat{\sigma}_1 + \left(1 + 4\alpha^2\right)\hat{\sigma}_2. \tag{6.28}$$

Therefore, the matrix of $f^\dagger f$ in the basis $(\hat{\sigma}_1, \hat{\sigma}_2)$ is

$$[f^\dagger f] = \begin{bmatrix} 1 & 2\alpha \\ 2\alpha & 1 + 4\alpha^2 \end{bmatrix}.$$

The eigenvalues of this matrix are

$$\lambda_\pm^2 = (2\alpha^2 + 1) \pm 2\alpha\sqrt{\alpha^2 + 1}, \tag{6.29}$$

whose square roots are,

$$\lambda_\pm = \sqrt{\alpha^2 + 1} \pm \alpha. \tag{6.30}$$

These are the required eigenvalues of the operator

$$S = (f^\dagger f)^{1/2}.$$

Exercise   Employ Mohr's algorithm to find the eigenvectors of $f^\dagger f$, using Eq. (6.28) with $\hat{\sigma}_2 = i\hat{\sigma}_1$.

Answer

$$\mathbf{u}_\pm = \hat{\sigma}_1 \pm \lambda_\pm \hat{\sigma}_2.$$

These are also the eigenvectors of the operator S.   □

To get the rotation in the polar decomposition of f we treat $\hat{\sigma}_1\hat{\sigma}_2$ plane to be the complex plane. Note that the vectors $\hat{\sigma}_1, \hat{\sigma}_2$ are represented by the numbers 1 and i on the complex plane. Thus, the vectors $\mathbf{u}_\pm$ are represented by the numbers $1 \pm i\lambda_\pm$ on the complex plane and the vectors $S\mathbf{u}_+ = \lambda_+\mathbf{u}_+$ and $f(\mathbf{u}_+) = \mathbf{u}_+ + 2\alpha\hat{\sigma}_1$ $(\hat{\sigma}_2 \cdot \mathbf{u}_+)$ are represented by the complex numbers $\lambda_+(1 + i\lambda_+)$ and $(1 + 2\alpha\lambda_+) + i\lambda_+$ respectively. We know that the operator $\mathscr{R}$ rotates the vector $S\mathbf{u}_+$ to the vector $f(\mathbf{u}_+)$. This gives the required rotation by (check it!)

$$\tan\theta = \frac{-2\alpha\lambda_+^2}{1 + 2\alpha\lambda_+ + \lambda_+^2}.$$

6.3   Rotations

We need a canonical form of an operator which gives the vector $\mathbf{x}'$ obtained as a result of rotating a vector $\mathbf{x}$ about the direction implied by a unit vector $\hat{\mathbf{n}}$. Proceeding on the lines similar to reflection (subsection 6.1.1), we arrive at the following canonical form for the rotation operator

$$\mathscr{R}(\mathbf{x}) = (\mathbf{x} \cdot \hat{\mathbf{n}})\hat{\mathbf{n}} + e^{i\theta}(\hat{\mathbf{n}} \times \mathbf{x}) \times \hat{\mathbf{n}}. \tag{6.31}$$

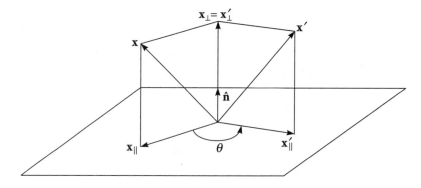

Fig. 6.5   Rotation of a vector

This operator can be understood by analyzing Fig. 6.5. First, we resolve $\mathbf{x}$ in its components $\mathbf{x}_\parallel$ and $\mathbf{x}_\perp$ lying in the plane normal to $\hat{\mathbf{n}}$ and along $\hat{\mathbf{n}}$ respectively. The first term in the expression for $\mathscr{R}(\mathbf{x})$ is $\mathbf{x}_\perp$ which remains invariant under rotation while the second term corresponds to the vector obtained by rotating $\mathbf{x}_\parallel$ counterclockwise through angle θ. ($\mathbf{x}'_\parallel$ in Fig. 6.5). Here, we treat the plane normal to $\hat{\mathbf{n}}$ to be the complex plane and multiplication by $e^{i\theta}$ rotates a vector counterclockwise by an angle θ. Since we have introduced a complex coefficient in the expression for the operator, the rule for the invariance of the scalar product has to be replaced by

$$f^*\mathbf{x} \cdot f\mathbf{y} = \mathbf{x} \cdot \mathbf{y}. \tag{6.32}$$

where f^* is obtained from f by complex conjugation. The operator f satisfying Eq. (6.32) is called unitary.

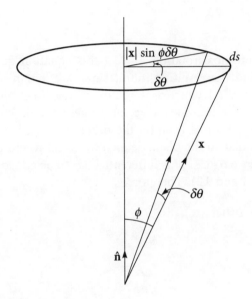

Fig. 6.6   Infinitesimal rotation $\delta\theta$ of $\mathbf{x}$ about $\hat{\mathbf{n}}$

Exercise Show that the operator $\mathcal{R}(\mathbf{x})$ in Eq. (6.31) satisfies Eq. (6.32). (Hint: Use identity II).   □

Thus, the rotation operator in Eq. (6.31) preserves scalar products as it should. That the determinant of $\mathcal{R}(\mathbf{x})$ in Eq. (6.31) is $+1$ can be proved along the same lines as we did for the reflection operator. This establishes the operator $\mathcal{R}(\mathbf{x})$ in Eq. (6.31) as the rotation operator. However, if we wish to carry on with the operator in Eq. (6.31) to get the structure and properties of rotation, we need a general algebraic setting incorporating the multiplication of a vector by a complex number as an integral part of it. Such an algebra is the geometric algebra which can be used to model rotations in a general and elegant manner [10, 7, 11]. Nevertheless we can develop the theory of rotations using only the algebra of vectors we have learnt. We proceed to do that.

   We first study infinitesimal rotations and then build up finite rotations as succession of infinitesimal rotations. Consider an infinitesimal rotation of a vector $\mathbf{x}$ about the direction implied by a unit vector $\hat{\mathbf{n}}$, through an angle $\delta\theta$ (see Fig. 6.6). The tip of vector $\mathbf{x}$ then moves over an infinitesimal arc length ds of a circle of radius $|\mathbf{x}|\sin\phi$ giving $ds = |\mathbf{x}|\sin\phi\,\delta\theta$ (Fig. 6.6). Since the circle is a smooth curve, we can choose the arc length ds generated by the rotation to be so small that the change $d\mathbf{x}$ in vector $\mathbf{x}$ due to rotation (see Fig. 6.7) can replace the arc length ds with a totally negligible (see discussion after Eq. (6.33)) error. Further, when the sense of rotation is positive or counterclockwise, a right handed screw advances in the direction of $\hat{\mathbf{n}}$ and the sense in which the rotating vector $\mathbf{x}$ traces the arc ds corresponds to the direction of the vector $\hat{\mathbf{n}} \times \mathbf{x}$. Thus, we can take

$$|\mathbf{x}|\sin\phi\delta\theta = |\hat{\mathbf{n}} \times \mathbf{x}|\delta\theta = ds = |d\mathbf{x}|$$

and

$$d\mathbf{x} = \delta\theta\hat{\mathbf{n}} \times \mathbf{x}.$$

for every possible infinitesimal rotation. In fact this equation quantitatively defines an infinitesimal rotation and the resulting infinitesimal arc length ds. The quantity $d\mathbf{x}$ is called the differential of $\mathbf{x}(\theta)$ which is a vector valued function of θ. In the limit as $\delta\theta \mapsto 0$, $d\mathbf{x}/\delta\theta = \hat{\mathbf{n}} \times \mathbf{x}$ becomes a vector tangent to the circle of rotation. Thus, corresponding to an infinitesimal rotation the differential $d\mathbf{x}$ has magnitude $|d\mathbf{x}| = ds$ and direction perpendicular to the plane defined by $\mathbf{x}$ and $\hat{\mathbf{n}}$ and tangent to the circle of rotation as shown in Figs 6.6, 6.7. This differential has to be added to $\mathbf{x}$ to get the rotated vector $\mathbf{x}'$ (see sections 9.1 and 9.2). Therefore,

$$\mathbf{x}' = \mathbf{x} + d\mathbf{x} = \mathbf{x} + \delta\theta(\hat{\mathbf{n}} \times \mathbf{x}). \qquad (6.33)$$

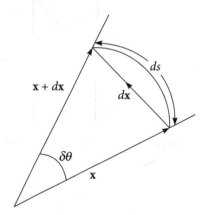

Fig. 6.7   Vectors $d\mathbf{x}$ and arc length ds as radius $|\mathbf{x}|\sin\theta$ is rotated through angle $\delta\theta$. As $\delta\theta \mapsto 0$ $d\mathbf{x}$ becomes tangent to the circle.

As we shall see later, (see section 9.6), the first equality in Eq. (6.33) becomes exact for any angle of rotation θ if we replace its RHS by the Taylor series of the function $\mathbf{x}(\theta)$ whose successive terms involve successive powers of θ. Thus, the RHS of the first equality in Eq. (6.33) is obtained by truncating this Taylor series after the term linear in θ which is justified if the angle of rotation is small, so that the higher powers $\theta^2, \theta^3 \cdots$ are orders of magnitude smaller than θ and hence can be neglected. In such a case, we replace θ by $\delta\theta$ to emphasize the smallness of the angle of rotation. Thus, the first equality in Eq. (6.33) essentially corresponds to an infinitesimal rotation.

Let the vector $\mathbf{x}$ be rotated by an infinitesimal angle $\delta\theta_1$ about the direction given by a unit vector $\hat{\mathbf{n}}_1$ to get a vector $\mathbf{x}'$. Next rotate $\mathbf{x}'$ through angle $\delta\theta_2$ about the direction given by unit vector $\hat{\mathbf{n}}_2$ to get the vector $\mathbf{x}''$. Using Eq. (6.33) and keeping the terms linear in $\delta\theta_1$ and $\delta\theta_2$ we get (do this algebra),

$$\mathbf{x}'' = \mathbf{x} + \delta\theta_1(\hat{\mathbf{n}}_1 \times \mathbf{x}) + \delta\theta_2(\hat{\mathbf{n}}_2 \times \mathbf{x}). \tag{6.34}$$

Now we reverse the order of rotations: Rotate $\mathbf{x}$ about $\hat{\mathbf{n}}_2$ by $\delta\theta_2$ to get $\mathbf{x}'$ and rotate $\mathbf{x}'$ about $\hat{\mathbf{n}}_1$ by $\delta\theta_1$ to get $\mathbf{x}''$. Going through the same algebra as above, keeping terms linear in $\delta\theta_1$ and $\delta\theta_2$, one can check that $\mathbf{x}''$ is again given by Eq. (6.34) which proves that infinitesimal rotations commute. The fact that finite rotations do not commute will become clear below.

Now let a vector $\mathbf{x}$ be rotated about a unit vector $\hat{\mathbf{n}}$ through a finite angle θ to get a vector $\mathbf{x}'$. The process is depicted in Fig. 6.5. As is shown in Fig. 6.5, we resolve $\mathbf{x}$ into two components, $\mathbf{x}_\parallel$ in the plane of rotation and $\mathbf{x}_\perp$ normal to this plane, i.e., in the direction of $\hat{\mathbf{n}}$. Rotation affects only the component $\mathbf{x}_\parallel$ while $\mathbf{x}_\perp$ remains invariant.

We imagine that the rotation of $\mathbf{x}_\parallel$ through θ is effected by N successive rotations about $\hat{\mathbf{n}}$, each of magnitude θ/N. We assume that N is so large (or θ/N is so small) that Eq. (6.33) applies to each of these rotations. Denote by $\mathbf{x}_1, \mathbf{x}_2, \ldots, \mathbf{x}_N = \mathbf{x}_\parallel'$ the successively rotated vectors. We have,

$$\mathbf{x}_1 = \frac{\theta}{N}(\hat{\mathbf{n}} \times \mathbf{x}_\parallel) + \mathbf{x}_\parallel.$$

$$\mathbf{x}_2 = \frac{\theta}{N}(\hat{\mathbf{n}} \times \mathbf{x}_1) + \mathbf{x}_1$$

$$= \frac{\theta}{N}\,\hat{\mathbf{n}} \times \left[\left(\frac{\theta}{N}\right)\hat{\mathbf{n}} \times \mathbf{x}_\parallel + \mathbf{x}_\parallel\right] + \frac{\theta}{N}\,\hat{\mathbf{n}} \times \mathbf{x}_\parallel + \mathbf{x}_\parallel$$

$$= \left[\left(\frac{\theta}{N}\right)^2 \hat{\mathbf{n}} \times (\hat{\mathbf{n}} \times + \left(\frac{2\theta}{N}\right)(\hat{\mathbf{n}} \times + 1\right]\mathbf{x}_\parallel).$$

Proceeding in this way, after N iterations we get

$$\mathbf{x}_\parallel' = \left[(1 + \binom{N}{1}\left(\frac{\theta}{N}\right)(\hat{\mathbf{n}} \times + \binom{N}{2}\left(\frac{\theta}{N}\right)^2 \hat{\mathbf{n}} \times (\hat{\mathbf{n}} \times + \cdots\right.$$

$$\left. + \binom{N}{N}\left(\frac{\theta}{N}\right)^N \hat{\mathbf{n}} \times (\hat{\mathbf{n}} \times (\cdots \right]\mathbf{x}_\parallel)$$

$$= \left(1 + \frac{\theta}{N}\,\hat{\mathbf{n}} \times\right)^N \mathbf{x}_\parallel. \tag{6.35}$$

Now let the parameter $N \longrightarrow \infty$ to get

$$\mathbf{x}'_{\|} = \lim_{N \mapsto \infty} \left(1 + \frac{\theta}{N}\,\hat{\mathbf{n}}\times\right)^N \mathbf{x}_{\|} \equiv e^{\theta\hat{\mathbf{n}}\times}\mathbf{x}_{\|}. \tag{6.36}$$

Note that Eqs (6.35) and (6.36) define operators $(1 + \frac{\theta}{N}\,\hat{\mathbf{n}}\times)^N$ and $e^{\theta\hat{\mathbf{n}}\times}$ respectively, on $\mathscr{E}_3$. The action of $e^{\theta\hat{\mathbf{n}}\times}$ on any vector $\mathbf{x}$ can be obtained by expanding it in powers of θ. We have,

$$e^{\theta\hat{\mathbf{n}}\times} \equiv \left(1 + \theta\,\hat{\mathbf{n}}\times + \frac{\theta^2}{2!}\,\hat{\mathbf{n}}\times(\hat{\mathbf{n}}\times + \frac{\theta^3}{3!}\,\hat{\mathbf{n}}\times(\hat{\mathbf{n}}\times(\hat{\mathbf{n}}\times +\cdots\right). \tag{6.37}$$

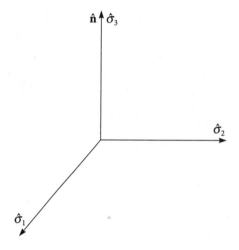

Fig. 6.8   Orthonormal triad to study the action of the rotation operator

To understand the effect of $e^{\theta\hat{\mathbf{n}}\times}$ on this space, we operate by it on a suitable basis. We choose the basis triad to be the set of three orthogonal unit vectors $(\hat{\sigma}_1, \hat{\sigma}_2, \hat{\sigma}_3)$ with $(\hat{\sigma}_1, \hat{\sigma}_2)$ lying in the plane containing $\mathbf{x}'_{\|}$ and $\hat{\sigma}_3 = \hat{\mathbf{n}}$. (see Fig. 6.8).

From Fig. 6.8 it is clear that

$$\hat{\mathbf{n}}\times\hat{\sigma}_1 = \hat{\sigma}_2 \quad ; \quad \hat{\mathbf{n}}\times\hat{\sigma}_2 = -\hat{\sigma}_1 \tag{6.38}$$

To see the effect of $e^{\theta\hat{\mathbf{n}}\times}$ on $\hat{\sigma}_1$ we evaluate RHS of Eq. (6.37) acting on $\hat{\sigma}_1$ and use Eq. (6.38) to get

$$e^{\theta\hat{\mathbf{n}}\times}\hat{\sigma}_1 = \hat{\sigma}_1 + \theta\hat{\sigma}_2 - \frac{\theta^2}{2!}\hat{\sigma}_1 - \frac{\theta^3}{3!}\hat{\sigma}_2 + \frac{\theta^4}{4!}\hat{\sigma}_1 + \cdots$$

Collecting the coefficients of $\hat{\sigma}_1$ and $\hat{\sigma}_2$ we get

$$e^{\theta\hat{\mathbf{n}}\times}\hat{\sigma}_1 = \cos\theta\,\hat{\sigma}_1 + \sin\theta\,\hat{\sigma}_2 \tag{6.39}$$

Similarly,

$$e^{\theta \hat{\mathbf{n}} \times} \hat{\sigma}_2 = -\sin \theta \hat{\sigma}_1 + \cos \theta \hat{\sigma}_2 \tag{6.40}$$

To get the result of $e^{\theta \hat{\mathbf{n}} \times} \mathbf{x}_{\parallel}$ we resolve $\mathbf{x}_{\parallel}$ with respect to the basis $(\hat{\sigma}_1, \hat{\sigma}_2, \hat{\sigma}_3)$:

$$\mathbf{x}_{\parallel} = a \hat{\sigma}_1 + b \hat{\sigma}_2. \tag{6.41}$$

Operating on the RHS of Eq. (6.41) by $e^{\theta \hat{\mathbf{n}} \times}$ and using Eq. (6.39) and Eq. (6.40) we get

$$\mathbf{x}_{\parallel}' = e^{\theta \hat{\mathbf{n}} \times} \mathbf{x}_{\parallel} = (a \hat{\sigma}_1 + b \hat{\sigma}_2) \cos \theta + (a \hat{\sigma}_2 - b \hat{\sigma}_1) \sin \theta.$$

By Eqs (6.38) and (6.41) this reduces to

$$\mathbf{x}_{\parallel}' = e^{\theta \hat{\mathbf{n}} \times} \mathbf{x}_{\parallel} = \mathbf{x}_{\parallel} \cos \theta + (\hat{\mathbf{n}} \times \mathbf{x}_{\parallel}) \sin \theta,$$

or,

$$\mathbf{x}_{\parallel}' = \mathbf{x}_{\parallel} + (\cos \theta - 1) \mathbf{x}_{\parallel} + \sin \theta (\hat{\mathbf{n}} \times \mathbf{x}_{\parallel}). \tag{6.42}$$

Since $\hat{\mathbf{n}}$ is a unit vector perpendicular to $\mathbf{x}_{\parallel}$, we have

$$\mathbf{x}_{\parallel} = -\hat{\mathbf{n}} \times (\hat{\mathbf{n}} \times \mathbf{x}_{\parallel}).$$

Substituting this in the above expression for $\mathbf{x}_{\parallel}$ we get

$$\mathbf{x}_{\parallel}' = \mathbf{x}_{\parallel} + (1 - \cos \theta) \hat{\mathbf{n}} \times (\hat{\mathbf{n}} \times \mathbf{x}_{\parallel}) + \sin \theta (\hat{\mathbf{n}} \times \mathbf{x}_{\parallel}).$$

Since $\mathbf{x}_{\perp}$ and $\hat{\mathbf{n}}$ are parallel, we can add $(\hat{\mathbf{n}} \times \mathbf{x}_{\perp}) = \mathbf{0} = \hat{\mathbf{n}} \times (\hat{\mathbf{n}} \times \mathbf{x}_{\perp})$ on the RHS and $\mathbf{x}_{\perp} (= \mathbf{x}_{\perp}')$ on both sides of the above equation, finally giving the desired result,

$$\mathbf{x}' = \mathbf{x} + (1 - \cos \theta) \hat{\mathbf{n}} \times (\hat{\mathbf{n}} \times \mathbf{x}) + \sin \theta (\hat{\mathbf{n}} \times \mathbf{x}). \tag{6.43}$$

Equation (6.43) is equivalent to the operator identity, defining the rotation operator $\mathscr{R}$

$$\mathscr{R}(\mathbf{x}) \equiv e^{\theta \hat{\mathbf{n}} \times} \mathbf{x} \equiv [\mathbf{x} + (1 - \cos \theta) \hat{\mathbf{n}} \times (\hat{\mathbf{n}} \times \mathbf{x}) + \sin \theta (\hat{\mathbf{n}} \times \mathbf{x})]. \tag{6.44}$$

Exercise   Show that the rotation operator $\mathscr{R}$ can be equivalently expressed by

$$\mathscr{R}(\mathbf{x}) = \cos \theta \mathbf{x} + (1 - \cos \theta)(\hat{\mathbf{n}} \cdot \mathbf{x}) \hat{\mathbf{n}} + \sin \theta (\hat{\mathbf{n}} \times \mathbf{x}). \tag{6.45}$$

Hint   Use identity I.

This expression for the rotation operator was used by Josiah Willard Gibbs sometime in the first decade of 20th century.   □

Exercise   Show that the rotation operator as defined above is orthogonal.   □

Exercise   Resolving $\mathbf{x} = \mathbf{x}_{\parallel} + \mathbf{x}_{\perp}$ with $\mathbf{x}_{\parallel}$ parallel and $\mathbf{x}_{\perp}$ perpendicular to $\hat{\mathbf{n}}$, show that $\mathscr{R}(\mathbf{x}) = \cos\theta\mathbf{x}_{\perp} + \sin\theta(\hat{\mathbf{n}} \times \mathbf{x}_{\perp}) + \mathbf{x}_{\parallel}$.   □

6.3.1   Matrices representing rotations

To get the matrix elements of the rotation operator on the RHS of Eqs (6.43), (6.44) we choose an orthonormal basis $(\hat{\sigma}_1, \hat{\sigma}_2, \hat{\sigma}_3)$ (not necessarily the same as that in Fig. 6.8) and transform each of the vectors $\{\hat{\sigma}_k\}, k = 1, 2, 3$ by this operator. This will give us a new set of orthonormal vectors $\{\hat{\mathbf{e}}_k\}, k = 1, 2, 3$. The matrix elements of the operator are the coordinates of $\{\hat{\mathbf{e}}_k\}$ with respect to the basis $\{\hat{\sigma}_k\}$. We have,

$$\hat{\mathbf{e}}_k = \sum_{j=1}^{3} \hat{\sigma}_j(\hat{\sigma}_j \cdot \hat{\mathbf{e}}_k) = \sum_{j=1}^{3} \hat{\sigma}_j e_{jk} \tag{6.46}$$

with its matrix version

$$[\hat{\mathbf{e}}_k]^T = [\hat{\sigma}_j]^T [e_{jk}] \tag{6.47}$$

where $[\hat{\sigma}_j]^T$ and $[\hat{\mathbf{e}}_k]^T$ are the row (1×3) matrices with elements as the basis vectors $\{\hat{\sigma}_j\}$ and $\{\hat{\mathbf{e}}_k\}$ respectively. Equation (6.46) gives, $e_{jk} = \hat{\sigma}_j \cdot \hat{\mathbf{e}}_k$, or,

$$e_{jk} = \hat{\sigma}_j \cdot [\hat{\sigma}_k + (1 - \cos\theta)\,\hat{\mathbf{n}} \times (\hat{\mathbf{n}} \times \hat{\sigma}_k) + \sin\theta\,\hat{\mathbf{n}} \times \hat{\sigma}_k],$$

which reduces, via identity I to

$$e_{jk} = \delta_{jk} + \hat{\sigma}_j \cdot [(\hat{\mathbf{n}} \cdot \hat{\sigma}_k)\hat{\mathbf{n}} - \hat{\sigma}_k](1 - \cos\theta) + \hat{\sigma}_j \cdot (\hat{\mathbf{n}} \times \hat{\sigma}_k)\sin\theta.$$

Let $\theta_k = \hat{\mathbf{n}} \cdot \hat{\sigma}_k$ denote the direction cosines of $\hat{\mathbf{n}}$ with respect to the basis $\{\hat{\sigma}_k\}$. We can then write

$$e_{jk} = \delta_{jk} + [\theta_j\theta_k - \delta_{jk}](1 - \cos\theta) - \varepsilon_{jkm}\theta_m\sin\theta,$$

or,

$$e_{jk} = \delta_{jk}\cos\theta + \theta_j\theta_k(1 - \cos\theta) - \varepsilon_{jkm}\theta_m\sin\theta. \tag{6.48}$$

where $\hat{\mathbf{n}} = \sum_m \theta_m\hat{\sigma}_m$ and $\varepsilon_{jkm} = \hat{\sigma}_j \cdot (\hat{\sigma}_k \times \hat{\sigma}_m)$ are the Levi-Civita symbols.

Thus, if $\hat{\mathbf{n}} = \hat{\sigma}_3$ the matrix of rotation becomes

$$\begin{bmatrix} \cos\theta & -\sin\theta & 0 \\ \sin\theta & \cos\theta & 0 \\ 0 & 0 & 1 \end{bmatrix}. \tag{6.49}$$

Note that this matrix relates the rotated vector $\mathbf{x}'$ obtained by rotating the basis vectors $\{\hat{\sigma}_{1,2}\}$ in the plane normal to $\hat{\mathbf{n}} = \hat{\sigma}_3$ that is, by operating the corresponding rotation operator on $\mathbf{x} = \sum_k x_k \hat{\sigma}_k$, while its transpose relates the coordinates of the same vector with respect to $\{\hat{\sigma}_k\}$ and $\{\hat{\mathbf{e}}_k\}$ respectively.

Exercise   Show that the components of $\mathbf{x}$ given by column vectors $[x_j']$ and $[x_j]$ with respect to the orthonormal bases $\{\hat{\mathbf{e}}_k\}$ and $\{\hat{\sigma}_k\}$ respectively are related by

$$[x_k'] = [e_{jk}]^T [x_j]$$

where $[e_{jk}]$ is the matrix defined by the rotation about $\hat{\mathbf{n}} = \hat{\sigma}_3$.

Solution   Note that $\mathbf{x} = x_1' \hat{\mathbf{e}}_1 + x_2' \hat{\mathbf{e}}_2 + x_3' \hat{\mathbf{e}}_3 = x_1' \mathcal{R} \hat{\sigma}_1 + x_2' \mathcal{R} \hat{\sigma}_2 + x_3' \mathcal{R} \hat{\sigma}_3$. This gives, using Eq. (6.46),

$$\mathbf{x} = \sum_j \left[\sum_k x_k' e_{jk} \right] \hat{\sigma}_j$$

or,

$$x_j = \sum_k x_k' e_{jk}$$

or,

$$[x_k'] = [e_{jk}]^T [x_j] \tag{6.50}$$

where we have used $[e_{jk}]^{-1} = [e_{jk}]^T$ since $[e_{jk}]$ is orthogonal.   □

We make a few observations.

It is straightforward to show (Exercise) that the rotation operator $\mathcal{R}(\hat{\mathbf{n}}, \theta)$ defined in Eqs (6.43), (6.44) is an orthogonal operator, that is,

$$\mathcal{R}(\hat{\mathbf{n}}, \theta)\mathbf{x} \cdot \mathcal{R}(\hat{\mathbf{n}}, \theta)\mathbf{y} = \mathbf{x} \cdot \mathbf{y}$$

for all $\mathbf{x}, \mathbf{y} \in \mathscr{E}_3$. This also proves that the matrix $[e_{jk}]$ representing $\mathcal{R}(\hat{\mathbf{n}}, \theta)$ is orthogonal, because we have already proved that a matrix representing an orthogonal operator is orthogonal. If we denote by S the orthogonal matrix of the rotation operator defined by Eq. (6.48), then the orthogonality condition means,

$$S^T S = I = S S^T \text{ or } S^T = S^{-1}, \tag{6.51}$$

where I is the unit matrix of size 3×3.

The determinant of the orthogonal matrix representing a rotation is $+1$. First, it is straightforward to show that the determinant of the rotation operator $\mathcal{R}(\hat{\mathbf{n}}, \theta)$ defined in Eqs (6.43), (6.44) is $+1$, that is,

$$\mathcal{R}(\hat{\mathbf{n}}, \theta)\hat{\sigma}_1 \cdot (\mathcal{R}(\hat{\mathbf{n}}, \theta)\hat{\sigma}_2 \times \mathcal{R}(\hat{\mathbf{n}}, \theta)\hat{\sigma}_3) = 1$$

by choosing $\hat{\mathbf{n}} = \hat{\sigma}_1$ as we did for the reflection operator. This means that the matrix $[e_{kj}]$ in Eq. (6.48) representing the rotation operator has determinant $+1$, because, we have proved in section 4.4 that the determinant of the matrix representing a linear operator is identical with the determinant of the operator. There is a one to one correspondence between the set of rotations and the set of 3×3 orthogonal matrices with determinant $+1$. To see this, note that the equality of matrices $[\mathcal{R}_1] = [\mathcal{R}_2]$ representing rotations $\mathcal{R}_1$ and $\mathcal{R}_2$ implies equality of rotations $\mathcal{R}_1 = \mathcal{R}_2$ because the equality of matrices would mean, via Eq. (6.46), that the action of $\mathcal{R}_1$ and $\mathcal{R}_2$ on an orthonormal basis is identical and by linearity of the operators this implies $\mathcal{R}_1 \mathbf{x} = \mathcal{R}_2 \mathbf{x}$ for all $\mathbf{x} \in \mathcal{E}_3$. This establishes the required one to one correspondence. In section 4.5 we have already seen that the matrix representing a product of operators is the product of the matrices representing the individual operators. This means, coupled with their one to one correspondence, that the set of 3×3 orthogonal matrices with determinant $+1$ is isomorphic with the set of rotations.

Note that the operator in Eqs (6.43), (6.44), which gives the *counterclockwise* rotation of the vector $\mathbf{x}$ by an angle θ also gives the *clockwise* rotation of $\mathbf{x}$ through the angle $2\pi - \theta$ (see Fig. 6.9), because the operator remains the same if we replace in its expression θ by $-(2\pi - \theta)$. This is in conformity with whatever we have said while dealing with rotation as the means of changing direction (section 1.2). Thus, these two rotations give rise to the same matrix representative apparently destroying the one to one correspondence between the rotations and the set of 3×3 orthogonal matrices with determinant $+1$. However, without losing generality we can stick only to the counterclockwise rotations alone, which establishes the required one to one correspondence.

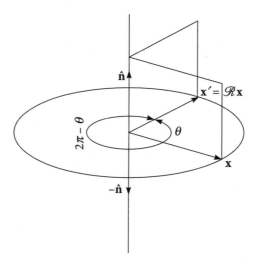

Fig. 6.9   Equivalent rotations: One counterclockwise and the other clockwise

Exercise The sum of the diagonal matrix elements f_{kk} of a linear transformation f is called the trace of f and denoted $Tr\ f$. Show that the trace of rotation $\mathscr{R}(\hat{\mathbf{n}}, \theta)$ is given by

$$Tr\ \mathscr{R} = \sum_k \hat{\sigma}_k \cdot (\mathscr{R}\hat{\sigma}_k) = 1 + 2\cos\theta \tag{6.52}$$

Hint This result follows trivially by explicitly summing the diagonal matrix elements of $\mathscr{R}(\hat{\mathbf{n}}, \theta)$ remembering that $\sum_j \theta_j^2 = 1$. □

Note that the trace is independent of the basis used to set up the matrix of $\mathscr{R}$. In fact this result is quite general.

Exercise Show that the trace of a linear operator f is independent of the basis used to compute it. □

We define the composition of two rotations (in the same way as the composition of two operators) as their successive application to a vector and denote it by a ∘ separating two rotations. We have already seen that the set of rotations on $\mathscr{E}_3$ and that of 3×3 orthogonal matrices with determinant $+1$ are in one to one correspondence. Taking, the composition of rotations and the matrix multiplication as the respective binary operations on these sets, we see that this one to one correspondence is actually an isomorphism. This is because $\mathbf{x}'' = \mathscr{R}_2\mathbf{x}' = \mathscr{R}_2 \circ \mathscr{R}_1\mathbf{x}$ corresponds to the following equation involving the matrix representatives and the column matrices for the vectors $[\mathbf{x}''] = [\mathscr{R}_2][\mathbf{x}'] = [\mathscr{R}_2][\mathscr{R}_1][\mathbf{x}]$. It is easy to see that the product of two orthogonal matrices with determinant $+1$ is an orthogonal matrix with determinant $+1$ (Exercise). This product matrix must correspond to a single rotation about some axis through some angle, because of the one to one correspondence between these two sets. Thus, the matrix representing the result of the composition of rotations is the product of the matrices representing the individual rotations. This establishes the required isomorphism. As a byproduct we have found that the set of rotations is closed under their composition. Also, it is easy to see that if $\mathscr{R}(\hat{\mathbf{n}}_1, \theta_1)\mathbf{x} = \mathbf{x}'$ and $\mathscr{R}(\hat{\mathbf{n}}_2, \theta_2)\mathbf{x}' = \mathbf{x}''$ then the single rotation corresponding to their composition $\mathscr{R}(\hat{\mathbf{n}}, \theta)$ is the one about the unit vector $\hat{\mathbf{n}}$ normal to the plane containing the vectors $\mathbf{x}$ and $\mathbf{x}''$ and through the angle given by

$$\cos\theta = \frac{\mathbf{x} \cdot \mathbf{x}''}{|\mathbf{x}||\mathbf{x}''|}.$$

The fact that two finite rotations say $\mathscr{R}(\hat{\mathbf{n}}_1, \theta_1)$ and $\mathscr{R}(\hat{\mathbf{n}}_2, \theta_2)$ do not commute in general, that is,

$$\mathscr{R}(\hat{\mathbf{n}}_2, \theta_2) \circ \mathscr{R}(\hat{\mathbf{n}}_1, \theta_1)\mathbf{x} \neq \mathscr{R}(\hat{\mathbf{n}}_1, \theta_1) \circ \mathscr{R}(\hat{\mathbf{n}}_2, \theta_2)\mathbf{x} \tag{6.53}$$

is amply clear from Fig. 6.10. To see this analytically, we make use of the isomorphism between the set of rotations (with $0 \le \theta < 2\pi$) and the set of 3×3 orthogonal matrices with determinant $+1$ representing them. Since the multiplication of matrices is not commutative, the matrices representing the LHS and the RHS of Eq. (6.53) are, in general, different, corresponding to different rotations.

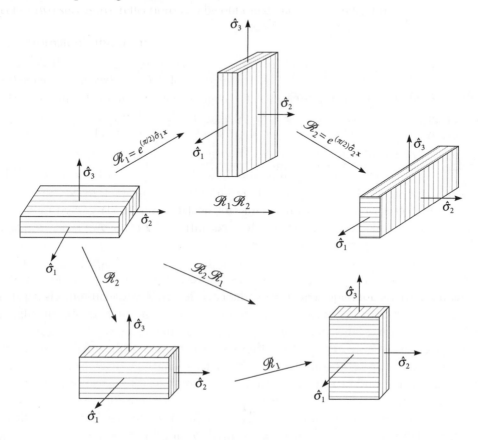

Fig. 6.10   Composition of rotations. Rotations do not commute.

Exercise   Show that two rotations about the same axis commute.

Hint   Just visualize it! Note that the matrices for both the rotations have the form given by the matrix representing a rotation about $\hat{\sigma}_z$, if we take $\hat{\sigma}_z$ along the axis of rotation. Show explicitly that these matrices commute.   □

6.4   Active and Passive Transformations: Symmetries

We know that a rotation operator $\mathscr{R}(\hat{\mathbf{n}}, \theta)$ connects a vector $\mathbf{x}$ with the vector $\mathbf{x}'$ obtained by counterclockwise rotating $\mathbf{x}$ by angle θ about an axis implied by a unit vector $\hat{\mathbf{n}}$. The transformation $\mathbf{x} \mapsto \mathbf{x}'$ which involves the actual rotation of a vector $\mathbf{x}$ giving a new vector $\mathbf{x}'$ is called an active transformation. Physically, the active transformation involves the actual change in the state of the system, like the rotation of an object or the change in the vector giving a vector quantity due to some external agency like magnetic field. Alternatively, the rotation operator can connect the coordinates of a vector with respect to a coordinate system with the coordinates of the same vector with respect to a new coordinate system obtained by rotating the initial one about the same unit vector n̂ by the same angle. This transformation, which does not involve an actual rotation of the vector (so that there is no change in the state of the physical system), is called a passive transformation. Whenever the successive application of the active and the passive transformations amounts to the application of the identity transformation, we say that the corresponding rotation (about the given axis through the given angle) is a symmetry or a symmetry element for the physical system.

For example, the figure at the tip of vector **F** in Fig. 6.11(a), is actively rotated (about the axis perpendicular to the xy plane and passing through the origin) with no change of shape into a new position with position vector **F'**. The components of the rotated vector are related to those of the initial vector by (see Eq. (6.49)),

$$\begin{bmatrix} F'_x \\ F'_y \end{bmatrix} = \begin{bmatrix} \cos\theta & -\sin\theta \\ \sin\theta & \cos\theta \end{bmatrix} \begin{bmatrix} F_x \\ F_y \end{bmatrix}.$$

In Fig. 6.11(b) the figure (and the vector **F**) is not rotated however, the coordinate axes are, by the same angle and in the same sense. This is the passive transformation and the coordinates of the vector along the new axes are (see Eq. (6.50)),

$$\begin{bmatrix} F_{x'} \\ F_{y'} \end{bmatrix} = \begin{bmatrix} \cos\theta & \sin\theta \\ -\sin\theta & \cos\theta \end{bmatrix} \begin{bmatrix} F_x \\ F_y \end{bmatrix}.$$

Note that the transformation matrices are orthogonal and are transpose and hence inverses of each other. We have already proved this fact generally in Eq. (6.50). Therefore, if both transformations are successively performed, as in Fig. 6.11(c), we get

$$F'_{x'} = F_x$$

$$F'_{y'} = F_y \tag{6.54}$$

Thus, the numerical values of the new components are the same as those of the old components. Therefore, a mere knowledge of these values does not indicate whether the transformation was performed. This indistinguishably is due to a physical property of plane surfaces: It is possible to rigidly rotate any plane figure. On the other hand, an irregular surface does not allow any rigid motion. It still allows the passive coordinate transformations which amount to mere relabeling of its points. However, there are no corresponding active transformations, which leave the displaced body unaltered. For example, suppose you are in a ship on the open sea and mark your position with respect to some reference ship at a distance. If your ship and the reference ship are both rotated about the same axis by the same angle, your position relative to the reference ship is unaltered. This invariance is sometimes expressed by saying that the hallmark of a symmetry is the impossibility of acquiring some physical knowledge.

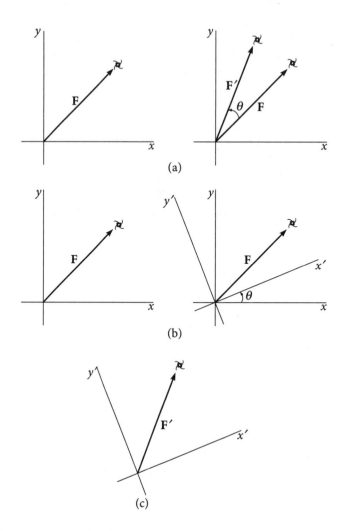

Fig. 6.11   Active and passive transformations

In the above analysis, we have taken the basis vector $\hat{\sigma}_3$ (or the z axis) along the axis of rotation. This is not necessary. Even if we take an arbitrary orthonormal basis and the corresponding coordinate system, the matrices for the active and passive transformations are transposes and inverses of each other, so that applying them in succession is the same as applying the identity transformation. Thus, whether a given rotation is a symmetry element does not depend on the orthonormal basis chosen to implement the active and passive transformations.

Exercise   If a right hand glove is turned inside out, it becomes a left hand glove. This is an example of an active transformation (assume that inside and outside textures and colors are identical). What is the corresponding passive transformation?   □

Consistent with our Newtonian view of space as a continuum of points making up an inert vacuum is the assumption that the whole space is like an ideal rigid body, that is, the distance between every pair of points in space remains constant despite all events taking place in it. Thus, when a single vector is rotated about any axis by any angle, the whole space is rotated along with the vector. The subsequent passive transformation relabels all the points in space to reproduce the initial situation. Therefore, for a single vector in space (which could be the position vector of a single particle in space), every possible rotation or reflection (which is equivalent to two rotations by Hamilton's theorem), is a symmetry transformation. If we consider a system of non-interacting particles we can apply the symmetry transformations to each particle separately, independent of other particles, so that the same conclusion applies to such a system. Thus, the system of non-interacting particles such as an ideal gas possesses highest symmetry. In contrast, the symmetry elements of a figure like an equilateral triangle or a square, or a cube or a tetrahedron act only on the points making up the figure and not on the rest of space. However, after the succession of the active and the passive transformations, the whole space, including the figure, must reproduce the initial situation. This is possible, only when the active transformation reproduces the initial configuration of the figure. Only a finite set of rotations and reflections meets this requirement. Thus, the symmetry elements of a solid which leave its unit cell invariant, form a finite set. Thus, when a gas or a liquid condenses to make a solid, the symmetry of the system is drastically reduced. This phenomenon is called 'symmetry breaking'. Generally, such a transition from liquid to solid phase, called a phase transition, occurs at a particular temperature at which the symmetry breaks spontaneously. Spontaneous symmetry breaking is responsible for the fact that the quantities like volume, magnetization, mole numbers of chemical species etc are macroscopically observable, that is, these variables are time independent on the atomic scale of time and spatially homogeneous on the atomic scale of distance. On the other hand, symmetries themselves are of far reaching significance as they give rise to all the conserved quantities like energy, angular momentum, linear momentum etc, which make the understanding of the dynamics of the system possible. For example, the dynamics of a particle driven by a central force is completely known because of the conservation of energy and angular momentum of such a particle. Further, Kepler's laws of planetary motion can be easily obtained using an additional conserved quantity, namely the Runge–Lenz vector. The underlying symmetries and symmetry breaking is crucial for the understanding of our physical world.

Exercise   Find all the symmetry elements of a equilateral triangle and a square (see Figs 7.1 and 7.2).   □

We now show that if the rotations $\mathcal{R}_1(\hat{\mathbf{n}}_1, \theta_1)$ and $\mathcal{R}_2(\hat{\mathbf{n}}_2, \theta_2)$ are symmetry elements for a system, then so is their composition. Let $\mathcal{R}_1$ rotate a vector $\mathbf{F}$ to $\mathbf{F}'$ and $\mathcal{R}_2$ rotate a vector $\mathbf{F}'$ to $\mathbf{F}''$. The composite rotation $\mathcal{R}_{12}(\hat{\mathbf{n}}, \theta) = \mathcal{R}_2(\hat{\mathbf{n}}_2, \theta_2) \circ \mathcal{R}_1(\hat{\mathbf{n}}_1, \theta_1)$ must rotate $\mathbf{F}$ to $\mathbf{F}''$. The matrix for the corresponding active transformation is the product $[\mathcal{R}_2][\mathcal{R}_1]$ and that for the passive transformation is the inverse of this product. Thus, applying the composite active and passive transformation gives us the identity transformation. This proves the result.

6.5   Euler Angles

We know that a rotation is completely specified by a unit vector $\hat{\mathbf{n}}$ giving the axis of rotation and the angle of rotation χ. Thus, the set of all possible rotations can be spanned by varying the direction ($\hat{\mathbf{n}}$) in space and the angle of rotation χ over the range $0 \leq \chi < 2\pi$. In other words, the rotation operator is parameterized by the unit vector $\hat{\mathbf{n}}$ and the angle of rotation. We have seen before (see subsection 1.7.1) that two independent parameters are required to specify a direction, namely the polar and the azimuthal angles. Thus, a rotation is parametrized by three independent angles, namely, the angle of rotation χ and the polar and azimuthal angles (θ, ϕ) which specify the direction about which the (counterclockwise) rotation takes place. A very useful way to specify a rotation is by specifying the orthonormal basis $\{\hat{\mathbf{e}}_k\}$ $k = 1, 2, 3$ obtained by rotating the standard basis $\{\hat{\sigma}_k\}$ $k = 1, 2, 3$ about a given direction $\hat{\mathbf{n}}$ by the given angle χ. Thus, given the bases $\{\hat{\mathbf{e}}_k\}$ $k = 1, 2, 3$ and $\{\hat{\sigma}_k\}$ $k = 1, 2, 3$ corresponding to the given rotation, we need to find three independent rotations through three angles say ϕ, θ and ψ such that, when performed successively, will rotate $\{\hat{\sigma}_k\}$ $k = 1, 2, 3$ to $\{\hat{\mathbf{e}}_k\}$ $k = 1, 2, 3$. The angles ϕ, θ, ψ are called Euler angles. The required three rotations can simply be read out from Fig. 6.12. First, we rotate the $\hat{\sigma}_1$ about $\hat{\sigma}_3$ axis by an angle ϕ so as to make it perpendicular to the plane defined by $\hat{\sigma}_3$ and $\hat{\mathbf{e}}_3$. The corresponding line is called the line of nodes. We denote the corresponding rotated vector by $\hat{\mathbf{e}}_N$. Next, we rotate $\hat{\sigma}_3$ about the line of nodes by angle θ to make it coincide with $\hat{\mathbf{e}}_3$. Finally, we rotate the line of nodes about $\hat{\mathbf{e}}_3$ by an angle ψ to make it coincide with $\hat{\mathbf{e}}_1$. Thus, the successive Euler rotations rotate the orthonormal frame $\{\hat{\sigma}_k\}$ $k = 1, 2, 3$ to $\{\hat{\mathbf{e}}_k\}$ $k = 1, 2, 3$ which was obtained by rotating $\{\hat{\sigma}_k\}$ $k = 1, 2, 3$ about the direction $\hat{\mathbf{n}}$ by an angle χ.

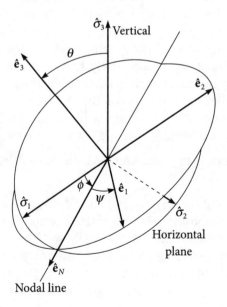

Fig. 6.12   Euler angles

Thus, to every triple of Euler angles ϕ, θ, ψ the above construction associates a rotation of 3-D space taking frame $\{\hat{\sigma}_k\}$ $k = 1, 2, 3$ into the frame $\{\hat{\mathbf{e}}_k\}$ $k = 1, 2, 3$. The ranges of the Euler angles are

$$0 < \phi < 2\pi, \ \ 0 < \psi < 2\pi, \ \ 0 < \theta < \pi.$$

Thus, by continuously varying the Euler angles, we can generate all possible rotations. Thus, the set of all possible rotations about a point is parameterized by three Euler angles varying in their specified ranges.

The net rotation is given by the composition of Euler rotations in the order stated above. We have,

$$\mathscr{R}(\hat{\mathbf{n}}, \chi) = e^{\psi \hat{\mathbf{e}}_3 \times} e^{\theta \hat{\mathbf{e}}_N \times} e^{\phi \hat{\sigma}_3 \times} \tag{6.55}$$

Exercise   Show that the line of nodes has the direction

$$\hat{\mathbf{e}}_N = e^{\theta \hat{\mathbf{e}}_N \times} \hat{\sigma}_1 = \frac{\hat{\sigma}_3 \times \hat{\mathbf{e}}_3}{|\hat{\sigma}_3 \times \hat{\mathbf{e}}_3|}. \qquad \square$$

Let us now set up the matrix representing $\mathscr{R}(\hat{\mathbf{n}}, \chi)$ in terms of its Euler angles. To do this, we have to expand the vectors $\{\hat{\mathbf{e}}_k\}$ $k = 1, 2, 3$ in terms of the basis $\{\hat{\sigma}_k\}$ $k = 1, 2, 3$. To get $\hat{\mathbf{e}}_3$ we have to first evaluate $e^{\phi \hat{\sigma}_3 \times} \hat{\sigma}_1$ and then evaluate $e^{\phi \hat{\mathbf{n}} \times} \hat{\sigma}_3$ where $\hat{\mathbf{n}} = e^{\phi \hat{\sigma}_3 \times} \hat{\sigma}_1$ using Eq. (6.43) or Eq. (6.45). Carrying out this calculation we get,

$$\hat{\mathbf{e}}_3 = \sin \theta \sin \phi \hat{\sigma}_1 - \sin \theta \cos \phi \hat{\sigma}_2 + \cos \theta \hat{\sigma}_3.$$

Evaluating $\hat{\mathbf{e}}_1$ and $\hat{\mathbf{e}}_2$ in the same way, we get, for the matrix representing $\mathscr{R}(\hat{\mathbf{n}}, \chi)$ in terms of its Euler angles,

$$\begin{bmatrix} \cos \psi \cos \phi - \sin \psi \sin \phi \cos \theta & -\sin \psi \cos \phi - \cos \psi \sin \phi \cos \theta & \sin \theta \sin \phi \\ \cos \psi \sin \phi + \sin \psi \cos \phi \cos \theta & -\sin \psi \sin \phi + \cos \psi \cos \phi \cos \theta & -\sin \theta \cos \phi \\ \sin \theta \sin \psi & \sin \theta \cos \psi & \cos \theta \end{bmatrix}.$$

If we multiply the row vector $[\hat{\sigma}_1 \hat{\sigma}_2 \hat{\sigma}_3]$ on the right by this matrix, then we get the row vector $[\hat{\mathbf{e}}_1 \hat{\mathbf{e}}_2 \hat{\mathbf{e}}_3]$. The Euler rotations corresponding to arbitrary rotation, defined above, are marred by the fact that their axes of rotation are not fixed directions in space. We can define Euler rotations using a construction by which every rotation $\mathscr{R}(\hat{\mathbf{n}}, \chi)$ is reduced to a composition of rotations about fixed axes of a standard basis. In this construction, an arbitrary rotation is decomposed into Euler rotations as

$$\mathscr{R} = \mathscr{R}(\hat{\mathbf{n}}, \chi) = e^{\phi \hat{\sigma}_3 \times} e^{\theta \hat{\sigma}_1 \times} e^{\psi \hat{\sigma}_3 \times} = \mathscr{R}_\phi \mathscr{R}_\theta \mathscr{R}_\psi \text{say} \tag{6.56}$$

Thus, the first rotation is about $\hat{\sigma}_3$ by an angle ψ the second rotation is about $\hat{\sigma}_1$ by an angle θ and the third one is about $\hat{\sigma}_3$ by an angle ϕ. Note that $\hat{\mathbf{e}}_k = \mathscr{R} \hat{\sigma}_k = \mathscr{R}_\phi \mathscr{R}_\theta \mathscr{R}_\psi \hat{\sigma}_k$ so that it is quite easy to calculate the matrix elements of a rotation in terms of Euler angles.

Consider, for example, the rotation of $\hat{\sigma}_3$. $\mathscr{R}_\psi$ is a rotation about $\hat{\sigma}_3$ and hence will leave $\hat{\sigma}_3$ invariant. Next, we have, using Eq. (6.43) or Eq. (6.45),

$$e^{\theta \hat{\sigma}_1 \times} \hat{\sigma}_3 = \hat{\sigma}_3 \cos\theta - \hat{\sigma}_2 \sin\theta.$$

Therefore,

$$
\begin{aligned}
\hat{\mathbf{e}}_3 &= e^{\phi \hat{\sigma}_3 \times} (\hat{\sigma}_3 \cos\theta - \hat{\sigma}_2 \sin\theta) \\
&= \hat{\sigma}_3 \cos\theta - e^{\phi \hat{\sigma}_3 \times} \hat{\sigma}_2 \sin\theta \\
&= \hat{\sigma}_3 \cos\theta - (\hat{\sigma}_2 \cos\phi - \hat{\sigma}_1 \sin\phi) \sin\theta.
\end{aligned}
\tag{6.57}
$$

From this, the matrix elements $e_{j3} = \hat{\sigma}_j \cdot \hat{\mathbf{e}}_3$ can be read off directly. We get exactly the same matrix representing $\mathscr{R}$ as before. Figure 6.13 shows the Euler rotations of a standard basis one after the other, in the given order.

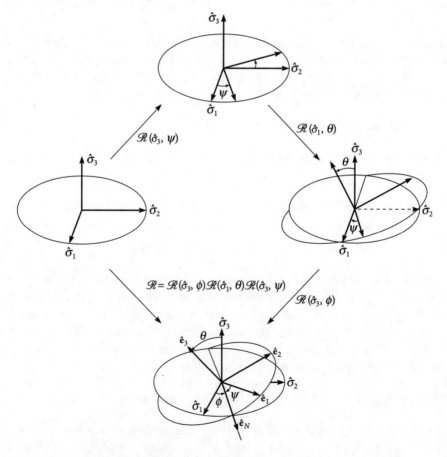

Fig. 6.13   Rotations corresponding to Euler angles

Note that the order of Euler rotations in Eq. (6.55) is opposite to that in Eq. (6.56). However, both the expressions describe the same rotation $\mathscr{R}(\hat{\mathbf{n}}, \chi)$. We see that the same set of Euler angles can be used to give two different parameterizations of the same rotation with two different sequences of Euler rotations. The first parameterization is preferred by astronomers because $\hat{\sigma}_3$ and $\hat{\mathbf{e}}_3$ can be associated with easily measured directions. On the other hand Eq. (6.56) has the advantage of fixed rotation axes for Euler rotations even when the Euler angles change with time ($\mathscr{R}(\hat{\mathbf{n}}, \chi)$ depends on time).

To show the equivalence of Eq. (6.55) with Eq. (6.56) we note that $e^{\theta \hat{\mathbf{e}}_N \times} = e^{\phi \hat{\sigma}_3 \times} e^{\theta \hat{\sigma}_1 \times} e^{-\phi \hat{\sigma}_3 \times}$ and $e^{\psi \hat{\mathbf{e}}_3 \times} = e^{\phi \hat{\sigma}_3 \times} e^{\theta \hat{\sigma}_1 \times} e^{\psi \hat{\sigma}_3 \times} e^{-\theta \hat{\sigma}_1 \times} e^{-\phi \hat{\sigma}_3 \times}$ Substituting in Eq. (6.55) and noting that the successive rotations by equal and opposite angles about the same axis result in identity transformation, we get Eq. (6.56).

Exercise   In addition to Euler rotations engineers use three independent rotations called *roll, pitch* and *yaw*, as shown in Fig. 6.14, to implement arbitrary rotation of the body via

$$\hat{\mathbf{e}}_k = (\text{yaw})(\text{pitch})(\text{roll})\hat{\sigma}_k = e^{\phi \hat{\sigma}_1 \times} e^{\theta \hat{\sigma}_2 \times} e^{\psi \hat{\sigma}_3 \times} \hat{\sigma}_k,$$

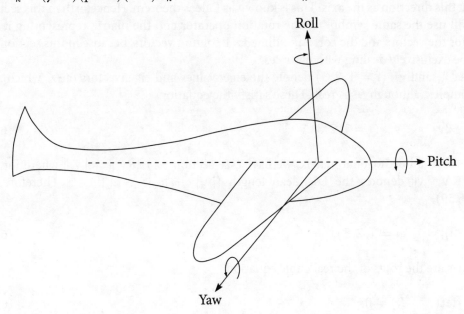

Fig. 6.14   Roll, pitch and yaw

where ψ, θ, ϕ are the angles of rotation corresponding to roll, pitch and yaw respectively. Show that the transformed basis is given by

$$\hat{\mathbf{e}}_1 = \cos\psi \cos\theta \, \hat{\sigma}_1 + (\cos\psi \sin\theta \sin\phi + \sin\psi \cos\phi)\hat{\sigma}_2$$

$$+ (\sin\psi \sin\phi - \cos\psi \sin\theta \cos\phi)\hat{\sigma}_3$$

$$\hat{\mathbf{e}}_2 = -\sin\psi\cos\theta\hat{\sigma}_1 + (\cos\psi\cos\phi - \sin\psi\sin\theta\sin\phi)\hat{\sigma}_2$$

$$+ (\cos\psi\sin\phi + \sin\psi\sin\theta\cos\phi)\hat{\sigma}_3$$

$$\hat{\mathbf{e}}_3 = \sin\theta\hat{\sigma}_1 - \cos\theta\sin\phi\hat{\sigma}_2 + \cos\theta\cos\phi\hat{\sigma}_3 \qquad (6.58)$$

Write down the matrix for the corresponding rotation. ☐

6.6 Euler's Theorem

In section 6.3, we analyzed a rotation about a given axis and found the orthogonal matrix of the corresponding rotation operator with respect to an arbitrary orthonormal basis. We now do the reverse: Given a 3×3 orthogonal real matrix $[\mathscr{R}]$ with determinant $+1$, we show that the transformation $[\mathbf{x}] \mapsto [\mathscr{R}][\mathbf{x}]$; $\mathbf{x} \in \mathscr{E}_3$ can be realized by first choosing a fixed direction in space through the origin and then rotating $\mathbf{x}$ through a suitable angle about this direction as the axis. This is known as Euler's theorem. Henceforth in this section, we will use the same symbol for the rotation operator and the matrix representing it and also for the vectors and the corresponding 3×1 column vectors, because in this section, we will be exclusively dealing with matrices.

Let λ_i and $\mathbf{v}_i$, $(i = 1, 2, 3)$ denote the eigenvalues and eigenvectors of $\mathscr{R}$ which may be complex, although $\mathscr{R}$ is real. These satisfy the equations

$$\mathscr{R}\mathbf{v}_i = \lambda_i\mathbf{v}_i \quad (i = 1, 2, 3). \qquad (6.59)$$

Since $\mathscr{R}$ is an orthogonal matrix, we have (see section 6.1) $\|R\mathbf{v}_i\| = \|\mathbf{v}_i\|$ where for any vector $\mathbf{v}$, $\|\mathbf{v}\|$ denotes the Euclidean length $(|v_x|^2 + |v_y|^2 + |v_z|^2)^{1/2}$. Therefore, by Eq. (6.59),

$$|\lambda_i| = 1 \quad (i = 1, 2, 3). \qquad (6.60)$$

The λ_is are the roots of the real cubic equation

$$\det(\lambda I - R) = 0. \qquad (6.61)$$

The product of the roots is

$$\lambda_1\lambda_2\lambda_3 = \det\mathscr{R} = 1. \qquad (6.62)$$

At least one of the roots is real. To see this note that for large enough $|\lambda|$, the cubic term dominates, so that the sign of the cubic polynomial in Eq. (6.61) is the same as that of λ. This means that the graph of the cubic polynomial (which is a continuous function) has to cut the λ axis at least once. If the other two eigenvalues (say λ_2, λ_3) are complex, then $\lambda_3 = \lambda_2^*$ (superfix $*$ denotes complex conjugation) and by Eq. (6.60) $\lambda_2\lambda_3 = 1$, hence by

Eq. (6.62) $\lambda_1 = 1$. If all the three roots are real, they can be $(1,1,1)$ or $(1,-1,-1)$. In any case there is always one root, say λ_1, equal to $+1$, hence

$$\mathscr{R}\mathbf{v}_1 = \mathbf{v}_1 \tag{6.63}$$

which shows that the straight line through the origin in the direction of $\mathbf{v}_1$, is invariant under the transformation $\mathbf{x} \mapsto \mathscr{R}\mathbf{x}$. Obviously, this is the axis of rotation.

Let $\lambda_1 = 1$, $\lambda_2 = e^{i\theta}$, $\lambda_3 = e^{-i\theta}$ and let $\mathbf{v}_1, \mathbf{v}_2, \mathbf{v}_3$ form an orthonormal set. The eigenvectors of a orthogonal matrix can always be orthonormalized. Call

$$\mathbf{u}_1 = \mathbf{v}_1$$

$$\mathbf{u}_2 = \frac{1}{\sqrt{2}}(\mathbf{v}_2 + \mathbf{v}_3)$$

$$\mathbf{u}_3 = \frac{i}{\sqrt{2}}(\mathbf{v}_2 - \mathbf{v}_3). \tag{6.64}$$

$\mathbf{u}_i$s form a orthonormal set (check it!) and can be taken to be real, because $\mathbf{v}_2$ and $\mathbf{v}_3$ can be taken to be complex conjugates.[2] From Eq. (6.64) and the values of λ_i $i = 1, 2, 3$ we get,

$$\mathscr{R}\mathbf{u}_1 = \mathbf{u}_1$$

$$\mathscr{R}\mathbf{u}_2 = \cos\theta\,\mathbf{u}_2 + \sin\theta\,\mathbf{u}_3$$

$$\mathscr{R}\mathbf{u}_3 = -\sin\theta\,\mathbf{u}_2 + \cos\theta\,\mathbf{u}_3. \tag{6.65}$$

We see that the transformation $\mathscr{R}$ is a rotation in the plane perpendicular to $\mathbf{u}_1$.

When the matrix $\mathscr{R}$ is given, the corresponding angle and axis of rotation can be obtained as follows. Since the sum of the eigenvalues of a matrix equals its trace, the angle θ is given by

$$1 + e^{i\theta} + e^{-i\theta} = \mathscr{R}_{11} + \mathscr{R}_{22} + \mathscr{R}_{33},$$

or,

$$\cos\theta = \frac{1}{2}\left(\mathscr{R}_{11} + \mathscr{R}_{22} + \mathscr{R}_{33} - 1\right).$$

Let the axis of rotation be in the direction of the eigenvector $\mathbf{v}$, that corresponds to the eigenvalue $\lambda = 1$, so that $\mathscr{R}\mathbf{v} = \mathbf{v}$. Since $\mathscr{R}$ is orthogonal, $\mathscr{R}^T\mathscr{R} = I$, hence $\mathbf{v} = \mathscr{R}^T\mathbf{v}$.

---

[2]Just take the complex conjugate of $\mathscr{R}\mathbf{v}_2 = \lambda_2\mathbf{v}_2$ and compare with $\mathscr{R}\mathbf{v}_3 = \lambda_3\mathbf{v}_3$ noting that $\lambda_3 = \lambda_2^*$.

Therefore, $(\mathscr{R} - \mathscr{R}^T)\mathbf{v} = \mathbf{0}$ which is a homogeneous system of simultaneous linear equations in the components v_1, v_2, v_3 of $\mathbf{v}$. Thus, the components of $\mathbf{v}$ are in the ratio

$$v_1 : v_2 : v_3 = (\mathscr{R}_{23} - \mathscr{R}_{32}) : (\mathscr{R}_{31} - \mathscr{R}_{13}) : (\mathscr{R}_{12} - \mathscr{R}_{21}). \qquad (6.66)$$

Exercise   Establish Eq. (6.66). □

In many cases the matrix of the rotation operator with respect to some basis is what is known, so we have to carry out the procedure in this section in order to get the specific rotation represented by the matrix. Such a specification is required in order to get the kinematical and dynamical description of a rotating physical system.

Transformation Groups

7.1 Definition and Examples

A state of a physical system at a time t is given by specifying the values of different vector (and scalar) physical quantities pertaining to the system at that time. The values of the vector physical quantities form a part of $\mathscr{E}_3$. Thus, the action of an operator or transformation on $\mathscr{E}_3$ will, in general, change the state of the system. Thus, all possible changes in the state correspond to a collection of transformations on $\mathscr{E}_3$. Such a set of transformations may form an extremely important algebraic structure called a *group*. The evolution of a system in time, due to its interaction with other systems, is controlled by its Lagrangian (or Hamiltonian). The symmetry element of the system, which leaves its Lagrangian (or Hamiltonian) invariant, gives rise to a conservation law, that is, it gives rise to an expression involving the position and momentum vectors of the system, whose value remains the same at all times, throughout the motion of the system. This result is called Noether's theorem. The set of all such symmetry elements form a group. This fact turns out to be of great advantage in the theoretical development of mechanics, quantum mechanics and of physics in general. In fact whole of mechanics can be developed from the group theoretical point of view, as in the book by N. Mukunda and E. C. G. Sudarshan [22]. Here our intention is to give elementary group theory with an emphasis on the rotation group and the group of isometries over $\mathscr{E}_3$ (also called Euclidean group) with a view to understand rigid body motion, which is a combination of the rotational and translational motion.

A group G is any set of elements $\{a, b, c, \ldots, x, y, z, \ldots\}$, finite or infinite, together with the law of composition, denoted $\circ$, such that

(i) (*Closure*)   If a and b are any two elements of G, then $a \circ b$ is an element of G.

(ii) (*Associative law*)   If $a, b, c \in G$ then

$$(a \circ b) \circ c = a \circ (b \circ c) \tag{7.1}$$

(iii) If $a, b \in G$ then there exist unique elements $x, y \in G$ such that

$$a \circ x = b \text{ and } y \circ a = b \qquad (7.2)$$

If the elements are numbers, vectors, matrices etc, the composition $a \circ b$ may either be the sum or the product of a and b. In the case of mappings, transformations, rotations, permutations. etc, the law is understood to be the usual law of composition; if a, b are transformations, then $a \circ b$ is the transformation which results from performing b first, then a.

Exercise Show that the set of all rotations in a plane $\{\mathscr{R}_\phi : 0 \le \phi < 2\pi\}$ forms a group.

Hint All the rotations are about the same axis, perpendicular to the plane, so that $\mathscr{R}_{\phi_1} \circ \mathscr{R}_{\phi_2} = \mathscr{R}_{\phi_1 + \phi_2}$. $\qquad \square$

Exercise Prove the following laws which are the consequences of axioms (i), (ii), (iii) above.

(iv) (*Law of cancellation*) If $a, b, c \in G$ then

$$a \circ b = a \circ c \text{ implies } b = c$$

$$b \circ a = c \circ a \text{ implies } b = c \qquad (7.3)$$

Hint Use axiom (iii) and the fact that the elements x and y defined in (iii) are unique.

(v) (*Identity*) There is a unique element $e \in G$ such that

$$a \circ e = a = e \circ a$$

for all $a \in G$.

Hint Use (iii) with b replaced by a to get

$$a \circ e = a \quad e' \circ a = a.$$

To show that $e = e'$ put $a = e$ and use the law of cancellation.

(vi) (*Inverse*) For every $a \in G$, there exists a unique $a^{-1} \in G$ such that

$$a^{-1} \circ a = e = a \circ a^{-1}.$$

(vii) (*Extended associative law*)

$$(a \circ (b \circ (c \circ (\cdots)))) \cdots) \circ h = a \circ b \circ c \cdots \circ h$$

so that unnecessary parentheses can be omitted.

(viii) (*Extended inverse*) $(a \circ b \circ c \cdots \circ x \circ y)^{-1} = y^{-1} \circ x^{-1} \circ \cdots \circ b^{-1} \circ a^{-1}.$ $\qquad \square$

Note that the law of composition need not be commutative, that is, in general, $a \circ b \neq b \circ a$. $a, b \in G$ are said to commute if $a \circ b = b \circ a$. If all pairs of elements of G commute, then G is said to be *commutative* or *Abelian*.

Let $a \in G$ and $m \geq 0$ be an integer. Then, a^m is defined as follows.

$$a^0 = e, \ a^1 = a, \ a^2 = a \circ a, \ a^3 = a^2 \circ a, \ \ldots, \ a^m = a^{m-1} \circ a; \ a^{-m} = (a^{-1})^m$$

If all the elements a^n $(n = 0, \pm 1, \pm 2, \cdots)$ are distinct, then the element a is said to be of infinite order, otherwise, there is a smallest positive integer l, called the *order* of a, such that $a^l = e$. Then, $a^m = e$ provided l is a divisor of m and every power of a equals one of the elements $e, a, a^2, \ldots, a^{l-1}$. The group comprising $e, a, a^2, \ldots, a^{l-1}$ is called the cyclic group of l elements.

If a subset $G' \subseteq G$ of a group G is a group with the same law of composition as G, it is called a subgroup of G. For example, the rotations about a fixed axis form a subgroup of the group of rotations on $\mathscr{E}_3$. The distinct powers of an element a form a subgroup called a subgroup generated by the element a. This could be the cyclic subgroup of finite or infinite order. The order of a group is the number of elements in it which can be finite or infinite. If G' is a subgroup of G we write $G' < G$. In any case, $G < G$ and $\{e\} < G$. If $G' \neq G$, G' is a proper subgroup, If $G' = \{e\}$, G' is a trivial subgroup.

Examples

(i) The vector space $\mathscr{E}_3$ is an additive Abelian group containing infinite elements. This is obvious from the properties of vector addition listed in section 1.4.

(ii) Let G denote the following set of 2×2 real matrices,

$$e = \begin{pmatrix} 1 & 0 \\ 0 & 1 \end{pmatrix} \ a = \begin{pmatrix} 0 & -1 \\ 1 & 0 \end{pmatrix} \ b = \begin{pmatrix} -1 & 0 \\ 0 & -1 \end{pmatrix} \ c = \begin{pmatrix} 0 & 1 \\ -1 & 0 \end{pmatrix}.$$

It is straightforward to check that this set forms a group under matrix multiplication. For example, $a \circ c = e$ and $a^{-1} = c$.

(iii) Let C_4 denote the group of the rotational symmetries of a square, under the composition of rotations, namely,

$e =$ identity (rotation through 0)

$a =$ counterclockwise rotation through $\pi/2$

$b =$ counterclockwise rotation through π

$a =$ counterclockwise rotation through $3\pi/2$ (clockwise rotation through $\pi/2$)

Exercise   Show that the groups in examples (ii) and (iii) are simply two different realizations of 'cyclic group of four elements'. □

(iv) The sets $\mathbb{Z}_2$ of integers modulo 2 and $((1, -1), \cdot)$ are groups under the respective binary operations and are isomorphic. We name them $\mathbb{Z}_2$ and $\mathbb{C}_2$ respectively. Both are cyclic groups of two elements $\{e, a\}$ with $a^2 = e$. The three element group $\mathbb{C}_3$ is given by $\{1, \omega, \omega^2\}$ where $\omega = e^{2\pi i/3}$. This is isomorphic with the group of three rotations of angles $0, 2\pi/3, 4\pi/3$ in the plane, which account for all the rotations forming the symmetry elements of an equilateral triangle centered at the origin.

(v) We can consider the group of *all* symmetries of the equilateral triangle (see Fig. 7.1). Thus, we allow reflections about the perpendicular bisectors as well. This is a six element group and we denote it by S_3. Labeling the vertices $\{1, 2, 3\}$ we can link every element in S_3 with some permutation of the vertices of the triangle. Let (12) denote the permutation which interchanges vertices 1 and 2 while leaving the vertex 3 fixed. This permutation is obtained by the reflection in the perpendicular bisector of the edge joining 1 to 2. Similarly, the permutation (123), sending vertex 1 into 2, 2 into 3 and 3 into 1 is obtained by rotating the triangle through $120°$. The permutation (132) sending vertex 1 into 3, 3 into 2 and 2 into 1 is obtained by rotating the triangle through $240°$. Thus, we see that the group of symmetries of an equilateral triangle is the same as the group of all permutations on three symbols.

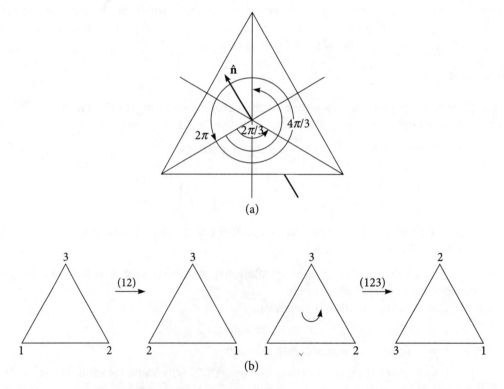

Fig. 7.1 (a) Symmetry elements of an equilateral triangle i) Reflections in three planes shown by $\perp$ bisectors of sides. ii) Rotations through $2\pi/3, 4\pi/3$ and 2π (= identity) about the axis $\perp$ to the plane of the triangle passing through the center. (b) Isomorphism with S_3 (see text).

Exercise Show that the group of permutations of 4 symbols, S_4, has 24 elements. Generalize to n symbols to show that S_n has $n!$ elements. □

(vi) We now consider the group of all symmetries of a square denoted D_4. This is an eight element group, four rotations and four reflections, reflections in two diagonals and the reflections in two perpendicular bisectors (see Fig. 7.2). Each element of D_4 permutes the vertices $1, 2, 3, 4$ of the square. Thus, we may regard D_4 as the subgroup of S_4, which has $4! = 24$ elements. Similarly, the group of symmetry elements of a regular polygon of n sides, called D_n, is the subgroup of S_n, the group of all permutations of n symbols.

Exercise Show that the group D_n contains $2n$ elements. □

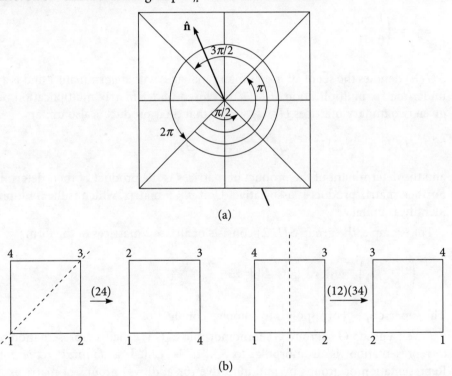

(a)

(b)

Fig. 7.2   (a) Symmetry elements of a square (group D_4) i) Reflections in planes through the diagonal and bisectors of the opposite sides. ii) Rotations about the axis through the center and $\perp$ to the square by angles $\pi/2, pi, 3\pi/2$ and 2π (= identity). (b) D_4 is isomorphic with a subgroup of S_4 (see text).

(vii) We now deal with groups with infinite number of elements. Let $SL(2, \mathbb{C})$ denote the set of 2×2 matrices with complex entries, whose determinant equals 1. Thus, an element of $SL(2, \mathbb{C})$ is given by

$$A = \begin{pmatrix} a & b \\ c & d \end{pmatrix},$$

where a, b, c, d are complex numbers satisfying

$$ad - bc = 1.$$

Exercise Show that $SL(2, \mathbb{C})$ forms a non-commutative group under matrix multiplication.

Hint Since the determinant of the product of matrices is the product of their determinants, $SL(2, \mathbb{C})$ is closed under matrix multiplication. Further, matrix product is associative. Since $\det A = 1$, A is invertible, and $\det A^{-1} = 1 / \det A = 1$, implying A^{-1} exists and is in $SL(2, \mathbb{C})$. The identity is given by

$$e = \begin{pmatrix} 1 & 0 \\ 0 & 1 \end{pmatrix}.$$

$\square$

(viii) $SU(n)$ denotes the set of all $n \times n$ unitary matrices with determinant 1 and is a group under matrix multiplication. $SU(n)$ is closed under matrix multiplication because given two unitary matrices U_1, U_2 we see that their product is also unitary,

$$(U_1 U_2)^\dagger = U_2^\dagger U_1^\dagger = U_2^{-1} U_1^{-1} = (U_1 U_2)^{-1} \tag{7.4}$$

and the determinant of the product of matrices is the product of their determinants. Further, matrix product is associative. Unit $n \times n$ matrix, which is the multiplicative identity, is unitary.

For example, the group $SU(2)$ consists of all 2×2 matrices of the form

$$\begin{pmatrix} a & b \\ -b^* & a^* \end{pmatrix}, \text{ where } |a|^2 + |b|^2 = 1.$$

The superscript $*$ corresponds to complex conjugation.

Given a group G, a group G' homomorphic to G is called a representation of G. If a representation is isomorphic to G, it is called a *faithful* representation. Representation of groups by multiplicative (or additive) groups of matrices is very useful, especially when the representation is faithful, or even otherwise, because many properties of the original group can be obtained by studying the corresponding group of matrices which is, generally, much easier to do.

Exercise Show that the set of all orthogonal matrices with determinant $+1$ forms a group.

$\square$

7.2 The Rotation Group $\mathcal{O}^+(3)$

We have already seen that the composition of two counterclockwise rotations is a counterclockwise rotation. Thus, the set of all rotations on $\mathcal{E}_3$ is closed under the composition of rotations. The composition of rotations is associative because by its definition, both the compositions $(\mathscr{R}_1 \circ \mathscr{R}_2) \circ \mathscr{R}_3$ and $\mathscr{R}_1 \circ (\mathscr{R}_2 \circ \mathscr{R}_3)$ can be implemented in only one way, namely, by applying the individual rotations in the order $\mathscr{R}_3, \mathscr{R}_2, \mathscr{R}_1$ in succession. The rotation with zero angle of rotation is the identity rotation, which does not rotate anything at all, so that its composition with any other rotation gives back the same rotation. The inverse of a rotation $\mathscr{R}(\hat{\mathbf{n}}, \theta)$ is $\mathscr{R}(\hat{\mathbf{n}}, 2\pi - \theta)$. Thus, the set of all possible rotations on $\mathscr{E}_3$ is a group under the composition of rotations, called $\mathscr{O}^+(3)$. All the rotations in $\mathscr{O}^+(3)$ together leave one point in space invariant, a point which is common to all the axes of rotation, taken to be the origin. Physically, a body which is only rotating has to leave at least one point in it undisplaced or stationary because the displacement of all points in the body corresponds to the translation of the whole body. Note that this group is not only infinite but is uncountable. In fact, it is parameterized by three Euler angles and can be scanned by continuously varying these parameters covering their ranges. These continuous parameters scanning the group form a region in $\mathbb{R}^3$ and the continuous variations in these parameters correspond to different possible paths in this region. In particular, starting from any rotation, its three Euler angles can be continuously reduced to zero to reach the identity. Thus, every rotation operator is continuously connected to the identity element $e^{0\hat{\mathbf{n}}\times} = I$ corresponding to zero rotation. Because of this property, the group of rotations, $\mathscr{O}^+(3)$, is called a continuous group.

We have seen that, having chosen an orthonormal basis $\{\hat{\sigma}_k\}$ $k = 1, 2, 3$ in $\mathscr{E}_3$, a matrix representing every rotation $\mathscr{R}(\hat{\mathbf{n}}, \theta)$ is given by

$$e_{jk} = \hat{\sigma}_j \cdot \mathscr{R} \hat{\sigma}_k,$$

where e_{jk} is the jkth element of the matrix. By subsection 6.3.1 we know that every such matrix is a 3×3 orthogonal matrix with determinant $+1$ and that the sets of rotations and their matrix representatives are isomorphic. The last exercise tells us that the set of all orthogonal matrices with determinant $+1$ is a group under matrix multiplication which we call $SO(3)$. All this just means that the group of 3×3 matrices with determinant $+1$, $SO(3)$, is a faithful matrix representation of the rotation group $\mathscr{O}^+(3)$. Thus, these two groups have the same structure and properties and it is enough to study $SO(3)$ to understand rotations in $\mathscr{E}_3$. In fact each 3×3 real matrix A defines a linear map $f : \mathbf{x} \mapsto A\mathbf{x}$ on $\mathscr{E}_3$, so that, by the isomorphism between $SO(3)$ and $\mathscr{O}^+(3)$, the group formed by the maps $\mathbf{x} \mapsto A\mathbf{x}$ with $A \in SO(3)$ is just $\mathscr{O}^+(3)$. Since $\mathscr{O}^+(3)$ is a three parameter continuous group, so must be the isomorphic group $SO(3)$.

Exercise Show that $SO(3)$ is a three parameter group.

Solution The conditions of orthogonality on a 3×3 matrix $A = [a_{kj}]$ are, by Eq. (6.7),

$$\sum_{k=1}^{3} a_{kj}^2 = 1 \quad (j = 1, 2, 3)$$

$$\sum_{k=1}^{3} a_{ki}a_{kj} \;=\; 0 \quad (i,j)=(1,2),(1,3),(2,3) \tag{7.5}$$

amounting to 6 constraints to be satisfied by 9 elements of the 3×3 matrix. This leaves only 3 independent parameters out of 9 elements of A. Actually we have not counted the constraint $\det A = 1$. However, it turns out that this constraint does not reduce the number of independent parameters, but eliminates all the matrices with determinant -1 from the parent set of orthogonal matrices with determinant ± 1. □

The set of all orthogonal transformations on $\mathscr{E}_3$ forms a group. We know that the set of orthogonal transformations is partitioned into two classes, characterized by transformations with determinant ± 1 corresponding to rotations and reflections respectively. The composition of two rotations is a rotation while the composition of two reflections is a rotation by Hamilton's theorem (subsection 6.1.2). Thus, the composition of two orthogonal transformations is an orthogonal transformation. The composition of rotations is associative and by the same argument the composition of reflections is also associative. Thus, the composition of orthogonal transformations is associative. The inverse of an orthogonal transformation is uniquely given by its adjoint. Finally, the identity transformation is orthogonal. This makes the set of all orthogonal transformations on $\mathscr{E}_3$ a group under the composition of transformations and we call it $\mathscr{O}(3)$. Obviously, $\mathscr{O}^+(3)$ is a subgroup of $\mathscr{O}(3)$, however, the class of reflections is not, because it is not closed under the composition of reflections.

Exercise   Show that the product of two orthogonal transformations (matrices) is an orthogonal transformation (matrix).

Hint   Proceed as in Eq. (7.4) for unitary matrices. □

In section 4.5 we proved that the matrix representing the product of two transformations is the product of the matrices representing the factors, (in the same order). In section 6.1 we showed that the matrix representing an orthogonal operator is orthogonal. By the above exercise, the product of two orthogonal matrices is orthogonal. If two orthogonal matrices are equal, then the corresponding orthogonal operators are equal, just as in the case of rotations. The set of all 3×3 orthogonal matrices forms a group under matrix multiplication (Exercise) also called $\mathscr{O}(3)$. All this just means that the group of orthogonal 3×3 matrices is a faithful representation of the group of orthogonal transformations on $\mathscr{E}_3$. It is then enough to analyze the group of matrices $\mathscr{O}(3)$, in order to get the structure and properties of the group of orthogonal transformations on $\mathscr{E}_3$. In fact the group of orthogonal transformations is identical to the group of linear maps $\mathbf{x} \mapsto A\mathbf{x}$ on $\mathscr{E}_3$ where A is a 3×3 orthogonal matrix. $\mathscr{O}(3)$ is also a continuous group driven by three independent parameters as we saw for its subgroup $SO(3)$.

7.3   The Group of Isometries and the Euclidean Group

We first define the translation group. A translation $\tau_{\mathbf{a}}$ in $\mathcal{E}_3$ is defined by

$$\tau_{\mathbf{a}}(\mathbf{x}) = \mathbf{x} + \mathbf{a} \tag{7.6}$$

In physical applications we apply this transformation to position vectors of particles comprising a physical object as shown in Fig. 7.3. Notice that the translation operator is not linear. We have,

$$\tau_{\mathbf{a}}(\mathbf{x} + \mathbf{y}) = \mathbf{x} + \mathbf{y} + \mathbf{a} \neq \tau_{\mathbf{a}}(\mathbf{x}) + \tau_{\mathbf{a}}(\mathbf{y}) = \mathbf{x} + \mathbf{y} + 2\mathbf{a}.$$

We show that the set of all translations in $\mathcal{E}_3$ forms an Abelian group. We have,

(i) (*Closure*) $(\tau_{\mathbf{a}}\tau_{\mathbf{b}})\mathbf{x} = \tau_{\mathbf{a}+\mathbf{b}}\mathbf{x} = (\tau_{\mathbf{b}}\tau_{\mathbf{a}})\mathbf{x}.$

(ii) (*Associativity*) $(\tau_{\mathbf{a}}\tau_{\mathbf{b}})\tau_{\mathbf{c}}\mathbf{x} = \tau_{\mathbf{a}+\mathbf{b}+\mathbf{c}}\mathbf{x} = \tau_{\mathbf{a}}(\tau_{\mathbf{b}}\tau_{\mathbf{c}})\mathbf{x}.$

(iii) (*Identity*) $\tau_{\mathbf{0}}(\mathbf{x}) = \mathbf{x} + \mathbf{0} = \mathbf{x}$ implies $I = \tau_{\mathbf{0}}$ is the identity.

(iv) (*Inverse*) $\tau_{-\mathbf{a}}$ is the inverse of $\tau_{\mathbf{a}}$.

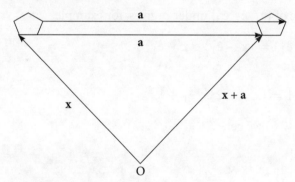

Fig. 7.3   Translation of a physical object by **a**

This proves what we wanted. All these properties follow from those of vector addition in $\mathcal{E}_3$. In fact the translation group is isomorphic with the group formed by $\mathcal{E}_3$ under vector addition (Exercise).

An isometry of Euclidean space $\mathcal{E}_3$ is a bijective (one to one and onto) transformation $\sigma : \mathcal{E}_3 \mapsto \mathcal{E}_3$ such that $d(\sigma(\mathbf{x}), \sigma(\mathbf{y})) = d(\mathbf{x}, \mathbf{y})$, where $d(\mathbf{x}, \mathbf{y}) = +\sqrt{(\mathbf{x} - \mathbf{y}) \cdot (\mathbf{x} - \mathbf{y})}$ is the Euclidean distance between $\mathbf{x}$ and $\mathbf{y}$, for all $\mathbf{x}, \mathbf{y} \in \mathcal{E}_3$.

We first show that all the isometries $\{\sigma\}$ form a group.

(i) (*Closure*)   Clearly, the composition of two isometries is an isometry, as it is the successive application of two transformations, each preserving distance. For the composition $\eta\sigma$ of two isometries η and σ we have

$$d(\eta\sigma(\mathbf{x}), \eta\sigma(\mathbf{y})) = d(\sigma(\mathbf{x}), \sigma(\mathbf{y})) = d(\mathbf{x}, \mathbf{y}).$$

(ii) (*Associativity*)   Let $\sigma_1, \sigma_2, \sigma_3$ be isometries. Then, both $(\sigma_1\sigma_2)\sigma_3$ and $\sigma_1(\sigma_2\sigma_3)$ have to be obtained by successively applying $\sigma_3, \sigma_2, \sigma_1$ (in that order), making them equal.

(iii) (*Identity*)   The identity transformation $I(\mathbf{x}) = \mathbf{x}$ is an isometry.

(iv) (*Inverse*)   By the bijection property, every isometry σ has an inverse, σ^{-1} and since σ is an isometry

$$d(\sigma^{-1}(\mathbf{x}), \sigma^{-1}(\mathbf{y})) = d(\sigma\sigma^{-1}(\mathbf{x}), \sigma\sigma^{-1}(\mathbf{y})) = d(\mathbf{x}, \mathbf{y})$$

so that σ^{-1} is an isometry.

Items (i)–(iv) above show that the set of all isometries in $\mathscr{E}_3$ form a group.

We now obtain some of the basic properties of an isometry.

Consider an orthonormal basis $\{\hat{\mathbf{e}}_1, \hat{\mathbf{e}}_2, \hat{\mathbf{e}}_3\}$ and an isometry σ which leaves the vectors $\{\mathbf{0}, \hat{\mathbf{e}}_1, \hat{\mathbf{e}}_2, \hat{\mathbf{e}}_3\}$ invariant. Then, we want to show that σ is the identity. Let $\mathbf{x}, \mathbf{x}' \in \mathscr{E}_3$ and $\sigma(\mathbf{x}) = \mathbf{x}'$. Since $\sigma(\mathbf{0}) = \mathbf{0}$ we have $d(\mathbf{x}, \mathbf{0}) = d(\sigma(\mathbf{x}), \sigma(\mathbf{0})) = d(\mathbf{x}', \mathbf{0})$. This gives,

$$\mathbf{x}^2 = (\mathbf{x}')^2. \tag{7.7}$$

Similarly, invariance of $\{\hat{\mathbf{e}}_1, \hat{\mathbf{e}}_2, \hat{\mathbf{e}}_3\}$ under σ gives, for example,

$$(\mathbf{x} - \hat{\mathbf{e}}_1) \cdot (\mathbf{x} - \hat{\mathbf{e}}_1) = (\mathbf{x}' - \hat{\mathbf{e}}_1) \cdot (\mathbf{x}' - \hat{\mathbf{e}}_1)$$

or,

$$x^2 - 2\mathbf{x} \cdot \hat{\mathbf{e}}_1 + 1 = (x')^2 - 2\mathbf{x}' \cdot \hat{\mathbf{e}}_1 + 1 \tag{7.8}$$

From Eqs (7.7) and (7.8) we get,

$$\mathbf{x} = \mathbf{x}'$$

or, $\sigma(\mathbf{x}) = \mathbf{x}$ for all $\mathbf{x} \in \mathscr{E}_3$, giving $\sigma = I$. Note that this conclusion is trivial for a linear operator as it follows directly from linearity. However, isometry is not linear in general.

Let σ be an isometry which leaves $\mathbf{0}$ invariant, that is, σ leaves one point in $\mathscr{E}_3$ fixed. Then we know that σ is an orthogonal transformation. In fact from Eq. (7.7) we know that $\sigma(\mathbf{0}) = \mathbf{0}$ implies $\sigma(\mathbf{x}) \cdot \sigma(\mathbf{x}) = \mathbf{x} \cdot \mathbf{x}$, or, σ preserves the length of vectors in $\mathscr{E}_3$. Hence, σ is an orthogonal transformation.

Let σ be an isometry with $\sigma(\mathbf{0}) = \mathbf{a}$. Then

$$\sigma(\mathbf{x}) = A\mathbf{x} + \mathbf{a} \quad \mathbf{x} \in \mathscr{E}_3 \tag{7.9}$$

where A is an orthogonal transformation. To see this, define a translation $\tau_{\mathbf{a}}(\mathbf{x}) = \mathbf{x} + \mathbf{a}$. This is an isometry with inverse $\tau_{-\mathbf{a}}(\mathbf{x}) = \mathbf{x} - \mathbf{a}$. Thus, $\tau_{-\mathbf{a}}\sigma(\mathbf{0}) = \mathbf{0}$ so that $\tau_{-\mathbf{a}}\sigma$ is an isometry fixing $\mathbf{0}$. Therefore, $\tau_{-\mathbf{a}}\sigma$ must be an orthogonal transformation which we denote by A. We can then write

$$\sigma(\mathbf{x}) = \tau_{\mathbf{a}}\tau_{-\mathbf{a}}\sigma(\mathbf{x}) = \tau_{\mathbf{a}}A(\mathbf{x}) = A(\mathbf{x}) + \mathbf{a} \tag{7.10}$$

In fact every isometry is given by the form in Eq. (7.9), because when $\mathbf{a} \neq \mathbf{0}$ ($\mathbf{a} = \mathbf{0}$) in $\sigma(\mathbf{0}) = \mathbf{a}$, it is given by Eq. (7.9) (Eq. (7.9) with $\mathbf{a} = \mathbf{0}$) and there are no other cases.

We can now conclude that the group of isometries is a six parameter group, three parameters are required to fix the orthogonal transformation A while three more are required to fix the translation $\mathbf{a}$. We are interested in the subgroup consisting of isometries given by the product of a rotation and a translation, called Euclidean group. Each such isometry is physically realized by a displacement of a rigid body. A rigid body is a system of particles with fixed distances from one another, so every displacement of a rigid body must be an isometry. A finite rigid body displacement must unfold continuously, so it must be continuously connected to the identity. In the last subsection we saw that this property is availed by rotations which are the elements of SO(3). Thus, only the isometries composed of a rotation and a translation have this property. An isometry of this kind is called a rigid displacement. Thus, all rigid displacements form a continuous group of isometries having the canonical form (see Fig. 7.4)

$$\sigma(\mathbf{x}) = \tau_{\mathbf{a}} \mathcal{R}(\mathbf{x}) = \mathcal{R}(\mathbf{x}) + \mathbf{a} \tag{7.11}$$

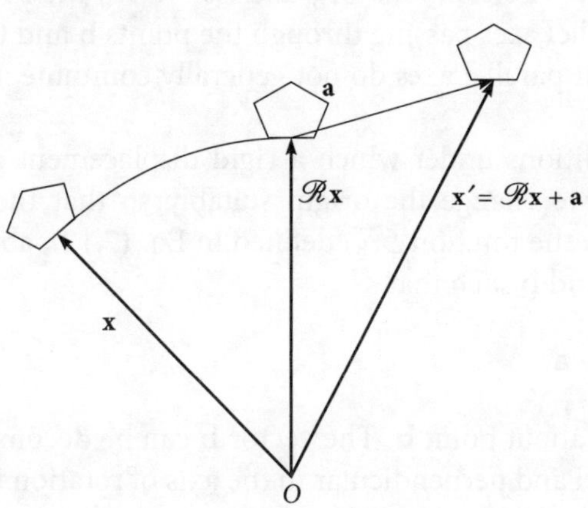

Fig. 7.4   A rigid displacement is the composite of a rotation and a translation. The translation vector $\mathbf{a}$ need not be in the plane of rotation.

where $\mathcal{R} \in SO(3)$ is a rotation. Note that the rotation $\mathcal{R}$ is about an axis through the origin so the origin is a distinguished point in this representation of the rigid displacement. However, the choice of origin was completely arbitrary in getting Eq. (7.11), so different choices of the origin give different decompositions of a rigid displacement into a rotation and a translation. Next, we show how these are related.

Let $\mathcal{R}_{\mathbf{b}}$ denote a rotation about a point $\mathbf{b}$ and let $\mathcal{R}_{\mathbf{0}} = \mathcal{R}$ denote the same rotation about the origin $\mathbf{0}$. The rotation about the point $\mathbf{b}$ can be effected via the following sequence of operations. (i) Translate the body by $-\mathbf{b}$ to shift the point $\mathbf{b}$ to the origin. (ii) Perform the rotation $\mathcal{R}$ about the origin. (iii) Translate by $\mathbf{b}$ to shift the origin back to the point $\mathbf{b}$. The resulting transformation is given by

$$\mathcal{R}_{\mathbf{b}}(\mathbf{x}) = \tau_{\mathbf{b}} \mathcal{R} \tau_{-\mathbf{b}}(\mathbf{x}) = \mathcal{R}(\mathbf{x} - \mathbf{b}) + \mathbf{b} = \mathcal{R}(\mathbf{x}) - \mathcal{R}(\mathbf{b}) + \mathbf{b} \tag{7.12}$$

which expresses $\mathscr{R}_b$ in terms of $\mathscr{R}$.

Next, we find the equation to the axis of rotation through point $\mathbf{b}$. The rotation axis for $\mathscr{R}_b$ is the set of points invariant under $\mathscr{R}_b$. This is the set of points $\mathbf{x}$ satisfying the equation

$$\mathscr{R}_b(\mathbf{x}) = \mathbf{x} \tag{7.13}$$

The points $\mathbf{x}$ satisfying Eq. (7.13) are the fixed points of $\mathscr{R}_b$. Combining Eqs (7.12) and (7.13) we get

$$\mathscr{R}(\mathbf{x} - \mathbf{b}) + \mathbf{b} = \mathbf{x} \tag{7.14}$$

As a check we find that $\mathscr{R}_b \mathbf{b} = \mathbf{b}$ as it should. If $\mathscr{R}_b$ is not an identity transformation, Eq. (7.14) determines a straight line passing through the point $\mathbf{b}$. To see this, note that Eq. (7.14) can be written $\mathscr{R}(\mathbf{x} - \mathbf{b}) = \mathbf{x} - \mathbf{b}$ which means that the rotation axis for the rotation $\mathscr{R}$ passing through the new origin $\mathbf{b}$ is given by $\mathbf{x} = \mathbf{x}' + \mathbf{b}$ where $\mathbf{x}' = \mathbf{x} - \mathbf{b}$ defines the axis through origin. The rotations $\mathscr{R}_b$ and $\mathscr{R} = \mathscr{R}_0$ then rotate the body through equal angles about parallel axes passing through the points $\mathbf{b}$ and $\mathbf{0}$ respectively. However, the rotations about such parallel axes do not generally commute, that is, $\mathscr{R}\mathscr{R}_b \neq \mathscr{R}_b \mathscr{R}$, as seen from Eq. (7.12).

We obtain the conditions under which a rigid displacement given by Eq. (7.11) is a rotation. That is, can we change the origin suitably so that the rigid displacement in Eq. (7.11) is effected via the rotation $\mathscr{R}_b$, defined in Eq. (7.12), about the shifted origin at $\mathbf{b}$? That is, we try and find $\mathbf{b}$ such that

$$\mathscr{R}_b(\mathbf{x}) = \mathscr{R}(\mathbf{x}) + \mathbf{a}. \tag{7.15}$$

where $\mathscr{R}_b$ is a rotation about point $\mathbf{b}$. The vector $\mathbf{b}$ can be decomposed into components $\mathbf{b}_\parallel$ and $\mathbf{b}_\perp$ being parallel and perpendicular to the axis of rotation respectively to give

$$\mathbf{b} = \mathbf{b}_\parallel + \mathbf{b}_\perp \tag{7.16}$$

Putting this in Eq. (7.12) we get

$$\mathscr{R}_b = \mathscr{R}(\mathbf{x}) + \mathbf{b}_\perp - \mathscr{R}(\mathbf{b}_\perp) \tag{7.17}$$

Comparison between Eqs (7.15) and (7.17) tells us that the following condition must be satisfied by the required vector $\mathbf{b}$.

$$\mathbf{a} = \mathbf{b}_\perp - \mathscr{R}(\mathbf{b}_\perp)$$

The vector on the RHS of this equation lies in a plane perpendicular to the rotation axis determined by $\mathscr{R}$. We can conclude from the above condition on $\mathbf{b}$ that a rigid displacement $\mathscr{R}(\mathbf{x}) + \mathbf{a}$ is a rotation if and only if the translation vector $\mathbf{a} = \mathbf{a}_\perp$ is perpendicular to the axis of rotation. To emphasize this fact, we rewrite the condition on **b** as

$$\mathbf{a}_\perp = \mathbf{b}_\perp - \mathscr{R}(\mathbf{b}_\perp) \tag{7.18}$$

We note that both the axes of rotation, through the origin **0** and through **b** are parallel and share the same plane of rotation perpendicular to both of them. Both vectors $\mathbf{a}_\perp$ and $\mathbf{b}_\perp$ lie in the plane of rotation which we can view as a complex plane and replace the rotation operator $\mathscr{R}$ in Eq. (7.18) by $e^{i\phi}$ where ϕ is the angle of rotation and treat vectors $\mathbf{a}_\perp$ and $\mathbf{b}_\perp$ like complex numbers. This gives

$$\mathbf{b}_\perp = \frac{\mathbf{a}_\perp}{1 - e^{i\phi}} = \frac{1}{2}\mathbf{a}_\perp \left(1 + i \cot\frac{\phi}{2}\right)$$

or, switching over to vectors,

$$\mathbf{b}_\perp = \frac{1}{2}\left(\mathbf{a}_\perp + (\hat{\mathbf{n}} \times \mathbf{a}_\perp)\cot\frac{\phi}{2}\right) \tag{7.19}$$

where $\hat{\mathbf{n}}$ is the unit vector defining the axis of rotation. Note that the transformation $\mathscr{R}(\mathbf{x}) + \mathbf{a}_\perp$ leaves every plane perpendicular to the rotation axis invariant and it consists of a rotation-translation in each such plane. Thus, we have proved that every rotation-translation $\mathscr{R}(\mathbf{x}) + \mathbf{a}_\perp$ in a plane is equivalent to the rotation centered at the point $\mathbf{b}_\perp$ given by Eq. (7.19) as shown in Fig. 7.5. Our proof fails if there is no rotation ($\phi = 0$), in which case we have pure translation. Thus, we have proved that every rigid displacement in a plane is either a rotation or a translation.

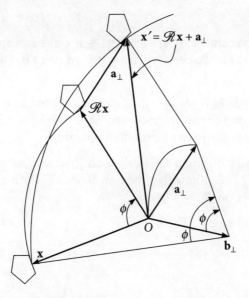

Fig. 7.5   Equivalence of a rotation/translation in a plane to a pure rotation

It is immediate from Eq. (7.17) that $\mathbf{b}_\perp = \mathbf{0}$ implies $\mathscr{R}_\mathbf{b} = \mathscr{R}$. Thus, the rotations differing by the shift of origin along the rotation axis are equivalent. Indeed, no parameters defining the rotation change by a translation along the axis of rotation.

7.3.1   Chasles theorem

Given any rigid displacement $\sigma(\mathbf{x}) = \mathscr{R}(\mathbf{x}) + \mathbf{a}$, we decompose the translation $\mathbf{a}$ into components $\mathbf{a}_\parallel$ and $\mathbf{a}_\perp$, parallel and perpendicular to the rotation axis defined by $\mathscr{R}$, so that

$$\sigma(\mathbf{x}) = \mathscr{R}(\mathbf{x}) + \mathbf{a}_\perp + \mathbf{a}_\parallel \tag{7.20}$$

Now $\mathscr{R}(\mathbf{x}) + \mathbf{a}_\perp$ can be treated as a rotation $\mathscr{R}_\mathbf{b}$, so that

$$\sigma(\mathbf{x}) = \tau_{\mathbf{a}_\parallel} \mathscr{R}_\mathbf{b}(\mathbf{x}) \tag{7.21}$$

where $\tau_{\mathbf{a}_\parallel}$ is the translation parallel to the rotation axis $\mathscr{R}_\mathbf{b}$. Equation (7.21) proves Chasles theorem: Any rigid displacement can be expressed as a screw displacement. A screw displacement consists of a product of rotation with a translation along the axis of rotation (the screw axis). We have done more than proving Chasles theorem, we have shown how to find the screw axis of a given rigid displacement. Although elegant, Chasles theorem is seldom used in practice. Equation (7.11) is usually more useful, because the center of rotation (the origin) can be specified at will to simplify the problem at hand. Finally, note that $\mathbf{b} = \mathbf{b}_\parallel$ (i.e., $\mathbf{b}_\perp = \mathbf{0}$ in Eq. (7.16)) gives, via Eq. (7.12),

$$\mathscr{R}_\mathbf{b}(\mathbf{x}) = \mathscr{R}(\mathbf{x}) \tag{7.22}$$

as it should.

Exercise   A rigid displacement $\sigma(\mathbf{x}) = \mathscr{R}(\mathbf{x}) + \mathbf{a}$ can be expressed as a product of a translation $\tau_\mathbf{c}$ and a rotation $\mathscr{R}_\mathbf{b}$ centered at a specified point $\mathbf{b}$. Determine the translation vector $\mathbf{c}$.

Hint   Using Eq. (7.12) $\mathscr{R}(\mathbf{x}) + \mathbf{a} = \tau_\mathbf{c} \mathscr{R}_\mathbf{b}$ can be reduced to $\mathbf{c} = \mathbf{a} - \mathbf{b} + \mathscr{R}(\mathbf{b})$. $\mathbf{a}, \mathbf{b}$ may be specified as column or row matrices and $\mathscr{R} \in SO(3)$ as a 3×3 special orthogonal matrix. Otherwise $\mathscr{R}$ may be given as a rotation operator.   □

Exercise   A subgroup H of group G is called an invariant subgroup if $g^{-1}hg \in H$ for every $h \in H$ and every $g \in G$. Show that the translations T form an invariant subgroup of the group E of isometries on $\mathscr{E}_3$.

Solution   Let $\sigma \in E$ and $\tau_\mathbf{a} \in T$. Then,

$$(\sigma^{-1}\tau_\mathbf{a}\sigma)(\mathbf{x}) = \mathbf{x} + \sigma^{-1}(\mathbf{a})$$

which is a translation $\tau_{\sigma^{-1}(\mathbf{a})} \in T$.   □

Exercise Let S denote the reflection in the plane normal to a non-zero vector **a**. If $\tau_{\mathbf{a}}$ is the translation by **a** then $S_{\mathbf{a}} = \tau_{\mathbf{a}} S \tau_{-\mathbf{a}}$ is the reflection S shifted to the point **a**. Show that

$$SS_{-\mathbf{a}} = \tau_{2\mathbf{a}}.$$

Thus, a translation by **a** can be expressed as a product of reflections in parallel planes separated by $\frac{1}{2}\mathbf{a}$.

Solution Since S is a linear operator, $S^2 = I$ and $S(\mathbf{a}) = -\mathbf{a}$, we have,

$$S_{-\mathbf{a}}(\mathbf{x}) = S(\mathbf{x} + \mathbf{a}) - \mathbf{a} = S(\mathbf{x}) + S(\mathbf{a}) - \mathbf{a}$$

$$= S(\mathbf{x}) - 2\mathbf{a}$$

giving

$$SS_{-\mathbf{a}} = S^2(\mathbf{x}) - 2S(\mathbf{a}) = \mathbf{x} + 2\mathbf{a} = \tau_{2\mathbf{a}}. \qquad \Box$$

7.4 Similarities and Collineations

Isometries preserve lengths of vectors as well as the angles between vectors. We call a non-empty subset of $\mathscr{E}_3$ a *figure*. Two figures S and S^* in $\mathscr{E}_3$ are *congruent* if and only if $S^* = \sigma(S)$ for some isometry σ on $\mathscr{E}_3$.

Exercise Show that congruence is an equivalence relation.

Solution This is obvious because isometries form a group.

(i) Since identity is an isometry, a figure is congruent to itself.

(ii) $S^* = \sigma(S)$ implies $S = \sigma^{-1} S^*$ so that congruence is reflexive.

(iii) Since a composition of isometries is an isometry, if S_1 is congruent to S_2 and S_2 is congruent to S_3 then S_1 is congruent to S_3. Thus, congruence is transitive. $\qquad \Box$

Two figures are said to be *similar* if they have the same shape but not the same size, so that one is congruent to an enlargement of the other. Two figures S and S^* are similar if and only if $S^* = \Sigma(S)$ where Σ, is called a similarity transformation on $\mathscr{E}_3$, and is given by

$$\Sigma : \mathbf{x} \mapsto \lambda A(\mathbf{x}) + \mathbf{a}, \quad \lambda \in \mathbb{R}, \quad \lambda \neq 0, A \text{ orthogonal}$$

If $\lambda < 0$ then we take $-A$ to be the orthogonal transformation. Similarity transformations form a group which contains isometries as a subgroup. The similarity transformations do not preserve distance however, they preserve ratios of distances, that is,

$$\frac{d(\Sigma(\mathbf{a}), \Sigma(\mathbf{b}))}{d(\Sigma(\mathbf{c}), \Sigma(\mathbf{d}))} = \frac{d(\mathbf{a}, \mathbf{b})}{d(\mathbf{c}, \mathbf{d})}.$$

Both isometries and similarities are subgroups of a more general group of transformations called *collineations* which transform lines into lines. All transformations of the form

$$\mathscr{A} : \mathbf{x} \mapsto A(\mathbf{x}) + \mathbf{a} \quad A \text{ invertible}$$

are collineations and are called *Affine* transformations. Affine transformations form a group called Affine group. Note that both isometries and similarities are affine transformations.

Let G be the affine group and let Ω be the set which is either $\mathscr{E}_3$ or a class of figures in $\mathscr{E}_3$ but not both. We define a relation $\equiv$ on Ω namely, $\alpha \equiv \beta$ if and only if there exists $\sigma \in G$ such that $\sigma(\alpha) = \beta$.

Exercise Show that $\equiv$ is an equivalence relation.

Hint Again, this follows from the fact that affine transformations form a group. So proceed just the way we showed congruence to be an equivalence relation. □

Consider a subset of Ω consisting of all elements which are related via $\equiv$. Such a subset is called an equivalence class of $\equiv$. To construct such a subset pick up an element in Ω and collect all elements of Ω related to it. If the complement of this subset in Ω is not empty, pick out an element from the complement and collect all elements related to it. Repeat this procedure until all of Ω is exhausted. Obviously, all these subsets, or equivalence classes, are mutually exclusive, because if any two of them have an element in common, by transitivity property it will be related to all the elements of both the subsets, so that their union will form a single equivalence class. Thus, Ω is partitioned by its equivalence classes, that is, two equivalence classes have empty intersection and the union of all of them is Ω.

When G is the affine group the elements of the equivalence class of $\equiv$ on Ω via G are called *affine equivalent.*

Instead of defining via the affine group, we can define $\equiv$ via the similarity group or the isometry group to get the same results.

We now classify the set of all central conics, (defined below), which are the orbits of particles driven by the inverse-square law of force, using group of affine transformations or groups of isometries and similarities.

Conics are the loci of the second degree, that is, the non-empty point sets in $\mathscr{E}_2$, given by Sprienger

$$\Gamma = \{(x,y) | ax^2 + 2hxy + by^2 + 2gx + 2fy + c = 0 \ \ a \neq 0 \text{ or } h \neq 0 \text{ or } b \neq 0\}$$

Conics for which $ab \neq h^2$ are called central conics.

We intend to examine the effect of an affine (or isometry or similarity) transformation on a conic Γ. The equation of Γ, mentioned in its definition can be alternatively expressed in the matrix form as

$$uAu^T + 2uk^T + c = 0 \tag{7.23}$$

where u, k are 1×2 matrices and a is a 2×2 symmetric matrix

$$u = \begin{pmatrix} x & y \end{pmatrix} A = \begin{pmatrix} a & h \\ h & b \end{pmatrix} k = \begin{pmatrix} g & f \end{pmatrix}$$

and c is a 1×1 matrix. Now we make an affine transformation $\sigma : u \mapsto u' = [x', y']$ so that $u = u'S + w$ (S invertible) and obtain the matrix equation

$$(u'S + w)A(S^T(u')^T + w^T) + 2(u'S + w)k^T + c = 0$$

which can be simplified to

$$u'A'(u')^T + 2u'(k')^T + c' = 0 \tag{7.24}$$

where $A' = SAS^T$, $k' = kS^T + wAS^T$ and $c' = c + 2wk^T + wAw^T$. Equation (7.24) is again a second degree equation so that (x', y') must lie on a conic

$$\Gamma' = \{(x, y) \mid a'x^2 + 2h'xy + b'y^2 + 2g'x + 2f'y + c' = 0 \ \ a' \neq 0 \text{ or } h' \neq 0 \text{ or } b' \neq 0\}$$

Since $\det A' = (\det S)^2 \det A$ ($\det S \neq 0$) we have $ab \neq h^2$ if and only if $a'b' \neq (h')^2$; in other words, central conics are transformed into central conics. Now choose the transformation $w = -kA^{-1}$ giving $k' = 0$, thus eliminating all the first degree terms from Eq. (7.24). The point represented by the vector $-kA^{-1}$ is called the center of the conic Γ. Note that when $ab = h^2$, A^{-1} does not exists and Γ cannot have a center. Using $w = -kA^{-1}$ we obtain $c' = c - kA^{-1}k^T$ which on evaluation gives

$$c' = \frac{\Delta}{ab - h^2}$$

$$\Delta = abc + 2fgh - af^2 - bg^2 - ch^2 \tag{7.25}$$

To find the affine equivalent class of central conics, we have to find the criteria which guarantee (or otherwise) the existence of an affine transformation connecting the given conics Γ and Γ'. That is, given Γ and Γ', as in Eqs (7.23) and (7.24), when can one find an invertible matrix S transforming Γ' to Γ. We differ this question until we have obtained the effect of the Euclidean transformations (isometries) on central conics and find its equivalence classes.

When $\sigma : u \mapsto u'$ is an isometry, the above analysis goes through, with the reservation that the matrix S defined by $u = u'S + w$ must be orthogonal. We are interested in the isometries continuously connected to identity, so we restrict to the Euclidean group and require S to be special orthogonal ($\det S = +1$). Since A is symmetric and S is special orthogonal, we can choose S such that the matrix $A' = SAS^T$ is diagonal with the diagonal elements as the eigenvalues of A. Thus, we can write $A' = \operatorname{diag}(\lambda, \mu)$ where λ, μ are the roots of the equation $t^2 - (a + b)t + ab - h^2 = 0$. We can therefore find an Euclidean transformation which takes the central conic Γ into the conic Γ' with equation

$$\lambda x^2 + \mu y^2 + \Delta/(ab - h^2) = 0 \tag{7.26}$$

If $\Delta \neq 0$ Eq. (7.26) can be rewritten as

$$\alpha x^2 + \beta y^2 = 1 \tag{7.27}$$

where $\alpha + \beta = -(a + b)(ab - h^2)/\Delta$, $\alpha\beta = (ab - h^2)^3/\Delta^2$.

We will now show that the pair of numbers $\{\alpha, \beta\}$ characterizes the Euclidean equivalence class of Γ. If Γ is Euclidean equivalent to a conic Γ'' with the equation

$$\gamma x^2 + \delta y^2 = 1 \tag{7.28}$$

then there is a transformation $[x\ y] \mapsto [x\ y]U + c$ (U orthogonal) taking Γ' to Γ''. It is easily seen that we must have $c = 0$ and

$$\begin{pmatrix} \gamma & 0 \\ 0 & \delta \end{pmatrix} = U \begin{pmatrix} \alpha & 0 \\ 0 & \beta \end{pmatrix} U^T$$

which is possible if and only if $\{\gamma, \delta\} = \{\alpha, \beta\}$. Thus, two central non-degenerate (i.e., $\Delta \neq 0$) conics are Euclidean equivalent if and only if they have the same values for α and β or, equivalently, for $\alpha + \beta$ and $\alpha\beta$ given by Eq. (7.27). In other words, the quantities

$$\frac{-(a + b)(ab - h^2)}{\Delta} \quad \text{and} \quad \frac{(ab - h^2)^3}{\Delta^2} \tag{7.29}$$

are invariants for the central ($ab \neq h^2$) and non-degenerate ($\Delta \neq 0$) conics under the action of the Euclidean group.

Under the similarity group, any central non-degenerate conic again reduces to a conic with Eq. (7.27), but this conic is equivalent to the conic in Eq. (7.28) if and only if either $\gamma/\delta = \alpha/\beta$ or $\gamma/\delta = \beta/\alpha$. The pair $\{\alpha/\beta, \beta/\alpha\}$ or equivalently the number $(\alpha/\beta) + (\beta/\alpha)$ or equivalently the number

$$\frac{(\alpha + \beta)^2}{\alpha\beta} = \frac{(a + b)^2}{(ab - h^2)} \tag{7.30}$$

is the required invariant under the similarity group.

Under the affine group, the conics with Eqs (7.27) and (7.28) are equivalent if and only if $\alpha\beta$ and $\gamma\delta$ have the same sign, because in this case (with U an invertible matrix not necessarily orthogonal) the determinants of the corresponding matrices are related by

$$\gamma\delta = (\det\ U)^2 \alpha\beta \tag{7.31}$$

and since the conic is central, $\alpha\beta \neq 0$. We also note that both α and β cannot be < 0 because in that case, no (x,y) can satisfy Eq. (7.27). Thus, Eq. (7.31) does imply that $\alpha\beta$ and $\gamma\delta$ have the same sign. There are thus only two affine equivalent classes of central non-degenerate conics, namely those for which $ab - h^2 > 0$ (ellipses) and those for which $ab - h^2 < 0$ (hyperbolae). Note that in the affine geometry, *any* two ellipses are equivalent, while in Euclidean geometry they are equivalent if they have the same pair of Euclidean invariants given by Eq. (7.29), which means that the two ellipses must be of the same size.

All ellipses are affine equivalent to the locus of the equation $x^2 + y^2 = 1$ that is the unit circle. All hyperbolae are affine equivalent to the locus of the equation $x^2 - y^2 = 1$. This is a disconnected set with two components, namely,

$$\{(x,y) \mid x^2 - y^2 = 1,\ x > 0\} \text{ and } \{(x,y) \mid x^2 - y^2 = 1,\ x < 0\}.$$

Finally, we note that the Euclidean equivalent figures have the following property: One figure can be superposed on the other by rigid displacement. Thus, the group of rigid displacements describes all possible relations of congruency. These relations underlie all physical measurements. A ruler is a rigid body and any measurement of length involves rigid displacements to compare a ruler with the object being measured.

Exercise This is a small project for the students:

Discuss the Euclidean, similarity and affine equivalence classes of non-singular central quadrics in $\mathcal{E}_3$ i.e., the loci

$$\left\{(x,y,z) \mid ax^2 + by^2 + cz^2 + 2fyz + 2gzx + 2hxy + 2ux + 2vy + 2wz + d = 0\right\}$$

with

$$\begin{vmatrix} a & h & g \\ h & b & f \\ g & f & c \end{vmatrix} \neq 0 \quad \begin{vmatrix} a & h & g & u \\ h & b & f & v \\ g & f & c & w \\ u & v & w & d \end{vmatrix} \neq 0,$$

where vertical bars mean the determinants of the corresponding matrices. Show in particular, that there are three affine equivalent classes and find simple canonical representatives of these classes. □

Part III

Vector Analysis

Nihatya chapavargena chapaṁ tat-tat phalani-cha.

Haret samulyuvargaiḥ trijyavargahataiḥ kramat.

Chapaṁ phalani-cha adho-adho nasyoparyuparityajet.

Jeevapatyaiḥ sangrahosyaiva vidvan ityadinaḥ kritaḥ.

This may be translated as follows:[1]

Multiply the arc by the square of the arc and take the result of repeating that [any number of times]. Divide [each of the above numetrators] by the squares of successive even numbers increased by that number [lit. the root] and multiplied by the square of the radius. Place the arc and the successive results so obtained one below the other and subtract each from the one above. These together give the *Jiva*, as collected together in the verse beginning with "*vidvan*" etc.

Indian mathematics and astronomy dealt not directly with present-day sines and cosines but with these quantities multiplied by the radius r of a standard circle. Thus, *jiva* corresponds to $r\sin\theta$ while *sara* corresponds to $r(1-\cos\theta)$.

In the present-day mathematical terminology the above passage says the following. Let r denote the radius of the circle, s denote the arc and t_n the nth expression obtained by applying the rule cited above. The rule requires us to calculate as follows.

1. Numerator: Multiply the arc s by its square s^2, this multiplication being repeated n times to obtain $s \cdot \Pi_1^n s^2$.

2. Denominator: Multiply the square of the radius, r^2, by $[(2k)^2 + 2k]$ ("squares of successive even numbers increased by that number") for successive values of k, repeating this product n times to obtain $\Pi_{k=1}^n r^2 [(2k)^2 + 2k]$.

Thus, the nth iterate is obtained by

$$t_n = \frac{s^{2n} \cdot s}{(2^2 + 2) \cdot (4^2 + 4) \cdots [(2n)^2 + 2n] \cdot r^{2n}}$$

The rule further says:

$$jiva \;=\; s - t_1 + t_2 - t_3 + t_4 - t_5 + \cdots$$

$$=\; s - \frac{s^3}{r^2 \cdot (2^2 + 2)} + \frac{s^5}{r^4 (2^2 + 2)(4^2 + 4)} - \cdots$$

---

[1] This epigraph is taken from ref.[18]

Substituting

  (i) $jiva = r\sin\theta$,

  (ii) $s = r\theta$, so that $s^{2n+1}/r^{2n} = r\theta^{2n+1}$ and noticing that

(iii) $[(2k)^2 + 2k] = 2k \cdot (2k+1)$ so that

(iv) $(2^2 + 2) \cdot (4^2 + 4) \cdots [(2n)^2 + 2n] = (2n+1)!$,

and cancelling r from both sides, we see that the infinite series for *Jiva* is entirely equivalent to the well known Taylor series for $\sin\theta$:

$$\sin\theta = \theta - \frac{\theta^3}{3!} + \frac{\theta^5}{5!} - \frac{\theta^7}{7!} + \cdots$$

It is now well known that calculus was developed in India starting mid-fifth century (Aryabhata in Bihar) until mid-fourteenth century (Madhava in Kerala) with a long list of brilliant mathematicians filling in the gap. Indians invented powerful techniques to accelerate convergence of a series and to sum a given series to the required accuracy [18]. Thus, Madhava produced a table of values of $\sin\theta$ and $\cos\theta$ exact upto ten decimal digits by summing up their Taylor series (better called Madhava series!). Values to this accuracy were required for navigation (locating ships and finding directions on open sea) and timekeeping (yearly scheduling of agricultural activities, vis-a-vis rainy season, to maximize production).

Preliminaries

8.1 Fundamental Notions

This part deals with the basic concepts and applications of differential and integral calculus to functions involving vector variables. By a function we mean a one to one or many to one mapping between non-empty sets say X and Y and denote it by $f : X \mapsto Y$. In general, f maps a subset of X, called its domain and denoted $\mathcal{D}(f)$, to a subset of Y called its range or image set and denoted $\mathcal{R}(f)$. If $\mathcal{R}(f) = Y$ then the function is called onto. If f is one to one and onto, it is invertible (see section 4.1). Note that the sets X and Y can be identical, $X = Y$, so that the function is $f : X \mapsto X$ and both the domain and the range of f are the subsets of the same set X. If $x \in \mathcal{D}(f)$ is mapped to $y \in \mathcal{R}(f)$ under f, then x is called the argument of f, y is called the image of x under f and is denoted $f(x)$, that is, $y = f(x)$. $f(x)$ is said to be the value of the function f at x. In general, we can say that x is a variable taking values in $\mathcal{D}(f)$ and $f(x)$ are the corresponding values in $\mathcal{R}(f)$. The image set of a subset $E \subseteq \mathcal{D}(f)$ under f is denoted $f(E)$. The equality, addition as well as the composition of two or more functions is exactly as given in section 4.1.

In this book we are concerned with the following three classes of functions.

- Vector valued functions of a scalar variable $f : \mathbb{R} \mapsto \mathscr{E}_3$. These functions generally occur as a part of the kinematics and dynamics of a physical system. For example, the velocity of a particle as a function of time $\mathbf{v}(t)$.

- Scalar valued functions of a vector variable, $f : \mathscr{E}_3 \mapsto \mathbb{R}$. All scalar fields $\phi(\mathbf{x})$ fall in this category, as a scalar field is a scalar valued function of position vectors or points in space, e.g., the temperature profile in a region of space.

- Vector valued functions of a vector variable, $f : \mathscr{E}_3 \mapsto \mathscr{E}_3$. All linear operators on $\mathscr{E}_3$ fall in this category. All vector fields are also functions (of position vectors) falling in this class.

In what follows we assume that the space $\mathscr{E}_3$ or ($\mathbb{R}^3$) and a real line $\mathbb{R}$ form a continuum (see section 1.2). We also treat these as metric spaces with Euclidean metric.

In this chapter, a vector is referred to either as a vector or as a point in space. Further, in this chapter we use the same symbol to indicate a vector or a scalar, because whatever is said about it applies to both the cases. At any rate, its being a vector or a scalar can be understood with reference to context. Also, by a function we mean a function in one of the three categories described above.

8.2   Sets and Mappings

We need the following properties of sets and mappings all shared by the subsets of $\mathscr{E}_3$ and $\mathbb{R}$.

Two sets A and B are said to be in $1-1$ correspondence if a one to one and onto map can be found between them. Such sets are said to have the same cardinality or are said to be equivalent and we write $A \sim B$. Clearly, the relation $A \sim B$ has the following properties.

- Reflexivity: $A \sim A$.
- Symmetry: If $A \sim B$ then $B \sim A$.
- Transitivity: If $A \sim B$ and $B \sim C$ then $A \sim C$.

Exercise   Prove the above properties.

Hint   The identity $I : A \mapsto A$ is a $1-1$ correspondence. Inverse of a $1-1$ correspondence is a $1-1$ correspondence. Composition of two $1-1$ correspondences is a $1-1$ correspondence.

□

Let $\mathbb{N}_k$ denote the set $\{1, 2, \ldots, k\}$ for some integer $k > 0$ and let $\mathbb{N}$ be the set $\{1, 2, 3, \ldots\}$ of all integers > 0. Given a set A we say

- A is *finite* if $A \sim \mathbb{N}_k$ for some $k \geq 0$. The empty set corresponding to $k = 0$ is also considered to be finite.
- A is *infinite* if it is not finite.
- A is *countable* if $A \sim \mathbb{N}$.
- A is *uncountable* if it is neither finite nor countable.

A countable set is sometimes called enumerable or denumerable.

For two finite sets A and B we evidently have $A \sim B$ if and only if they contain the same number of elements. The set $\mathbb{I}$ of all integers is countable as can be seen from the following $1-1$ correspondence between $\mathbb{I}$ and $\mathbb{N}$.

$$\mathbb{I} : 0 \;\; 1 \;\; -1 \;\; 2 \;\; -2 \;\; 3 \;\; -3 \cdots$$

$$\mathbb{N} : 1 \;\; 2 \;\; 3 \;\; 4 \;\; 5 \;\; 6 \;\; 7 \cdots$$

Exercise   Find $f : \mathbb{N} \mapsto \mathbb{I}$ generating this $1-1$ correspondence.

Answer

$$f(n) = \begin{cases} \frac{n}{2} & \text{(n even)} \\ -\frac{n-1}{2} & \text{(n odd)}. \end{cases}$$ □

This example shows that an infinite set can be put to $1 - 1$ correspondence with one of its proper subsets. This is not possible for finite sets.

Since $\mathbb{R}$, $\mathbb{R}^3$ and $\mathscr{E}_3$ are continua, we expect each of them to form an uncountable set. Also, every subset of these spaces, which forms a continuous region of space must also be an uncountable set. We accept this to be true without supplying any proofs.

8.3 Convergence of a Sequence

All analysis, be it real, complex or vector analysis, can be constructed on the basis of a single fundamental concept, namely, the convergence of an infinite sequence of points (or sequence for short) in the given space.

A sequence is a function defined on the set of all positive integers $\{1, 2, 3, \ldots\}$. We are basically interested in sequences defined by the functions $f : \mathbb{N} \mapsto \mathbb{R}$ and $f : \mathbb{N} \mapsto \mathscr{E}_3$ which are the sequences of scalars and vectors respectively. We denote the sequence $f(n) = x_n$, $(n \in \mathbb{N})$ by the symbol $\{x_n\}$ or by $x_1, x_2, x_3, \ldots$. The elements x_n forming the sequence are called the terms of the sequence. If A is a set and if $x_n \in A$ for all $n \in \mathbb{N}$ then $\{x_n\}$ is said to be a sequence in A. Note that the terms of a sequence may be distinct or identical. The set of all points x_n, $(n = 1, 2, \ldots)$ is the range of the sequence $\{x_n\}$. The range of a sequence may be a finite set or it may be infinite. A sequence $\{x_n\}$ is said to be *bounded* if its range is bounded (that is, the set formed by the distinct elements of a sequence is a bounded set, see below). We are interested in sequences in $\mathbb{R}$ or in $\mathscr{E}_3$.

The concept of the convergence of a sequence in a metric space can be defined without referring to a particular metric space. Therefore, we define the the convergence of a sequence in a metric space X which stands for both $\mathbb{R}$ and $\mathscr{E}_3$. A subset $S \subset X$ is said to be *bounded* if there is a real $M > 0$ satisfying $d(p, q) \leq M$ for all $p, q \in S$. The smallest M satisfying this condition is called the *diameter* of S. A r-*neighborhood* of a point $p \in X$ is a set $N_r(p)$ consisting of all points q such that $d(p, q) < r$. The number r is called the *radius* of $N_r(p)$. An *open set* is a subset E of X such that every point in it has a neighborhood which is a proper subset of that set. Each such point is called an *interior point* so an open set is the one whose every element is an interior point. In particular, a r-neighborhood of any point in a metric space is an open set. A point $p \in E$ is its *boundary point* if every neighborhood of p has a point $q \in E$, $q \neq p$, but is not a subset of E. A set containing all its interior as well as its boundary points is called a *closed set*. Thus, the set of all points inside a sphere of radius R is an open set while the points on the sphere form the set of boundary points. In general, in a metric space, given $\epsilon > 0$, the set of points with distance $< \epsilon$ from a given point form the ϵ-neighborhood of that point. The set of points at a distance ϵ from the given point form the set of boundary points of this ϵ-neighborhood.

A sequence of points in the metric space X, say, $x_1, x_2, x_3, \ldots$ is said to be *convergent* if for *every* $\epsilon > 0$, however small, there is an open set of diameter ϵ such that *all except finitely many* points of the sequence are elements of this set (see Fig. 8.1). Consider the sequence of real numbers $0 < \epsilon_1 > \epsilon_2 > \epsilon_3 > \cdots \epsilon_{n-1} > \epsilon_n > \epsilon_{n+1} > \cdots$ and the open sets of diameters $\epsilon_1 > \epsilon_2 > \epsilon_3 \cdots$ each of which contains all except finitely many elements of the converging sequence. Obviously, the set corresponding to ϵ_k is a proper subset of all sets corresponding to ϵ_n, $n < k$. If the diameter of these subsets is reduced without bounds, then these sets keep on approaching a set with singleton point, that is, the set corresponding to $\epsilon = 0$. This point is called the *limit* of the converging sequence.

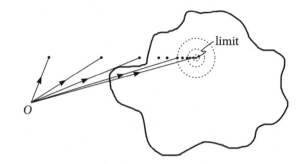

Fig. 8.1   A converging sequence in $\mathscr{E}_3$

Exercise   Show that the limit of a converging sequence is unique.

Hint   Assume two distinct limits and arrive at a contradiction. We have to also assume that two distinct points can have disjoint neighborhoods, a property possessed by $\mathscr{E}_3$ and $\mathbb{R}$.   □

Exercise   If two sequences $\{x_i\}$ and $\{y_i\}$ in $\mathscr{E}_3$ or $\mathbb{R}$ converge to x^* and y^* respectively in $\mathscr{E}_3$ or $\mathbb{R}$, show that the sequence $\{x_i + y_i\}$ converges to $x^* + y^*$ in $\mathscr{E}_3$ or $\mathbb{R}$. Further, if these sequences are in $\mathbb{R}$ and converge to these limits in $\mathbb{R}$, then show that the sequence $\{x_i y_i\}$ converges to $x^* y^*$ in $\mathbb{R}$.

Hint   We have to show that if the Euclidean distances $d(x_n, x^*) < \epsilon$ and $d(y_n, y^*) < \epsilon$ then $d(x_n + y_n, x^* + y^*) < \alpha \epsilon$ and $d(x_n y_n, x^* y^*) < \beta \epsilon$ where α, β are constants independent of n.   □

Exercise   A sequence $\{x_i\}$ in a metric space X converges to x^* in X. Show that its isomorphic image $\{y_i\}$ in space Y isometrically isomorphic to X converges to the isomorphic image $y^* \in Y$ of the limit $x^* \in X$.

Hint   Two linear spaces X and Y are said to be isometrically isomorphic if the isomorphism T satisfies $\|T(x)\| = \|x\|$ for all $x \in X$. Obviously, such an isomorphism preserves distance,

$$d(x,y) = \|x - y\| = \|T(x-y)\| = \|T(x) - T(y)\| = d(T(x), T(y))$$

from which the result follows. Thus, a sequence in $\mathscr{E}_3$ converging to a vector in $\mathscr{E}_3$ is also a sequence in $\mathbb{R}^3$ converging to a point represented by the vector at the limit.   □

Uniqueness of the limit of a converging sequence enables us to re-define its convergence as follows.

A sequence $\{x_i\}$ in a metric space X is a sequence converging to x^* if for every $\epsilon > 0$ there is an integer $n_0 > 0$ such that $d(x_n, x^*) < \epsilon$ whenever $n > n_0$. The fact that x^* is the limit of a converging sequence $\{x_k\}$ is summarily expressed as $\lim_{k \to \infty} x_k = x^*$.

Exercise   Suppose $\{x_n\}$ is in $\mathbb{R}$ and $\lim_{n \to \infty} x_n = x^*$. Show that $\lim_{n \to \infty} \frac{1}{x_n} = \frac{1}{x^*}$ provided $x_n \neq 0$, $(n = 1, 2, \ldots)$ and $x^* \neq 0$.   □

Exercise

(a) Suppose $\mathbf{x}_n \in \mathbb{R}^3 (n = 1, 2, 3, \ldots)$ and $\mathbf{x}_n = (\alpha_{1,n}, \alpha_{2,n}, \alpha_{3,n})$. Then $\mathbf{x}_n$ converges to $\mathbf{x} = (\alpha_1, \alpha_2, \alpha_3)$ if and only if $\lim_{n \to \infty} \alpha_{j,n} = \alpha_j, j = 1, 2, 3$.

(b) Suppose $\{\mathbf{x}_n\} \{\mathbf{y}_n\}$ are sequences in $\mathbb{R}^3$ and $\{\beta_n\}$ is a sequence in (R) and $\mathbf{x}_n \to \mathbf{x}$, $\mathbf{y}_n \to \mathbf{y}$, $\beta_n \to \beta$. Then,

$$\lim_{n \to \infty} (\mathbf{x}_n + \mathbf{y}_n) = \mathbf{x} + \mathbf{y} \quad \lim_{n \to \infty} (\mathbf{x}_n \cdot \mathbf{y}_n) = \mathbf{x} \cdot \mathbf{y} \quad \lim_{n \to \infty} \beta_n \mathbf{x}_n = \beta \mathbf{x}.$$

Solution

(a) If $\mathbf{x}_n \to \mathbf{x}$, the inequalities

$$|\alpha_{j,n} - \alpha_j| \leq |\mathbf{x}_n - \mathbf{x}|$$

which follow immediately from the definition of the norm in $\mathbf{R}^3$ show that $\lim_{n \to \infty} \alpha_{j,n} = \alpha_j, j = 1, 2, 3$.

Conversely, if $\lim_{n \to \infty} \alpha_{j,n} = \alpha_j, j = 1, 2, 3$, then to each $\epsilon > 0$ there is an integer N such that $n \geq N$ implies

$$|\alpha_{j,n} - \alpha_j| < \frac{\epsilon}{\sqrt{3}} \quad j = 1, 2, 3.$$

Hence, $n \geq N$ implies

$$|\mathbf{x}_n - \mathbf{x}| = \left\{ \sum_{j=1}^{3} |\alpha_{j,n} - \alpha_j|^2 \right\}^{\frac{1}{2}} < \epsilon,$$

so that $\mathbf{x}_n \to \mathbf{x}$, which proves (a).

(b) **Hint**   Use part (a).   □

8.4 Continuous Functions

Consider a converging sequence $x_1, x_2, x_3, \ldots$ in the domain $\mathcal{D}(f)$ of a function f with its limit $x^* \in \mathcal{D}(f)$. The function f is said to be continuous at x^* if the sequence $f(x_1), f(x_2), f(x_3), \ldots$ converges to the limit $f(x^*)$ and this happens for *all* sequences in $\mathcal{D}(f)$ converging to x^*. The continuity of a function at a point can be expressed as

$$\lim_{x \to x^*} f(x) = f(x^*),$$

or,

$$\lim_{x \to x^*} d(f(x), f(x^*)) = 0,$$

or, assuming the Euclidian distance

$$\lim_{x \to x^*} \|f(x) - f(x^*)\| = 0.$$

Exercise Show that if the functions $f(x)$ and $g(x)$ are continuous at x^* then so is their sum $f(x) + g(x)$ and their product $f(x)g(x)$. □

In general, we say that

$$\lim_{x \to x^*} f(x)$$

exists if for *every* sequence $\{x_n\}$ converging to x^*, the corresponding sequence $\{f(x_n)\}$ converges to the *same* limit. In terms of this definition, the result of the third exercise of this section can be used to get

$$\lim_{x \to x^*} [f(x) + g(x)] = \lim_{x \to x^*} f(x) + \lim_{x \to x^*} g(x) \tag{8.1}$$

and

$$\lim_{x \to x^*} [f(x)g(x)] = [\lim_{x \to x^*} f(x)][\lim_{x \to x^*} g(x)]. \tag{8.2}$$

provided the limits on the RHS of these equations exist.

Vector Valued Functions of a Scalar Variable

We start with the functions in the first of the three categories described above, namely, the vector valued functions of a scalar variable, denoted $\mathbf{f}(t)$.

9.1 Continuity and Differentiation

The derivative of $\mathbf{f}(t)$ with respect to the scalar variable t is a new function denoted $\frac{d\mathbf{f}(t)}{dt}$ or $\dot{\mathbf{f}}(t)$ and is defined by

$$\dot{\mathbf{f}}(t) = \frac{d\mathbf{f}(t)}{dt} = \lim_{\Delta t \to 0} \frac{\mathbf{f}(t + \Delta t) - \mathbf{f}(t)}{\Delta t}. \tag{9.1}$$

This limit, when evaluated at a particular value $t = t_0$, gives the value of the derivative of $\mathbf{f}(t)$ at t_0, that is, the value of $\dot{\mathbf{f}}(t_0)$ or $\frac{d\mathbf{f}}{dt}(t_0)$. We say that the function $\mathbf{f}(t)$ is differentiable at t_0 if this limit exists at $t = t_0$.

Note that, to be differentiable at t_0, $\mathbf{f}(t)$ must be continuous at t_0, that is,

$$\lim_{\Delta t \to 0} \mathbf{f}(t_0 + \Delta t) = \mathbf{f}(t_0)$$

Otherwise, the RHS of Eq. (9.1) will blow up as $\Delta t \to 0$ because the numerator remains finite while the denominator tends to zero.

The derivative $\dot{\mathbf{f}}(t)$ is a function of t in its own right, therefore we can differentiate it by applying Eq. (9.1) to it, provided the corresponding limit exists. The resulting derivative function is called the second derivative of $\mathbf{f}(t)$ and is denoted $\ddot{\mathbf{f}}(t)$ or $\frac{d^2\mathbf{f}}{dt^2}(t)$. Continuing in this way we can define the third and higher order derivatives of $\mathbf{f}(t)$.

As an important application, we consider a particle moving along a path which is a continuous and differentiable curve, that is, the curve is the graph of a continuous and differentiable function $\mathbf{x}(t)$ of time t, giving the position vector of the particle at time t on the path. The derivative $\dot{\mathbf{x}} = \dot{\mathbf{x}}(t)$ is called the velocity of the particle, defined by Eq. (9.1), which we can abbrivate as

$$\dot{\mathbf{x}} = \frac{d\mathbf{x}}{dt} = \lim_{\Delta t \to 0} \frac{\Delta \mathbf{x}}{\Delta t}, \text{ which defines } \Delta \mathbf{x} = \mathbf{x}(t + \Delta t) - \mathbf{x}(t).$$

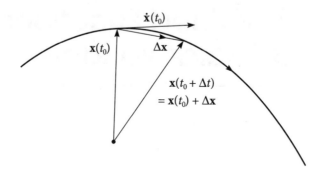

Fig. 9.1   Geometry of the derivative

The curve and the vectors involved in the derivative are shown in Fig. 9.1. Note that the derivative $\dot{\mathbf{x}}$ or the velocity vector is always tangent to the curve. The derivative of the velocity

$$\ddot{\mathbf{x}} = \frac{d^2\mathbf{x}}{dt^2} = \lim_{\Delta t \to 0} \frac{\Delta \dot{\mathbf{x}}}{\Delta t}$$

is called the acceleration of the particle.

Using Eq. (8.2) we easily get, for functions $\mathbf{f}(t)$ and $\mathbf{g}(t)$,

$$\frac{d}{dt}(\mathbf{f}(t) + \mathbf{g}(t)) = \frac{d\mathbf{f}(t)}{dt} + \frac{d\mathbf{g}(t)}{dt} = \dot{\mathbf{f}}(t) + \dot{\mathbf{g}}(t) \tag{9.2}$$

and for two scalar valued functions of a scalar variable $f(t)$ and $g(t)$ we get

$$\frac{d}{dt}(f(t)g(t)) = \frac{df(t)}{dt}g(t) + f(t)\frac{dg(t)}{dt} = \dot{f}(t)g(t) + f(t)\dot{g}(t) \tag{9.3}$$

Using the definition of the dot product in terms of vector components and Eq. (9.3) we can write

$$\frac{d}{dt}(\mathbf{f}(t) \cdot \mathbf{g}(t)) = \frac{d}{dt}(f_x(t)g_x(t) + f_x(t)g_x(t) + f_x(t)g_x(t))$$

$$= \dot{\mathbf{f}}(t) \cdot \mathbf{g}(t) + \mathbf{f}(t) \cdot \dot{\mathbf{g}}(t). \tag{9.4}$$

In particular, for a particle with velocity $\mathbf{v}(t)$ and speed function $v(t) = |\mathbf{v}(t)|$ we get

$$\frac{d}{dt}v^2(t) = \frac{d}{dt}(\mathbf{v}(t) \cdot \mathbf{v}(t)) = 2\dot{\mathbf{v}}(t) \cdot \mathbf{v}(t).$$

This equation relates the rate of change of kinetic energy of a particle with its velocity and acceleration. On the other hand, if the particle is moving along a straight line, so that its direction $\hat{\mathbf{v}}$ is constant while its speed changes with time, $(\dot{\mathbf{v}}(t) = \dot{v}(t)\hat{\mathbf{v}})$, then,

$$\frac{d}{dt}v^2 = 2v\dot{v} = 2v\dot{v}\hat{\mathbf{v}} \cdot \hat{\mathbf{v}} = 2\dot{\mathbf{v}} \cdot \mathbf{v}.$$

We shall now show that a vector valued function $\mathbf{v}(t)$ has constant magnitude if and only if there is a vector ω satisfying

$$\dot{\mathbf{v}} = \omega \times \mathbf{v} \tag{9.5}$$

To show that Eq. (9.5) implies constant magnitude for $\mathbf{v}$, we just dot both sides by $\mathbf{v}$ to get $\mathbf{v} \cdot \omega \times \mathbf{v}$ on RHS which is zero. This means $2\dot{\mathbf{v}} \cdot \mathbf{v} = \frac{d}{dt}v^2 = 0$ or $|\mathbf{v}|$ is constant.

To show that constant magnitude of $\mathbf{v}$, that is, $2\dot{\mathbf{v}} \cdot \mathbf{v} = \frac{d}{dt}v^2 = 0$ implies the existence of some ω satisfying Eq. (9.5), we choose $\omega = (\hat{\mathbf{v}} \times \dot{\mathbf{v}})/v$. Using identity I and the fact that $\dot{\mathbf{v}} \cdot \mathbf{v} = 0$ we can easily check that this ω satisfies Eq. (9.5).

Exercise   If $\hat{\mathbf{n}}$ is a unit vector function of the scalar variable t, then show that

$$\left| \hat{\mathbf{n}} \times \frac{d\hat{\mathbf{n}}}{dt} \right| = \left| \frac{d\hat{\mathbf{n}}}{dt} \right|.$$

Solution   We make use of the fact that the vector of constant magnitude is perpendicular to its derivative. Thus, $\hat{\mathbf{n}}$ is perpendicular to $\frac{d\hat{\mathbf{n}}}{dt}$. Therefore, we have,

$$\left| \hat{\mathbf{n}} \times \frac{d\hat{\mathbf{n}}}{dt} \right| = |\hat{\mathbf{n}}| \left| \frac{d\hat{\mathbf{n}}}{dt} \right| \sin \frac{\pi}{2} = \left| \frac{d\hat{\mathbf{n}}}{dt} \right|$$

since $|\hat{\mathbf{n}}| = 1$.   □

Exercise   Let $\mathbf{u} = \mathbf{u}(t)$ be a vector valued function and write $u = |\mathbf{u}|$. Show that

$$\frac{d}{dt}(\hat{\mathbf{u}}(t)) = \frac{d}{dt}\left(\frac{\mathbf{u}}{u}\right) = \frac{(\mathbf{u} \times \dot{\mathbf{u}}) \times \mathbf{u}}{u^3}.$$

Solution   By straightforward differentiation we get

$$\frac{d}{dt}\left(\frac{\mathbf{u}}{u}\right) = \frac{u\dot{\mathbf{u}} - \dot{u}\mathbf{u}}{u^2}.$$

Now consider

$$\frac{(\mathbf{u} \times \dot{\mathbf{u}}) \times \mathbf{u}}{u^3} = \frac{u^2 \dot{\mathbf{u}} - (\mathbf{u} \cdot \dot{\mathbf{u}}) \mathbf{u}}{u^3} = \frac{u \dot{\mathbf{u}} - \dot{u} \mathbf{u}}{u^2}$$

where the last equality follows from $\mathbf{u} \cdot \dot{\mathbf{u}} = \frac{1}{2} \frac{d}{dt} u^2 = u \dot{u}$. □

Exercise   Show that the conservation of angular momentum ($\mathbf{h}$) of a particle driven by a central force, ($\dot{\mathbf{h}} = \mathbf{0}$), implies that both the magnitude and the direction of $\mathbf{h}$ are conserved separately. Use this to show that the orbit of the earth around the sun never changes the direction of its circulation about the sun.

Solution   To prove the first part consider $\dot{\mathbf{h}} = \mathbf{0}$ implies $\mathbf{h} \cdot \dot{\mathbf{h}} = 0$ which implies $\frac{d}{dt}(\mathbf{h} \cdot \mathbf{h}) = \frac{d}{dt}(h^2) = 0$, where $h = |\mathbf{h}|$. Thus, the magnitude of $\mathbf{h}$ is conserved separately. Now, $h = $ constant and $h\hat{\mathbf{h}} = $ constant together imply $\hat{\mathbf{h}} = $ constant so that the direction of $\mathbf{h}$ is separately conserved.

To get the second part, note that, for constant magnitude of $\mathbf{h}$,

$$0 \le |\mathbf{h}| = h = mr^2 \dot{\theta}, \tag{9.6}$$

where r is the distance of the particle from the center of force. Equation (9.6) implies that $\dot{\theta} \ge 0$ always, in a dextral (that is, right handed) frame so $\theta = \theta(t)$ increases monotonically with time if $h \ne 0$. In a left handed frame $\dot{\theta} \le 0$. What is important (and physical) is that $\dot{\theta}$ cannot ever change its sign. This means that the orbit of the earth in the central force field of the sun never changes the direction of its circulation, as the angular momentum of its orbital motion around the sun is conserved. Note that this result applies to all central forces. □

Let us now see the effect of differentiation on the vector product of two functions and the product of a vector valued and the scalar valued function. Let $\mathbf{A}(t)$ and $\mathbf{B}(t)$ be two vector valued functions of a scalar variable t and $\phi(t)$ be a scalar valued function of t. Differentiating $(\mathbf{A}(t) \times \mathbf{B}(t))_i = \varepsilon_{ijk} A_j(t) B_k(t)$ we get,

$$\frac{d}{dt}(\mathbf{A}(t) \times \mathbf{B}(t)) = \frac{d\mathbf{A}}{dt} \times \mathbf{B} + \mathbf{A} \times \frac{d\mathbf{B}}{dt}. \tag{9.7}$$

Also, by differentiating the product of functions we get,

$$\frac{d}{dt}(\phi \mathbf{A}) = \frac{d\phi}{dt} \mathbf{A} + \phi \frac{d\mathbf{A}}{dt}. \tag{9.8}$$

We can summarily conclude

- If $\frac{d\mathbf{A}}{dt} \cdot \mathbf{A} = 0$ then $|\mathbf{A}|$ is constant.

- If $\mathbf{A} \times \frac{d\mathbf{A}}{dt} = \mathbf{0}, \mathbf{A} \ne \mathbf{0}$, then $\frac{d\mathbf{A}}{dt}$ is parallel to $\mathbf{A}$ implying that $\mathbf{A}$ has constant direction.

9.2   Geometry and Kinematics: Space Curves and Frenet–Seret Formulae

Frenet–Seret formulae help us connect the geometry of the path of a particle with its kinematics. We have seen that a path of a particle, which we assume to be a smooth curve given by a continuous and differentiable function $\mathbf{x}(t)$, is parameterized by time t. That is, evaluation of $\mathbf{x}(t)$ at some value of the scalar parameter t, say $\mathbf{x}(t_0)$ at $t = t_0$, corresponds to a unique point on the path giving the position of the particle at time $t = t_0$. The vector valued function $\mathbf{x}(t)$ is equivalent to the triplet of scalar valued 'coordinate functions' $(x(t), y(t), z(t))$ which are the components of $\mathbf{x}(t)$ with respect to some orthonormal basis.

For a curve $\mathcal{C}$, the function $\mathbf{x}(t) \equiv (x(t), y(t), z(t))$ above, defines a *one to one map* of the *t-axis onto the curve*, that is, a point on the t-axis is mapped to the unique point $\mathbf{x}(t) \equiv (x(t), y(t), z(t))$ on the curve $\mathcal{C}$. Since the function $\mathbf{x}(t) \equiv (x(t), y(t), z(t))$ is assumed continuous, neighboring points on the t-axis correspond to the neighboring points on the curve. Since the points on the t-axis are ordered, we can assign an order or the 'sense' to the points of $\mathcal{C}$ by saying that the point $\mathbf{x}(t_1)$ on $\mathcal{C}$ precedes point $\mathbf{x}(t_2)$ on $\mathcal{C}$ if $t_1 < t_2$. The parametric representation thus gives a precise meaning to the sense in which a curve is traversed, using the order of points on a line. This still allows for the possibility $\mathbf{x}(t_1) = \mathbf{x}(t_2)$ on $\mathcal{C}$ even if $t_1 \neq t_2$ which just means that the particle was at the same point on the curve at two different times t_1 and t_2. This is possible if path is a simple closed curve or has a loop. A point on the curve at which $\frac{d\mathbf{x}}{dt} \neq \mathbf{0}$ is called a *regular point*.

The same path can be parameterized by different parameters, given by different monotonic functions of t. For example, a circle can be parameterized by angle θ made by the radius vector with the positive direction of the x axis say $\theta = \omega t$ where ω is the angular or rotational velocity of the particle along the circle. Another possible parameterization is by arc length. This parameter is given by the distance $s(t)$ traversed by the particle along the path, measured from a fixed point on the path which corresponds to $t = 0$. The path then becomes the graph of the function $\mathbf{x}(s)$. The value $\mathbf{x}(s_0)$ at $s = s_0$ simply gives the position vector of the particle at a point on the path, reached by traversing the path of length s_0 from the chosen fixed point on the path. While measuring s_0 the path is traversed in the same sense in which the moving particle traverses the path, with increasing time, as we saw in the above paragraph. All this is depicted in Fig. 9.2.

Mathematically, we change the parameter from arc length s to time t, in the range $s_1 \leq s \leq s_2$, by means of an analytic function $s = s(t)$ with $s_1 = s(t_1)$ and $s_2 = s(t_2)$ such that $\frac{ds}{dt} > 0$ in $t_1 \leq t \leq t_2$. This ensures that the inverse function $t(s)$ exists and is analytic in $s_1 \leq s \leq s_2$ and that $\frac{dt}{ds} > 0$ there. This ensures 1-1 correspondence between the values of s and t in their domains and both parameterizations traverse the curve in the same sense as they increase through their values. As $\frac{d\mathbf{x}}{dt} = \frac{d\mathbf{x}}{ds}\frac{ds}{dt}$ and $\frac{ds}{dt} \neq 0$ a regular point for the parameter s is also the regular point for the parameter t.

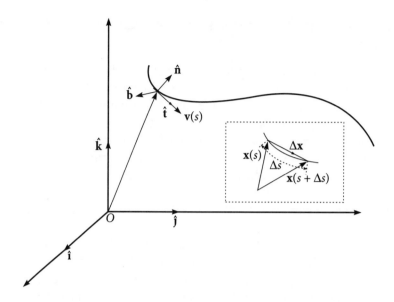

Fig. 9.2   Parameterization by arc length

Exercise   A circular helix is represented by

$$\mathbf{x} = a\cos t\hat{\mathbf{i}} + a\sin t\hat{\mathbf{j}} + bt\hat{\mathbf{k}} \quad -\infty < t < +\infty,$$

where $\hat{\mathbf{k}}$ is along the axis of the helix. Provide the equation for the circular helix with (i) z coordinate and (ii) arc length s as a parameter.

Solution   A circular helix is a curve which winds on a circular cylinder of radius a with its axis along the z axis. When a point moving along the helix completes one turn, t increases by 2π; x and y coordinates assume their original values, and z is increased by $2\pi b$. As $\frac{d\mathbf{x}}{dt} \neq \mathbf{0}$, for all t, all points of the helix are regular for the parameter t.

Let z be the new parameter and $b \neq 0$. Then $t = z/b$ and the equation to the helix becomes

$$\mathbf{x} = a\cos\frac{z}{b}\hat{\mathbf{i}} + a\sin\frac{z}{b}\hat{\mathbf{j}} + z\hat{\mathbf{k}}.$$

Since t is an analytic function of z and $dt/dz = 1/b \neq 0$ every point of the helix is a regular point for the new parameter z.

Now for the parameter arc length s, we know that,

$$ds = \sqrt{\left(\frac{dx}{dt}\right)^2 + \left(\frac{dy}{dt}\right)^2 + \left(\frac{dz}{dt}\right)^2}\, dt.$$

For the circular helix this becomes

$$ds = \sqrt{a^2 + b^2}\, dt.$$

We choose $s = 0$ at $t = 0$ and integrate to get,

$$s = t\sqrt{a^2 + b^2}.$$

Therefore, in terms of s we get,

$$\mathbf{x} = a\cos\frac{s}{\sqrt{a^2 + b^2}}\hat{\mathbf{i}} + a\sin\frac{s}{\sqrt{a^2 + b^2}}\hat{\mathbf{j}} + b\frac{s}{\sqrt{a^2 + b^2}}\hat{\mathbf{k}}.$$

Since $dt/ds \neq 0$, every point on the helix is regular with respect to parameter s. $\square$

Consider a point $\mathbf{x}(s_0)$ on the path corresponding to $s = s_0$. Let $\mathbf{x} + \Delta\mathbf{x}$ be the position vector of a neighboring point corresponding to the parametric value $s + \Delta s$. Since the curve is smooth and $\mathbf{x}(s)$ is differentiable, there is a small enough neighborhood of $\mathbf{x}(s_0)$ such that we can take $|\Delta\mathbf{x}| = |\Delta s|$, that is, we can take the Euclidean distance between $\mathbf{x}(s_0)$ and $\mathbf{x}(s_0 + \Delta s)$ to be the same as the distance traversed along the path between these points. In the limit,

$$\lim_{\Delta s \to 0}\frac{\mathbf{x}(s_0 + \Delta s) - \mathbf{x}(s)}{\Delta s} = \left[\frac{d\mathbf{x}}{ds}\right]_{s=s_0}$$

then becomes a unit vector tangential to the path at the point $\mathbf{x}(s_0)$ pointing along the direction given by the increasing values of s. Denoting this tangential unit vector by $\hat{\mathbf{t}}$ we can write

$$\hat{\mathbf{t}} = \frac{d\mathbf{x}}{ds}.$$

Since $\hat{\mathbf{t}}$ is a unit vector we have $\hat{\mathbf{t}} \cdot \hat{\mathbf{t}} = 1$ which gives

$$\frac{d\hat{\mathbf{t}}}{ds} \cdot \hat{\mathbf{t}} = 0$$

that is, the vector $\frac{d\hat{\mathbf{t}}}{ds}$ is orthogonal to $\hat{\mathbf{t}}$. This vector measures the amount by which the direction of $\hat{\mathbf{t}}$ changes as s increases i.e., as the particle moves along the path. We write

$$\frac{d\hat{\mathbf{t}}}{ds} = \left|\frac{d\hat{\mathbf{t}}}{ds}\right|\hat{\mathbf{n}} = \kappa\hat{\mathbf{n}} \tag{9.9}$$

where $\hat{\mathbf{n}}$ is the unit vector in the direction of $\frac{d\hat{\mathbf{t}}}{ds}$ and $\kappa = \left|\frac{d\hat{\mathbf{t}}}{ds}\right|$ is the rate of change of direction of $\hat{\mathbf{t}}$ with s. κ is called the curvature of the path at the point $\mathbf{x}(s_0)$. $\hat{\mathbf{n}}$ is called the *principal normal* unit vector. Note that $\hat{\mathbf{n}}$ is always in the direction of $\frac{d\hat{\mathbf{t}}}{ds}$ as κ is chosen to be non-negative.

The equation $\kappa = \frac{1}{\rho}$ defines the radius of curvature ρ at the corresponding point. A straight line is a curve with zero curvature and infinite radius of curvature. In this case $\hat{\mathbf{t}}$ is along the line and $\hat{\mathbf{n}}$ can be in any direction perpendicular to $\hat{\mathbf{t}}$. The vector $\mathbf{X} = \mathbf{x} + \rho\hat{\mathbf{n}}$

determines C, the center of curvature. The circle with center at C, radius ρ and in the plane determined by $\hat{\mathbf{n}}$ and $\hat{\mathbf{t}}$ is called the *circle of curvature* or the *osculating circle* (see Fig. 9.3).

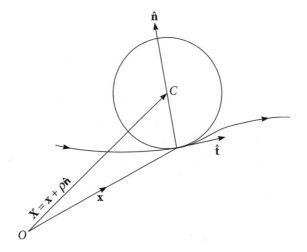

Fig. 9.3   The Osculating circle

Exercise   Determine the curvature for the circular helix.
   Referring to the previous exercise we get for the circular helix,

$$\hat{\mathbf{t}} = \frac{-a}{\sqrt{a^2 + b^2}} \sin \frac{s}{\sqrt{a^2 + b^2}}\hat{\mathbf{i}} + \frac{a}{\sqrt{a^2 + b^2}} \cos \frac{s}{\sqrt{a^2 + b^2}}\hat{\mathbf{j}} + \frac{b}{\sqrt{a^2 + b^2}}\hat{\mathbf{k}}.$$

So that

$$\frac{d\hat{\mathbf{t}}}{ds} = \frac{-a}{a^2 + b^2}\left[\cos \frac{s}{\sqrt{a^2 + b^2}}\hat{\mathbf{i}} + \sin \frac{s}{\sqrt{a^2 + b^2}}\hat{\mathbf{j}}\right]$$

Hence,

$$\kappa = \left|\frac{d\hat{\mathbf{t}}}{ds}\right| = \frac{a}{a^2 + b^2}$$

and

$$\hat{\mathbf{n}} = -\cos \frac{s}{\sqrt{a^2 + b^2}}\hat{\mathbf{i}} - \sin \frac{s}{\sqrt{a^2 + b^2}}\hat{\mathbf{j}}.$$

Note that the curvature is the same for all points of the helix, while $\hat{\mathbf{n}}$ changes as we go along the helix.   □

Exercise   Obtain the parameterization of a circle of radius R by arc length. Find the vectors $\hat{\mathbf{t}}$ and $\hat{\mathbf{n}}$ and hence the curvature and the radius of curvature at a point on the circle. Show that these quantities are the same for the whole circle.

Solution   The arc length parameterization of a circle of radius R is given by

$$\mathbf{x}(s) \equiv \left(R\cos\frac{s}{R}, R\sin\frac{s}{R} \right).$$

Differentiating with respect to s we immediately get

$$\hat{\mathbf{t}} \equiv \left(-\sin\frac{s}{R}, \cos\frac{s}{R} \right).$$

giving $|\hat{\mathbf{t}}| = 1$. Differentiating again with respect to s gives

$$\frac{d\hat{\mathbf{t}}}{ds} = -\frac{1}{R}\left(\cos\frac{s}{R}, \sin\frac{s}{R} \right)$$

so that the curvature $\kappa = |\frac{d\hat{\mathbf{t}}}{ds}| = \frac{1}{R}$ and the radius of curvature is R. Since these quantities depend only on the circle radius R, they are the same for all points of the circle, characterizing the circle as a whole. □

Exercise

(a) For a scalar valued function of a scalar variable, $y(x)$, which is continuous and has a continuous first derivative, the curvature κ is defined by $\frac{d\alpha}{ds}$ where s is the arch length parameter of the graph of $y(x)$ verses x, $\alpha(s)$ is the angle made by the tangent to the graph at s with the positive direction of the x axis (see Fig. 9.4). Show that

$$\kappa = \frac{y''}{(1+y'^2)^{3/2}} \qquad (9.10)$$

where prime denotes differentiation with respect to x.

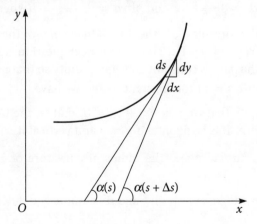

Fig. 9.4   Curvature of a planar curve

(b) If the graph of $y(x)$ is the path of a particle parameterized by $\mathbf{x}(t) \equiv (x(t), y(t))$, show that the curvature is given by

$$\kappa = \frac{\dot{x}\ddot{y} - \dot{y}\ddot{x}}{(\dot{x}^2 + \dot{y}^2)^{3/2}}, \tag{9.11}$$

where $\dot{x} \equiv \frac{dx}{dt}$ etc. When can we have $\kappa = \dot{x}\ddot{y} - \dot{y}\ddot{x}$?

Solution

(a) Since $y(x)$ is continuous and differentiable, the piece of curve traversed by a small enough increment ds can be approximated by a straight line, in which case we have (see Fig. 9.4),

$$ds = \sqrt{dx^2 + dy^2} = dx\sqrt{1 + y'^2}.$$

Further, $y' = \tan \alpha$ or $\alpha = \arctan y'$, $-\frac{\pi}{2} \le \alpha \le \frac{\pi}{2}$, We have,

$$\frac{d\alpha}{ds} = \frac{d\alpha}{dx}\frac{dx}{ds}$$

$$= \frac{\frac{d}{dx}(\arctan y')}{\sqrt{1 + y'^2}}$$

$$= \frac{y''}{(1 + y'^2)^{3/2}}. \tag{9.12}$$

(b) To get Eq. (9.11) just note that $y' = \frac{\dot{y}}{\dot{x}} = \frac{\sin \alpha}{\cos \alpha} = \tan \alpha$ and transform Eq. (9.10). Note that $\cos \alpha = \pm \frac{\dot{x}}{\sqrt{\dot{x}^2 + \dot{y}^2}}$ and $\sin \alpha = \pm \frac{\dot{y}}{\sqrt{\dot{x}^2 + \dot{y}^2}}$ (where the same sign must be taken in both the formulas) are the direction cosines of the tangent vector $\dot{\mathbf{x}} \equiv (\dot{x}, \dot{y})$ to the path at $(x(t), y(t))$. The claim in the next question is satisfied if the speed of the particle along the path is constant and equals unity so that parameters s and t become identical (because $s = vt$ for constant v) and we have $\left|\frac{d\mathbf{x}}{ds}\right| = \left|\frac{d\mathbf{x}}{dt}\right| = \sqrt{\dot{x}^2 + \dot{y}^2} = 1$.

Finally, we note that we take $\dot{x}^2 + \dot{y}^2 \neq 0$, that is, the tangent always exists at all points of the path. It is horizontal if $\dot{y} = 0$ and vertical if $\dot{x} = 0$. □

Exercise   Find the curvature and the radius of curvature of a circle of radius R using Eq. (9.11). □

A third unit vector, orthogonal to both $\hat{\mathbf{t}}$ and $\hat{\mathbf{n}}$ is uniquely defined as

$$\hat{\mathbf{b}} = \hat{\mathbf{t}} \times \hat{\mathbf{n}}$$

and is called the *binormal* unit vector.

We see that the triplet $\{\hat{\mathbf{t}}, \hat{\mathbf{n}}, \hat{\mathbf{b}}\}$ forms a right handed system of orthonormal vectors at each point of the curve. Since the triplet $\{\hat{\mathbf{t}}, \hat{\mathbf{n}}, \hat{\mathbf{b}}\}$ changes from point to point on the curve, the corresponding coordinate system also changes and is called a *moving trihedral*.

Since $\hat{\mathbf{t}} \cdot \hat{\mathbf{b}} = 0$, we have,

$$0 = \frac{d\hat{\mathbf{t}}}{ds} \cdot \hat{\mathbf{b}} + \hat{\mathbf{t}} \cdot \frac{d\hat{\mathbf{b}}}{ds} = \hat{\mathbf{t}} \cdot \frac{d\hat{\mathbf{b}}}{ds}$$

implying $\hat{\mathbf{t}}$ and $\frac{d\hat{\mathbf{b}}}{ds}$ are orthogonal. Since $\hat{\mathbf{b}} \cdot \hat{\mathbf{b}} = 1$, $\hat{\mathbf{b}} \cdot \frac{d\hat{\mathbf{b}}}{ds} = 0$. Thus, $\frac{d\hat{\mathbf{b}}}{ds}$ is a vector perpendicular to both $\hat{\mathbf{t}}$ and $\hat{\mathbf{b}}$ so that the vector $\frac{d\hat{\mathbf{b}}}{ds}$ is along $\hat{\mathbf{n}}$ and measures the rotation of $\hat{\mathbf{b}}$ in the plane of $\hat{\mathbf{b}}$ and $\hat{\mathbf{n}}$ perpendicular to $\hat{\mathbf{t}}$, as the particle moves along the curve, or as s changes. We write

$$\frac{d\hat{\mathbf{b}}}{ds} = \tau\hat{\mathbf{n}} \tag{9.13}$$

and call τ the torsion of the curve.

Exercise Find the binormal vector and the torsion for the circular helix.

Answer Using the previously obtained expressions for $\hat{\mathbf{t}}$ and $\hat{\mathbf{n}}$ for the helix,

$$\hat{\mathbf{b}} = \frac{b}{c}\sin\frac{s}{c}\hat{\mathbf{i}} - \frac{b}{c}\cos\frac{s}{c}\hat{\mathbf{j}} + \frac{a}{c}\hat{\mathbf{k}}$$

where $c = \sqrt{a^2 + b^2}$. Further,

$$\tau = -\frac{b}{c^2}. \qquad \Box$$

Exercise A helix is defined to be a curve with non-zero curvature, such that the tangent at every point makes the same angle with a fixed line in space called the axis. Show that a necessary and sufficient condition that a curve be a helix is that the ratio of torsion to curvature is constant.

Solution We first show that the all tangents making the same angle with the axis implies a constant ratio of κ and τ. This condition can be expressed as

$$\hat{\mathbf{t}} \cdot \hat{\mathbf{e}} = \cos\theta = c,$$

where $\hat{\mathbf{t}}$ is a unit tangent vector to the helix, $\hat{\mathbf{e}}$ is a unit vector along the axis and θ is the (constant) angle between the tangent and the axis. Differentiating this equation with respect to s gives

$$\frac{d\hat{\mathbf{t}}}{ds} \cdot \hat{\mathbf{e}} = \kappa\hat{\mathbf{n}} \cdot \hat{\mathbf{e}} = 0.$$

Since $\kappa \neq 0$ we must have $\hat{\mathbf{n}} \cdot \hat{\mathbf{e}} = 0$. Hence, $\hat{\mathbf{e}}$ is in the plane spanned by $\hat{\mathbf{t}}$ and $\hat{\mathbf{b}}$ and can be expressed as a linear combination of them. Since $\hat{\mathbf{t}} \cdot \hat{\mathbf{e}} = \cos\theta$ and $\hat{\mathbf{e}}$ is a unit vector,

$$\hat{\mathbf{e}} = \cos\theta\hat{\mathbf{t}} + \sin\theta\hat{\mathbf{b}}.$$

Differentiating with respect to s we get, since the derivatives of $\hat{\mathbf{t}}$ and $\hat{\mathbf{b}}$ are both proportional to $\hat{\mathbf{n}}$,

$$0 = (\kappa\cos\theta + \tau\sin\theta)\hat{\mathbf{n}},$$

or,

$$\frac{\kappa}{\tau} = -\tan\theta = \text{constant}.$$

We now assume that

$$\frac{\kappa}{\tau} = -\tan\theta = -\frac{\sin\theta}{\cos\theta} = \text{constant}.$$

This means we can write

$$(\kappa\cos\theta + \tau\sin\theta)\hat{\mathbf{n}} = \mathbf{0}.$$

Now, we substitute the derivatives of $\hat{\mathbf{t}}$ and $\hat{\mathbf{b}}$ for $\kappa\hat{\mathbf{n}}$ and $\tau\hat{\mathbf{n}}$ respectively and then integrate with respect to s to get,

$$\cos\theta\hat{\mathbf{t}} + \sin\theta\hat{\mathbf{b}} = \hat{\mathbf{e}}$$

where $\hat{\mathbf{e}}$ is the constant of integration. Dotting with $\hat{\mathbf{t}}$ we get $\hat{\mathbf{t}} \cdot \hat{\mathbf{e}} = \cos\theta = \text{constant}$, that is, the angle between $\hat{\mathbf{t}}$ and $\hat{\mathbf{e}}$ is constant, or, $\hat{\mathbf{t}}$ is a tangent to an helix and $\hat{\mathbf{e}}$ is along its axis.   □

Using the relations between the orthonormal triad $(\hat{\mathbf{t}}, \hat{\mathbf{n}}, \hat{\mathbf{b}})$ and their derivatives with respect to the arc length parameter s we can show (Exercise) that,

$$\hat{\mathbf{n}} = \hat{\mathbf{b}} \times \hat{\mathbf{t}}$$

$$\frac{d\hat{\mathbf{n}}}{ds} = \frac{d\hat{\mathbf{b}}}{ds} \times \hat{\mathbf{t}} + \hat{\mathbf{b}} \times \frac{d\hat{\mathbf{t}}}{ds}$$

$$= \tau\hat{\mathbf{n}} \times \hat{\mathbf{t}} + \kappa\hat{\mathbf{b}} \times \hat{\mathbf{n}}$$

$$= -\tau\hat{\mathbf{b}} - \kappa\hat{\mathbf{t}}. \tag{9.14}$$

Equations (9.13) and (9.14) constitute Frenet–Seret formulae.

Exercise Show that we can cast the Frenet–Seret formulae in the form

$$\frac{d\hat{\mathbf{t}}}{ds} = \hat{\mathbf{d}} \times \hat{\mathbf{t}}, \quad \frac{d\hat{\mathbf{n}}}{ds} = \hat{\mathbf{d}} \times \hat{\mathbf{n}}, \quad \frac{d\hat{\mathbf{b}}}{ds} = \hat{\mathbf{b}} \times \hat{\mathbf{d}}$$

where $\hat{\mathbf{d}} = \tau\hat{\mathbf{t}} + \kappa\hat{\mathbf{b}}$ is the *Darboux vector* of the curve. $\square$

We can express the instantaneous velocity and acceleration of the particle as it moves along a smooth path in terms of the orthonormal basis $(\hat{\mathbf{t}}, \hat{\mathbf{n}}, \hat{\mathbf{b}})$. From the definition of the parameter s we see that the quantity $\frac{ds}{dt}$ is simply the instantaneous speed v of the particle. We then have, for the instantaneous velocity of the particle

$$\mathbf{v} = \frac{d\mathbf{x}}{dt} = \frac{d\mathbf{x}}{ds} \cdot \frac{ds}{dt} = v\hat{\mathbf{t}}. \tag{9.15}$$

Thus, the direction of the instantaneous velocity is always along the unit tangent vector to the path in the direction of motion of the particle.

We get the acceleration of the particle by differentiating Eq. (9.15).

$$\begin{aligned}
\mathbf{a} &= \frac{d\mathbf{v}}{dt} \\[2mm]
&= \frac{dv}{dt}\hat{\mathbf{t}} + v\frac{d\hat{\mathbf{t}}}{dt} \\[2mm]
&= \frac{d^2 s}{dt^2}\hat{\mathbf{t}} + v\frac{ds}{dt} \cdot \frac{d\hat{\mathbf{t}}}{ds} \\[2mm]
&= \frac{d^2 s}{dt^2}\hat{\mathbf{t}} + v^2 \kappa\hat{\mathbf{n}} \\[2mm]
&= \frac{dv}{dt}\hat{\mathbf{t}} + v^2 \kappa\hat{\mathbf{n}}. \tag{9.16}
\end{aligned}$$

Thus, the acceleration has two components, one given by the rate of change of instantaneous speed along the direction of motion and the other, with magnitude $v^2\kappa$, called centripetal acceleration, along the principal normal. We have thus connected the kinametical quantities velocity and acceleration of the particle with the local geometry of its path given by the triad $(\hat{\mathbf{t}}, \hat{\mathbf{n}}, \hat{\mathbf{b}})$.

Exercise A kinematical quantity called jerk (denoted $\mathbf{j}$) is defined as the third order derivative of the position vector with respect to time. Show that,

$$\mathbf{j} \equiv \frac{d^3\mathbf{x}}{dt^3} = -\kappa^2\hat{\mathbf{t}} + \frac{d\kappa}{ds}\hat{\mathbf{n}} - \kappa\tau\hat{\mathbf{b}} \tag{9.17}$$

The acceleration does not involve the torsion of the orbit, but the jerk does. Show further that,

$$\mathbf{v} \cdot (\mathbf{a} \times \mathbf{j}) = -\kappa \tau v^3 \tag{9.18}$$

and

$$|\mathbf{v} \times \mathbf{a}| = v^3 \kappa. \tag{9.19}$$

These equations can be used to find the curvature κ and the torsion τ at any point of the orbit by using the kinematical values $\mathbf{v}$, $\mathbf{a}$ and $\mathbf{j}$ at that point.   □

Exercise   Find the curvature and the torsion of the spiralling path of a charged particle in a uniform magnetic field $\mathbf{B}$.

Solution   The Newtonian equation of motion is

$$m\frac{d\mathbf{v}}{dt} = e(\mathbf{v} \times \mathbf{B})$$

which implies

$$\mathbf{v} \cdot \frac{d\mathbf{v}}{dt} = 0$$

so that $|\mathbf{v}| = v_0$ is a constant. The solution of the equation of motion is

$$\mathbf{v} = \mathbf{v}_0 + \frac{e}{m}\{(\mathbf{x} - \mathbf{x}_0) \times \mathbf{B}\}$$

where $\mathbf{v}_0$ and $\mathbf{x}_0$ are the constants of integration. This gives

$$\mathbf{v} \cdot \mathbf{B} = \mathbf{v}_0 \cdot \mathbf{B} = v_0 B \cos\theta$$

where θ is the angle between $\mathbf{v}_0$ and $\mathbf{B}$. Taking the vector product of $\mathbf{v}$ on both sides of the equation of motion, we get, using identity I,

$$\mathbf{v} \times \frac{d\mathbf{v}}{dt} = \frac{e}{m}[(\mathbf{v} \cdot \mathbf{B})\mathbf{v} - v^2\mathbf{B}].$$

Similarly, differentiating the equation of motion once with respect to t we get

$$\mathbf{j} = \frac{d^2\mathbf{v}}{dt^2} = \left(\frac{e}{m}\right)^2 [(\mathbf{v} \cdot \mathbf{B})\mathbf{B} - B^2\mathbf{v}].$$

We can now use Eqs (9.18), (9.19) to get the curvature κ and toesion τ as

$$\kappa = \frac{e}{m}\frac{B\sin\theta}{v_0}$$

and

$$\tau = \frac{e}{m} \frac{B\cos\theta}{v_0}.$$

Exercise   A spaceship of mass m_0 moves in the absence of external forces with a constant velocity $\mathbf{v}_0$. To change the motion direction, a jet engine is switched on. It starts ejecting a gas jet with velocity $\mathbf{u}$ which is constant relative to the spaceship and at right angle to the spaceship motion. The engine is shut down when the mass of the spaceship decreases to m. Through what angle θ does the direction of the motion of the spaceship deviate due to the jet engine operation?

Solution   Figure 9.5 shows a possible path of the satellite when the jet engine is on (the actual path will depend on $\mathbf{v}_0$). Since there are no external forces, the equation of motion is

$$m\frac{d\mathbf{v}}{dt} + u\frac{dm}{dt}\hat{\mathbf{n}} = \mathbf{0},$$

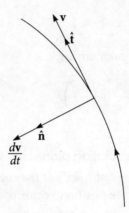

Fig. 9.5   A possible path of the satellite

where $\mathbf{u} = u\hat{\mathbf{n}}$ is the velocity of the gas jet relative to the satellite and $\hat{\mathbf{n}}$ is the principal normal. However, we know, via Eq. (9.16), that

$$\frac{d\mathbf{v}}{dt} = v^2\kappa\hat{\mathbf{n}} + \frac{dv}{dt}\hat{\mathbf{t}},$$

where κ is the curvature and s is the length along the path of the satellite (arc length). Dotting the equation of motion with $\mathbf{v}$ and noting that $\mathbf{v}\cdot\hat{\mathbf{n}} = 0$ we get $\mathbf{v}\cdot\frac{d\mathbf{v}}{dt} = \frac{dv^2}{dt} = 0$ which means that the speed of the satellite as it moves along its path is constant in time. This follows also from the fact that there are no external forces. Thus, only the centripetal acceleration survives giving $\frac{d\mathbf{v}}{dt} = v^2\kappa\hat{\mathbf{n}}$. When substituted in the equation of motion it becomes

$$mv^2\kappa = -u\frac{dm}{dt},$$

or,

$$\frac{mv^2}{R} = -u\frac{dm}{dt},$$

or,

$$dt = -\frac{uR}{v^2}\frac{dm}{m}.$$

Here, we have used $\kappa = \frac{1}{R}$ where R is the radius of curvature. In order to get the angular advance of the satellite we transform this equation using $vdt = Rd\theta$ (which is justified because the path is continuous and differentiable) to get

$$\frac{Rd\theta}{v} = dt = -\frac{uR}{v^2}\frac{dm}{m},$$

or

$$d\theta = -\frac{u}{v}\frac{dm}{m}.$$

Integrating, we get the required angular advance,

$$\theta = \int d\theta = -\frac{u}{v}\int_{m_0}^{m}\frac{dm}{m} = \frac{u}{v}\ln\left(\frac{m_0}{m}\right). \qquad \square$$

9.2.1   Normal, rectifying and osculating planes

We fix a point on the curve by fixing t at t_0 or s at the corresponding value s_0, that is, $s_0 = s(t_0)$. Let $\mathbf{x}(t_0) = \mathbf{x}(s_0) = \mathbf{x}_p$ be the position vector of this point, say P. The coordinate planes of the coordinate system given by $\{\hat{\mathbf{t}}, \hat{\mathbf{n}}, \hat{\mathbf{b}}\}$ at P are

  The plane normal to $\hat{\mathbf{t}}$, spanned by $\{\hat{\mathbf{n}}, \hat{\mathbf{b}}\}$ called normal plane.

  The plane normal to $\hat{\mathbf{n}}$, spanned by $\{\hat{\mathbf{t}}, \hat{\mathbf{b}}\}$ called rectifying plane and

  The plane normal to $\hat{\mathbf{b}}$, spanned by $\{\hat{\mathbf{t}}, \hat{\mathbf{n}}\}$ called osculating plane.

  These planes are tangent to the space curve at P. Note that these planes change with the triad $\{\hat{\mathbf{t}}, \hat{\mathbf{n}}, \hat{\mathbf{b}}\}$ as the point P moves along the curve or as the parameters t or s change. Therefore, the position vector of a point on each of these planes has to be labelled by either t or s. So let $\mathbf{x}(t)$ be the position vector of an arbitrary point of each of the planes in turn. Then, the equation of the normal plane is, suppressing the parameter,

$$(\mathbf{x} - \mathbf{x}_p)\cdot\hat{\mathbf{t}} = 0,$$

the equation of the rectifying plane is

$$(\mathbf{x} - \mathbf{x}_p)\cdot\hat{\mathbf{n}} = 0,$$

and the equation of the osculating plane is

$$(\mathbf{x} - \mathbf{x}_p) \cdot \hat{\mathbf{b}} = 0.$$

Using the definitions of $\hat{\mathbf{t}}$ and $\hat{\mathbf{n}}$, we see that $\hat{\mathbf{b}}$ is parallel to $\mathbf{x}'_p \times \mathbf{x}''_p$ where prime denotes the differentiation with respect to s, and this notation will be used subsequently. Thus, the equation to the osculating plane gets the form

$$(\mathbf{x} - \mathbf{x}_p) \cdot \mathbf{x}'_p \times \mathbf{x}''_p = 0.$$

To get to the t parameterization, note that

$$\mathbf{x}'_p = \dot{\mathbf{x}}_p \frac{dt}{ds}$$

and

$$\mathbf{x}''_p = \ddot{\mathbf{x}}_p \left(\frac{dt}{ds} \right)^2 + \dot{\mathbf{x}}_p \frac{d^2 t}{ds^2}.$$

Exercise Show that $\dot{\mathbf{x}}_p \times \ddot{\mathbf{x}}_p$ is parallel to $\mathbf{x}'_p \times \mathbf{x}''_p$. □

Hence, the equation for the osculating plane, in terms of t can be written in the form

$$(\mathbf{x} - \mathbf{x}_p) \cdot \dot{\mathbf{x}}_p \times \ddot{\mathbf{x}}_p = 0.$$

If the curve is a straight line, or a point, $\dot{\mathbf{x}}_p$ and $\ddot{\mathbf{x}}_p$ are parallel, so that equation to the osculating plane is satisfied by every $\mathbf{x}$ in space which means that the equation does not determine the osculating plane. For a straight line, the osculating plane is determined by the choice of the principal normal $\hat{\mathbf{n}}$ (see the text below the place where we have defined $\hat{\mathbf{n}}$).

In Cartesian coordinates x, y, z, the equation to the osculating plane becomes

$$\begin{vmatrix} x - x_p & y - y_p & z - z_p \\ \dot{x}_p & \dot{y}_p & \dot{z}_p \\ \ddot{x}_p & \ddot{y}_p & \ddot{z}_p \end{vmatrix} = 0.$$

Exercise Find the equation of the osculating plane to the circular helix.

Answer

$$\begin{vmatrix} x - a\cos t & y - a\sin t & z - bt \\ -a\sin t & a\cos t & b \\ \cos t & \sin t & 0 \end{vmatrix} = 0,$$

or,

$$xb\sin t - yb\cos t + az = abt. \qquad \qquad \Box$$

9.2.2   Order of contact

Consider an osculating plane tangent to a space curve $\mathbf{x}(s)$ at a point P with position vector $\mathbf{x}(s_0)$. In order to estimate how 'close' a space curve is to a tangent plane at a point P, we make use of the concept of *order of contact* of a plane and a curve. Higher the order of contact closer is the plane to the curve. Using this concept we show that the osculating plane at a point on a space curve is closest to it amongst all the planes tangent to the curve at the same point.

A plane with a common point P at $\mathbf{x}(s_0)$ with a space curve $\mathbf{x}(s)$ has a contact of order n at P if the distance of a point $\mathbf{x}(s)$ on the curve from the plane is a function $\delta(s)$ satisfying

$$\delta^{(k)}(s_0) = 0, \quad k = 0, 1, \ldots, n,$$

$$\delta^{(n+1)}(s_0) \neq 0.$$

where $\delta^{(k)}$ is the kth derivative of $\delta(s)$ with respect to s.

The distance of a point $\mathbf{x}(s)$ on the curve from the osculating plane is

$$\delta(s) = \pm[\mathbf{x}(s) - \mathbf{x}(s_0)] \cdot \hat{\mathbf{b}},$$

where $\hat{\mathbf{b}} = \hat{\mathbf{b}}(s_0)$ is the binormal. We see that

$$\delta^{(1)}(s_0) = \pm\mathbf{x}'(s_0) \cdot \hat{\mathbf{b}} = \hat{\mathbf{t}} \cdot \hat{\mathbf{b}} = 0$$

and

$$\delta^{(2)}(s_0) = \pm\mathbf{x}''(s_0) \cdot \hat{\mathbf{b}} = \kappa\hat{\mathbf{n}} \cdot \hat{\mathbf{b}} = 0,$$

since the first and the second derivatives of $\mathbf{x}(s)$ with respect to s equal $\hat{\mathbf{t}}$ and $\kappa\hat{\mathbf{n}}$ respectively and $\hat{\mathbf{t}}, \hat{\mathbf{n}}, \hat{\mathbf{b}}$ form an orthonormal triad. Hence, the osculating plane has contact of *at least* order two with the curve.

Now consider a second plane tangent to the curve at P. The distance function $\delta(s)$ for this plane is

$$\delta(s) = \pm[\mathbf{x}(s) - \mathbf{x}(s_0)] \cdot \hat{\mathbf{c}}$$

where $\hat{\mathbf{c}}$ is a unit vector normal to the plane. The first two derivatives of $\delta(s)$ at P are

$$\delta^{(1)}(s_0) = \pm\mathbf{x}'(s_0) \cdot \hat{\mathbf{c}} = \hat{\mathbf{t}} \cdot \hat{\mathbf{c}}$$

and

$$\delta^{(2)}(s_0) = \pm\mathbf{x}''(s_0) \cdot \hat{\mathbf{c}} = \kappa\hat{\mathbf{n}} \cdot \hat{\mathbf{c}}.$$

Therefore, the derivatives are non-zero, unless $\hat{\mathbf{c}}$ is parallel to $\hat{\mathbf{b}}$ making two planes coincide. Thus, the order of contact of any plane other than the osculating plane is less than two.

Exercise Find the order of contact of the osculating plane to the circular helix.

Hint We know that the order of contact is at least two. Using the equation of the helix with arc length as parameter, show that $\delta^{(3)} = \pm\mathbf{x}'''(s_0) \cdot \hat{\mathbf{b}} = \pm\frac{ab}{c^4} \neq 0$, where $c = \sqrt{a^2 + b^2}$. Therefore, the required order of contact is two.   □

9.2.3 The osculating circle

Let P, Q, R be three distinct points on a space curve such that the curve has a non-zero curvature at each of them. Let $\mathbf{x}(s_0), \mathbf{x}(s_1), \mathbf{x}(s_2)$ be the corresponding position vectors with $s_0 < s_1 < s_2$. We further assume that the points P, Q, R also lie on a sphere $(\mathbf{x} - \mathbf{x}_0)^2 = a^2$, $\mathbf{x}_0$ being the position vector of the center. We want to find what happens to this sphere in the limiting case as Q and R approach P.

We start by defining the function

$$f(s) = (\mathbf{x}(s) - \mathbf{x}_0)^2 - a^2,$$

where s is the arc length parameter. Note that

$$f(s_0) = f(s_1) = f(s_2) = 0.$$

Therefore, by Rolle's theorem, we get,

$$f'(\xi_1) = f'(\xi_2) = 0, \quad s_0 \leq \xi_1 \leq s_1 \leq \xi_2 \leq s_2.$$

Applying Rolle's theorem again to $f'(s)$ we get,

$$f''(\xi_3) = 0, \quad \xi_1 \leq \xi_3 \leq \xi_2.$$

As Q and R approach P, $s_1, s_2, \xi_1, \xi_2, \xi_3$ approach s_0. Therefore,

$$f(s_0) = (\mathbf{x}(s_0) - \mathbf{x}_0)^2 - a^2 = 0,$$

$$f'(s_0) = \mathbf{x}'(s_0) \cdot (\mathbf{x}(s_0) - \mathbf{x}_0) = 0,$$

$$f''(s_0) = \mathbf{x}''(s_0) \cdot (\mathbf{x}(s_0) - \mathbf{x}_0) + (\mathbf{x}'(s_0))^2 = 0.$$

Since $\mathbf{x}' = \hat{\mathbf{t}}$, the second of these equations shows that $(\mathbf{x}(s_0) - \mathbf{x}_0)$ lies in the normal plane at P. Therefore, we can express it as a linear combination of $\hat{\mathbf{n}}$ and $\hat{\mathbf{b}}$, that is,

$$\mathbf{x}(s_0) - \mathbf{x}_0 = \alpha\hat{\mathbf{n}} + \beta\hat{\mathbf{b}}. \tag{9.20}$$

Since $\mathbf{x}''(s_0) = \kappa\hat{\mathbf{n}}$ and $\mathbf{x}'(s_0) = \hat{\mathbf{t}}$, the third of the above equations gives,

$$\hat{\mathbf{n}} \cdot (\mathbf{x}(s_0) - \mathbf{x}_0) + \rho = 0, \tag{9.21}$$

where ρ is the radius of curvature. Dotting Eq. (9.20) with $\hat{\mathbf{n}}$ and then using Eq. (9.21) we get $\alpha = -\rho$. Squaring each side of Eq. (9.20) and using $f(s_0) = 0$ (first of the above three equations) we get $\beta = \pm\sqrt{a^2 - \rho^2}$. Using Eq. (9.20) (with the corresponding expressions for α and β) we see that, for $a > \rho$, there are two limiting spheres the position vectors of the centers of which are given by

$$\mathbf{x}_0 = \mathbf{x}(s_0) + \rho\hat{\mathbf{n}} \pm \sqrt{a^2 - \rho^2}\hat{\mathbf{b}}. \tag{9.22}$$

If we select $a = \rho$ then the sphere has its center in the osculating plane. The intersection of this sphere and the osculating plane is a circle of radius ρ and is called the osculating circle, or the circle of curvature.

We define the order of contact between two curves in the same way as we did for a curve and a plane. It turns out that the order of contact between the osculating circle and the space curve is *at least* two.

9.2.4 Natural equations of a space curve

Two space curves are *congruent* if they can be made to coincide by only translating and rotating one of them (that is, via a rigid motion). During a rigid motion, both curvature and torsion at all points on the curve remain unaltered. Thus, the same curvature and torsion, as functions $\kappa(s)$ and $\tau(s)$ of the arc length parameter s, describe the whole class of mutually congruent space curves. The values of κ and τ at a point corresponding to s are given by the values of the functions $\kappa(s)$ and $\tau(s)$. This fact is expressed by the equations

$$\kappa = \kappa(s) \text{ and } \tau = \tau(s), \tag{9.23}$$

which are called the *natural*, or *intrinsic* equations of a curve. We know that two congruent curves have the same natural equations. We now show that the reverse implication is also true: Two curves having the same natural equations are congruent.

Let the two curves be $\mathbf{x} = \mathbf{x}_1(s)$ and $\mathbf{x} = \mathbf{x}_2(s)$. By a rigid motion, we can make the points corresponding to $s = 0$ coincide such that the moving trihedrals at these points coincide. Now using Eqs (9.9), (9.13) and (9.14) it is straightforward to show that

$$\frac{d}{ds}(\hat{\mathbf{t}}_1 \cdot \hat{\mathbf{t}}_2 + \hat{\mathbf{n}}_1 \cdot \hat{\mathbf{n}}_2 + \hat{\mathbf{b}}_1 \cdot \hat{\mathbf{b}}_2) = 0,$$

or,

$$\hat{\mathbf{t}}_1 \cdot \hat{\mathbf{t}}_2 + \hat{\mathbf{n}}_1 \cdot \hat{\mathbf{n}}_2 + \hat{\mathbf{b}}_1 \cdot \hat{\mathbf{b}}_2 = \text{constant}.$$

However, we know that at $s = 0$

$$\hat{\mathbf{t}}_1 = \hat{\mathbf{t}}_2, \hat{\mathbf{n}}_1 = \hat{\mathbf{n}}_2, \hat{\mathbf{b}}_1 = \hat{\mathbf{b}}_2. \tag{9.24}$$

Therefore,

$$\hat{\mathbf{t}}_1 \cdot \hat{\mathbf{t}}_2 + \hat{\mathbf{n}}_1 \cdot \hat{\mathbf{n}}_2 + \hat{\mathbf{b}}_1 \cdot \hat{\mathbf{b}}_2 = 3. \tag{9.25}$$

Since $\hat{\mathbf{t}}, \hat{\mathbf{n}}, \hat{\mathbf{b}}$ are unit vectors, it follows from Eq. (9.25) that

$$\hat{\mathbf{t}}_1 \cdot \hat{\mathbf{t}}_2 = \hat{\mathbf{n}}_1 \cdot \hat{\mathbf{n}}_2 = \hat{\mathbf{b}}_1 \cdot \hat{\mathbf{b}}_2 = 1$$

and that Eq. (9.24) applies for all s; not only at $s = 0$. From $\hat{\mathbf{t}}_1 \cdot \hat{\mathbf{t}}_2$ we get,

$$\mathbf{x}_1' = \mathbf{x}_2'$$

so that

$$\mathbf{x}_1 = \mathbf{x}_2 + \mathbf{c},$$

where $\mathbf{c}$ is the constant of integration. The initial condition $\mathbf{x}_1(0) = \mathbf{x}_2(0)$ gives $\mathbf{c} = \mathbf{0}$. Therefore, for all s

$$\mathbf{x}_1 = \mathbf{x}_2$$

which means that both the curves are congruent.

It can also be shown that given two analytic functions $\kappa(s) > 0$ and $\tau(s)$ there is a curve for which the curvature and torsion are given by Eq. (9.23). We skip the proof.

We may expand the function $\mathbf{x}(s)$ pertaining to the curve in Taylor series (see section 9.6) around $s = 0$:

$$\mathbf{x}(s) = \mathbf{x}(0) + s\mathbf{x}'(0) + \frac{s^2}{2}\mathbf{x}''(0) + \frac{s^3}{3!}\mathbf{x}'''(0) + \cdots.$$

Again, expressing the derivatives of $\mathbf{x}(s)$ in terms of curvature and torsion via Eqs (9.9), (9.13) and (9.14), we get,

$$\mathbf{x}(s) = \mathbf{x}(0) + s\hat{\mathbf{t}}(0) + \frac{s^2}{2}\kappa(0)\hat{\mathbf{n}}(0) + \frac{s^3}{3!}\left(-\kappa^2(0)\hat{\mathbf{t}}(0) + \kappa'(0)\hat{\mathbf{n}}(0)\right.$$

$$\left. + \kappa(0)\tau(0)\hat{\mathbf{b}}(0)\right) + \cdots.$$

This Taylor series is equivalent to three scalar equations in terms of the components $x_1(s), x_2(s), x_3(s)$ of $\mathbf{x}(s)$ along triad basis $\hat{\mathbf{t}}, \hat{\mathbf{n}}, \hat{\mathbf{b}}$ with origin at $s = 0$. These are

$$x_1(s) = s - \frac{\kappa^2(0)s^3}{6} + \cdots$$

$$x_2(s) = \frac{\kappa(0)s^2}{2} + \frac{\kappa'(0)s^3}{6} + \cdots$$

$$x_3(s) = \frac{\kappa(0)\tau(0)s^3}{6} + \cdots \tag{9.26}$$

We can use Eq. (9.26) to get the equations to the projections of the space curve on the coordinate planes corresponding to the $\hat{\mathbf{t}}, \hat{\mathbf{n}}, \hat{\mathbf{b}}$ basis in the neighborhood of $s = 0$. Keeping only the first terms in Eq. (9.26), the projections on the osculating plane, the rectifying plane and the normal plane respectively are given by

$$x_2(s) = \frac{\kappa(0)}{2} x_1^2(s)$$

$$x_3(s) = \frac{\kappa(0)\tau(0)}{6} x_1^3(s)$$

$$x_3^2(s) = \frac{2\tau^2(0)}{9\kappa(0)} x_2^3(s) \tag{9.27}$$

These projections are depicted in Fig. 9.6.

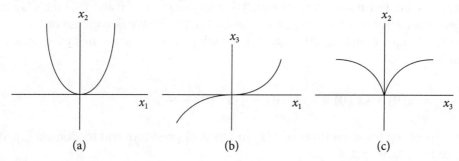

      (a)   (b)   (c)

Fig. 9.6   Projections of a space curve on the coordinate planes of a moving trihedral

Exercise   Find the natural equations for the cycloid, parametrically given by (see the next section on plane curves)

$$x = a(t - \sin t), \quad y = a(1 - \cos t), \quad z = 0.$$

Solution   Since the curve is planar, the unit vector $\hat{\mathbf{b}}$ is a constant vector always perpendicular to the plane of the curve. Therefore, $d\hat{\mathbf{b}}/ds = \mathbf{0}$, that is, $\tau = 0$. To get the equation in κ, we have to find the arc length measured from some fixed point on the curve, using the given parametric equations. We have,

$$ds = \sqrt{dx^2 + dy^2} = 2a \sin \frac{t}{2} dt,$$

giving

$$s = \int_0^s ds = 2a \int_\pi^t \sin \frac{t}{2} dt = -4a \cos \frac{t}{2},$$

where s is measured from the top of the cycloid, that is, $s = 0$ at $t = \pi$. From Eq. (9.19), the parametric equation of the curve and $\mathbf{v} = \dot{\mathbf{x}}$, $\mathbf{a} = \ddot{\mathbf{x}}$ we get

$$\kappa^2 = \frac{|[a(1 - \cos t)\hat{\mathbf{i}} + a \sin t \hat{\mathbf{j}}] \times [a \sin t \hat{\mathbf{i}} + a \cos t \hat{\mathbf{j}}]|^2}{[(a(1 - \cos t)\hat{\mathbf{i}} + a \sin t \hat{\mathbf{j}})^2]^3} = \frac{1}{8a^2(1 - \cos t)}.$$

Further,

$$s^2 = 16a^2 \cos^2 \frac{t}{2} = 8a^2(1 + \cos t)$$

giving us the required equation,

$$\frac{1}{\kappa^2} + s^2 = 16a^2. \qquad \qquad \square$$

9.2.5   Evolutes and involutes

We shall now use the Frenet–Seret formulae to learn about an important genera of curves called *evolutes* and *involutes*.

Definition: If there is a one to one correspondence between the points of two curves C_1 and C_2 such that the tangent to C_1 at any point on it is normal to C_2 at the corresponding point on C_2 then C_1 is called an *evolute* of C_2 and C_2 an *involute* of C_1.

We denote all the quantities pertaining to the evolute curve C_1 by small case letters, while those pertaining to the involute curve C_2 are denoted by the capital letters.

Suppose the equation for the evolute curve C_1 is given by $\mathbf{x} = \mathbf{x}(s)$. We want to find out the equation for its involute C_2 given by $\mathbf{X} = \mathbf{X}(S)$. We refer to Fig. 9.7. If the distance $P_1 P_2$ is taken to be u, the position vector OP_2 will be $\mathbf{X} = \mathbf{x} + u\hat{\mathbf{t}}$ where $\mathbf{x} = \mathbf{x}(s)$ and $\hat{\mathbf{t}} = \frac{d\mathbf{x}}{ds}$. Differentiating with respect to S, the arc length parameter of the involute, we get

$$\frac{d\mathbf{X}}{dS} = \hat{\mathbf{T}} = (\mathbf{x}' + u\hat{\mathbf{t}}' + u'\hat{\mathbf{t}}) \frac{ds}{dS}.$$

Using Eqs (9.9) and (9.13) this becomes

$$\hat{\mathbf{T}} = (\hat{\mathbf{t}} + u\kappa\hat{\mathbf{n}} + u'\hat{\mathbf{t}})\frac{ds}{dS}. \tag{9.28}$$

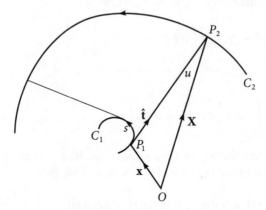

Fig. 9.7   A construction for finding the equation of an involute C_2 for a given evolute C_1 and vice versa

It follows from the definition of an involute that $\hat{\mathbf{t}} \cdot \hat{\mathbf{T}} = 0$. Hence,

$$\hat{\mathbf{t}} \cdot (\hat{\mathbf{t}} + u\kappa\hat{\mathbf{n}} + u'\hat{\mathbf{t}}) = 0,$$

or,

$$1 + u' = 0$$

or, integrating,

$$u = c - s,$$

where c is the constant of integration. Hence, the equation for the involute is

$$\mathbf{X} = \mathbf{x}(s) + (c - s)\hat{\mathbf{t}} \tag{9.29}$$

for any given evolute $\mathbf{x} = \mathbf{x}(s)$. Actually, for each value of c there will be an involute. So for a given evolute there exists a family of infinite number of involutes. The same is true for a given involute.

Let $\mathbf{X}_1$ and $\mathbf{X}_2$ be two points on two involutes for $c = c_1$ and $c = c_2$ in Eq. (9.29) corresponding to a point P on the evolute curve $\mathbf{x}(s)$. Subtracting the equation of one involute from that of the other, we get

$$\mathbf{X}_1 - \mathbf{X}_2 = (c_1 - c_2)\hat{\mathbf{t}}$$

or,

$$|\mathbf{X}_1 - \mathbf{X}_2| = c_1 - c_2.$$

Thus, the separation between two such corresponding points is constant.

The simplest realization of involutes to a given evolute is the case of winding strings on the surface of any object. The open end of the string, if forced to remain stretched during the process of winding, will describe an involute to the curve on the body traced by the winding thread. The latter is an evolute as the string touches it tangentially, and the open end of the string must move in a direction perpendicular to the string itself. Equation (9.29) suggests that the length of the string u used up in winding is just equal to the increase in arc length s of the evolute along which the winding takes place, that is, $|\mathbf{X} - \mathbf{x}| + s = c$, where c is the length of the string (see Fig. 9.8). Strings of different lengths generate different involutes. Thus, the involute of a circle is a spiral. There are families of curves such that both the evolutes and involutes belong to the same family such as cycloids, hypocycloids and epicycloids. Such families of self replicating evolute-involute curves are said to form *tesserals* [19].

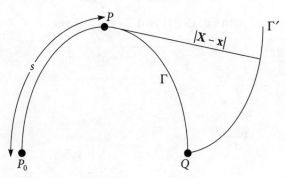

Fig. 9.8   Construction of a evolute-involute pair

Exercise   Find the equation for the involutes of a circular helix.

Solution   For the circular helix, Eq. (9.29) becomes,

$$\mathbf{X} = \mathbf{x} + c\hat{\mathbf{t}} - t\sqrt{a^2 + b^2}\hat{\mathbf{t}},$$

since $s = \sqrt{a^2 + b^2}\,t$. We get

$$\hat{\mathbf{t}} = \frac{d\mathbf{x}}{dt}\frac{dt}{ds} = (-a\sin t\hat{\mathbf{i}} + a\cos t\hat{\mathbf{j}} + b\hat{\mathbf{k}})(a^2 + b^2)^{-\frac{1}{2}}.$$

Substituting for the equation of the involute, we get,

$$\mathbf{X} = \left(a\cos t - \frac{ca}{\sqrt{a^2 + b^2}}\sin t + at\sin t\right)\hat{\mathbf{i}}$$

$$+ \left(a\sin t + \frac{ca}{\sqrt{a^2 + b^2}}\cos t - at\cos t\right)\hat{\mathbf{j}} + \frac{bc}{\sqrt{a^2 + b^2}}\hat{\mathbf{k}}. \qquad \square$$

Exercise   Show that the curvature K of the involute of a curve is given by

$$K^2 = \frac{\kappa^2 + \tau^2}{\kappa^2(c-s)^2}.$$

Solution   From Frenet formula

$$\frac{d\hat{\mathbf{T}}}{dS} = K\hat{\mathbf{T}}.$$

Equation (9.21) coupled with $\hat{\mathbf{T}} \cdot \hat{\mathbf{t}} = 0$ tells us that $\hat{\mathbf{T}} = \pm\hat{\mathbf{n}}$. Then

$$\frac{d\hat{\mathbf{T}}}{dS} = \pm\frac{d\hat{\mathbf{n}}}{ds}\frac{ds}{dS}.$$

Further, $u = c - s$ coupled with Eq. (9.21) and $\hat{\mathbf{T}} \cdot \hat{\mathbf{t}} = 0$ gives

$$\hat{\mathbf{T}} = \kappa(c-s)\hat{\mathbf{n}}\frac{ds}{dS},$$

from which we get

$$\hat{\mathbf{T}} \cdot \hat{\mathbf{T}} = 1 = \pm\kappa(c-s)\frac{ds}{dS}.$$

Therefore,

$$\frac{d\hat{\mathbf{T}}}{dS} = \frac{d\hat{\mathbf{n}}}{ds}\frac{1}{\kappa(c-s)} = \frac{-\kappa\hat{\mathbf{t}} - \tau\hat{\mathbf{b}}}{\kappa(c-s)} = K\hat{\mathbf{N}}.$$

and

$$K^2 = \frac{\kappa^2 + \tau^2}{\kappa^2(c-s)^2}. \qquad\qquad \square$$

We now solve the reversed problem: Given a space curve, C_2, to find space curves, denoted C_1, of which the given curve is an involute. We follow the same notational convention as before: Small case letters for the evolute C_1 and the capital letters for the involute C_2.

From the definition of the involute, we know that C_2 must be perpendicular to every tangent to the curve C_1 we are seeking. Therefore, $\hat{\mathbf{t}}$ lies in the plane of $\hat{\mathbf{N}}$ and $\hat{\mathbf{B}}$. From Eq. (9.29) we see that the targeted curve C_1, if it exists, is given by (see Fig. 9.9)

$$\mathbf{x} = \mathbf{X} - u t.$$

However, $\hat{\mathbf{t}}$ is a linear combination of $\hat{\mathbf{N}}$ and $\hat{\mathbf{B}}$. Therefore,

$$\mathbf{x} = \mathbf{X} + \alpha\hat{\mathbf{N}} + \beta\hat{\mathbf{B}}, \tag{9.30}$$

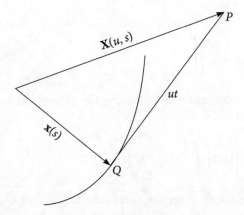

Fig. 9.9   Finding the evolute of an involute

where α and β are to be determined. Differentiating with respect to S we get,

$$\frac{d\mathbf{x}}{dS} = \frac{d\mathbf{X}}{dS} + \alpha \frac{d\hat{\mathbf{N}}}{dS} + \beta \frac{d\hat{\mathbf{B}}}{dS} + \hat{\mathbf{N}} \frac{d\alpha}{dS} + \hat{\mathbf{B}} \frac{d\beta}{dS}.$$

Using Eqs (9.9), (9.13) and (9.14) we get,

$$\frac{d\mathbf{x}}{dS} = (1 - \alpha K)\hat{\mathbf{T}} + \left(\frac{d\alpha}{dS} + T\beta \right)\hat{\mathbf{N}} + \left(\frac{d\beta}{dS} - T\alpha \right)\hat{\mathbf{B}}, \tag{9.31}$$

where K and T are respectively the curvature and the torsion of the involute C_2. As

$$\frac{d\mathbf{x}}{dS} = \frac{d\mathbf{x}}{ds} \frac{ds}{dS} = \hat{\mathbf{t}} \frac{ds}{dS}$$

and as $\hat{\mathbf{t}}$ must be a linear combination of $\hat{\mathbf{N}}$ and $\hat{\mathbf{B}}$, it follows that the coefficient of $\hat{\mathbf{T}}$ in Eq. (9.31) must vanish, leading to

$$\alpha = \frac{1}{K}.$$

Thus, $\alpha(S)$ is simply the radius of curvature of the involute at S.

Next convince yourself that $\mathbf{X} - \mathbf{x}$ is parallel to $d\mathbf{x}/dS$. Hence the coefficients of $\hat{\mathbf{N}}$ and $\hat{\mathbf{B}}$ in Eqs (9.30) and (9.31) must be in the same ratio. We have,

$$\frac{\alpha}{\beta} = \frac{\frac{d\alpha}{dS} + T\beta}{\frac{d\beta}{dS} - T\alpha}.$$

Integration with respect to S yields

$$\tan^{-1} \frac{\beta}{\alpha} = \int T dS + C,$$

or,

$$\beta = \alpha \left[\tan \left(\int T \, dS + C \right) \right],$$

where C is a constant of integration. Substituting the values of α and β in Eq. (9.30) we get the equation of the evolute:

$$\mathbf{x} = \mathbf{X} + \frac{1}{K} \hat{\mathbf{N}} + \frac{1}{K} \left[\tan \left(\int T \, dS + C \right) \right] \hat{\mathbf{B}}. \tag{9.32}$$

Note that for a point P of the involute the corresponding points $Q_1(\mathbf{x}_1), Q_2(\mathbf{x}_2), \ldots$ on the evolutes for different values of C $C_1, C_2, \ldots$ lie on a straight line parallel to the binormal $\hat{\mathbf{B}}$ at P because $\mathbf{x}_i - \mathbf{x}_j$, $i \neq j$, $i, j = 1, 2, \ldots$ is proportional to $\hat{\mathbf{B}}$. Further, this line is at a distance of $\frac{1}{K}$ (radius of curvature at P) because $\mathbf{x}$ has a component along $\hat{\mathbf{N}}$ which is normal to $\hat{\mathbf{B}}$ and has magnitude $\frac{1}{K}$.

Exercise   Obtain the equations for the evolutes of the circular helix.

Hint   Specialize Eq. (9.32) to circular helix. All the required results are available in previous exercises. ☐

9.3   Plane Curves

A separate study of plane curves, that is, curves on a plane, is worthwhile, because many aspects of the theory can be developed with them without losing generality and many characteristics of geometric parameters for these curves can be defined, which have no analogue for curves in three dimensional space. Thus, for example, we can define the sign of curvature, κ, for a plane curve, positive and negative sides of a plane curve or the interior and the exterior regions of a closed plane curve, all of which are not meaningful for a curve in three dimensional space.

A plane curve is parameterized by a vector valued function $\mathbf{x}(t)$ of parameter t where $\mathbf{x}(t) \equiv (x(t), y(t))$ is a planar vector with coordinate functions $(x(t), y(t))$. We assume that the functions $\mathbf{x}(t) \equiv (x(t), y(t))$ possess continuous derivatives with respect to t.

9.3.1   Three different parameterizations of an ellipse

We give three different ways to parameterize ellipse, first by the so called eccentric angle (called eccentric anomaly by the astronomers), the second by using the angle swept by the vector based at one of the foci counterclockwise from its pericenter (called true anomaly by the astronomers) and the third using the time taken by a planet to reach a given point on its elliptical path around the sun assuming $t = 0$ at the pericenter. On the way we shall pick up some geometrical characteristics of ellipse and also some of its physical realizations, most prominent being planetary motion.

We start with the non-parametric equation to the ellipse, namely,

$$\frac{x^2}{a^2} + \frac{y^2}{b^2} = 1$$

where (x, y) are the coordinates of a point on the ellipse with respect to the coordinate system based at the center of the ellipse and x, y axes along its major and minor axes respectively. a and b are the lengths of the semi-major and the semi-minor axes respectively. Introduce the parameter u by $x = a \cos u$ to get, via its non-parametric equation above, $y = b \sin u$. These are the parametric equations to the ellipse in terms of the eccentric angle u. The position vector of any point P on the ellipse is given by

$$\mathbf{z} = \mathbf{a} \cos u + \mathbf{b} \sin u \tag{9.33}$$

where $\mathbf{a}$ and $\mathbf{b}$ are vectors along the positive x and y directions with $|\mathbf{a}| = a$ and $|\mathbf{b}| = b$ so that $\mathbf{a} \cdot \mathbf{b} = 0$. This is depicted in Fig. 9.10.

The above equations to the ellipse tell us that an ellipse is obtained by reducing the ordinates (y values) of all points on the circumscribing circle (see Fig. 9.10) by the factor $\frac{b}{a}$. Thus, the ellipse can be viewed as the projection of a circle placed in an inclined position with respect to the $x - y$ plane. We see that the area of the ellipse is $\frac{b}{a}$ times that of a circle with radius equal to its semi-major axis a, that is, $A = \pi ab$.

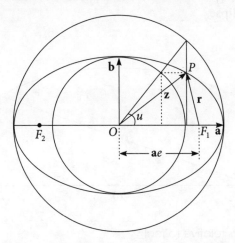

Fig. 9.10   Ellipse

Suppose a point performs two harmonic motions in two mutually perpendicular directions with the same angular velocity ω and with a phase difference of $\pi/2$ radians, with amplitudes a and b (Lissajous motion). Then, $x = a \cos \omega t$ and $y = b \sin \omega t$ and the curve traced by the particle is ellipse given by Eq. (9.33) with $u = \omega t$.

For a pendulum with small oscillations, the equation of motion is

$$m \ddot{\mathbf{r}} + k \mathbf{r} = 0$$

where **r** is the position vector of the bob.

Splitting this vector equation into its components we get

$$m\ddot{x} + kx = 0 \quad ; \quad m\ddot{y} + ky = 0$$

which have particular solutions

$$x = a\cos\sqrt{\frac{k}{m}}t \quad ; \quad y = b\sin\sqrt{\frac{k}{m}}t$$

giving rise to the motion along an ellipse given by Eq. (9.33) with $u = \sqrt{\frac{k}{m}}t$.

The two foci of the ellipse are the points situated on the major axis at a distance $c = \sqrt{a^2 - b^2}$ from the center (see Fig. 9.11). The ratio $e = c/a$ is called the eccentricity of the ellipse. It is zero if the ellipse degenerates into a circle ($a = b$). In order to write down the equation of the ellipse relative to one of the foci as origin, we add or subtract the constant vector $\mathbf{c} = \sqrt{a^2 - b^2}\hat{\mathbf{a}}$ to or from the position vector **z** given by Eq. (9.33). We get

$$(a\cos u \pm c)\hat{\mathbf{a}} + \sin u\,\mathbf{b} = \begin{cases} \mathbf{r}_1 \\ \mathbf{r}_2 \end{cases} .$$

We can easily calculate $|\mathbf{r}_1| = a + c\cos u$ and $|\mathbf{r}_2| = a - c\cos u$ giving us an important geometric property of ellipse,

$$|\mathbf{r}_1| + |\mathbf{r}_2| = 2a. \tag{9.34}$$

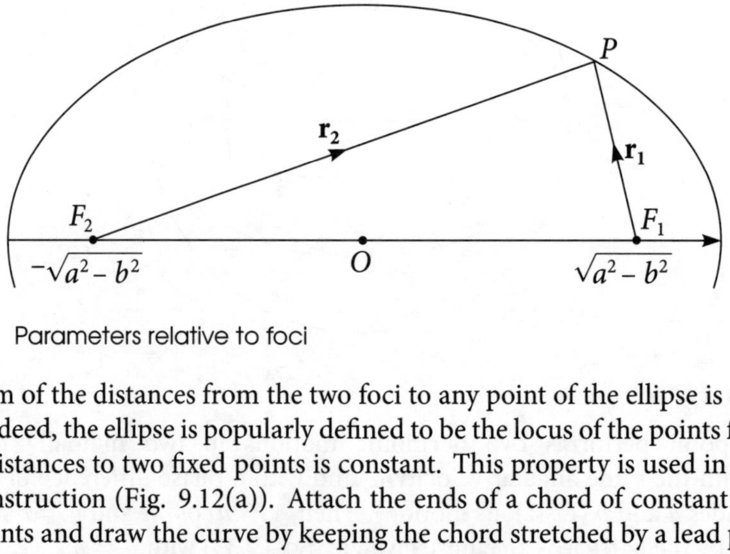

Fig. 9.11 Parameters relative to foci

Thus, the sum of the distances from the two foci to any point of the ellipse is constant and equals $2a$. Indeed, the ellipse is popularly defined to be the locus of the points for which the sum of the distances to two fixed points is constant. This property is used in the so called gardner's construction (Fig. 9.12(a)). Attach the ends of a chord of constant length $2a$ to two fixed points and draw the curve by keeping the chord stretched by a lead pencil.

For the ends of the minor axis, $|\mathbf{r}_1| = a = |\mathbf{r}_2|$. Figure 9.12(b) illustrates the relation $a^2 = b^2 + c^2$. For a point vertically above one of the foci, the coefficient of $\hat{\mathbf{a}}$ is zero. In this case, $\cos u = \pm c/a = \pm e$. Consequently, $\sin u = \sqrt{1 - e^2} = b/a$ and the value of y

is $b \sin u = b^2/a$. This value is denoted by p and is called the parameter or the semilatus-rectum of the ellipse (see Fig. 9.12(b)). ($2p$ is the latus-rectum.) The eccentricity e and the parameter p are sufficient to fix the shape and size of the ellipse, just as are a and b.

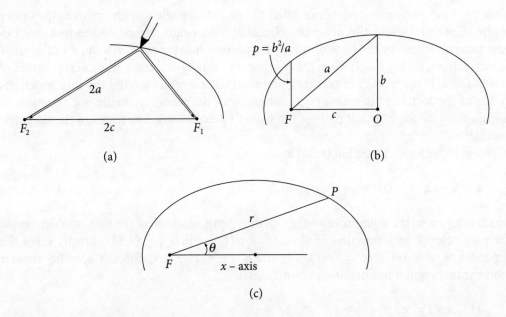

(a)

(b)

(c)

Fig. 9.12   (a) Drawing ellipse with a pencil and a string (b) Semilatus rectum
(c) Polar coordinates relative to a focus

To get the equation of the ellipse in polar coordinates we identify $r = |\mathbf{r}_1|$ to get, as derived before,

$$r = a + c \cos u. \tag{9.35}$$

To get the θ coordinate (focal azimuth, see Fig. 3.9(c)) we note that

$$\cos \theta = \frac{x}{r} = \frac{\text{coefficient of } \hat{\mathbf{a}} \text{ in } \mathbf{r}_1}{r} = \frac{a \cos u + c}{a + c \cos u}. \tag{9.36}$$

Eliminating u from Eqs (9.35) and (9.36) we find the polar equation to the ellipse

$$\frac{1}{r} = \frac{1}{p}(1 - e \cos \theta). \tag{9.37}$$

Exercise   Extend the position vector $\mathbf{r}_1$ of a point P on the ellipse in the opposite direction to get a chord of the ellipse. Let the chord be divided by the focus in the intercepts r_1 and r_2. Show that

$$\frac{1}{r_1} + \frac{1}{r_2} = \frac{2}{p}.$$

Hint Use Eq. (9.37) for r_1 and r_2 and note that $\cos(\theta + \pi) = -\cos\theta$. Thus, each chord passing through the focus is divided by it into two parts such that their hamonic mean is constant and equals p. □

Thus, we have parameterized ellipse using the eccentric angle u with origin at the center of the ellipse and using the polar coordinate θ with origin at one of the foci. We can parameterize ellipse by the time of travel of a particle moving on it, tracing it in the sense of increasing t, taking $t = 0$ when the particle was at the pericenter. Typical realization of this situation is the motion of planets along their elliptic orbits around the sun, which sits at one of the foci and interacts gravitationally with the planet. Actually, we are going to re-parameterize the elliptical path of the planet by expressing t in terms of the eccentric anomaly u.

We start with re-writing Eq. (9.33) as

$$\mathbf{r} = \mathbf{z} - e\mathbf{a} = \mathbf{a}(\cos u - e) + \mathbf{b}\sin u, \tag{9.38}$$

which is a parametric equation $\mathbf{r} = \mathbf{r}(u)$ of the elliptic orbit. Now the task is to determine the parameter u as a function of time $u = u(t)$ so that Eq. (9.38) directly gives the dependence of $\mathbf{r}$ on t, $\mathbf{r} = \mathbf{r}(t)$. From Eq. (9.38) we get, for the specific angular momentum (angular momentum per unit mass),

$$\mathbf{H} = \mathbf{r} \times \dot{\mathbf{r}} = \mathbf{z} \times \dot{\mathbf{z}} - e\mathbf{a} \times \dot{\mathbf{z}},$$

or,

$$\mathbf{H}dt = \mathbf{z} \times d\mathbf{z} - e\mathbf{a} \times d\mathbf{z}.$$

From Eq. (9.33) we get

$$d\mathbf{z} = -\mathbf{a}\sin u\, du + \mathbf{b}\cos u\, du, \tag{9.39}$$

so that using Eqs (9.33) and (9.39) we have

$$\mathbf{z} \times d\mathbf{z} = \mathbf{a} \times \mathbf{b}\, du.$$

Similarly,

$$\mathbf{a} \times d\mathbf{z} = \mathbf{a} \times \mathbf{b}\cos u\, du.$$

Therefore, $\mathbf{H}dt$ becomes

$$\mathbf{H}dt = \mathbf{a} \times \mathbf{b}\, du - e\mathbf{a} \times \mathbf{b}\cos u\, du. \tag{9.40}$$

Now we assume that $t = 0$ and $u = 0$ at the pericenter and u to be the angular advance of the planet from the pericenter in time t. Thus, integrating Eq. (9.40) and remembering that the angular momentum $\mathbf{H}$ is a conserved quantity so that it is constant in time, we get,

$$\mathbf{H} \int_0^t dt = \mathbf{a} \times \mathbf{b} \int_0^u du - e\mathbf{a} \times \mathbf{b} \int_0^u \cos u \, du,$$

or, $\mathbf{H}t = \mathbf{a} \times \mathbf{b}u - e(\mathbf{a} \times \mathbf{b}) \sin u.$ (9.41)

Taking moduli on both sides of Eq. (9.41) we get

$Ht = uab - e \sin u \, ab.$ (9.42)

We now make use of the fact that H is the arial velocity of the planet, or, $HP = 2\pi ab$ where P is the period of the orbit. Substituting for H from this equation into Eq. (9.42) and dividing out by ab, we finally get the desired equation relating u and t which can be combined with Eq. (9.38) to get the parameterization of the elliptic orbit in time,

$$\frac{2\pi t}{P} = u - e \sin u.$$ (9.43)

This equation is called Kepler's equation and can be used to obtain the position of the planet on its orbit at a given time. To make use of this equation, we have to solve it for u as a function of t. Unfortunately, the equation is transcendental and the solution cannot be expressed in terms of elementary functions. It can be solved numerically using the method of successive approximations [2, 17].

9.3.2 Cycloids, epicycloids and trochoids

These are the curves traced out by a point marked on the circumference of a circle which is rolling without slipping on a straight line or another circle. In the simplest case, a circle of radius a rolls along the x axis and the path of a point P on its circumference traces out a *cycloid*. We assume that at $t = 0$ the point P is at the origin of a cartesian coordinate system on the plane. Let us further assume that the circle turns clockwise with unit angular velocity so that the radius ending at P turns through an angle t in time t. Since the circle rolls uniformly without sliding the distance traversed by its centre equals the arc length rolled which equals at so that the coordinates of the centre of the circle at time t are (at, a). To get the position of the point P at time t we may imagine that its position vector at $t = 0$ is $-a\hat{\mathbf{j}}$ (see Fig. 9.13), rotate it *clockwise* through angle t and then translate by the vector $at\hat{\mathbf{i}} + a\hat{\mathbf{j}}$. Thus, we have

$$\mathbf{x}(t) = \mathscr{R}(-t, \hat{\mathbf{n}})(-a\hat{\mathbf{j}}) + at\hat{\mathbf{i}} + a\hat{\mathbf{j}},$$

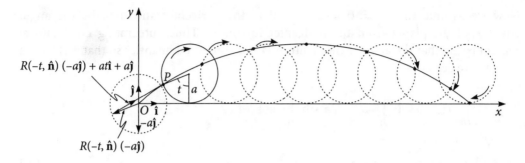

Fig. 9.13   Cycloid

where $\hat{n}$ is the vector normal to the plane defining the axis of rotation. Using Eq. (6.45) we get, for the position vector of P at time t,

$$a(t - \sin t)\hat{\mathbf{i}} + a(1 - \cos t)\hat{\mathbf{j}}.$$

Writing $\mathbf{x}(t) = x(t)\hat{\mathbf{i}} + y(t)\hat{\mathbf{j}}$ and equating the corresponding coefficients we get the parametric equations for the cycloid,

$$x(t) = a(t - \sin t),$$

$$y(t) = a(1 - \cos t). \tag{9.44}$$

An *epicycloid* is defined as the path of a point P on the circumference of a circle of radius c as it rolls at a uniform speed without slipping, along and outside the circumference of a second fixed circle of radius a. Let the center of the fixed circle be at the origin of a cartesian coordinate system on the $x - y$ plane. We assume that the center of the rolling circle rotates at the uniform angular speed of unit magnitude around the origin, so that the position vector of its center sweeps an angle t in time t (see Fig. 9.14). Let the position of P at $t = 0$ ($\mathbf{x}(0)$) be at the point of contact given by the tip of the vector $\mathbf{a}$ as in Fig. 9.14. Then, the position of P at time t ($\mathbf{x}(t)$) is (see Fig. 9.14)

$$\mathscr{R}\left(\frac{a}{c}t, \hat{n}\right)(-\mathscr{R}(t, \hat{n})\mathbf{c}) + \mathscr{R}(t, \hat{n})(\mathbf{a} + \mathbf{c}),$$

where $\hat{n}$ is the unit vector normal to the plane defining the axis of rotation. Using Eq. (6.45) to get the effect of rotation operators on vectors, we get, after some algebra,

$$\mathbf{x}(t) = \cos t(\mathbf{a} + \mathbf{c}) - \cos\left(\frac{a+c}{c}t\right)\mathbf{c} + \sin t\hat{n} \times (\mathbf{a} + \mathbf{c})$$

$$- \sin\left(\frac{a+c}{c}t\right)\hat{n} \times \mathbf{c}.$$

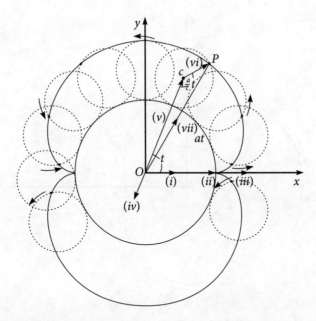

Fig. 9.14   Epicycloid. Vectors are (i) : $\mathbf{c}$, (ii) : $\mathbf{a}$, (iii) : $\mathbf{a} + \mathbf{c}$, (iv) : $-\mathscr{R}(t, \hat{\mathbf{n}})\mathbf{c}$, (v)
: $\mathscr{R}(t, \hat{\mathbf{n}})(\mathbf{a} + \mathbf{c})$, (vi) : $\mathscr{R}(\frac{a}{c}t, \hat{\mathbf{n}})(-\mathscr{R}(t, \hat{\mathbf{n}})\mathbf{c})$, (vii) : $\mathbf{x}(t)$

Resolving this into components we get the parametric equations for the epicycloid,

$$x(t) = (a + c)\cos t - c\cos\left(\frac{a + c}{c}t\right)$$

$$y(t) = (a + c)\sin t - c\sin\left(\frac{a + c}{c}t\right). \tag{9.45}$$

When $a = c$ the curve is called a *cardioid* (Fig. 9.15) and is given by the parametric equations

$$x(t) = 2a\cos t - a\cos(2t),$$

$$y(t) = 2a\sin t - a\sin(2t). \tag{9.46}$$

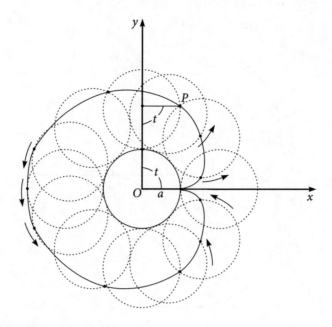

Fig. 9.15   Cardioid

A third kind of cycloid is the so called *hypocycloid* which is obtained exactly like the epicycloid, except that the rolling circle of radius c is interior to the fixed circle of radius a (see Fig. 9.16). Assuming that the initial position of the rolling point P is at the tip of the vector **a** and proceeding exactly as in the case of epicycloid,

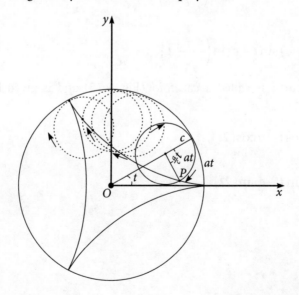

Fig. 9.16   Hypocycloid

we can show (Exercise) the parametric equations for the hypocycloid to be

$$x(t) = (a-c)\cos t + c\cos\left(\frac{a-c}{c}t\right),$$

$$y(t) = (a-c)\sin t - c\sin\left(\frac{a-c}{c}t\right).$$

In the special case $c = \frac{1}{2}a$ we find

$$x(t) = a\cos t, \quad y(t) = 0$$

and the hypocycloid degenerates into the diameter of the fixed circle, traced out back and forth (see Fig. 9.17). It is interesting to note that this example provides a way to draw a straight line merely by means of circular motions.

For the case $c = a/3$ the parametric equations for the hypocycloid become

$$x(t) = \frac{2}{3}a\cos t + \frac{1}{3}a\cos(2t),$$

$$y(t) = \frac{2}{3}a\sin t - \frac{1}{3}a\sin(2t).$$

This can be converted to

$$x^2 + y^2 = \frac{5}{6}a^2 + \frac{4}{9}a^2\cos(3t),$$

so that the hypocycloid meets the fixed circle exactly at three points and the corresponding curve appears in Fig. 9.16.

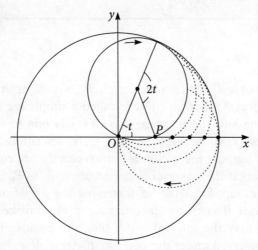

Fig. 9.17   A point P on the rim of a circle rolling inside a circle of twice the radius describes a straight line segment

More general curves called *trochoids* (epitrochoids, hypotrochoids) are obtained if we consider the motion of a point P attached to a circle, but not necessarily on its rim, when that circle rolls along a straight line or along the outside or inside of another circle (see Fig. 9.18). The same type of curve arises as the path of a point moving uniformly on a circle while the center of the circle moves uniformly along a line or a circle. For example, Eq. (9.44) go over to

$$x(t) = a(t - \sin t),$$

$$y(t) = a(1 - \cos t) - c \cos t. \tag{9.47}$$

where a is the radius of the circle and $a + c$ is the distance of P from its center. Note that, at $t = 0$ the position of P is $(0, -c)$, or the vector $\mathbf{c}_0$ in Fig. 9.18. These curves appear as the brachistochrones and tautochrones inside a gravitating homogeneous sphere [19].

9.3.3 Orientation of curves

We are interested in *connected* curves in a plane, consisting of one piece (unlike e.g., hyperbola which has two distinct branches). A connected curve can intersect itself like the trochoid in Fig. 9.18. A connected curve without self intersections is called *simple.* Within simple curves we can distinguish *closed curves*, such as circles or ellipses from the curves such as parabolas or straight line segments.

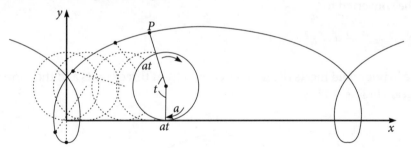

Fig. 9.18   Trochoid

Suppose a planar curve C with endpoints P_0, P_1 is parameterized by $t \mapsto \mathbf{x}(t)$ or equivalently $t \mapsto (x(t), y(t))$. Such a curve is called a *simple arc* if t varies over a finite interval on the real line and the mapping $t \mapsto \mathbf{x}(t)$ is one to one and onto, that is, $\mathbf{x}(t_1) = \mathbf{x}(t_2)$ implies $t_1 = t_2$. Further, as t *increases* continuously in the interval $a \leq t \leq b$ from a to b, suppose the vector $\mathbf{x}(t)$ traverses the arc continuously from P_0 to P_1. In this case, we say that the traversal of the arc from P_0 to P_1 is the *positive sense* of traversing the arc. The opposite sense of traversing the arc (from P_1 to P_0) is called *negative* sense of traversal. If a new parameterization $\tau(t)$ is invoked such that τ increases monotonically with t, over the interval $[a, b]$, then the positive (or negative) sense of traversing the arc is preserved under the new parameter τ. If τ decreases monotonically with increasing t, then the positive sense for t becomes the negative sense for τ and vice versa.

As an example of a curve with a loop, consider the curve given by the parametric equations $x(t) = t^2 - 1$, $y(t) = t^3 - t$. As t varies from $-\infty$ to $+\infty$ the curve crosses the origin twice for $t = -1$ and $t = +1$ while $\mathbf{x}(t)$ is unique for all other values of t (Fig. 9.19). The interval $-1 < t < +1$ corresponds to a *loop* of the curve. The sense of increasing t defines the sense of traversing the curve if we imagine the points corresponding to $t = -1$ and $t = +1$ as distinct, one lying on top of the other.

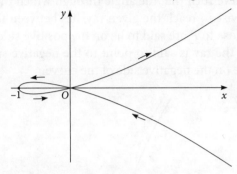

Fig. 9.19   A curve with a loop

The whole oriented curve can be decomposed into simple arcs, for example, into the arcs corresponding to $n \leq t \leq n+1$ where n runs over all integers. The standard example of a closed curve is a circle parameterized by $x(t) = a\cos t$, $y(t) = a\sin t$, which physically describes the uniform motion of a particle on a circle of radius a with t as time. If t varies in any half-open interval $\alpha \leq t < \alpha + 2\pi$ the point $P(x,y)$ traverses the circle counterclockwise exactly once. In general, a pair of continuous functions $x(t), y(t)$ defined in a closed interval $a \leq t \leq b$ represents a closed curve provided $x(a) = x(b)$ and $y(a) = y(b)$. The closed curve will be simple if $(x(t_1), y(t_1)) = (x(t_2), y(t_2))$ implies $t_1 = t_2$ whenever $a \leq t < b$.

The positive sense of traversing a closed curve is defined by the ordering of the points $P_0 P_1 P_2$ corresponding to $t_0 < t_1 < t_2$ respectively (see Fig. 9.20). Note that any cyclic permutation of the points $P_0 P_1 P_2$ does not change the sense of traversing a closed curve.

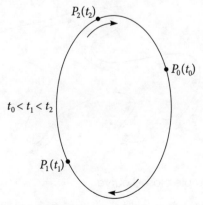

Fig. 9.20   Positive sense of traversing a closed curve

Positive and negative sides of a curve

We can distinguish between two sides, *positive* (or *left*) side and *negative* (or *right*) side of a oriented plane curve locally as follows.

Consider a ray issuing from a point P on the curve. Then this ray points to the positive side of the curve if there are points Q on the curve, arbitrarily close to P and following P in the sense given to the curve such that the angle through which the line from P to Q must be rotated counterclockwise to reach the given ray, lies between 0 and π (Fig. 9.21). The points on the ray lying close to P are said to lie on the positive side of the curve.

In the opposite case, the ray is said to point to the negative side of the curve and the points on it are said to lie on the negative side of the curve.

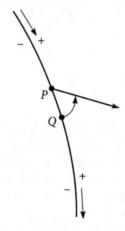

Fig. 9.21 Positive and negative sides of an oriented arc

If the curve C is a simple closed curve, it divides all points of the plane into two classes, those interior to C and those exterior to C. We say that C has *counterclockwise orientation* if its interior lies on the positive (that is, left) side (Fig. 9.22).

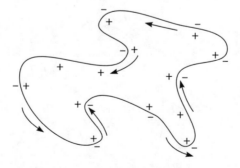

Fig. 9.22 Orientated simple closed curve

If the closed curve C consists of several loops, then it is not always possible to describe C such that all enclosed regions are on the positive side of C (see Fig. 9.23).

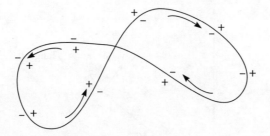

Fig. 9.23   Orientation of a curve with loops

Directions of tangent and normal

The two possible choices of the direction cosines of the tangent, namely,

$$\cos\alpha = \pm\frac{\dot{x}}{\sqrt{\dot{x}^2 + \dot{y}^2}} \quad \text{and} \quad \sin\alpha = \pm\frac{\dot{y}}{\sqrt{\dot{x}^2 + \dot{y}^2}},$$

(where the same sign must be taken in both the formulas) correspond to directions in which the tangent can be traversed. The corresponding angles α differ by an odd multiple of π. One of the two directions correspond to increasing t, while the other one to decreasing t. Since $y' = \frac{\dot{y}}{\dot{x}} = \frac{\sin\alpha}{\cos\alpha}$ the positive direction of the tangent that corresponds to increasing values of t is the one that forms with the positive direction of x axis an angle α for which $\cos\alpha$ has the same sign as $\dot{x}$ and $\sin\alpha$ has the same sign as $\dot{y}$. The corresponding direction cosines are given by

$$\cos\alpha = \frac{\dot{x}}{\sqrt{\dot{x}^2 + \dot{y}^2}} \quad \text{and} \quad \sin\alpha = \frac{\dot{y}}{\sqrt{\dot{x}^2 + \dot{y}^2}}.$$

If $\dot{x} > 0$, then the direction of increasing t on the tangent is that of increasing x and the angle α has a positive cosine. Similarly, the normal direction resulting due to the rotation of the positive tangent (given by increasing t) in the counterclockwise sense by $\frac{\pi}{2}$ has the unambiguous direction cosines

$$\cos\left(\alpha + \frac{\pi}{2}\right) = \frac{-\dot{y}}{\sqrt{\dot{x}^2 + \dot{y}^2}}, \quad \sin\left(\alpha + \frac{\pi}{2}\right) = \frac{\dot{x}}{\sqrt{\dot{x}^2 + \dot{y}^2}}.$$

It is called positive normal direction and points to the 'positive side' of the curve (see Fig. 9.24).

If we introduce a new parameter $\tau = \chi(t)$ on the curve, then the values of $\cos\alpha$ and $\sin\alpha$ remain unchanged if $\frac{d\tau}{dt} > 0$ and they change sign if $\frac{d\tau}{dt} < 0$ that is, if we change the sense of the curve, then the positive sense of tangent and normal is likewise changed.

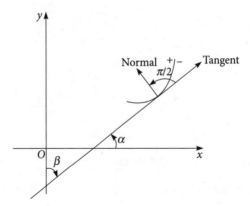

Fig. 9.24   Positive direction of the tangent and the normal

Sign of curvature

We know that the curvature of a plane curve is defined by the rate of change of direction of the tangent to the curve with the arc length parameter s, measured by $\frac{d\alpha}{ds}$ where α is the angle made by the tangent with the positive direction of the x-axis. Since the absolute value of the difference between two values of s has a invariant geometric meaning, namely the distance between two points of the curve measured along the curve, the absolute value of κ namely $|\kappa| = \left|\frac{d\alpha}{ds}\right|$ does not depend on the choice of a parameter. However, the *sign* of the difference must always be taken to be the same as the sign of the difference of the corresponding s values.

Since we defined s to be an increasing function of t, the sign of κ depends on the sense of the curve corresponding to increasing t. Obviously, $\kappa > 0$ if α increases with s, that is, if the tangent to the curve turns counterclockwise as we trace the curve with increasing s or t. This happens when the curve is convex towards the x-axis and the sense of increasing s is from left to right, while the tangent turns clockwise, when traced in the same sense of increasing s, if the curve is concave towards the x-axis. When $\kappa > 0$ The orientation of the curve C is such that the positive side of C is also the inner side of C, that is, the side towards which C curves (see Fig. 9.25).

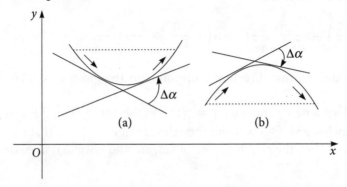

Fig. 9.25   (a) A convex function with positive curvature, and (b) a concave function with negative curvature

Exercise   Find the curvature of the function $y = x^3$ and find its sign in the regions $x < 0$ and $x > 0$. Check how the tangent turns as x increases in these regions.   □

9.4   Chain Rule

Let $\mathbf{f}(s)$ be a vector valued function of a scalar variable s, which, in turn, is a scalar valued function of another scalar variable t. By substitution, one would then have, $\mathbf{f}(s(t)) = \mathbf{f}(t)$ for the corresponding values of t and s. $\mathbf{f}(s)$ and $\mathbf{f}(t)$ are generally different functions but their values match for the values t and $s(t)$. This is the reason why the same symbol $\mathbf{f}$ is used to denote both the functions. We assume that both $\mathbf{f}(s)$ and $s(t)$ are continuous and differentiable wherever required. This implies that as $\Delta t \to 0$, both $\Delta\mathbf{f} = (\mathbf{f}(s(t + \Delta t)) - \mathbf{f}(s(t))) \to \mathbf{0}$ and $\delta s = (s(t + \Delta t) - s(t)) \to 0$. Thus, for the compound function $\mathbf{f}(s(t)) = \mathbf{f}(t)$ we have,

$$\frac{d\mathbf{f}}{dt} = \lim_{\Delta t \to 0} \frac{\Delta\mathbf{f}(t)}{\Delta t} = \lim_{\Delta t \to 0} \left(\frac{\Delta\mathbf{f}(s(t))}{\Delta s(t)} \frac{\Delta s(t)}{\Delta t} \right).$$

Note that $\mathbf{f}(s(t)) = \mathbf{f}(s)$ since the corresponding values match. By Eq. (8.2) we can write

$$\frac{d\mathbf{f}}{dt} = \left(\lim_{\Delta t \to 0} \frac{\Delta\mathbf{f}(s(t))}{\Delta s(t)} \right) \left(\lim_{\Delta t \to 0} \frac{\Delta s(t)}{\Delta t} \right)$$

$$= \left(\lim_{\Delta t \to 0} \frac{\Delta\mathbf{f}(s)}{\Delta s} \right) \left(\lim_{\Delta t \to 0} \frac{\Delta s(t)}{\Delta t} \right)$$

$$= \left(\frac{d\mathbf{f}}{ds} \right) \left(\frac{ds}{dt} \right). \tag{9.48}$$

Equation (9.48) gives us a rule for differentiating a compound function called the chain rule.

9.5   Scalar Integration

The rules of integration of a vector valued function of a scalar variable are similar to those for integration of a scalar valued function of a scalar variable. These are

$$\int_a^b \mathbf{f}(t)dt = -\int_b^a \mathbf{f}(t)dt \tag{9.49}$$

and

$$\int_a^b [\mathbf{f}(t) + \mathbf{g}(t)]dt = \int_a^b \mathbf{f}(t)dt + \int_a^b \mathbf{g}(t)dt. \tag{9.50}$$

For $a < c < b$,

$$\int_a^b \mathbf{f}(t)dt = \int_a^c \mathbf{f}(t)dt + \int_c^b \mathbf{f}(t)dt. \tag{9.51}$$

If $\mathbf{a}$ is a constant vector independent of t, then,

$$\int_a^b \mathbf{a} \cdot \mathbf{f}(t)dt = \mathbf{a} \cdot \left[\int_a^b \mathbf{f}(t)dt \right],$$

$$\int_a^b \mathbf{a} \times \mathbf{f}(t)dt = \mathbf{a} \times \left[\int_a^b \mathbf{f}(t)dt \right]$$

$$= -\left[\int_a^b \mathbf{f}(t)dt \right] \times \mathbf{a}. \tag{9.52}$$

Further, we have the "fundamental formula for the integral calculus" which evaluates the integral of a derivative.

$$\int_a^b \frac{d\mathbf{f}(t)}{dt}dt = \mathbf{f}(t) \Big|_a^b = \mathbf{f}(b) - \mathbf{f}(a). \tag{9.53}$$

Another fundamental result is the following formula for the derivative of an integral.

$$\frac{d}{dt} \int_a^t \mathbf{f}(s)ds = \mathbf{f}(t), \tag{9.54}$$

where s is the dummy variable of integration.

9.6   Taylor Series

Let us assume that a function $\mathbf{f}(t)$ possesses derivatives of all orders in some non-empty interval of values of the real (scalar) variable t. Let s be a scalar variable whose values are measured from a point t in this interval. Then, the value of the function at $t + s$ can be evaluated by summing the infinite converging series in powers of s with coefficients given by the values of derivatives of $\mathbf{f}$ evaluated at t. This is called Taylor series for $\mathbf{f}$ and is given by

$$\mathbf{f}(t + s) = \mathbf{f}(t) + s\dot{\mathbf{f}}(t) + \frac{s^2}{2!}\ddot{\mathbf{f}}(t) + \cdots$$

$$= \sum_{k=0}^{\infty} \frac{s^k}{k!} \frac{d^k}{dt^k}\mathbf{f}(t). \tag{9.55}$$

Thus, if we know the values of the function and all its derivatives at t then its value at $(t+s)$ can be obtained as a power series in s. Such a function is said to be analytic at t. A function analytic at all points in an interval is called *analytic* in that interval. A function analytic over its entire domain is called an *entire function*. Taylor series is very useful in applications because it can approximate a complicated analytic function by a polynomial obtained after truncating its Taylor series ensuring the required accuracy. For a given analytic function, it is always possible to find the minimum number of terms in its Taylor series whose sum will give the value of the function within the required accuracy.

We can use the fundamental formula, Eq. (9.53), to obtain the Taylor expansion of an analytic function along with the remainder after k terms.

The fundamental formula gives us

$$I = \int_t^{t+s} \dot{\mathbf{f}}(v)dv = \mathbf{f}(t+s) - \mathbf{f}(t).$$

This integral can be transformed to

$$I = \int_0^s \dot{\mathbf{f}}(t+s-u)du$$

via the change of variables $v = t+s-u$. We can now integrate by parts to get, with $\dot{\mathbf{f}}(t) = \frac{d\mathbf{f}}{du}\big|_{u=t}$,

$$I = u\dot{\mathbf{f}}(t+s-u)\Big|_0^s + \int_0^s u\ddot{\mathbf{f}}(t+s-u)du = s\dot{\mathbf{f}}(t) + \int_0^s u\ddot{\mathbf{f}}(t+s-u)du.$$

Integrating the second term by parts yields

$$I = s\dot{\mathbf{f}}(t) + \frac{s^2}{2!}\ddot{\mathbf{f}}(t) + \int_0^s \frac{u^2}{2!}\frac{d^3}{du^3}\mathbf{f}(t+s-u)du.$$

Thus, we have obtained

$$
\begin{aligned}
\mathbf{f}(t+s) &= \mathbf{f}(t) + I \\
&= \mathbf{f}(t) + s\dot{\mathbf{f}}(t) + \frac{s^2}{2!}\ddot{\mathbf{f}}(t) + \int_0^s \frac{u^2}{2!}\frac{d^3}{du^3}\mathbf{f}(t+s-u)du
\end{aligned}
\tag{9.56}
$$

giving the first three terms in the Taylor series, the last integral being the remainder term. $k-1$ successive integrations by parts give the first k terms of the series with the corresponding remainder term involving kth derivative of $\mathbf{f}(t)$. The remainder term can be used to estimate the truncation error incurred by truncating the series after k terms.

10

Functions with Vector Arguments

We now deal with the functions of vector arguments. These functions are either scalar valued or vector valued, with corresponding one to one or many to one maps given by $f : \mathscr{E}_3 \mapsto \mathbb{R}$ or by $\mathbf{f} : \mathscr{E}_3 \mapsto \mathscr{E}_3$. A vector valued function of vector argument is equivalent to a triplet of scalar valued functions of vector argument given by

$$\mathbf{f}(\mathbf{x}) = f_1(\mathbf{x})\hat{\mathbf{i}} + f_2(\mathbf{x})\hat{\mathbf{j}} + f_3(\mathbf{x})\hat{\mathbf{k}}, \tag{10.1}$$

where $f_{1,2,3}(\mathbf{x})$ are the scalar valued functions of $\mathbf{x}$ given by the components of $\mathbf{f}(\mathbf{x})$ with respect to some orthonormal basis $\{\hat{\mathbf{i}}, \hat{\mathbf{j}}, \hat{\mathbf{k}}\}$.

10.1 Need for the Directional Derivative

We have to first address the question of differentiating such functions. For a function of scalar argument, say $f(t)$, the derivative is defined via the difference quotient $(f(t + \Delta t) - f(t))/\Delta t$ which is the difference between the function values at t and at the incremented value $t + \Delta t$ divided by the increment Δt. For a function with a vector argument, say $f(\mathbf{x})$, the increment in the argument, say $\Delta \mathbf{x}$, in different directions will, in general, lead to different values of $f(\mathbf{x} + \Delta \mathbf{x}) - f(\mathbf{x})$. This leads to different derivatives in different directions which we call directional derivatives. Further, in the absence of an invertible product like the geometric product between vectors, division by the vector increment $\Delta \mathbf{x}$ is not possible.

10.2 Partial Derivatives

The standard way of dealing with this situation is to treat a scalar valued function of vector argument as a function of three scalar variables, $f : \mathbb{R}^3 \mapsto \mathbb{R}$. Equation (10.1) can be used to replace a vector valued function of a vector argument by a triplet of scalar valued functions of vector argument, each of which can then be treated as the function of three scalar variables. Thus, in this subsection it will be sufficient to deal with the scalar valued functions of three variables. A given function of three variables $f(x,y,z)$ can be reduced to a function of a single variable by giving constant fixed values to any two of the variables, say y and z and treat x as the only variable varying over the allowed domain of x values. Such a function of a single variable, say x, can then be differentiated by using the standard definition of its derivative, assuming that it is a continuous and differentiable function of x. This derivative is called the partial derivative of $f(x,y,z)$ with respect to x. If we fix $z = z_0$ then $f(x,y,z)$ is reduced to the function $f(x,y,z_0) = f(x,y)$ which defines a surface in $\mathbb{R}^3$. If we now fix $y = y_0$ we get the function $f(x,y_0,z_0) = f(x)$ whose graph is the curve giving the intersection of the surface $f(x,y)$ and the plane $y = y_0$. Geometrically, the partial derivative of $f(x,y,z)$ with respect to x is given by the tangent of the angle between a parallel line to the x axis and the tangent line to the curve $u = f(x,y_0,z_0)$. It is, therefore, slope of the surface $u = f(x,y,z_0)$ in the direction of the x axis (see Fig. 10.1). Thus, the partial derivatives of $f(x,y,z)$ with respect to x,y,z are given by

$$\lim_{\Delta x \to 0} \frac{f(x+\Delta x,y,z) - f(x,y,z)}{\Delta x} = \frac{\partial f}{\partial x}(x,y,z) = f_x(x,y,z)$$

$$\lim_{\Delta y \to 0} \frac{f(x,y+\Delta y,z) - f(x,y,z)}{\Delta y} = \frac{\partial f}{\partial y}(x,y,z) = f_y(x,y,z)$$

$$\lim_{\Delta z \to 0} \frac{f(x,y,z+\Delta z) - f(x,y,z)}{\Delta z} = \frac{\partial f}{\partial z}(x,y,z) = f_z(x,y,z). \tag{10.2}$$

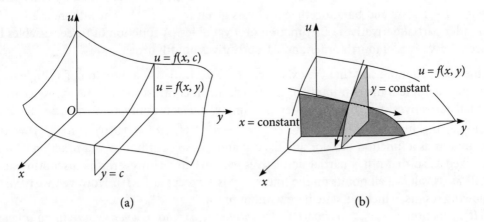

(a)   (b)

Fig. 10.1   Sections of $u = f(x,y)$

where the variables which are not incremented are not varied and are held constant. We have to be careful while indicating for what values of the independent variables the derivatives are taken. For example, the x-derivative of $f(x,y) = x^2 + 2xy + 4y^2$ evaluated at the point $x = 1, y = 2$ can be written as

$$\left(\frac{\partial f(x,y)}{\partial x}\right)_{x=1,y=2} = f_x(1,2) = (2x+2y)_{x=1,y=2} = 6.$$

We should not write it simply as $\frac{\partial f(1,2)}{\partial x}$ since $f(1,2) = 21$ is a constant and has 0 as its x-derivative.

Since the partial derivatives $f_{x,y,z}(x,y,z)$ are the functions of three variables, they can be again partially differentiated with respect to x,y,z. Assuming that the order of differentiation does not matter, we get the six derivatives, namely, $f_{xx}, f_{xy}, f_{xz}, f_{yy}, f_{yz}, f_{zz}$ where $f_{xx} = \frac{\partial^2 f}{\partial x^2} = \frac{\partial f_x}{\partial x}$, $f_{xy} = \frac{\partial^2 f}{\partial x \partial y} = \frac{\partial f_y}{\partial x}$ etc.

Exercise   Assuming that the order of differentiation does not matter, how many partial derivatives of order r of a function of n variables are possible?

Solution   Let $r_1, r_2, \ldots, r_n$ denote the number of occurrences of the variables $x_1, x_2, \ldots, x_n$ in a rth order possible partial derivative of a function $f(x_1, x_2, \ldots, x_n)$. We must have $r_1 + r_2 + \cdots + r_n = r$. A general arrangement can be viewed as n stars separated by $n-1$ bars. For example, the eighth order partial derivative of a six variable function $\frac{\partial^8 f}{\partial x_1^3 \partial x_2 \partial x_6^4}$ corresponds to ($r = 8$ and $n = 6$) $***|*|||****$ where the string of stars ending at the kth bar ($1 \leq k \leq n-1$) gives the order of differentiation with respect to the variable x_k and the string of stars starting after the $n-1$th bar gives the order of differentiation with respect to the variable x_n. If a pair of bars does not sandwitch any stars, or if the last string of stars is absent, the differentiation with respect to the corresponding variable is absent. The total number of distinct distributions is then given by the number of ways of selecting r places out of $n+r-1$ places to be filled by stars and rest of the places are filled by bars. (there are $n+r-1$ stars and bars together). This is given by $\binom{n+r-1}{r}$. Thus, there are $\binom{n+r-1}{r}$ rth order partial derivatives of a function of n variables. A function of three variables has fifteen derivatives of fourth order and 21 derivatives of fifth order.   □

In the last section we saw that the existence of the derivative of a function of a single scalar variable guarantees the continuity of the function. In contrast to this, the existence of the partial derivatives $f_{x,y,z}(x,y,z)$ does not imply the continuity of $f(x,y,z)$. Thus for example, the function $u(x,y) = 2xy/(x^2 + y^2)$, $(x,y) \neq (0,0)$; $u(0,0) = 0$ is continuous as a function of x for any fixed y and is also continuous as a function of y for any fixed x, so that it has partial derivatives everywhere. However, it is discontinuous at $(0,0)$ as its value at all points on the line $x = y$ is 1 except at $(0,0)$. However, we have the following results, which we state here without proof.

If a function $f(x,y,z)$ has partial derivatives f_x, f_y and f_z everywhere in an open set $\mathcal{R}$ and these derivatives everywhere satisfy the inequalities

$$|f_x(x,y,z)| < M, \quad |f_y(x,y,z)| < M,$$

where M is independent of x,y,z then $f(x,y,z)$ is continuous everywhere in $\mathcal{R}$.

Further, if both the partial derivative of order r and the partial derivative obtained by changing the order of differentiation in any way are continuous in a region $\mathcal{R}$, then both these derivatives are equal in $\mathcal{R}$, that is, the order of differentiation is immaterial. This makes the number of partial derivatives of rth order of $f(x,y,z)$ decidedly smaller than otherwise expected, as we have calculated in the previous exercise.

10.3 Chain Rule

Consider a function $u(x,y,z) = u(\xi(x,y,z),\eta(x,y,z),\dots)$ to be a differentiable function of n variables $\xi,\eta,\dots$ each of which is a differentiable function of x,y,z. Let the functions $\xi,\eta,\dots$ have as their common domain the region $\mathcal{R}$ in $\mathbb{R}^3$. All the n functions $\xi,\eta,\dots$ together map a point in $\mathcal{R}$ to a point in the region S in $\mathbb{R}^n$. The function u then maps this point to a scalar value. Thus, u is a differentiable function of x,y,z ; $u : \mathbb{R}^3 \mapsto \mathbb{R}$. The partial derivatives of u with respect to x,y,z are then given by

$$u_x = \frac{\partial u}{\partial \xi}\frac{\partial \xi}{\partial x} + \frac{\partial u}{\partial \eta}\frac{\partial \eta}{\partial x} + \cdots = u_\xi \xi_x + u_\eta \eta_x + \cdots$$

$$u_y = \frac{\partial u}{\partial \xi}\frac{\partial \xi}{\partial y} + \frac{\partial u}{\partial \eta}\frac{\partial \eta}{\partial y} + \cdots = u_\xi \xi_y + u_\eta \eta_y + \cdots$$

$$u_z = \frac{\partial u}{\partial \xi}\frac{\partial \xi}{\partial z} + \frac{\partial u}{\partial \eta}\frac{\partial \eta}{\partial z} + \cdots = u_\xi \xi_z + u_\eta \eta_z + \cdots \tag{10.3}$$

Replacing x,y,z by x_1,x_2,x_3 and $\xi,\eta,\dots$ by $\xi_1,\xi_2,\dots$ we can summarize the above equations by

$$u_{x_k} = \sum_{i=1}^{n} \frac{\partial u}{\partial \xi_i}\frac{\partial \xi_i}{\partial x_k} \quad k = 1,2,3. \tag{10.4}$$

In order to prove Eq. (10.3) all that we need to use is that all functions involved are differentiable. We have,

$$\xi(x+\Delta x,y+\Delta y,z+\Delta z) - \xi(x,y,z) = \xi(x+\Delta x,y+\Delta y,z+\Delta z) - \xi(x,y+\Delta y,z+\Delta z)$$

$$+\xi(x,y+\Delta y,z+\Delta z) - \xi(x,y,z+\Delta z) + \xi(x,y,z+\Delta z) - \xi(x,y,z).$$

If we multiply three terms on RHS by $\frac{\Delta x}{\Delta x}, \frac{\Delta y}{\Delta y}$ and $\frac{\Delta z}{\Delta z}$ respectively, we get an expression linear in $\Delta x, \Delta y, \Delta z$, that is,

$$\Delta \xi = \frac{\xi(x+\Delta x, y+\Delta y, z+\Delta z) - \xi(x, y+\Delta y, z+\Delta z)}{\Delta x} \Delta x$$

$$+ \frac{\xi(x, y+\Delta y, z+\Delta z) - \xi(x, y, z+\Delta z)}{\Delta y} \Delta y$$

$$+ \frac{\xi(x, y, z+\Delta z) - \xi(x, y, z)}{\Delta z} \Delta z. \tag{10.5}$$

By differentiability of $\xi(x, y, z)$ we mean that replacing the difference quotients on the RHS of this equation by the respective partial derivatives would give an error

- linear in the Euclidean distance traversed as we go from x, y, z to $x+\Delta x, y+\Delta y, z+\Delta z$, that is, the error is given by $\epsilon \rho$, where $\rho = \sqrt{\Delta x^2 + \Delta y^2 + \Delta z^2}$ and
- the error goes to zero faster than $\rho \to 0$, that is, $\epsilon \to 0$ faster than $\rho \to 0$.

Thus, we can write, upto first order of smallness in ρ, (That is, neglecting the terms of the second and higher order in ρ in the expression for error if any,)

$$\Delta \xi = \xi_x \Delta x + \xi_y \Delta y + \xi_z \Delta z.$$

This is exactly the same as replacing the distance traversed between two points along a path by the Euclidean distance between these two points, a procedure we have incurred before.

Similarly, we get,

$$\Delta \eta = \eta_x \Delta x + \eta_y \Delta y + \eta_z \Delta z.$$

Since u is a differentiable function of $\xi, \eta, \ldots$ we can again write

$$\Delta u = u_\xi \Delta \xi + u_\eta \Delta \eta + \cdots$$

Substituting, the expressions for $\Delta \xi$, $\Delta \eta \cdots$ we get Δu as a result of Δx, Δy Δz as

$$\Delta u = (u_\xi \xi_x + u_\eta \eta_x + \cdots)\Delta x + (u_\xi \xi_y + u_\eta \eta_y + \cdots)\Delta y + (u_\xi \xi_z + u_\eta \eta_z + \cdots)\Delta z.$$

However, considering u as a function of x, y, z we must have

$$\Delta u = u_x \Delta x + u_y \Delta y + u_z \Delta z.$$

Comparing the last two equations for Δu we get Eq. (10.3), which is called the chain rule for differentiating a compound function of several variables.

Exercise   Find expressions for all second order derivatives of u.   □

Exercise   Find all partial derivatives of the first and the second order with respect to x and y for the following functions of x, y:

(i) $u = v \log w$ where $v = x^2$ and $w = \frac{1}{1+y}$.

(ii) $u = e^{vw}$, where $v = ax$ and $w = \cos y$.

(iii) $u = v \tan^{-1} w$ where $v = \frac{xy}{x-y}$ and $w = x^2y + y - x$.

(iv) $u = g(x^2 + y^2, e^{x-y})$.

(v) $u = \tan(x \tan^{-1} y)$. $\square$

10.4   Directional Derivative and the Grad Operator

As we have seen above, for a function of three variables $f(\mathbf{x}) \equiv f(x,y,z)$ we can write upto first order in ρ,

$$\Delta f = f(\mathbf{x} + \Delta\mathbf{x}) - f(\mathbf{x}) = \frac{\partial f}{\partial x}\Delta x + \frac{\partial f}{\partial y}\Delta y + \frac{\partial f}{\partial z}\Delta z = \nabla f \cdot \Delta\mathbf{x} \qquad (10.6)$$

Equations (10.6), (10.7) define a new operator, called '**grad**' or '*del*' operator which operates on a scalar valued function $f(\mathbf{x})$ and returns a vector valued function $(\nabla f)(\mathbf{x})$ via

$$(\nabla f)(\mathbf{x}) = \frac{\partial f}{\partial x}(\mathbf{x})\hat{\mathbf{i}} + \frac{\partial f}{\partial y}(\mathbf{x})\hat{\mathbf{j}} + \frac{\partial f}{\partial z}(\mathbf{x})\hat{\mathbf{k}}. \qquad (10.7)$$

where $\hat{\mathbf{i}}, \hat{\mathbf{j}}, \hat{\mathbf{k}}$ is the orthonormal basis in which coordinates of $\mathbf{x}$ are (x,y,z). Note that the notation $\nabla(f(\mathbf{x}))$ is meaningless because $f(\mathbf{x})$ is a number and the *del* operator does not act on a number.

In order to be useful, we must show that the definition of the *del* operator is invariant under the change of basis, that is, it is the same for all orthonormal bases, so that the *del* operator $(\nabla f)(\mathbf{x})$ has the same value at $\mathbf{x}$ irrespective of the basis used to evaluate it. We do this by treating the *del* operator as a vector with coordinates $u_1 = \frac{\partial f}{\partial x_1}$, $u_2 = \frac{\partial f}{\partial x_2}$, $u_3 = \frac{\partial f}{\partial x_3}$ with respect to the coordinate system corresponding to the basis $\hat{\mathbf{i}}, \hat{\mathbf{j}}, \hat{\mathbf{k}}$. Let the coordinates of a vector $\mathbf{x}$ in this coordinate system be x_1, x_2, x_3. We know that a new coordinate system is obtained from the old one by rotating and/or translating it. Hence, the new coordinates say x_1', x_2', x_3' are related to the old ones by

$$x_j' = \sum_{k=1}^{3} a_{jk}x_k + b_j$$

where $[a_{jk}]$ is an orthogonal matrix, whose inverse equals its transpose, and $\mathbf{b}$ is the vector by which the origin of the old system is translated. Due to orthogonality of the transformation $[a_{jk}]$, the old coordinates can be re-expressed in terms of the new ones as

$$x_k = \sum_{j=1}^{3} a_{kj}(x_j' - b_j), \quad k = 1, 2, 3.$$

Under this coordinate transformation, a function $f(x_1, x_2, x_3)$ will get transformed to $g(x_1', x_2', x_3')$ so that the operator ∇f will get transformed to $\nabla f \equiv \left(\frac{\partial g}{\partial x_1'}, \frac{\partial g}{\partial x_2'}, \frac{\partial g}{\partial x_3'} \right)$. To evaluate these partial derivatives we note that

$$g(x_1', x_2', x_3') = f\left(\sum_{k=1}^{3} a_{k1}(x_k' - b_k), \sum_{k=1}^{3} a_{k2}(x_k' - b_k), \sum_{k=1}^{3} a_{k3}(x_k' - b_k) \right).$$

Thus, the coordinates of ∇g with respect to the new coordinate system are given by

$$v_j = \frac{\partial g}{\partial x_j'} = \sum_{k=1}^{3} \frac{\partial f}{\partial x_k} \frac{\partial x_k}{\partial x_j'} = \sum_{k=1}^{3} a_{jk} u_k.$$

where we have used the chain rule. Thus, under the coordinate transformation the operator ∇f transforms like a vector and its components in the transformed system are given by the partial derivatives of the transformed function with respect to the transformed coordinates. Given a vector $\mathbf{x}$ the vector $(\nabla f)(\mathbf{x})$ is the same irrespective of the coordinate system used to evaluate it.

We are now equipped to define the directional derivative of a function of three variables. Given a scalar valued function $f(\mathbf{x}) \equiv f(x, y, z)$, its derivative in a direction $\hat{\mathbf{a}}$ is given by

$$(\hat{\mathbf{a}} \cdot \nabla) f = n_x \frac{\partial f}{\partial x} + n_y \frac{\partial f}{\partial y} + n_z \frac{\partial f}{\partial z} \tag{10.8}$$

where (n_x, n_y, n_z) are the direction cosines of $\hat{\mathbf{a}}$ with respect to the basis $\hat{\mathbf{i}}, \hat{\mathbf{j}}, \hat{\mathbf{k}}$. This is called the directional derivative of $f(\mathbf{x})$ in the direction $\hat{\mathbf{a}}$. Henceforth, we shall drop the parentheses in the expressions for the *del* operator and the directional derivative, implying their actions implicitly. Also, we may allow replacing the unit vector $\hat{\mathbf{a}}$ by a general vector $\mathbf{a}$ (with magnitude different than unity) in the definition of the directional derivative. In that case the direction cosines in Eq. (10.8) are replaced by the components of $\mathbf{a}$.

Exercise   Let $f(\mathbf{x}) \equiv f(x_1, x_2, x_3)$ be a differentiable scalar valued function with $\{x_1, x_2, x_3\}$ referring to the orthonormal basis $\{\hat{\mathbf{i}}_1, \hat{\mathbf{i}}_2, \hat{\mathbf{i}}_3\}$. Show that $\frac{\partial f}{\partial x_k}$, $k = 1, 2, 3$ are the directional derivatives along $\{\hat{\mathbf{i}}_1, \hat{\mathbf{i}}_2, \hat{\mathbf{i}}_3\}$ respectively.

Solution   Notice that $\frac{\partial f}{\partial x_k} = \hat{\mathbf{i}}_k \cdot \Delta f$, $k = 1, 2, 3$. $\qquad\qquad\square$

Exercise   Find the directional derivative of a scalar field $f(\mathbf{x})$ along a continuous and differentiable curve parameterized by time t.

Answer   This is simply the total time derivative of the function $f(\mathbf{x}(t))$ with respect to t as can be seen from (see section 10.7)

$$\frac{df}{dt} = \dot{\mathbf{x}} \cdot \nabla f(\mathbf{x}).$$

The RHS is just the directional derivative of $f(\mathbf{x})$ in the direction of the velocity or the tangent vector to the curve. $\qquad\square$

The concept of the directional derivative can be quite simply generalized to vector fields as follows. The directional derivative of a vector field $\mathbf{f}(\mathbf{x}) \equiv (f_1(\mathbf{x}), f_2(\mathbf{x}), f_3(\mathbf{x}))$ along $\hat{\mathbf{a}}$ is given by a vector with components $(\hat{\mathbf{a}} \cdot \nabla f_1(\mathbf{x}), \hat{\mathbf{a}} \cdot \nabla f_2(\mathbf{x}), \hat{\mathbf{a}} \cdot \nabla f_3(\mathbf{x}))$ in the same basis in which the field $\mathbf{f}(\mathbf{x})$ is resolved. Since each component of $\nabla \mathbf{f}$ is invarient under the change of basis, so is $\nabla \mathbf{f}$ itself.

Another elegant approach called geometric calculus is developed by D. Hestenes and collaborators in the context of functions with multivector arguments. This approach can be adapted to both the scalar as well as vector valued functions of vector arguments, vectors being a special case of multivectors. This is a coordinate-free approach, where arguments of functions are treated as vectors as such, without resolving them into components using a particular basis. The increment $\Delta \mathbf{x}$ in the vector argument $\mathbf{x}$ is decomposed as $\mathbf{a}\tau$ where the vector $\mathbf{a}$ gives the direction and τ is a scalar variable. The directional derivative is then defined as[1]

$$\mathbf{a} \cdot \nabla f(\mathbf{x}) = \lim_{\tau \to 0} \frac{f(\mathbf{x} + \mathbf{a}\tau) - f(\mathbf{x})}{\tau}. \tag{10.9}$$

Note that this definition is meaningful even if the function f is vector valued, because the limit defining it is meaningful in that case. We will show below, for a scalar valued function, that the definitions of the directional derivative given by Eqs (10.8) and (10.9) are equivalent. Thus, the LHS of Eq. (10.9) can be viewed as the dot product of $\mathbf{a}$ and $\nabla f(\mathbf{x})$. In this section, unless stated otherwise, the same symbol f will represent both the scalar and vector valued function and the corresponding result applies in both the cases.

We now obtain some basic results regarding the directional derivative. Consider

$$
\begin{aligned}
(\mathbf{a} + \mathbf{b}) \cdot \nabla f(\mathbf{x}) &= \lim_{\tau \to 0} \frac{f(\mathbf{x} + \mathbf{a}\tau + \mathbf{b}\tau) - f(\mathbf{x})}{\tau} \\[2ex]
&= \lim_{\tau \to 0} \left[\frac{f(\mathbf{x} + \mathbf{a}\tau + \mathbf{b}\tau) - f(\mathbf{x} + \mathbf{a}\tau)}{\tau} + \frac{f(\mathbf{x} + \mathbf{a}\tau) - f(\mathbf{x})}{\tau} \right] \\[2ex]
&= \mathbf{a} \cdot \nabla f(\mathbf{x}) + \mathbf{b} \cdot \nabla f(\mathbf{x}).
\end{aligned}
\tag{10.10}
$$

Similarly, for a scalar constant c,

$$(c\mathbf{a}) \cdot \nabla f(\mathbf{x}) = c \lim_{c\tau \to 0} \frac{f(\mathbf{x} + c\tau\mathbf{a}) - f(\mathbf{x})}{c\tau} = c(\mathbf{a} \cdot \nabla f(\mathbf{x})). \tag{10.11}$$

Exercise   Let $f(\mathbf{x})$ and $g(\mathbf{x})$ be two functions of vector argument $\mathbf{x}$.

---

[1] See also ref [21]

(i) Show that

$$\mathbf{a} \cdot \nabla(f + g) = \mathbf{a} \cdot \nabla f + \mathbf{a} \cdot \nabla g. \tag{10.12}$$

(ii) Assuming either f or g or both to be scalar valued, or, by replacing the product fg by the dot product $\mathbf{f} \cdot \mathbf{g}$ if both are vector valued, show that

$$\mathbf{a} \cdot \nabla(fg) = (\mathbf{a} \cdot \nabla f)g + f(\mathbf{a} \cdot \nabla g). \tag{10.13}$$

We refer to this as the "product rule". It is trivial to check that $\mathbf{a} \cdot \nabla cf(\mathbf{x}) = c\mathbf{a} \cdot \nabla f(\mathbf{x})$. This equation and Eq. (10.12) together show that the directional derivative is a linear operator.

Now let f be a scalar valued function of a scalar argument and let $\lambda(\mathbf{x})$ be a scalar valued function of a vector argument. Then, the directional derivative of the compound function $f(\lambda(\mathbf{x}))$ is

$$
\begin{aligned}
\mathbf{a} \cdot \nabla f &= \lim_{\tau \to 0} \left[\frac{f(\lambda(\mathbf{x} + \mathbf{a}\tau)) - f(\lambda(\mathbf{x}))}{\lambda(\mathbf{x} + \mathbf{a}\tau) - \lambda(\mathbf{x})} \frac{\lambda(\mathbf{x} + \mathbf{a}\tau) - \lambda(\mathbf{x})}{\tau} \right] \\[2ex]
&= \left[\lim_{\Delta\lambda \to 0} \frac{f(\lambda + \Delta\lambda) - f(\lambda)}{\Delta\lambda} \right] \left[\lim_{\tau \to 0} \frac{\lambda(\mathbf{x} + \mathbf{a}\tau) - \lambda(\mathbf{x})}{\tau} \right] \\[2ex]
&= (\mathbf{a} \cdot \nabla\lambda) \frac{df}{d\lambda}. \tag{10.14}
\end{aligned}
$$

This is the chain rule for the directional derivative of a compound function.

The directional derivative of the vector valued and the scalar valued constant functions $\mathbf{f}(\mathbf{x}) = \mathbf{b}$ and $f(\mathbf{x}) = c$ are trivially zero, as seen from its definition. We have

$$\mathbf{a} \cdot \nabla\mathbf{b} = 0 = \mathbf{a} \cdot \nabla c.$$

It follows directly from the definition of the directional derivative that the directional derivative of the identity function $I(\mathbf{x}) = \mathbf{x}$ is

$$\mathbf{a} \cdot \nabla\mathbf{x} = \mathbf{a}.$$

We can use general rules Eqs (10.12) and (10.13) to find the derivatives of more complicated functions. The derivatives of algebraic functions of $\mathbf{x}$ can be obtained in this way. For example, we note that the "magnitude function" $|\mathbf{x}|$ is related to $\mathbf{x}$ by the algebraic equation $|\mathbf{x}|^2 = \mathbf{x} \cdot \mathbf{x}$. Using Eq. (10.13) we can write

$$\mathbf{a} \cdot \nabla(\mathbf{x} \cdot \mathbf{x}) = (\mathbf{a} \cdot \nabla\mathbf{x}) \cdot \mathbf{x} + \mathbf{x} \cdot (\mathbf{a} \cdot \nabla\mathbf{x}) = \mathbf{a} \cdot \mathbf{x} + \mathbf{x} \cdot \mathbf{a} = 2\mathbf{a} \cdot \mathbf{x}. \tag{10.15}$$

If we apply the chain rule (Eq. (10.14)) we get

$$\mathbf{a} \cdot \nabla|\mathbf{x}|^2 = 2|\mathbf{x}|\mathbf{a} \cdot \nabla|\mathbf{x}|.$$

Equating the RHS of both these equations we get

$$\mathbf{a} \cdot \nabla |\mathbf{x}| = \frac{\mathbf{a} \cdot \mathbf{x}}{|\mathbf{x}|} = \mathbf{a} \cdot \hat{\mathbf{x}}. \tag{10.16}$$

Next, we find the derivative of the "direction function" $\hat{\mathbf{x}}$. We use the product rule (Eq. (10.13)) and the chain rule (Eq. (10.14)) as follows.

$$\mathbf{a} \cdot \nabla \left(\frac{\mathbf{x}}{|\mathbf{x}|} \right) = \frac{\mathbf{a} \cdot \nabla \mathbf{x}}{|\mathbf{x}|} - \frac{\mathbf{a} \cdot \nabla |\mathbf{x}|}{|\mathbf{x}|^2} \mathbf{x} = \frac{\mathbf{a}}{|\mathbf{x}|} - \frac{(\mathbf{a} \cdot \hat{\mathbf{x}}) \mathbf{x}}{|\mathbf{x}|^2}.$$

Hence,

$$\mathbf{a} \cdot \nabla \hat{\mathbf{x}} = \frac{\mathbf{a} - (\mathbf{a} \cdot \hat{\mathbf{x}}) \hat{\mathbf{x}}}{|\mathbf{x}|}. \tag{10.17}$$

Exercise Find the derivatives

(a) $\mathbf{a} \cdot \nabla (\mathbf{x} \times \mathbf{b})$ Where $\mathbf{b}$ is a constant vector independent of $\mathbf{x}$.

Answer $\mathbf{a} \times \mathbf{b}$. Follows from the definition of the directional derivative.

(b) $\mathbf{a} \cdot \nabla (\mathbf{x} \times (\mathbf{x} \times \mathbf{b}))$.

Answer $(\mathbf{a} \cdot \mathbf{b}) \mathbf{x} + (\mathbf{x} \cdot \mathbf{b}) \mathbf{a} - 2(\mathbf{a} \cdot \mathbf{x}) \mathbf{b}$.

Hint Use identity I and the product rule. ☐

Exercise Let $\mathbf{r} = \mathbf{r}(\mathbf{x}) = \mathbf{x} - \mathbf{x}'$, $r = |\mathbf{r}| = |\mathbf{x} - \mathbf{x}'|$ where $\mathbf{x}'$ is independent of $\mathbf{x}$. Show that

(a) $\mathbf{a} \cdot \nabla r = \mathbf{a} \cdot \hat{\mathbf{r}}$.

(b) $\mathbf{a} \cdot \nabla \hat{\mathbf{r}} = \dfrac{\mathbf{a} - (\mathbf{a} \cdot \hat{\mathbf{r}}) \hat{\mathbf{r}}}{r}$.

(c) $\mathbf{a} \cdot \nabla (\hat{\mathbf{r}} \cdot \mathbf{a}) = \dfrac{a^2 - (\mathbf{a} \cdot \hat{\mathbf{r}})^2}{r}$.

(d) $\mathbf{a} \cdot \nabla (\hat{\mathbf{r}} \times \mathbf{a}) = \dfrac{(\mathbf{a} \cdot \hat{\mathbf{r}})(\mathbf{a} \times \hat{\mathbf{r}})}{r}$.

(e) $\mathbf{a} \cdot \nabla |\hat{\mathbf{r}} \times \mathbf{a}|^2 = -\dfrac{(\hat{\mathbf{r}} \cdot \mathbf{a}) |\hat{\mathbf{r}} \times \mathbf{a}|}{r}$.

(f) $\mathbf{a} \cdot \nabla \dfrac{\hat{\mathbf{r}}}{r} = \dfrac{\mathbf{a} - 2(\mathbf{a} \cdot \hat{\mathbf{r}}) \hat{\mathbf{r}}}{r^2}$.

(g) $\mathbf{a} \cdot \nabla \dfrac{1}{r^2} = -2 \dfrac{\mathbf{a} \cdot \hat{\mathbf{r}}}{r^3}$.

(h) $\dfrac{1}{2} (\mathbf{a} \cdot \nabla)^2 \dfrac{1}{r^2} = \dfrac{3(\mathbf{a} \cdot \hat{\mathbf{r}})^2 - |\hat{\mathbf{r}} \times \mathbf{a}|^2}{r^4}$.

(i) $\dfrac{1}{6} (\mathbf{a} \cdot \nabla)^3 \dfrac{1}{r^2} = 4\mathbf{a} \cdot \hat{\mathbf{r}} \dfrac{(\mathbf{a} \cdot \hat{\mathbf{r}})^2 + |\hat{\mathbf{r}} \times \mathbf{a}|^2}{r^5}$.

(j) $\mathbf{a} \cdot \nabla \log r = \dfrac{\mathbf{a} \cdot \hat{\mathbf{r}}}{r}$.

(k) $\mathbf{a} \cdot \nabla r^{2k} = 2k(\mathbf{a} \cdot \mathbf{r})r^{2(k-1)}$.

(l) $\mathbf{a} \cdot \nabla r^{2k+1} = r^{2k}(\mathbf{a} + 2k(\mathbf{a} \cdot \hat{\mathbf{r}})\hat{\mathbf{r}})$.

In the last two cases $k \neq 0$ is an integer and $\mathbf{r} \neq \mathbf{0}$ if $k < 0$. $\square$

It is quite easy to see that the definition of the directional derivative in Eq. (10.8) follows from that in Eq. (10.9). Choosing an orthonormal basis $\{\hat{\mathbf{e}}_1, \hat{\mathbf{e}}_2, \hat{\mathbf{e}}_3\}$ and denoting the components of $\mathbf{x}$ with respect to this basis by x_1, x_2, x_3 we get

$$
\begin{aligned}
\hat{\mathbf{a}} \cdot \nabla f(\mathbf{x}) &= (n_1\hat{\mathbf{e}}_1 + n_2\hat{\mathbf{e}}_2 + n_3\hat{\mathbf{e}}_3) \cdot \nabla f(\mathbf{x}) \\[2mm]
&= n_1\hat{\mathbf{e}}_1 \cdot \nabla f(\mathbf{x}) + n_2\hat{\mathbf{e}}_2 \cdot \nabla f(\mathbf{x}) + n_3\hat{\mathbf{e}}_3 \cdot \nabla f(\mathbf{x}) \\[2mm]
&= n_1\frac{\partial f}{\partial x_1} + n_2\frac{\partial f}{\partial x_2} + n_3\frac{\partial f}{\partial x_3}.
\end{aligned}
\tag{10.18}
$$

The second equality follows from Eq. (10.10) and the last equality follows because the directional derivative (Eq. (10.9)) along the direction of one of the basis vectors reduces to the corresponding partial derivative (Eq. (10.8)).

We note that the action of the '*del*' operator on a scalar valued function $f(\mathbf{x})$ is the same as that of the linear operator

$$
\nabla \equiv \sum_{j=1}^{3} \hat{\mathbf{e}}_j \frac{\partial}{\partial x_j} = \hat{\mathbf{e}}_1 \frac{\partial}{\partial x_1} + \hat{\mathbf{e}}_2 \frac{\partial}{\partial x_2} + \hat{\mathbf{e}}_3 \frac{\partial}{\partial x_3}.
\tag{10.19}
$$

Using the linearity of the directional derivative and Eq. (10.18) we can express the directional derivative of a vector valued function in terms of the partial derivatives of its component functions in an orthonormal basis $(\hat{\mathbf{e}}_1, \hat{\mathbf{e}}_2, \hat{\mathbf{e}}_3)$. We have,

$$
\begin{aligned}
\hat{\mathbf{a}} \cdot \nabla \mathbf{f}(\mathbf{x}) &= \hat{\mathbf{a}} \cdot \nabla(f_1(\mathbf{x})\hat{\mathbf{e}}_1 + f_2(\mathbf{x})\hat{\mathbf{e}}_2 + f_3(\mathbf{x})\hat{\mathbf{e}}_3) \\[2mm]
&= \hat{\mathbf{a}} \cdot \nabla f_1(\mathbf{x})\hat{\mathbf{e}}_1 + \hat{\mathbf{a}} \cdot \nabla f_2(\mathbf{x})\hat{\mathbf{e}}_2 + \hat{\mathbf{a}} \cdot \nabla f_3(\mathbf{x})\hat{\mathbf{e}}_3 \\[2mm]
&= \left(n_1\frac{\partial f_1}{\partial x_1} + n_2\frac{\partial f_1}{\partial x_2} + n_3\frac{\partial f_1}{\partial x_3} \right)\hat{\mathbf{e}}_1 + \left(n_1\frac{\partial f_2}{\partial x_1} + n_2\frac{\partial f_2}{\partial x_2} + n_3\frac{\partial f_2}{\partial x_3} \right)\hat{\mathbf{e}}_2 \\[2mm]
&\quad + \left(n_1\frac{\partial f_3}{\partial x_1} + n_2\frac{\partial f_3}{\partial x_2} + n_3\frac{\partial f_3}{\partial x_3} \right)\hat{\mathbf{e}}_3.
\end{aligned}
\tag{10.20}
$$

We can replace the unit vector $\hat{\mathbf{a}}$ by a vector $\mathbf{a}$ of arbitrary (usually small) magnitude in the same direction, without losing generality. In this case the components of the unit vector $\hat{\mathbf{a}}$, namely, the direction cosines n_1, n_2, n_3 are replaced by the components of $\mathbf{a}$ that is, by a_1, a_2, a_3. The components of the directional derivative of the vector valued function $\mathbf{f}(\mathbf{x})$, usually called a vector field, are completely specified by the matrix product

$$
\begin{bmatrix}
\dfrac{\partial f_1}{\partial x_1} & \dfrac{\partial f_1}{\partial x_2} & \dfrac{\partial f_1}{\partial x_3} \\[2mm]
\dfrac{\partial f_2}{\partial x_1} & \dfrac{\partial f_2}{\partial x_2} & \dfrac{\partial f_2}{\partial x_3} \\[2mm]
\dfrac{\partial f_3}{\partial x_1} & \dfrac{\partial f_3}{\partial x_2} & \dfrac{\partial f_3}{\partial x_3}
\end{bmatrix}
\begin{bmatrix} a_1 \\[2mm] a_2 \\[2mm] a_3 \end{bmatrix}
=
\begin{bmatrix} \mathbf{a} \cdot \nabla f_1 \\[2mm] \mathbf{a} \cdot \nabla f_2 \\[2mm] \mathbf{a} \cdot \nabla f_3 \end{bmatrix}.
$$

The linear map defined by the matrix

$$
J = \frac{d(f_1, f_2, f_3)}{d(x_1, x_2, x_3)} =
\begin{bmatrix}
\dfrac{\partial f_1}{\partial x_1} & \dfrac{\partial f_1}{\partial x_2} & \dfrac{\partial f_1}{\partial x_3} \\[2mm]
\dfrac{\partial f_2}{\partial x_1} & \dfrac{\partial f_2}{\partial x_2} & \dfrac{\partial f_2}{\partial x_3} \\[2mm]
\dfrac{\partial f_3}{\partial x_1} & \dfrac{\partial f_3}{\partial x_2} & \dfrac{\partial f_3}{\partial x_3}
\end{bmatrix}
$$

is called the Jacobian matrix of the differentiable map $\mathbf{x} \mapsto \mathbf{f}(\mathbf{x})$. When evaluated at a particular value of $\mathbf{x}$, we get a matrix whose elements are numbers, called Jacobian matrix at $\mathbf{x}$, denoted $J(\mathbf{x})$. The Jacobian matrix plays the role of the derivative of the vector valued function of a vector variable, because it gives a linear approximation to $\mathbf{f}$ at $\mathbf{x}$ just as the derivative of a function of a single variable. Extending this analogy further, we call the linear map defined by the Jacobian $J(\mathbf{x})$ to be the map tangent to $\mathbf{f}$ at $\mathbf{x}$. The Jacobian matrix can be generalized to a differentiable map $f : \mathbb{R}^n \mapsto \mathbb{R}^m$ defining the derivative of such a map. When $m = n$ (in our case $m = n = 3$) we can evaluate the determinant of the Jacobian $J(\mathbf{x})$ which is called the Jacobian determinant of $\mathbf{f}(\mathbf{x})$ at $\mathbf{x}$, denoted $|J(\mathbf{x})|$.

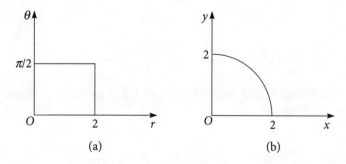

Fig. 10.2   Mapping polar to cartesian coordinates

Exercise   Let $F : \mathbb{R}^2 \mapsto \mathbb{R}^2$ be the map defined by

$$F(r,\theta) = (r\cos\theta, r\sin\theta) \quad r \geq 0$$

In other words, the polar coordinates map $(r,\theta) \mapsto (x,y)$ as

$$x = r\cos\theta, \quad y = r\sin\theta$$

which maps a rectangle into a circular sector (see Fig. 10.2). Find the Jacobian matrix and the Jacobian determinant of this mapping. Find all points (r,θ) where the Jacobian determinant vanishes.   □

10.5 Taylor Series

We can extend the Taylor series approximation to the functions of vector argument. This enables us to approximate the arbitrary functions of vectors (mostly position vectors) by simpler functions. Such a Taylor series involves directional derivatives, and applies to functions for which directional derivatives (or, equivalently, partial derivatives) of all orders (see below) exist. The basic idea is to use the Taylor series expansion of the function with scalar argument. Given a scalar or vector valued function $f(\mathbf{x})$ to be approximated, we invoke a new function of scalar argument

$$G(\tau) = f(\mathbf{x} + \mathbf{a}\tau).$$

Using this definition of $G(\tau)$ and the definition of the directional derivative (Eq. (10.9)) it is clear that

$$\frac{dG(0)}{d\tau} = \mathbf{a} \cdot \nabla f(\mathbf{x}),$$

$$\frac{d^2G(0)}{d\tau^2} = \mathbf{a} \cdot \nabla(\mathbf{a} \cdot \nabla f(\mathbf{x})) \equiv (\mathbf{a} \cdot \nabla)^2 f(\mathbf{x}),$$

$$\frac{d^kG(0)}{d\tau^k} = \mathbf{a} \cdot \nabla((\mathbf{a} \cdot \nabla)^{k-1} f(\mathbf{x})) = (\mathbf{a} \cdot \nabla)^k f(\mathbf{x}). \tag{10.21}$$

We now expand the function with scalar argument $G(\tau)$ in Taylor series about $\tau = 0$ and evaluate it at $\tau = 1$. We get

$$G(1) = G(0) + \frac{dG(0)}{d\tau} + \frac{1}{2}\frac{d^2G(0)}{d\tau^2} + \cdots = \sum_{k=0}^{\infty} \frac{1}{k!}\frac{d^kG(0)}{d\tau^k}.$$

Using Eq. (10.21) we can express this Taylor series in terms of $f(\mathbf{x})$. This gives the desired Taylor expansion

$$f(\mathbf{x}+\mathbf{a}) = f(\mathbf{x}) + \mathbf{a} \cdot \nabla f(\mathbf{x}) + \frac{(\mathbf{a} \cdot \nabla)^2}{2!} f(\mathbf{x}) + \cdots$$

$$= \sum_{k=0}^{\infty} \frac{(\mathbf{a} \cdot \nabla)^k}{k!} f(\mathbf{x}) \equiv e^{\mathbf{a} \cdot \nabla} f(\mathbf{x}), \tag{10.22}$$

where the last equivalence *defines* the operator $e^{\mathbf{a} \cdot \nabla}$.

If f is a vector valued function $\mathbf{f}(\mathbf{x})$ we can resolve it in terms of its component functions with respect to some orthonormal basis and use Eq. (10.20) iteratively to get the Taylor expansion

$$\mathbf{f}(\mathbf{x}+\mathbf{a}) = \begin{bmatrix} f_1(\mathbf{x}) \\ f_2(\mathbf{x}) \\ f_3(\mathbf{x}) \end{bmatrix} + \begin{bmatrix} \mathbf{a} \cdot \nabla f_1(\mathbf{x}) \\ \mathbf{a} \cdot \nabla f_2(\mathbf{x}) \\ \mathbf{a} \cdot \nabla f_3(\mathbf{x}) \end{bmatrix} + \frac{1}{2!} \begin{bmatrix} (\mathbf{a} \cdot \nabla)^2 f_1(\mathbf{x}) \\ (\mathbf{a} \cdot \nabla)^2 f_2(\mathbf{x}) \\ (\mathbf{a} \cdot \nabla)^2 f_3(\mathbf{x}) \end{bmatrix} + \cdots$$

Each element in the second term is simply the dot product of $\mathbf{a}$ and $\nabla f_k(\mathbf{x})$, $k = 1, 2, 3$. The second term is given by the product of the Jacobian matrix and the vector $\mathbf{a} \leftrightarrow [a_1 a_2 a_3]^T$.

10.6 The Differential

The general form of the remainder after two terms in the Taylor series of a scalar valued function $f(\mathbf{x})$ can be found by the following argument. We say that $f(\mathbf{x})$ is differentiable at $\mathbf{x}$ if all its partial derivatives exist at $\mathbf{x}$, or, the vector $\nabla f(\mathbf{x})$ is well defined. Since we cannot divide by a vector increment $\Delta \mathbf{x}$ we can re-write the Newtonian quotient as

$$df = f(\mathbf{x} + \Delta \mathbf{x}) - f(\mathbf{x}) = \Delta \mathbf{x} \cdot \nabla f(\mathbf{x}) + |\Delta \mathbf{x}| g(\Delta \mathbf{x}) \tag{10.23}$$

such that $g(\Delta \mathbf{x}) \to 0$ as $|\Delta \mathbf{x}| \to 0$. Note that the first term on RHS is simply the directional derivative in the direction of $\Delta \mathbf{x}$. This equation implies that, for any required accuracy, we can choose $|\mathbf{a}|$ small enough so as to make the first two terms of the Taylor series in Eq. (10.22) give the value of $f(\mathbf{x} + \mathbf{a})$ within the required accuracy. In other words, the remainder term in the series obtained after truncating it after the second term, namely the last term in the equation

$$f(\mathbf{x} + \mathbf{a}) = f(\mathbf{x}) + \mathbf{a} \cdot \nabla f(\mathbf{x}) + |\mathbf{a}| g(\mathbf{a}) \tag{10.24}$$

can be chosen as small as we please by choosing $|\mathbf{a}|$ small enough.[2] We call the directional derivative appearing in this equation, namely, $\mathbf{a} \cdot \nabla f(\mathbf{x})$, the *differential* of the function $f(\mathbf{x})$. For a scalar valued function, $f(\mathbf{x})$, Eq. (10.23) is the equation for a line in 3-D in the range $\mathbf{x}$ and $\mathbf{x} + d\mathbf{x}$. Thus, we see that, for any scalar valued differentiable function, the differential provides a linear approximation to that function in a small enough range of its argument. For a vector valued function $\mathbf{f}(\mathbf{x})$ Eq. (10.24) now becomes a vector equation, with f replaced by

$$\mathbf{f}(\mathbf{x} + \mathbf{a}) = \begin{pmatrix} f_1(\mathbf{x}) \\ f_2(\mathbf{x}) \\ f_1(\mathbf{x}) \end{pmatrix} + \begin{pmatrix} \mathbf{a} \cdot \nabla f_1(\mathbf{x}) \\ \mathbf{a} \cdot \nabla f_2(\mathbf{x}) \\ \mathbf{a} \cdot \nabla f_3(\mathbf{x}) \end{pmatrix} + |\mathbf{a}| \begin{pmatrix} g_1(\mathbf{a}) \\ g_1(\mathbf{a}) \\ g_1(\mathbf{a}) \end{pmatrix},$$

where the scalar valued functions $f_k(\mathbf{x})$, $k = 1, 2, 3$ are the components of $\mathbf{f}(\mathbf{x})$ with respect to some orthonormal basis. The term in the middle, involving the gradients, is precisely equal to the product of the Jacobian matrix times $\mathbf{a} \equiv [a_1 a_2 a_3]^T$. Since $\lim_{|\mathbf{a}| \to 0} g_k(\mathbf{a}) = 0$; $k = 1, 2, 3$ we can make the linear approximation to $\mathbf{f}(\mathbf{x})$ at $\mathbf{x}$ by the Jacobian matrix $J(\mathbf{x})$ as accurate as we please by making $|\mathbf{a}|$ small enough.

To appreciate the importance of the differential, (which is the same as the directional derivative of a scalar valued or vector valued function $f(\mathbf{x})$ in the direction of fixed vector $(\mathbf{a})$, we view it as a function of $\mathbf{a}$ for fixed $\mathbf{x}$, say $F(\mathbf{a})$. We have already shown that the differential is a linear function of $\mathbf{a}$ (see Eqs (10.10),(10.11)). Expanding the Taylor series about the point $\mathbf{x}_0$ and putting $\Delta \mathbf{x} = \mathbf{x} - \mathbf{x}_0$ we have, for small enough $|\Delta \mathbf{x}|$,

$$f(\mathbf{x}_0 + \Delta \mathbf{x}) = f(\mathbf{x}) = f(\mathbf{x}_0) + \Delta \mathbf{x} \cdot \nabla f(\mathbf{x}_0) = (\mathbf{x} - \mathbf{x}_0) \cdot \nabla f(\mathbf{x}_0). \tag{10.25}$$

Note that the vector $\mathbf{x} - \mathbf{x}_0$ in the differential $(\mathbf{x} - \mathbf{x}_0) \cdot \nabla f(\mathbf{x}_0)$ plays the role of vector $\mathbf{a}$ in $\mathbf{a} \cdot \nabla f(\mathbf{x})$ which is a linear function of $\mathbf{a}$. Therefore, using this linearity and Eq. (10.25) we get, to the first order in $\Delta \mathbf{x}$

$$f(\mathbf{x}) - f(\mathbf{x}_0) = (\mathbf{x} - \mathbf{x}_0) \cdot \nabla f(\mathbf{x}_0) = \mathbf{x} \cdot \nabla f(\mathbf{x}_0) - \mathbf{x}_0 \cdot \nabla f(\mathbf{x}_0) = F(\mathbf{x}) - F(\mathbf{x}_0). \tag{10.26}$$

If we couple linearity of $F(\mathbf{x})$ with Eq. (10.26), we see that the differential provides a linear approximation to any differentiable function. Since linear functions are simple enough to be analyzed completely, Eq. (10.26) establishes the importance of the differential. Note that Eqs (10.25) and (10.26) apply to both the scalar valued as well as the vector valued function $f(\mathbf{x})$.

---

[2] Compare with

$$f(a + h) = f(a) + \frac{df}{dx}\Big|_{x=a} h + |h| g(h)$$

where

$$\lim_{h \to 0} g(h) = 0.$$

10.7   Variation on a Curve

We are often interested in the variation of a function $f(\mathbf{x})$ along the path of a moving particle parametrically given by $\mathbf{x} = \mathbf{x}(t)$. Let us first assume that $f(\mathbf{x})$ is scalar valued. We know that the general variation of such a function is given by

$$f(\mathbf{x} + \Delta\mathbf{x}) = f(\mathbf{x}) + \Delta\mathbf{x} \cdot \nabla f(\mathbf{x}).$$

However, both $\mathbf{x}$ and $\Delta\mathbf{x}$ are now not arbitrary, but $\mathbf{x}$ must satisfy $\mathbf{x} = \mathbf{x}(t)$ and $\Delta\mathbf{x}$ must join the point $\mathbf{x}(t)$ and a neighboring point on the path given by $\mathbf{x}(t + \Delta t)$, that is, $\Delta\mathbf{x} = \mathbf{x}(t + \Delta t) - \mathbf{x}(t)$. Therefore, the variation of $f(\mathbf{x})$ *along the curve* is given by

$$f(\mathbf{x}(t + \Delta t)) = f(\mathbf{x}(t)) + (\mathbf{x}(t + \Delta t) - \mathbf{x}(t)) \cdot \nabla f(\mathbf{x}(t)).$$

Now we subtract $f(\mathbf{x}(t))$ from both sides, divide by Δt on both sides and take the limit as $\Delta t \to 0$ on both sides to get the desired result,

$$\frac{df}{dt}(\mathbf{x}(t)) = \dot{\mathbf{x}}(t) \cdot \nabla f(\mathbf{x}(t)) = \sum_{i=1}^{3} \dot{x}_i(t) \frac{\partial f}{\partial x_i}, \tag{10.27}$$

where $\dot{x}_i \ \ i = 1,2,3$ and $x_i \ \ i = 1,2,3$ are the components of $\dot{\mathbf{x}}(t)$ and $\mathbf{x}(t)$ respectively, with respect to some orthonormal basis. Thus, the time rate of change of a function of the position vector of a particle, as it moves along its path, is given by the directional derivative of this function along the direction of the velocity vector, which is tangent to the path in the same sense as traversed by the particle.

Exercise   The Lagrangian of a system with n degrees of freedom is a function of $2n + 1$ variables, namely, $\mathcal{L}(\mathbf{q}(t); \dot{\mathbf{q}}(t); t)$ where $\mathbf{q}(t) \equiv q_1(t), q_2(t), \dots, q_n(t)$ are the generalized coordinates and $\dot{\mathbf{q}}(t) \equiv \dot{q}_1(t), \dot{q}_2(t), \dots, \dot{q}_n(t)$ are the generalized velocities. The motion is viewed as the path traced by a point in the configuration space spanned by the n generalized coordinates. Similarly, the Hamiltonian of such a system is given as a function of $2n + 1$ coordinates, namely, $\mathcal{H}(\mathbf{q}(t); \mathbf{p}(t); t)$ where $\mathbf{p}(t) \equiv p_1, p_2, \dots, p_n$ are the generalized momenta. The motion is viewed as that of a point in phase space spanned by n generalized coordinates and n generalized momenta. Find the expressions for $\frac{d\mathcal{L}}{dt}$ and $\frac{d\mathcal{H}}{dt}$.

Answer

$$\frac{d\mathcal{L}}{dt} = \sum_{i=1}^{n} \frac{\partial \mathcal{L}}{\partial q_i} \dot{q}_i + \sum_{i=1}^{n} \frac{\partial \mathcal{L}}{\partial \dot{q}_i} \ddot{q}_i + \frac{\partial \mathcal{L}}{\partial t},$$

where $\ddot{q}_i = \frac{d}{dt}\dot{q}_i$.

$$\frac{d\mathcal{H}}{dt} = \sum_{i=1}^{n} \frac{\partial \mathcal{H}}{\partial q_i} \dot{q}_i(\mathbf{p}(t)) + \sum_{i=1}^{n} \frac{\partial \mathcal{H}}{\partial p_i} \dot{p}_i + \frac{\partial \mathcal{H}}{\partial t},$$

where the generalized velocities are the functions of generalized momentum vector $\mathbf{p}(t)$. ☐

If the function $\mathbf{f}(\mathbf{x}(t))$ is vector valued, Eq. (10.27) can be expressed invoking the Jacobian. We can write

$$\frac{d\mathbf{f}}{dt}(\mathbf{x}(t)) = \begin{pmatrix} \dot{\mathbf{x}}(t) \cdot \nabla f_1(\mathbf{x}(t)) \\ \dot{\mathbf{x}}(t) \cdot \nabla f_2(\mathbf{x}(t)) \\ \dot{\mathbf{x}}(t) \cdot \nabla f_3(\mathbf{x}(t)) \end{pmatrix},$$

where $f_i(\mathbf{x}(t))$ $i = 1,2,3$ are the components of the function $\mathbf{f}(\mathbf{x}(t))$. The RHS of this equation is simply the product of the Jacobian matrix of the function $\mathbf{f}(\mathbf{x}(t))$ and the column matrix comprising the components of the vector $\dot{\mathbf{x}}(t)$. Thus, we have found the *Chain rule* for differentiating the composite function $f(\mathbf{x}(t))$ or $\mathbf{f}(\mathbf{x}(t))$.

10.8   Gradient of a Potential

If a vector field $\mathbf{f}(\mathbf{x})$ is the differential of some scalar field, that is, $\mathbf{a} \cdot \mathbf{f}(\mathbf{x}) = \mathbf{a} \cdot \nabla \phi(\mathbf{x})$ for some scalar field $\phi(\mathbf{x})$, then we say that $\mathbf{f}$ is the *gradient* of ϕ and write

$$\mathbf{f} = \nabla \phi.$$

ϕ is called the *potential* of $\mathbf{f}$. We know that the differential of a function $\phi(\mathbf{x})$ is its directional derivative in the direction of $\mathbf{a}$. The directional derivative is simply the rate at which the value of ϕ changes in the direction of $\mathbf{a}$. If we choose $\hat{\mathbf{a}}$ to be unit vector giving the chosen direction, then $\hat{\mathbf{a}} \cdot \nabla \phi$ has its maximum value when $\hat{\mathbf{a}}$ and $\nabla \phi$ are in the same direction, that is, $\hat{\mathbf{a}} \cdot \nabla \phi = |\nabla \phi|$. Thus, the gradient $\nabla \phi(\mathbf{x})$ specifies both the direction as well as the magnitude of the maximum change in the value of $\phi(\mathbf{x})$ at any point $\mathbf{x}$ in the domain of ϕ. In general, the change in the values of ϕ, in any given direction $\hat{\mathbf{a}}$, based at a point $\mathbf{x}$, is given by the scalar product of $\hat{\mathbf{a}}$ with $\nabla \phi(\mathbf{x})$.

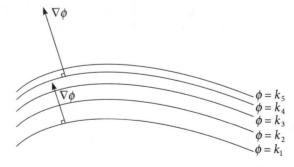

Fig. 10.3   The gradient vector is orthogonal to the equipotential at every point

It is interesting to find $\nabla \phi(\mathbf{x})$ at a point $\mathbf{x}$ on a surface defined by the equation $\phi(\mathbf{x}) = k$, that is, the surface, at each point of which ϕ has constant value k. Such a surface is called an *equipotential surface*. Actually, the equation $\phi(\mathbf{x}) = k$ defines a one-parameter family of equipotential surfaces, one surface for each constant value of k (see Fig. 10.3). At any point $\mathbf{x}$ on an equipotential surface the vector $\nabla\phi(\mathbf{x})$ cannot have a component tangential to the surface because a non-zero gradient tangential to the surface would mean that $\phi(\mathbf{x})$ changes as $\mathbf{x}$ changes along the surface, contradicting the equipotential nature of the surface. Thus, at every point $\mathbf{x}$ on an equipotential surface the vector $\nabla\phi(\mathbf{x})$ must be normal to the surface through that point. Further, it is directed towards the surfaces with larger values of k, because the sign of the directional derivative is the same as that of the difference in ϕ values and in the present case, the sign of the directional derivative is the same as that of $\nabla\phi(\mathbf{x})$. Figure 10.3 shows only a two dimensional cross section. In this figure, the change in k is the same for each pair of neighboring surfaces, so the separation provides a measure of the change in ϕ. The closer the surfaces, larger the gradient.

Given a scalar valued function $\phi(\mathbf{x})$ its gradient at $\mathbf{x}$ is easily found by evaluating the corresponding directional derivative $\mathbf{a} \cdot \nabla\phi(\mathbf{x})$ which is simply the scalar product of $\nabla\phi$ with an arbitrary vector $\mathbf{a}$. Thus, for $\phi(\mathbf{x}) = \mathbf{x} \cdot \mathbf{b}$ where $\mathbf{b}$ is a constant vector, we get $\mathbf{a} \cdot \nabla(\mathbf{x} \cdot \mathbf{b}) = \mathbf{a} \cdot \mathbf{b}$ which follows from $\mathbf{a} \cdot \nabla\mathbf{x} = \mathbf{a}$. Hence,

$$\nabla\mathbf{x} \cdot \mathbf{b} = \mathbf{b}.$$

Similarly, from Eqs (10.15) and (10.16) we get

$$\nabla\mathbf{x}^2 = 2\mathbf{x},$$

$$\nabla|\mathbf{x}| = \hat{\mathbf{x}}. \tag{10.28}$$

These formulas enable us to determine the gradients of certain functions without referring to the directional derivative at all. Thus, if $f(|\mathbf{x}|)$ is a function of the magnitude of $\mathbf{x}$ alone, then, by using the second of Eq. (10.28) while applying the chain rule Eq. (10.14), we get

$$\nabla f = \hat{\mathbf{x}} \frac{\partial f}{\partial|\mathbf{x}|}. \tag{10.29}$$

Later we will meet potential functions in connection with the line integrals over vector fields derivable from a potential.

10.9   Inverse Maps and Implicit Functions

We have already seen the conditions for the map $\mathbf{f} : \mathscr{E}_3 \mapsto \mathscr{E}_3$ to be invertible (subsection 4.1.2). Here, we are interested in a class of maps (or functions) which are differentiable, called $\mathcal{C}^1$ functions, so we define the inverse of a function over the set of $\mathcal{C}^1$ functions. Further, by $\mathscr{E}_3$ we mean $\mathscr{E}_3$ or $\mathbb{R}^3$. Let U denote some open set in $\mathscr{E}_3$. A map $\mathbf{f} : U \mapsto \mathscr{E}_3$ is called a $\mathcal{C}^1$-*map* on U if $\hat{\mathbf{a}} \cdot \nabla\mathbf{f}$ and $(\hat{\mathbf{a}} \cdot \nabla)^2\mathbf{f}$ exist at all $\mathbf{x} \in U$ and for all $\hat{\mathbf{a}}$. This is equivalent to saying that all partial derivatives of all the component functions $f_1(\mathbf{x}), f_2(\mathbf{x}), f_3(\mathbf{x})$ of $\mathbf{f}(\mathbf{x})$ exist and are continuous at all $\mathbf{x} \in U$. A $\mathcal{C}^1$-map $\mathbf{f} : U \mapsto \mathscr{E}_3$ is said to be C^1-*invertible* if the image set $\mathbf{f}(U)$ is an open set V and if there exists a C^1-map $\mathbf{g} : V \mapsto U$ such that $\mathbf{g} \circ \mathbf{f}$ and $\mathbf{f} \circ \mathbf{g}$ are the respective identity maps on U and V. For example, if $\mathbf{f} : \mathscr{E}_3 \mapsto \mathscr{E}_3$ is given by $\mathbf{f}(\mathbf{x}) = \mathbf{x} + \mathbf{b}$ where $\mathbf{b}$ is a fixed vector, then $\mathbf{f}$ is C^1-invertible, its inverse being the translation by $-\mathbf{b}$.

Exercise   Let U be the subset of $\mathbb{R}^2$ consisting of all pairs (r, θ) with $r > 0$ and $0 < \theta < \pi$. Let

$$\mathbf{f}(r\hat{\mathbf{i}} + \theta\hat{\mathbf{j}}) = r\cos\theta\hat{\mathbf{i}} + r\sin\theta\hat{\mathbf{j}}, \tag{10.30}$$

with $x = r\cos\theta$ and $y = r\sin\theta$. Show that this is a C^1-map and find the image set $\mathbf{f}(U)$. Show that the inverse map is given by

$$\mathbf{g}(x\hat{\mathbf{i}} + y\hat{\mathbf{j}}) = \sqrt{x^2 + y^2}\,\hat{\mathbf{i}} + \cos^{-1}\frac{x}{\sqrt{x^2 + y^2}}\,\hat{\mathbf{j}},$$

with $r = \sqrt{x^2 + y^2}$ and $\theta = \cos^{-1}\frac{x}{\sqrt{x^2+y^2}}$.

Answer   The image of U is the upper half plane consisting of all (x, y) such that $y > 0$, and arbitrary x. Inverse can be checked explicitly.   □

In many cases a map may not be invertible over the whole space or over arbitrary subsets of it, but can still be C^1-invertible locally in the following sense. Let a point $\mathbf{x} \in U$. We say that a map $\mathbf{f}$ is *locally C^1-invertible at* $\mathbf{x}$ if there exists an open set U_1 satisfying $\mathbf{x} \in U_1 \subset U$ such that $\mathbf{f}$ is C^1-invertible on U_1.

Exercise   Show that the map given by Eq. (10.30) is not C^1-invertible on all of $\mathbb{R}^2$, but given any point, it is locally invertible at that point.

Hint   If we take $r < 0$, the inverse map given in the previous exercise does not work. However, we can locally invert by choosing $r = -\sqrt{x^2 + y^2}$ in the inverse map at a point with $r < 0$.   □

In most cases the locally invertible map cannot be expressed in closed form. However, there is a very important result which gives computable criterion for local invertibility of a map.

10.9.1   Inverse mapping theorem

Let U be an open set in $\mathscr{E}_3$ and $\mathbf{f} : U \mapsto \mathscr{E}_3$ be a C^1 map. Let $\mathbf{x}$ be a point in U. If the Jacobian determinant $|j_{\mathbf{f}}(\mathbf{x})| \neq 0$ then $\mathbf{f}$ is locally C^1-invertible at $\mathbf{x}$.

We do not give a formal proof of this theorem which is quite involved. However, we note that the Jacobian matrix corresponding to a vector valued map $\mathbf{f}(\mathbf{x})$ plays the role of its derivative at $\mathbf{x}$. The Jacobian matrix itself is a linear map $\mathbf{a} \mapsto \mathbf{a} \cdot \nabla \mathbf{f}$ giving the directional derivative of $\mathbf{f}$ along $\mathbf{a}$. The determinant $|J_{\mathbf{f}}(\mathbf{x})| \neq 0$ means that the the Jacobian matrix is invertible at $\mathbf{x}$. Thus, the inverse mapping theorem states that the map $\mathbf{f}$ is locally invertible at $\mathbf{x}$ if the linear map defining its derivative, namely, its Jacobian matrix is invertible at $\mathbf{x}$.

Exercise Let $F : \mathbb{R}^2 \mapsto \mathbb{R}^2$ be given by $F(x,y) = (e^x \cos y, e^x \sin y)$. Show that F is locally invertible at every point.

Answer $|J_F(x,y)| = e^x \neq 0$ for all $(x,y) \in \mathbb{R}^2$ with $|x| < \infty$ and $|y| < \infty$. □

Exercise Let U be open in $\mathbb{R}^2$ and let $f : U \mapsto \mathbb{R}$ be a C^1 function. Let $(a,b) \in U$. Assume that $\frac{\partial f}{\partial y}(a,b) \neq 0$. Then, show that the map $F : \mathbb{R}^2 \mapsto \mathbb{R}^2$ given by

$$(x,y) \mapsto F(x,y) = (x, f(x,y))$$

is locally invertible at (a,b).

Answer We have to compute the Jacobian matrix and its determinant. We have

$$J_F(x,y) = \begin{pmatrix} 1 & 0 \\ \frac{\partial f}{\partial x} & \frac{\partial f}{\partial y} \end{pmatrix},$$

so that

$$|J_F(a,b)| = \frac{\partial f}{\partial y}(a,b),$$

which, by assumption, is not zero and the inverse mapping theorem then implies what we are asked to prove. □

The result of this exercise can be used to discuss *implicit functions*. We assume that the function $f : U \mapsto \mathbb{R}$ defined in the exercise has the value c at (a,b), or, $f(a,b) = c$. We wish to find out whether there is some differentiable function $y = \phi(x)$, defined near $x = a$, such that $\phi(a) = b$ and

$$f(x, \phi(x)) = c$$

for all x near a. If such a function ϕ exists, we say that $y = \phi(x)$ is the *function determined implicitly by f*.

10.9.2 Implicit function theorem

Let U be open in $\mathbb{R}^2$ and let $f : U \mapsto \mathbb{R}$ be a C^1 function. Let $(a,b) \in U$ and let $f(a,b) = c$. Assume that $\frac{\partial f}{\partial y}(a,b) \neq 0$. Then, there exists an implicit function $y = \phi(x)$ which is C^1 in some interval containing a with $\phi(a) = b$.

Proof We apply the above exercise and use its notation. Thus, we let

$$F(x,y) = (x, f(x,y)).$$

We know that $F(a,b) = (a,c)$ and that there exists a C^1-inverse G defined locally near (a,c). We can write

$$G(x, f(x,y)) = G(x,z) = (x,y) = (x, g(x,z))$$

for some function g. This equation shows that we have put $z = f(x,y)$ and $y = g(x,z)$. We define

$$\phi(x) = g(x,c).$$

Then on the one hand,

$$F(x, \phi(x)) = F(x, g(x,c)) = F(G(x,c)) = (x,c)$$

and on the other hand,

$$F(x, \phi(x)) = (x, f(x, \phi(x))).$$

This proves that $f(x, \phi(x)) = c$. Furthermore, by definition of an inverse map, $G(a,c) = (a,b)$ so that $\phi(a) = b$. This proves the implicit function theorem in two dimensions. $\square$

Exercise Show that the function $f(x,y) = x^2 + y^2$ implicitly defines a function $y = \phi(x)$ near $x = 1$. Find this function. Take (i) $(a,b) = (1,1)$, (ii) $(a,b) = (-1,-1)$.

Answer

(i) $c = f(1,1) = 2$. $\frac{\partial f}{\partial y}(1,1) = 2 \neq 0$, so the implicit function $y = \phi(x)$ near $x = 1$ exists. It can be found by explicitly solving $2 = x^2 + y^2 : y = \sqrt{2 - x^2}$.

(ii) $y = -\sqrt{2 - x^2}$.

In general, the equation $f(x,y) = c$ defines some curve as in Fig. 10.4(a). As indicated in Fig. 10.4(b), we see that there is an implicit function near the point (a,b), which exists only for points near $x = a$ and not for all x values. It is straightforward to generalize the implicit function theorem to higher dimensional functions $f : \mathbb{R}^n \mapsto \mathbb{R}$ but we will not pursue it here.

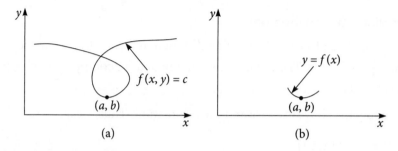

(a) $\qquad\qquad\qquad\qquad$ (b)

Fig. 10.4   Neighborhood of point (a,b) on $f(x,y) = c$ is locally given by the implicit function $y = f(x)$

10.9.3 Algorithm to construct the inverse of a map

We give an iterative algorithm [5], using the method of successive approximations, to construct the inverse of the locally C^1-invertible map $\mathbf{f} : \mathcal{E}_3 \mapsto \mathcal{E}_3$

$$\mathbf{u} = \mathbf{f}(\mathbf{x}) = u(\mathbf{x})\hat{\mathbf{i}} + v(\mathbf{x})\hat{\mathbf{j}} + w(\mathbf{x})\hat{\mathbf{k}}$$

with

$$u(\mathbf{x}) = \phi(x,y,z), \quad v(\mathbf{x}) = \psi(x,y,z), \quad w(\mathbf{x}) = \chi(x,y,z).$$

That is, we want to solve the equation $\mathbf{u} = \mathbf{f}(\mathbf{x})$ for $\mathbf{x}$ where $\mathbf{u}$ is a point near $\mathbf{u}_0 = \mathbf{f}(\mathbf{x}_0)$, where, at $\mathbf{x} = \mathbf{x}_0$ we must have, for the Jacobian determinant $|J_{\mathbf{f}}(\mathbf{x}_0)|$,

$$|J_{\mathbf{f}}(\mathbf{x}_0)| = \begin{vmatrix} \phi_x(\mathbf{x}_0) & \phi_y(\mathbf{x}_0) & \phi_z(\mathbf{x}_0) \\ \psi_x(\mathbf{x}_0) & \psi_y(\mathbf{x}_0) & \psi_z(\mathbf{x}_0) \\ \chi_x(\mathbf{x}_0) & \chi_y(\mathbf{x}_0) & \chi_z(\mathbf{x}_0) \end{vmatrix} \neq 0.$$

The differentials dx, dy, dz and du, dv, dw satisfy the linear relations (see Eq. (10.23))

$$\begin{aligned} du &= d\phi = \phi_x dx + \phi_y dy + \phi_z dz \\ dv &= d\psi = \psi_x dx + \psi_y dy + \psi_z dz \\ dw &= d\chi = \chi_x dx + \chi_y dy + \chi_z dz \end{aligned} \tag{10.31}$$

or,

$$d\mathbf{u} = J_{\mathbf{f}}(\mathbf{x})d\mathbf{x} \tag{10.32}$$

where

$$J_{\mathbf{f}}(\mathbf{x}) = \begin{pmatrix} \phi_x(\mathbf{x}) & \phi_y(\mathbf{x}) & \phi_z(\mathbf{x}) \\ \psi_x(\mathbf{x}) & \psi_y(\mathbf{x}) & \psi_z(\mathbf{x}) \\ \chi_x(\mathbf{x}) & \chi_y(\mathbf{x}) & \chi_z(\mathbf{x}) \end{pmatrix}$$

is the Jacobian giving the derivative of the map $\mathbf{u} = \mathbf{f}(\mathbf{x})$.

Exercise   Find an upper bound on the Euclidean distance of the images of the points $\mathbf{x}$ and $\mathbf{x} + \Delta\mathbf{x}$ under the map $\mathbf{f} : \mathcal{E}_3 \mapsto \mathcal{E}_3$.

Solution   The required distance is given by (see Equation following Eq. (10.24) and note that $\Delta\mathbf{x} \cdot \nabla f(\mathbf{x})$ is a vector),

$$\sqrt{(\mathbf{f}(\mathbf{x} + \Delta\mathbf{x}) - \mathbf{f}(\mathbf{x})) \cdot (\mathbf{f}(\mathbf{x} + \Delta\mathbf{x}) - \mathbf{f}(\mathbf{x}))} = \sqrt{(\Delta\mathbf{x} \cdot \nabla f(\mathbf{x})) \cdot (\Delta\mathbf{x} \cdot \nabla f(\mathbf{x}))}$$

or,

$$\sqrt{(\Delta \mathbf{x} \cdot \nabla f(\mathbf{x})) \cdot (\Delta \mathbf{x} \cdot \nabla f(\mathbf{x}))}$$

$$= \sqrt{(h\phi_x + k\phi_y + l\phi_z)^2 + (h\psi_x + k\psi_y + l\psi_z)^2 + (h\chi_x + k\chi_y + l\chi_z)^2} \quad (10.33)$$

where $\phi_{x,y,z}, \psi_{x,y,z}, \chi_{x,y,z}$ are the partial derivatives giving the row-wise elements of the Jacobian matrix and h, k, l are the components of $\Delta \mathbf{x}$. Let M denote an upper bound on the absolute values of all the elements of the Jacobian matrix taken at all points of the segment joining $\mathbf{x}$ and $\mathbf{x} + \Delta \mathbf{x}$. This gives

$$\sqrt{(h\phi_x + k\phi_y + l\phi_z)^2 + (h\psi_x + k\psi_y + l\psi_z)^2 + (h\chi_x + k\chi_y + l\chi_z)^2}$$

$$\leq \sqrt{3} M (|h| + |k| + |l|) \leq 3M \sqrt{h^2 + k^2 + l^2} \quad (10.34)$$

which is the required upper bound. □

Thus, the distance of the image points is at most $3M$ times that of the original ones. Writing $\mathbf{y} = \mathbf{x} + \Delta \mathbf{x}$ we can write Eq. (10.34) as

$$|\mathbf{f}(\mathbf{y}) - \mathbf{f}(\mathbf{x})| \leq 3M |\mathbf{y} - \mathbf{x}|. \quad (10.35)$$

We now consider the mapping $\mathbf{u} = \mathbf{f}(\mathbf{x})$ in a neighborhood

$$|\mathbf{x} - \mathbf{x}_0| < \delta \quad (10.36)$$

of the point $\mathbf{x}_0$ in the domain $\mathcal{R}$ of $\mathbf{f}$. Let $\mathbf{u}_0 = \mathbf{f}(\mathbf{x}_0)$. For a fixed $\mathbf{u}$ we write the equation $\mathbf{u} = \mathbf{f}(\mathbf{x})$ which is to be solved for $\mathbf{x}$, in the form

$$\mathbf{x} = \mathbf{g}(\mathbf{x}), \quad (10.37)$$

where

$$\mathbf{g}(\mathbf{x}) = \mathbf{x} + A(\mathbf{u} - \mathbf{f}(\mathbf{x})); \quad (10.38)$$

where A stands for an appropriately chosen fixed non-singular operator (or matrix) with inverse denoted by A^{-1}. Thus, Eq. (10.37) is equivalent to $A(\mathbf{u} - \mathbf{f}(\mathbf{x})) = 0$, which by multiplication with A^{-1} yields

$$A^{-1} A(\mathbf{u} - \mathbf{f}(\mathbf{x})) = I(\mathbf{u} - \mathbf{f}(\mathbf{x})) = (\mathbf{u} - \mathbf{f}(\mathbf{x})) = 0,$$

where I is the identity operator represented by the unit matrix. Thus, a solution $\mathbf{x}$ of Eq. (10.37), that is, a fixed point of the map $\mathbf{g}$, furnishes a solution of $\mathbf{u} = \mathbf{f}(\mathbf{x})$.

We show that a fixed point of the map $\mathbf{g}$ can be reached by reaching the limit of $\mathbf{x}_n$ defined by the recursion formula

$$\mathbf{x}_{n+1} = \mathbf{g}(\mathbf{x}_n) \quad n = 0, 1, 2, \dots \tag{10.39}$$

provided the Jacobian matrix, which in this case we denote by $\mathbf{g}'(\mathbf{x})$, representing the derivative of the vector mapping $\mathbf{g}$ is of sufficiently small size. This procedure is popularly known as the *method of successive approximations*. Making the 'small size' requirement more precise, we require that for all $\mathbf{x}$ in the neighborhood of $\mathbf{x}_0$ given by Eq. (10.36), the largest element of the matrix $\mathbf{g}'$ is less than $\frac{1}{6}$ in absolute value and that

$$|\mathbf{g}(\mathbf{x}_0) - \mathbf{x}_0| < \frac{1}{2}\delta.$$

The last equation is the condition on the initial value from which to start the iteration.

First, we prove by induction that, under the assumptions stated, the recursion formula in Eq. (10.39) successively gives vectors satisfying Eq. (10.36). This assures us that $\mathbf{x}_n$ lie in the domain of $\mathbf{g}$ so that the sequence can be continued indefinitely. From Eq. (10.35) with $M = \frac{1}{6}$ we see that,

$$|\mathbf{g}(\mathbf{y}) - \mathbf{g}(\mathbf{x})| \le \frac{1}{2}|\mathbf{y} - \mathbf{x}| \quad \text{for} \quad |\mathbf{x} - \mathbf{x}_0| < \delta, \ |\mathbf{y} - \mathbf{x}_0| < \delta. \tag{10.40}$$

Now the inequality in Eq. (10.36) holds trivially for $\mathbf{x} = \mathbf{x}_0$. If it holds for $\mathbf{x} = \mathbf{x}_n$, we find for the vector $\mathbf{x}_{n+1}$ defined by Eq. (10.39) that

$$|\mathbf{x}_{n+1} - \mathbf{x}_0| \le |\mathbf{x}_{n+1} - \mathbf{x}_1| + |\mathbf{x}_1 - \mathbf{x}_0| = |\mathbf{g}(\mathbf{x}_n) - \mathbf{g}(\mathbf{x}_0)| + |\mathbf{g}(\mathbf{x}_0) - \mathbf{x}_0| \le \frac{1}{2}|\mathbf{x}_n - \mathbf{x}_0| + \frac{1}{2}\delta.$$

This proves that $|\mathbf{x}_n - \mathbf{x}_0| < \delta$ for all n.

To see that the sequence $\{\mathbf{x}_n\}$ converges, we observe that by Eq. (10.40),

$$|\mathbf{x}_{n+1} - \mathbf{x}_n| = |\mathbf{g}(\mathbf{x}_n) - \mathbf{g}(\mathbf{x}_{n-1})| \le \frac{1}{2}|\mathbf{x}_n - \mathbf{x}_{n-1}|.$$

In the same way,

$$|\mathbf{x}_n - \mathbf{x}_{n-1}| \le \frac{1}{2}|\mathbf{x}_{n-1} - \mathbf{x}_{n-2}|,$$

$$|\mathbf{x}_{n-1} - \mathbf{x}_{n-2}| \le \frac{1}{2}|\mathbf{x}_{n-2} - \mathbf{x}_{n-3}|$$

and so on. These inequalities together imply

$$|\mathbf{x}_{n+1} - \mathbf{x}_n| \le \frac{1}{2^n}|\mathbf{x}_1 - \mathbf{x}_0| \le \frac{\delta}{2^{n+1}}. \tag{10.41}$$

Since the distance between successive iterates decreases exponentially, the sequence $\{\mathbf{x}_n\}$ must converge to its limit say $\mathbf{x}^*$. In this limit, the distance between successive iterates goes to zero. Therefore, the substitution of this limit $\mathbf{x}^*$ in $\mathbf{g}(\mathbf{x})$ must return the same vector $\mathbf{x}^*$. In other words this limit $\mathbf{x}^*$ solves Eq. (10.37). Another way to see this is the following. Since $\mathbf{g}(\mathbf{x})$ is continuous, if the sequence $\{\mathbf{x}_k\}$ $k = 1, 2, \ldots$ converges to $\mathbf{x}^*$ the sequence $\mathbf{g}(\mathbf{x}_k)$ $k = 1, 2, \ldots$ must converge to $\mathbf{g}(\mathbf{x}^*)$. However, by virtue of Eq. (10.39) these two sequences are identical, making their limits the same, that is, $\mathbf{x}^* = \mathbf{g}(\mathbf{x}^*)$.

Since the function $\mathbf{g}$ depends continuously on $\mathbf{u}$, the $\mathbf{x}_n$ obtained successively by recursion formula Eq. (10.37) also depends continuously on $\mathbf{u}$. Since the convergence of the sequence $\{\mathbf{x}_n\}$ does not depend on $\mathbf{u}$, it follows that its limit $\mathbf{x}^*$ is a continuous function of $\mathbf{u}$. Also, we have $|\mathbf{x}^* - \mathbf{x}_0| \leq \delta$ because $|\mathbf{x}_n - \mathbf{x}^*| < \delta$ for all n. If there existed a second solution $\mathbf{x}'$ with $\mathbf{x}' = \mathbf{g}(\mathbf{x}')$ and $|\mathbf{x}' - \mathbf{x}_0| \leq \delta$ we find from Eq. (10.40) that

$$|\mathbf{x}' - \mathbf{x}^*| = |\mathbf{g}(\mathbf{x}') - \mathbf{g}(\mathbf{x}^*)| \leq \frac{1}{2}|\mathbf{x}' - \mathbf{x}^*|$$

which makes $|\mathbf{x}' - \mathbf{x}^*| = 0$ and $\mathbf{x}' = \mathbf{x}^*$.

Thus, we have established the existence, uniqueness and continuity of a solution $\mathbf{x}^*$ of the equation $\mathbf{u} = \mathbf{f}(\mathbf{x})$, for which $|\mathbf{x}^* - \mathbf{x}_0| \leq \delta$, provided the function $\mathbf{g}(\mathbf{x})$ defined by Eq. (10.38) has the derivative $\mathbf{g}'$ with elements less than $\frac{1}{6}$ in absolute value for $|\mathbf{x}^* - \mathbf{x}_0| \leq \delta$ and provided $|\mathbf{g}(\mathbf{x}_0) - \mathbf{x}_0| < \frac{1}{2}\delta$. These requirements can be satisfied for all $\mathbf{u}$ sufficiently close to $\mathbf{u}_0$ by a suitable choice of the matrix A. By the definition of $\mathbf{g}$ (Eq. (10.38))

$$\mathbf{g}'(\mathbf{x}) = I - A\mathbf{f}'(\mathbf{x}),$$

where I is the identity. Then, for $\mathbf{x} = \mathbf{x}_0$

$$\mathbf{g}'(\mathbf{x}_0) = I - A\mathbf{f}'(\mathbf{x}_0) = \mathbf{0}$$

if we choose for A the inverse of the matrix $\mathbf{f}'(\mathbf{x}_0)$, that is,

$$A = (\mathbf{f}'(\mathbf{x}_0))^{-1}.$$

The existence of this inverse is guaranteed by our basic assumption that the matrix $\mathbf{f}'(\mathbf{x}_0)$ has a non-vanishing determinant, that is, the Jacobian of the mapping $\mathbf{f}$ does not vanish at the point $\mathbf{x}_0$. The assumed continuity of the first derivatives of the mapping $\mathbf{f}$ implies that $\mathbf{g}'(\mathbf{x})$ depends continuously on $\mathbf{x}$; hence the the elements of $\mathbf{g}'(\mathbf{x})$ are arbitrarily small, for instance less than $\frac{1}{6}$, for sufficiently small $|\mathbf{x} - \mathbf{x}_0|$, say for $|\mathbf{x} - \mathbf{x}_0| \leq \delta$. Moreover, by Eq. (10.38)

$$|\mathbf{g}(\mathbf{x}_0) - \mathbf{x}_0| = |A(\mathbf{u} - \mathbf{f}(\mathbf{x}_0))| = |A(\mathbf{u} - \mathbf{u}_0| < \frac{1}{2}\delta,$$

provided $\mathbf{u}$ lies in a sufficiently small neighborhood of $\mathbf{u}_0$. This completes the proof of the local existence of a continuous inverse for a continuously differentiable mapping with non-vanishing Jacobian.

The existence of the inverse of the Jacobian of the map $\mathbf{u} = \mathbf{f}(\mathbf{x})$ at a point $\mathbf{x}$ can be used to show the continuity and differentiability of the inverse map $\mathbf{x} = \mathbf{f}^{-1}(\mathbf{u})$. Since the Jacobian defines a linear, continuous and invertible map at $\mathbf{x}$ it must be one-to-one and onto on some neighborhood of $\mathbf{x}$. Furthermore, every point $\mathbf{v} \neq \mathbf{u}$ in this neighborhood, is given by $\mathbf{v} = \mathbf{f}(\mathbf{y})$, $\mathbf{y} \neq \mathbf{x}$. This means that as $\mathbf{v} \to \mathbf{u}$ through some sequence of points, $\mathbf{y} \to \mathbf{x}$. This enables us to invert the differential of $\mathbf{f}(\mathbf{x})$ in the following way.

$$\mathbf{f}(\mathbf{y}) - \mathbf{f}(\mathbf{x}) = \mathbf{v} - \mathbf{u} = J(\mathbf{x}) \cdot (\mathbf{y} - \mathbf{x}) + |\mathbf{y} - \mathbf{x}|\mathbf{h}(\mathbf{y} - \mathbf{x}),$$

or,

$$\mathbf{y} - \mathbf{x} = J^{-1}(\mathbf{x})(\mathbf{v} - \mathbf{u}) + |\mathbf{v} - \mathbf{u}|\epsilon(\mathbf{v} - \mathbf{u}),$$

where

$$\lim_{\mathbf{v} \to \mathbf{u}} \epsilon(\mathbf{v} - \mathbf{u}) = \mathbf{0}.$$

This equation just says that the vector $\mathbf{x}$ satisfying $\mathbf{u} = \mathbf{f}(\mathbf{x})$ is a differentiable function of vector $\mathbf{u}$ and that the Jacobian matrix of $\mathbf{x}$ with respect to $\mathbf{u}$ is the inverse of the matrix $\mathbf{f}'(\mathbf{x}) = J(\mathbf{x})$.

10.10   Differentiating Inverse Functions

Let $\mathbf{f}(\mathbf{x})$ be a differentiable and invertible function. We assume the differentiability of the inverse function. Let the components of $\mathbf{f}(\mathbf{x})$ be [3]

$$u = \phi(x,y,z) \quad v = \psi(x,y,z) \quad w = \chi(x,y,z),$$

and the components of the inverse be

$$x = g(u,v,w) \quad y = h(u,v,w) \quad z = k(u,v,w).$$

We substitute the inverse functions in the given functions to get the compound functions

$$\phi(g(u,v,w),h(u,v,w),k(u,v,w)), \; \psi(g(u,v,w),h(u,v,w),k(u,v,w)),$$

$$\chi(g(u,v,w),h(u,v,w),k(u,v,w)),$$

---

[3] The transformation $\mathbf{f}(\mathbf{x})$ could be passive, that is, the one which changes the coordinates of the same vector referring to a different basis.

which must be equal to u v and w respectively. Thus, we get the equations

$$u = \phi(g(u,v,w), h(u,v,w), k(u,v,w))$$

$$v = \psi(g(u,v,w), h(u,v,w), k(u,v,w))$$

$$w = \chi(g(u,v,w), h(u,v,w), k(u,v,w)) \tag{10.42}$$

These equations are identities as they hold for all values of u, v, w. We now differentiate each of these equations with respect to u v and w regarding them as independent variables and apply the chain rule to differentiate the compound functions. We then obtain the system of equations

$$1 = \phi_x g_u + \phi_y h_u + \phi_z k_u \quad 0 = \phi_x g_v + \phi_y h_v + \phi_z k_v \quad 0 = \phi_x g_w + \phi_y h_w + \phi_z k_w$$

$$0 = \psi_x g_u + \psi_y h_u + \psi_z k_u \quad 1 = \psi_x g_v + \psi_y h_v + \psi_z k_v \quad 0 = \phi_x g_w + \phi_y h_w + \phi_z k_w$$

$$0 = \chi_x g_u + \chi_y h_u + \chi_z k_u \quad 0 = \chi_x g_v + \chi_y h_v + \chi_z k_v \quad 1 = \chi_x g_w + \chi_y h_w + \chi_z k_w$$

Solving these equations for nine unknowns $g_{u,v,w}, h_{u,v,w}, k_{u,v,w}$ we get the partial derivatives of the inverse functions $x = g(u,v,w)$, $y = h(u,v,w)$, $z = k(u,v,w)$ with respect to u, v, w expressed in terms of the derivatives of the original functions $\phi(x,y,z)$, $\psi(x,y,z), \chi(x,y,z)$ with respect to x, y, z, namely,

$$g_u = \frac{1}{D}[\psi_y \chi_z - \psi_z \chi_y] \; g_v = \frac{1}{D}[\chi_y \phi_z - \chi_z \phi_y] \; g_w$$

$$= \frac{1}{D}[\phi_y \psi_z - \phi_z \psi_y]$$

$$h_u = \frac{1}{D}[\psi_z \chi_x - \psi_x \chi_z] \; h_v = \frac{1}{D}[\chi_z \phi_x - \chi_x \phi_z] \; h_w$$

$$= \frac{1}{D}[\phi_z \psi_x - \phi_x \psi_z]$$

$$k_u = \frac{1}{D}[\psi_x \chi_y - \psi_y \chi_x] \; k_v = \frac{1}{D}[\chi_x \phi_y - \chi_y \phi_x] \; k_w$$

$$= \frac{1}{D}[\phi_x \psi_y - \phi_y \psi_x] \tag{10.43}$$

where D stands for the Jacobian determinant

$$|J_f(\mathbf{x})| = D = \begin{vmatrix} \phi_x & \phi_y & \phi_z \\ \psi_x & \psi_y & \psi_z \\ \chi_x & \chi_y & \chi_z \end{vmatrix}.$$

This justifies calling the Jacobian the derivative of a differentiable map $\mathbf{f} : \mathscr{E}_3 \mapsto \mathscr{E}_3$. For a 2-D map Eq. (10.43) reduce to

$$g_u = \frac{\psi_y}{D}, \ g_v = -\frac{\phi_y}{D}, \ h_u = -\frac{\psi_x}{D}, \ h_v = \frac{\phi_x}{D}, \tag{10.44}$$

where the Jacobian determinant D is given by

$$D = \begin{vmatrix} \phi_x & \phi_y \\ \psi_x & \psi_y \end{vmatrix}.$$

Exercise For polar coordinates in the plane expressed in terms of rectangular coordinates,

$$u = r = \sqrt{x^2 + y^2}, \ v = \theta = \tan^{-1}\frac{y}{x},$$

find the partial derivatives $r_x, r_y, \theta_x, \theta_y$ and the Jacobian determinant.

Solution The partial derivatives are

$$r_x = \frac{x}{\sqrt{x^2 + y^2}} = \frac{x}{r}, \ r_y = \frac{y}{\sqrt{x^2 + y^2}} = \frac{y}{r},$$

$$\theta_x = \frac{-y}{x^2 + y^2} = -\frac{y}{r^2}, \ \theta_y = \frac{x}{x^2 + y^2} = \frac{x}{r^2}. \tag{10.45}$$

Hence, the Jacobian has the value

$$D = \frac{x}{r}\frac{x}{r^2} - \frac{y}{r}\left(-\frac{y}{r^2}\right) = \frac{1}{r}$$

and the partial derivatives of the inverse functions (cartesian coordinates expressed in terms of polar coordinates) are

$$x_r = \frac{x}{r}, \ x_\theta = -y, \ y_r = \frac{y}{r}, \ y_\theta = x,$$

as we could have found by direct differentiation of the inverse formulae $x = r\cos\theta, y = r\sin\theta$. $\square$

From the formulae for the derivatives of the inverse functions (Eq. (10.44)) for the 2-D case, we find that the Jacobian determinant of the functions $x = x(u,v)$ and $y = y(u,v)$ (where the coordinates themselves replace the function names g and h) with respect to u and v is given by

$$\frac{d(x,y)}{d(u,v)} = x_u y_v - x_v y_u = \frac{u_x v_y - u_y v_x}{D^2} = \frac{1}{D} = \left(\frac{d(u,v)}{d(x,y)}\right)^{-1}. \qquad (10.46)$$

Thus, the *Jacobian determinant of the inverse system of functions is the reciprocal of the Jacobian determinant of the original system.*[4] This is not surprising, because these Jacobians are the inverses of each other, as we have shown above (see the last para before the present subsection).

Exercise Find the second order derivatives for a 2-D map $x_{uu} = \frac{\partial^2 x}{\partial u^2} = g_{uu}$ and $y_{uu} = \frac{\partial^2 y}{\partial u^2} = h_{uu}$.

Hint Differentiate the equations (with $u_x = \phi_x$, $x_u = g_u$ etc.)

$$1 = u_x x_u + u_y y_u$$

$$0 = v_x x_u + v_y y_u \qquad (10.47)$$

again with respect to u and use the chain rule. Then, solve the resulting system of linear equations regarding the quantities x_{uu} and y_{uu} as unknowns and then replace x_u and y_u by the expressions already known for them. Note that the determinant of the doubly differentiated system is again D and hence, by hypothesis, is not zero.

Answer

$$x_{uu} = -\frac{1}{D^3} \begin{vmatrix} u_{xx}v_y^2 - 2u_{xy}v_x v_y + u_{yy}v_x^2 & u_y \\ v_{xx}v_y^2 - 2u_{xy}v_x v_y + v_{yy}v_x^2 & v_y \end{vmatrix}$$

and

$$y_{uu} = \frac{1}{D^3} \begin{vmatrix} u_{xx}v_y^2 - 2u_{xy}v_x v_y + u_{yy}v_x^2 & u_x \\ v_{xx}v_y^2 - 2v_{xy}v_x v_y + v_{yy}v_x^2 & v_x \end{vmatrix}. \qquad \square$$

10.11 Jacobian for the Composition of Maps

Let $\mathbf{f}(\mathbf{x})$ be a differentiable and $1-1$ map from open set R_1 to the open set R_2 and let $\mathbf{g}(\mathbf{x})$ be a differentiable and $1-1$ map from open set R_2 to the open set R_3 in $\mathscr{E}_3$. Then,

---

[4]This is the analogue of the rule for the derivative of the inverse of a function of a single variable. See, for example, [5] volume I.

we can compose these two maps to get a differentiable and $1-1$ map from open set $\mathcal{R}_1$ to the open set $\mathcal{R}_3$ as $\mathbf{g} \circ \mathbf{f}(\mathbf{x}) = \mathbf{g}(\mathbf{f}(\mathbf{x}))$. If the components of $\mathbf{f}(\mathbf{x})$ are

$$\xi = \phi(x,y,z), \ \eta = \psi(x,y,z), \ \zeta = \chi(x,y,z)$$

and the components of $\mathbf{g}(\mathbf{x})$ are

$$u = \Phi(\xi,\eta,\zeta), \ v = \Psi(\xi,\eta,\zeta), \ w = \Omega(\xi,\eta,\zeta)$$

then the components of the composite map $\mathcal{R}_1 \mapsto \mathcal{R}_3$ are

$$u = \Phi(\phi(x,y,z),\psi(x,y,z),\chi(x,y,z)), v = \Psi(\phi(x,y,z),\psi(x,y,z),\chi(x,y,z)),$$

$$w = \Omega(\phi(x,y,z),\psi(x,y,z),\chi(x,y,z)).$$

Using the chain rule to differentiate compound functions, we get

$$\frac{\partial u}{\partial x} = \Phi_\xi \phi_x + \Phi_\eta \psi_x + \Phi_\zeta \chi_x, \frac{\partial u}{\partial y} = \Phi_\xi \phi_y + \Phi_\eta \psi_y + \Phi_\zeta \chi_y,$$

$$\frac{\partial u}{\partial z} = \Phi_\xi \phi_z + \Phi_\eta \psi_z + \Phi_\zeta \chi_z,$$

$$\frac{\partial v}{\partial x} = \Psi_\xi \phi_x + \Psi_\eta \psi_x + \Psi_\zeta \chi_x, \frac{\partial v}{\partial y} = \Psi_\xi \phi_y + \Psi_\eta \psi_y + \Psi_\zeta \chi_y,$$

$$\frac{\partial v}{\partial z} = \Psi_\xi \phi_z + \Psi_\eta \psi_z + \Psi_\zeta \chi_z,$$

$$\frac{\partial w}{\partial x} = \Omega_\xi \phi_x + \Omega_\eta \psi_x + \Omega_\zeta \chi_x, \frac{\partial w}{\partial y} = \Omega_\xi \phi_y + \Omega_\eta \psi_y + \Omega_\zeta \chi_y,$$

$$\frac{\partial w}{\partial z} = \Omega_\xi \phi_z + \Omega_\eta \psi_z + \Omega_\zeta \chi_z. \tag{10.48}$$

Equation (10.48) can be written in the matrix form,

$$\begin{pmatrix} \frac{\partial u}{\partial x} & \frac{\partial u}{\partial y} & \frac{\partial u}{\partial z} \\ \frac{\partial v}{\partial x} & \frac{\partial v}{\partial y} & \frac{\partial v}{\partial z} \\ \frac{\partial w}{\partial x} & \frac{\partial w}{\partial y} & \frac{\partial w}{\partial z} \end{pmatrix} = \begin{pmatrix} \Phi_\xi & \Phi_\eta & \Phi_\zeta \\ \Psi_\xi & \Psi_\eta & \Psi_\zeta \\ \Omega_\xi & \Omega_\eta & \Omega_\zeta \end{pmatrix} \begin{pmatrix} \phi_x & \phi_y & \phi_z \\ \psi_x & \psi_y & \psi_z \\ \chi_x & \chi_y & \chi_z \end{pmatrix}.$$

Since the determinant of the product of matrices is the product of their determinants, we conclude that *the Jacobian determinant of the composition of two transformations is equal to the product of the Jacobian determinants of the individual transformations.* Using the notation we have introduced for the Jacobian determinant, we have,

$$\frac{d(u,v,w)}{d(x,y,z)} = \frac{d(u,v,w)}{d(\xi,\eta,\zeta)} \frac{d(\xi,\eta,\zeta)}{d(x,y,z)}. \tag{10.49}$$

Written in this form, we see that, *under the composition of transformations, the Jacobians behave in the same way as the derivatives behave under the composition of functions of a single variable.*

Exercise   Using Eq. (10.49) show that the Jacobian determinant of the differentiable inverse of a differentiable map is the reciprocal of its Jacobian determinant.   □

Consider a continuously differentiable map $\mathbb{R}^2 \mapsto \mathbb{R}^2$ mapping (x,y) plane to (ξ,η) plane given by $\xi = \phi(x,y), \eta = \psi(x,y)$ which has a non-vanishing Jacobian determinant at $(x_0,y_0) = P_0$. We can then determine the *mapping of directions* at the point P_0. A curve passing through P_0 can be described parametrically by equations $x = f(t)$, $y = g(t)$ where $x_0 = f(t_0), y_0 = g(t_0)$. The slope of the curve at P_0 is given by

$$m = \frac{g'(t_0)}{f'(t_0)} \tag{10.50}$$

Similarly, the slope of the image curve

$$\xi = \phi(f(t),g(t)), \quad \eta = \psi(f(t),g(t)) \tag{10.51}$$

at the point corresponding to P_0 is

$$\mu = \frac{d\eta/dt}{d\xi/dt} = \frac{\psi_x f' + \psi_y g'}{\phi_x f' + \phi_y g'} = \frac{c+dm}{a+bm}, \tag{10.52}$$

where a,b,c,d are the constants

$$a = \phi_x(x_0,y_0), b = \phi_y(x_0,y_0), c = \psi_x(x_0,y_0), d = \psi_y(x_0,y_0).$$

Since

$$\frac{d\mu}{dm} = \frac{ad - bc}{(a+bm)^2}$$

we find that μ is an increasing function of m if $ad - bc > 0$ and decreasing function if $ad - bc < 0$. More precisely, this holds locally, excluding the directions where m or μ become infinite.

Increasing slopes correspond to increasing angles of inclination or to counterclockwise rotation of the corresponding directions. Thus, $\frac{d\mu}{dm} > 0$ implies that the counterclockwise sense of rotation is preserved, while it is reversed for $\frac{d\mu}{dm} < 0$ Now $ad - bc$ is just the Jacobian determinant

$$\frac{d(\xi,\eta)}{d(x,y)} = \begin{vmatrix} \phi_x & \phi_y \\ \psi_x & \psi_y \end{vmatrix}$$

evaluated at the point P_0. We conclude that the mapping $\xi = \phi(x,y), \eta = \psi(x,y)$ *preserves or reverses orientations near the point* (x_0, y_0) *according to whether the Jacobian determinant at that point is positive or negative.*

10.12 Surfaces

As for curves, in most cases the parametric representation is found suitable for surfaces [5]. Since a surface is a two dimensional object, it requires two parameters to fix a point on it, as against one parameter required to fix a point on a curve. Thus, a parametric representation of a surface is given by parameterizing the position vector $\mathbf{x} \equiv (x,y,z)$ of a point on the surface,

$$\mathbf{x} = \boldsymbol{\Phi}(u,v) \equiv (x = \phi(u,v), y = \psi(u,v), z = \chi(u,v)) \tag{10.53}$$

where we assume the surface to be smooth, that is, $\mathbf{x} = \boldsymbol{\Phi}(u,v)$ is a continuously differentiable vector valued function or, equivalently, $x = \phi(u,v)$, $y = \psi(u,v)$, $z = \chi(u,v)$ are continuously differentiable scalar valued functions of two parameters (u,v). The point (u,v) ranges over some region $\mathcal{R}$ in the (u,v) plane. The corresponding point $\mathbf{x}(u,v) \equiv (x = \phi(u,v), y = \psi(u,v), z = \chi(u,v))$ ranges over a set in $\mathscr{E}_3$ or $\mathbb{R}^3$ spanning the surface. We can describe the surface in one of the three forms $z = f(x,y)$, $y = f(z,x)$, $x = f(y,z)$ by solving one of the three pairs of equations drawn out of $x = \phi(u,v), y = \psi(u,v), z = \chi(u,v)$. Solving any such pair of equations is equivalent to inverting the corresponding $\mathbb{R}^2 \mapsto \mathbb{R}^2$ map, say $(u,v) \mapsto (x = \phi(u,v), y = \psi(u,v))$ to express (u,v) as functions of (x,y) which can then be substituted in $z = \chi(u,v)$ to get $z = f(x,y)$. Thus, we require that not all of the three $\mathbb{R}^2 \mapsto \mathbb{R}^2$ maps corresponding to three pairs of equations be non-invertible, that is, we require that the three Jacobian determinants

$$\begin{vmatrix} \psi_u & \psi_v \\ \chi_u & \chi_v \end{vmatrix}, \begin{vmatrix} \chi_u & \chi_v \\ \phi_u & \phi_v \end{vmatrix}, \begin{vmatrix} \phi_u & \phi_v \\ \phi_u & \phi_v \end{vmatrix} \tag{10.54}$$

do not all vanish at once. We can summarize this condition in a single inequality

$$(\phi_u \psi_v - \phi_v \psi_u)^2 + (\psi_u \chi_v - \psi_v \chi_u)^2 + (\chi_u \phi_v - \chi_v \phi_u)^2 > 0 \tag{10.55}$$

If the inequality Eq. (10.55) is satisfied, in some neighbourhood of each point on the surface given by the $\mathbb{R}^2 \mapsto \mathbb{R}^3$ map in Eq. (10.53), it is certainly possible to express one of the three coordinates in terms of the other two.

At each point on the surface with parameters u, v we can partially differentiate the position vector to give

$$\mathbf{x}_u = (\phi_u, \psi_u, \chi_u) \quad \text{and} \quad \mathbf{x}_v = (\phi_v, \psi_v, \chi_v) \tag{10.56}$$

The differential of the vector $\mathbf{x}$ using the corresponding Jacobian, is given by

$$d\mathbf{x} = \begin{pmatrix} dx \\ dy \\ dz \end{pmatrix} = \begin{pmatrix} \phi_u & \phi_v \\ \psi_u & \psi_v \\ \chi_u & \chi_v \end{pmatrix} \begin{pmatrix} du \\ dv \end{pmatrix} = \mathbf{x}_u du + \mathbf{x}_v dv. \tag{10.57}$$

The three determinants Eq. (10.54) are just the components of the vector product $\mathbf{x}_u \times \mathbf{x}_v$. The expression on the left of the inequality in Eq. (10.55) is the square of the length of the vector $\mathbf{x}_u \times \mathbf{x}_v$ so that condition Eq. (10.55) is equivalent to

$$\mathbf{x}_u \times \mathbf{x}_v \neq \mathbf{0} \tag{10.58}$$

As an example, the spherical surface $x^2 + y^2 + z^2 = r^2$ of radius r is represented parametrically by the equations

$$x = r\cos u \sin v, \ y = r\sin u \sin v \ z = r\cos v, \ (0 \leq u < 2\pi, \ 0 \leq v \leq \pi) \tag{10.59}$$

where $v = \theta$ is the "polar inclination" or the polar angle and $u = \phi$ is the "longitude" or the azimuthal angle made by the point on the sphere. Note that the functions relating x, y, z to u, v are single valued and cover all the sphere. As v runs from $\pi/2$ to π the point x, y, z spans the lower hemisphere, that is,

$$z = -\sqrt{r^2 - x^2 - y^2}$$

while the values of v from 0 to $\pi/2$ give the upper hemisphere. Thus, for the parametric representation it is not necessary, as it is for the representation

$$z = \pm\sqrt{r^2 - x^2 - y^2},$$

to apply two single valued branches of the function in order to span the whole sphere.

We obtain another parametric representation of the sphere by means of *stereographic projection*. In order to project the sphere $x^2 + y^2 + z^2 - r^2 = 0$ stereographically from the north pole $(0, 0, r)$ on the equatorial plane $z = 0$, we join each point of the surface to the north pole N by a straight line and call the intersection of this line with the equatorial plane the *stereographic image* of the corresponding point of the sphere (see Fig. 10.5). We thus obtain a $1 - 1$ correspondence between the points of the sphere and the points of the plane, except for the north pole N. Using elementary geometry, we find that this correspondence is expressed by

$$x = \frac{2r^2 u}{u^2 + v^2 + r^2}, \; y = \frac{2r^2 v}{u^2 + v^2 + r^2}, \; z = \frac{(u^2 + v^2 - r^2)r}{u^2 + v^2 + r^2},$$ (10.60)

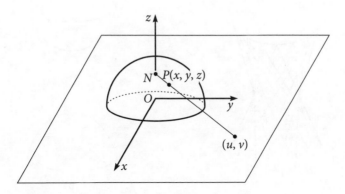

Fig. 10.5   Stereographic projection of the sphere

where (u, v) are the rectangular (cartesian) coordinates of the image point in the plane. These equations can be regarded as the parametric representation of the sphere, the parameters (u, v) being the rectangular coordinates in the u, v (equatorial) plane.

As a further example, we give parametric representation of surfaces

$$\frac{x^2}{a^2} + \frac{y^2}{b^2} - \frac{z^2}{c^2} = 1 \quad \text{and} \quad \frac{x^2}{a^2} + \frac{y^2}{b^2} - \frac{z^2}{c^2} = -1$$

called the *hyperboloid of one sheet* and the *hyperboloid of two sheets* respectively (see Fig. 10.6). The hyperboloid of one sheet is represented by

$$x = a \cos u \cosh v,$$

$$y = b \sin u \cosh v,$$

$$z = c \sinh v$$ (10.61)

where $0 \le u < 2\pi$; $-\infty < v < +\infty$ and the hyperboloid of two sheets by

$$x = a \cos u \sinh v,$$

$$y = b \sin u \sinh v,$$

$$z = \pm c \cosh v$$ (10.62)

where $0 \le u < 2\pi$; $0 < v < +\infty$.

In general, we may regard the *parametric representation* of a surface as the *mapping of the region $\mathcal{R}$ of the (u, v) plane onto the corresponding surface.* To each point of the region

$\mathcal{R}$ of the (u,v) plane there corresponds one point of the surface and typically the converse is also true.[5]

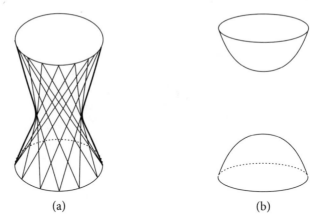

(a)   (b)

Fig. 10.6   (a) Hyperboloid of one sheet and (b) Hyperboloid of two sheets

Just as we can parameterize a surface by mapping a region in the u,v plane via Eq. (10.53), we can parameterize a curve on a surface by mapping an appropriate curve in the u,v plane onto the given curve on the surface. Thus, a curve $u = u(t)$, $v = v(t)$ in the u,v plane corresponds, by virtue of Eq. (10.53), to the curve

$$\mathbf{x}(t) = \mathbf{\Phi}(u(t),\, v(t)) \equiv (x(t) = \phi(u(t),\, v(t)),\, y(t) = \psi(u(t),\, v(t)),$$

$$z(t) = \chi(u(t), v(t))) \tag{10.63}$$

on the surface. Thus for example, the coordinate lines passing through a point on the sphere have the parametric equations $u = \phi = $ constant (longitudes) and $v = \theta = $ constant (latitudes). Corresponding curves in the u,v plane are the lines parallel to v and u axes respectively. The net of parametric curves (the mesh of latitudes and longitudes on the sphere) corresponds to the net of parallels to the axes in the u,v plane.

The tangent to the curve on the surface corresponding to the curve $u = u(t), v = v(t)$ in the u,v plane has the direction of the vector $\mathbf{x}_t = \frac{d\mathbf{x}}{dt}$, that is,

$$\mathbf{x}_t = (x_t, y_t, z_t) = \left(x_u \frac{du}{dt} + x_v \frac{dv}{dt}, y_u \frac{du}{dt} + y_v \frac{dv}{dt}, z_u \frac{du}{dt} + z_v \frac{dv}{dt} \right) = \mathbf{x}_u \frac{du}{dt} + \mathbf{x}_v \frac{dv}{dt}.$$

$$\tag{10.64}$$

At a given point on the surface, the tangential vectors $\mathbf{x}_t$ of all curves on the surface passing through that point are linear combinations of two vectors $\mathbf{x}_u, \mathbf{x}_v$ which respectively are tangential to to the parametric lines $v = $ constant and $u = $ constant passing through that

---

[5]This is not always the case. For example, in the representation Eq. (10.59) of the sphere by spherical coordinates, the poles of the sphere correspond to the whole line segments given by $v = 0$ and $v = \pi$.

point. (e.g., the vectors $\hat{\phi}$ and $\hat{\theta}$ for the spherical polar coordinates on a sphere.) This means that the tangents all lie in the plane through the point *spanned* by the vectors $\mathbf{x}_u$ and $\mathbf{x}_v$, that is, the *tangent plane to the surface* at that point. The *normal* to the surface at that point is perpendicular to all tangential directions, in particular to the vectors $\mathbf{x}_u$ and $\mathbf{x}_v$. Thus, the surface normal is parallel (or antiparallel) to the direction of the vector product

$$\mathbf{x}_u \times \mathbf{x}_v = (y_u z_v - y_v z_u, z_u x_v - z_v x_u, x_u y_v - x_v y_u). \tag{10.65}$$

One of the most important keys to the understanding of the given surface is the study of the curves that lie on it. Here, we give the expression for the arc length s of such a curve. We start with

$$\left(\frac{ds}{dt}\right)^2 = \left(\frac{dx}{dt}\right)^2 + \left(\frac{dy}{dt}\right)^2 + \left(\frac{dz}{dt}\right)^2 = \mathbf{x}_t \cdot \mathbf{x}_t,$$

so in view of Eq. (10.64) we get

$$\left(\frac{ds}{dt}\right)^2 = \left(\mathbf{x}_u \frac{du}{dt} + \mathbf{x}_v \frac{dv}{dt}\right) \cdot \left(\mathbf{x}_u \frac{du}{dt} + \mathbf{x}_v \frac{dv}{dt}\right)$$

$$= \left(x_u \frac{du}{dt} + x_v \frac{dv}{dt}\right)^2 + \left(y_u \frac{du}{dt} + y_v \frac{dv}{dt}\right)^2 + \left(z_u \frac{du}{dt} + z_v \frac{dv}{dt}\right)^2$$

$$= E\left(\frac{du}{dt}\right)^2 + 2F\left(\frac{du}{dt}\right)\left(\frac{dv}{dt}\right) + G\left(\frac{dv}{dt}\right)^2. \tag{10.66}$$

Here, the coefficients E, F, G, the *Gaussian fundamental quantities* of the surface, are given by

$$E = \left(\frac{\partial x}{\partial u}\right)^2 + \left(\frac{\partial y}{\partial u}\right)^2 + \left(\frac{\partial z}{\partial u}\right)^2 = \mathbf{x}_u \cdot \mathbf{x}_u$$

$$F = \frac{\partial x}{\partial u}\frac{\partial x}{\partial v} + \frac{\partial y}{\partial u}\frac{\partial y}{\partial v} + \frac{\partial z}{\partial u}\frac{\partial z}{\partial v} = \mathbf{x}_u \cdot \mathbf{x}_v$$

$$G = \left(\frac{\partial x}{\partial v}\right)^2 + \left(\frac{\partial y}{\partial v}\right)^2 + \left(\frac{\partial z}{\partial v}\right)^2 = \mathbf{x}_v \cdot \mathbf{x}_v \tag{10.67}$$

These depend only on $\mathbf{x}_u, \mathbf{x}_v$ and therefore on the surface and its parametric representation and not on the particular choice of the curve on the surface. The expression Eq. (10.66) for the derivative of the length of arc s with respect to the parameter t usually is written symbolically without reference to the parameter used along the curve. One says that the *line element* ds is given by the quadratic differential form ("fundamental form")

$$ds^2 = Edu^2 + 2Fdudv + Gdv^2. \tag{10.68}$$

The length of the cross product $\mathbf{x}_u \times \mathbf{x}_v$ can be expressed in terms of E, F, G as

$$|\mathbf{x}_u \times \mathbf{x}_v|^2 = |\mathbf{x}_u|^2 |\mathbf{x}_v|^2 - (\mathbf{x}_u \cdot \mathbf{x}_v)^2 = EG - F^2. \tag{10.69}$$

Our original condition on the parametric representation (inequality Eq. (10.55)) can now be formulated as the condition

$$EG - F^2 > 0 \tag{10.70}$$

for the fundamental quantities.

The direction cosines for one of the two normals to the surface are the components of the unit vector

$$\frac{1}{|\mathbf{x}_u \times \mathbf{x}_v|} \mathbf{x}_u \times \mathbf{x}_v = \frac{1}{\sqrt{EG - F^2}} \mathbf{x}_u \times \mathbf{x}_v.$$

It follows from Eq. (10.65) that the normal to a surface represented parametrically has the direction cosines

$$\cos\alpha = \frac{y_u z_v - y_v z_u}{\sqrt{EG - F^2}}, \quad \cos\beta = \frac{z_u x_v - z_v x_u}{\sqrt{EG - F^2}}, \quad \cos\gamma = \frac{x_u y_v - x_v y_u}{\sqrt{EG - F^2}}. \tag{10.71}$$

The tangent to a curve $u = u(t), v = v(t)$ on the surface has the direction of the vector

$$\mathbf{x}_t = \mathbf{x}_u \frac{du}{dt} + \mathbf{x}_v \frac{dv}{dt}.$$

If we now consider a second curve, $u = u(\tau), v = v(\tau)$ on the surface referred to a parameter τ, its tangent has the direction of the vector

$$\mathbf{x}_\tau = \mathbf{x}_u \frac{du}{d\tau} + \mathbf{x}_v \frac{dv}{d\tau}.$$

If the two curves pass through the same point on the surface, the cosine of the angle of intersection ω is the same as the cosine of the angle between $\mathbf{x}_t$ and $\mathbf{x}_\tau$. Hence,

$$\cos\omega = \frac{\mathbf{x}_t \cdot \mathbf{x}_\tau}{|\mathbf{x}_t||\mathbf{x}_\tau|}.$$

We have,

$$\mathbf{x}_t \cdot \mathbf{x}_\tau = \left(\mathbf{x}_u \frac{du}{dt} + \mathbf{x}_v \frac{dv}{dt} \right) \cdot \left(\mathbf{x}_u \frac{du}{d\tau} + \mathbf{x}_v \frac{dv}{d\tau} \right)$$

$$= E \frac{du}{dt} \frac{du}{d\tau} + F \left(\frac{du}{dt} \frac{dv}{d\tau} + \frac{du}{d\tau} \frac{dv}{dt} \right) + G \frac{dv}{dt} \frac{dv}{d\tau}. \qquad (10.72)$$

Consequently, the cosine of the angle between two curves on the surface is given by

$$\cos \omega = \frac{E \frac{du}{dt} \frac{du}{d\tau} + F \left(\frac{du}{dt} \frac{dv}{d\tau} + \frac{du}{d\tau} \frac{dv}{dt} \right) + G \frac{dv}{dt} \frac{dv}{d\tau}}{\sqrt{E \left(\frac{du}{dt} \right)^2 + 2F \left(\frac{du}{dt} \right) \left(\frac{dv}{dt} \right) + G \left(\frac{dv}{dt} \right)^2} \sqrt{E \left(\frac{du}{d\tau} \right)^2 + 2F \left(\frac{du}{d\tau} \right) \left(\frac{dv}{d\tau} \right) + G \left(\frac{dv}{d\tau} \right)^2}}$$
$$(10.73)$$

We end this subsection by giving one more example of parametrization of a surface which comes up frequently in applications. We consider torus. This is obtained by rotating a circle about a line which lies in the plane of the circle, but does not intersect with it (see Fig. 10.7). We take the axis of rotation as the z-axis and choose the y-axis so as to pass through the center of the circle, whose y-coordinate we denote by a. If the radius of the circle is $r < |a|$, we obtain

$$x = 0, \ y - a = r \cos \theta, \ z = r \sin \theta \, (0 \le \theta < 2\pi)$$

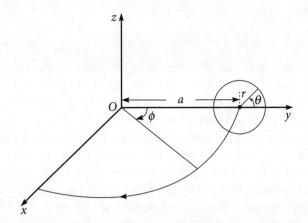

Fig. 10.7 Creation of torus by the rotation of a circle

as a parametric representation of the circle in the $y - z$ plane. Now letting the circle rotate about the z-axis, we find that for each point on the circle $x^2 + y^2$ remains constant; that is, $x^2 + y^2 = (a + r \cos \theta)^2$. If ϕ is the angle of rotation about the z-axis, we have

$$x = (a + r \cos \theta) \sin \phi,$$

$$y = (a + r\cos\theta)\cos\phi,$$

$$z = r\sin\theta \tag{10.74}$$

with $0 \le \phi < 2\pi, 0 \le \theta < 2\pi$ as a parametric representation of the torus in terms of the parameters θ and ϕ. In this representation the torus appears as the image of the square of side 2π in the θ, ϕ plane. Any pair of boundary points of this square lying on the same line $\theta = $ constant or $\phi = $ constant corresponds to only one point on the surface and the four corners of the square all correspond to the same point on the surface.

Equation (10.67) gives, for the line element on the torus,

$$ds^2 = r^2 d\theta^2 + (a + r\cos\theta)^2 d\phi^2.$$

10.13 The Divergence and the Curl of a Vector Field

We have already seen that the del or the grad operator has vector like structure and it also transforms like a vector under the rotation and translation of the coordinate system. This enables us to formally treat the del operator like a vector with components $\left(\frac{\partial}{\partial x_1}, \frac{\partial}{\partial x_2}, \frac{\partial}{\partial x_3}\right)$ and define its scalar and vector products with vector valued functions possibly giving a vector field.

The divergence

The corresponding   r product called the divergence of a field is given by

$$\nabla \cdot \mathbf{f}(\mathbf{x}) = \frac{\partial f_1}{\partial x_1} + \frac{\partial f_2}{\partial x_2} + \frac{\partial f_3}{\partial x_3} = \sum_{k=1}^{3} \frac{\partial f_k}{\partial x_k} \tag{10.75}$$

where $f_{1,2,3}(\mathbf{x})$ are the scalar valued component functions of the vector valued function $\mathbf{f}(\mathbf{x})$ with respect to some orthonormal basis (see Eq. (10.1)). If we fix a position vector $\mathbf{x}$, then we get the corresponding vector $\mathbf{f}(\mathbf{x})$ giving us the unique value of the divergence $\nabla \cdot \mathbf{f}(\mathbf{x})$. Thus, the divergence of a vector field is itself a scalar field and we can calculate 'the divergence at a point'. The value of the divergence of a vector field at a point is a measure of how much a vector $\mathbf{f}(\mathbf{x})$ spreads out from (or flows into) the point $\mathbf{x}$ in question. Thus, the vector function in Fig. 10.8(a) has large positive divergence (if the arrows pointed inward it would be a large *negative* divergence), the function in Fig. 10.8(b) has zero divergence and Fig. 10.8(c) again shows a function of positive divergence. Here is a nice possible observation of the divergence phenomenon [9]. Imagine standing at the edge of a pond. Sprinkle some sawdust on the surface. If the material spreads out then you have dropped it at a point of positive divergence; if it collects together, you have dropped it at a point of negative divergence. The vector function $\mathbf{v}$ in this model is the velocity of the water. This is a two dimensional example but it helps give us a feel for the meaning of divergence. A point of positive divergence is a sourse or 'foucet'; a point of negative divergence is a sink or 'drain'.

Exercise   If the functions in Fig. 10.8 are $\mathbf{v}_a = \mathbf{r} = x\hat{\mathbf{x}} + y\hat{\mathbf{y}} + z\hat{\mathbf{z}}$, $\mathbf{v}_b = \hat{\mathbf{z}}$ and $\mathbf{v}_c = z\hat{\mathbf{z}}$, calculate the divergences.

Answer $\nabla \cdot \mathbf{v}_a = 3, \nabla \cdot \mathbf{v}_b = 0, \nabla \cdot \mathbf{v}_c = 1$.   □

In fact the first result can be generalized to n dimensions as $\nabla \cdot \mathbf{x} = \sum_{k=1}^{n} \frac{\partial x_k}{\partial x_k} = n$.

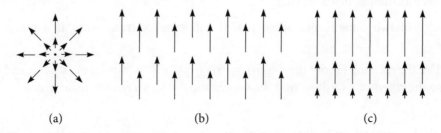

| (a) | (b) | (c) |

Fig. 10.8   Vector fields given by (a) $\mathbf{v}_a$ (b) $\mathbf{v}_b$ (c) $\mathbf{v}_c$ as defined in this exercise

Exercise   Calculate the divergence of the following vector functions.

(a) $\mathbf{v}_a = x^2\hat{\mathbf{x}} + 3xz^2\hat{\mathbf{y}} - 2xz\hat{\mathbf{z}}$

(b) $\mathbf{v}_b = xy\hat{\mathbf{x}} + 2yz\hat{\mathbf{y}} - 3zx\hat{\mathbf{z}}$

(c) $\mathbf{v}_c = y^2\hat{\mathbf{x}} + (2xy + z^2)\hat{\mathbf{y}} + 2yz\hat{\mathbf{z}}$ □ (10.76)

Exercise   Sketch the vector function $\mathbf{v} = \frac{\hat{\mathbf{r}}}{r^2}$ and compute its divergence except at $r = 0$.[6]

Hint   Write

$$\frac{\hat{\mathbf{r}}}{r^2} = \frac{x}{(x^2 + y^2 + z^2)^{3/2}}\hat{\mathbf{x}} + \frac{y}{(x^2 + y^2 + z^2)^{3/2}}\hat{\mathbf{y}} + \frac{z}{(x^2 + y^2 + z^2)^{3/2}}\hat{\mathbf{z}}$$

and evaluate $\nabla \cdot \mathbf{v}$.

Answer $\nabla \cdot \frac{\hat{\mathbf{r}}}{r^2} = 0$ □

The result of the above exercise can be explained as follows. The *flux* of a vector field across the surface enclosing a volume is simply the integral of the corresponding vector valued function on the surface. If we enclose the point of interest in an infinitesimal cube, then, as we will see later, this flux equals $\nabla \cdot \mathbf{v} dV$ where $\mathbf{v}$ defines the field and dV is the volume of the infinitesimal cube. For $\mathbf{v} = \frac{\hat{\mathbf{r}}}{r^2}$, looking at its expression with respect to the cartesian system $\hat{\mathbf{x}}, \hat{\mathbf{y}}, \hat{\mathbf{z}}$, it is clear that the flux through the opposite faces of the cube cancel each other so that the net flux through the cube is zero. Since $dV \neq 0$ we must have $\nabla \cdot \frac{\hat{\mathbf{r}}}{r^2} = 0$.

Note that the divergence of a vector field changes even if the field has a changing magnitude in a single direction. Thus, for the field given by $\mathbf{v}(\mathbf{x}) = \cos(\pi x)\hat{\mathbf{x}}$ the divergence is $\nabla \cdot \mathbf{v} = -\pi \sin(\pi x)$ and varies sinusoidally with x. At any point the field

---

[6]To find what happens at $r = 0$ read the appendix on Dirac delta function.

flows into the point along x axis if $\sin(\pi x) > 0$ and out of it if $\sin(\pi x) < 0$. For the field $\mathbf{v} = \frac{\hat{\mathbf{r}}}{r^2}$, the field spreads out as r^2 as we go out from the origin, but its magnitude falls as $\frac{1}{r^2}$ so that its divergence is zero.

Since the operator del transforms like a vector under the rotation and translation of a coordinate system, the divergence $\nabla \cdot \mathbf{v}$ of a vector field $\mathbf{v}$ transforms like the scalar product of two vectors, that is, like a scalar.

Exercise   In two dimensions, show that the divergence transforms as a scalar under rotation.

Hint   Use the rotation (about the z-axis) matrix explicitly to transform (v_x, v_y) and (x, y), then use the chain rule to show that the expression for $\nabla \cdot \mathbf{v}$ remains invariant.   □

The curl

The curl of a vector field is the vector product of the del operator with the vector valued function defining the field, say $\mathbf{v}$. It can be conveniently defined using Levi-Civita symbols,

$$(\nabla \times \mathbf{v})_i = \sum_{jk} \varepsilon_{ijk} \frac{\partial v_k}{\partial x_j} \quad i, j, k = 1, 2, 3. \tag{10.77}$$

Here ε_{ijk} are the Levi-Civita symbols, $\mathbf{v}_{1,2,3}(\mathbf{x})$ and $x_{1,2,3}$ are the components of $\mathbf{v}(\mathbf{x})$ and $\mathbf{x}$ respectively with res   to some orthonormal basis.

Exercise   Write dc $\sqrt{} \times \mathbf{v}$ explicitly in terms of its components.

Answer

$$\nabla \times \mathbf{v} = \left(\frac{\partial v_z}{\partial y} - \frac{\partial v_y}{\partial z} \right) \hat{\mathbf{x}} + \left(\frac{\partial v_x}{\partial z} - \frac{\partial v_z}{\partial x} \right) \hat{\mathbf{y}} + \left(\frac{\partial v_y}{\partial x} - \frac{\partial v_x}{\partial y} \right) \hat{\mathbf{z}}, \tag{10.78}$$

or, in terms of the determinantal definition of the cross product,

$$\nabla \times \mathbf{v} = \begin{vmatrix} \hat{\mathbf{x}} & \hat{\mathbf{y}} & \hat{\mathbf{z}} \\ \frac{\partial}{\partial x} & \frac{\partial}{\partial y} & \frac{\partial}{\partial z} \\ v_x & v_y & v_z \end{vmatrix}. \qquad \square \tag{10.79}$$

The value of $\nabla \times \mathbf{v}(\mathbf{x})$ at a point $\mathbf{x}$ is a measure of how much the vector $\mathbf{v}(\mathbf{x})$ "curls around" the point $\mathbf{x}$ in question. Thus, the three functions in Fig. 10.8 all have zero curl while the functions in Fig. 10.9 have a substantial curl, pointing in the z direction, as the rule of fixing the direction of a cross product would suggest. In anology with the illustration for divergence, imagine that you are standing at the edge of a pond. Float a small paddle wheel (like a cork with toothpicks pointing out radially); if it starts to rotate, you have placed it at a point of non-zero curl. A whirlpool would be a region of large curl. To furnish intuition further, we can read Eq. (10.78) geometrically.

Thus, in Fig. 10.10(a), the signs of $\frac{\partial v_z}{\partial y}$ and $\frac{\partial v_y}{\partial z}$ are opposite enhancing the first term in Eq. (10.78). In Fig. 10.10(b) these signs are the same, weakening the first term. Figure 10.10(c) shows that the sign of the gradient of a component along the corresponding axis can be determined by the change in its *value* along that axis, thus deciding its contribution to the curl of the field.

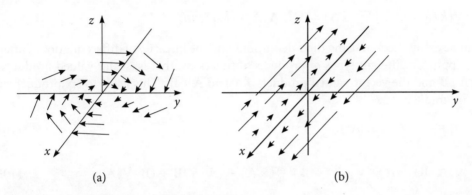

Fig. 10.9   Illustrating curl of a vector field

Exercise   Suppose the function sketched in Fig. 10.9(a) is $\mathbf{v}_a = y\hat{\mathbf{x}} - x\hat{\mathbf{y}}$ and that in Fig. 10.9(b) is $\mathbf{v}_b = y\hat{\mathbf{x}}$. Calculate their curls and the divergence.

Answer $\nabla \times \mathbf{v}_a = -2\hat{\mathbf{z}}$ and $\nabla \times \mathbf{v}_b = -\hat{\mathbf{z}}$. Both have zero divergence. This is consistant with Fig. 10.9, which shows the fields which are not spreading out, but are only curling around.   □

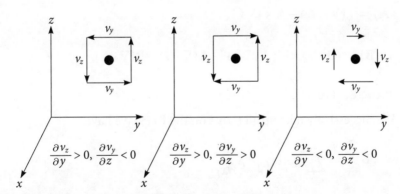

Fig. 10.10   Various cases of field curling around a point

After defining the divergence and the curl, we need to obtain rules for their action on expressions involving vector valued functions and also their combined action on such functions. For completeness we also state here the corresponding rules for the action of the del operator on the scalar valued functions. We have, for the scalar valued functions $f(\mathbf{x}), g(\mathbf{x})$ and the vector valued functions $\mathbf{A}(\mathbf{x}), \mathbf{B}(\mathbf{x})$

$$\nabla(f+g) = \nabla f + \nabla g, \quad \nabla \cdot (\mathbf{A} + \mathbf{B}) = \nabla \cdot \mathbf{A} + \nabla \cdot \mathbf{B}$$

$$\nabla \times (\mathbf{A} + \mathbf{B}) = \nabla \times \mathbf{A} + \nabla \times \mathbf{B},$$

and

$$\nabla(kf) = k\nabla f \quad \nabla \cdot (k\mathbf{A}) = k\nabla \cdot \mathbf{A} \quad \nabla \times (k\mathbf{A}) = k\nabla \times \mathbf{A},$$

as can be easily checked using their definitions and the linearity of differentiation. Different rules apply for different types of products of functions, that is, scalar valued products fg and $\mathbf{A} \cdot \mathbf{B}$ and the vector valued products $f\mathbf{A}$ and $\mathbf{A} \times \mathbf{B}$. This leads to six product rules, two for gradients,

$$\nabla(fg) = f\nabla g + g\nabla f, \tag{10.80}$$

$$\nabla(\mathbf{A} \cdot \mathbf{B}) = \mathbf{A} \times (\nabla \times \mathbf{B}) + \mathbf{B} \times (\nabla \times \mathbf{A}) + (\mathbf{A} \cdot \nabla)\mathbf{B} + (\mathbf{B} \cdot \nabla)\mathbf{A}, \tag{10.81}$$

two for divergences,

$$\nabla \cdot (f\mathbf{A}) = f(\nabla \cdot \mathbf{A}) + \mathbf{A} \cdot (\nabla f), \tag{10.82}$$

$$\nabla \cdot (\mathbf{A} \times \mathbf{B}) = \mathbf{B} \cdot (\nabla \times \mathbf{A}) - \mathbf{A} \cdot (\nabla \times \mathbf{B}) \tag{10.83}$$

and two for curls,

$$\nabla \times (f\mathbf{A}) = f(\nabla \times \mathbf{A}) - \mathbf{A} \times (\nabla f), \tag{10.84}$$

$$\nabla \times (\mathbf{A} \times \mathbf{B}) = (\mathbf{B} \cdot \nabla)\mathbf{A} - (\mathbf{A} \cdot \nabla)\mathbf{B} + \mathbf{A}(\nabla \cdot \mathbf{B}) - \mathbf{B}(\nabla \cdot \mathbf{A}). \tag{10.85}$$

Exercise   Prove Eq. (10.81).

Solution   We successively take up all terms on the RHS. We have,

$$[\mathbf{A} \times (\nabla \times \mathbf{B})]_i = \sum_{jklm} \varepsilon_{kij}\varepsilon_{klm} A_j \frac{\partial B_m}{\partial x_l}.$$

Using

$$\varepsilon_{kij}\varepsilon_{klm} = \delta_{il}\delta_{jm} - \delta_{im}\delta_{jl}$$

we get

$$[\mathbf{A} \times (\nabla \times \mathbf{B})]_i = \sum_j A_j \left(\frac{\partial B_j}{\partial x_i} - \frac{\partial B_i}{\partial x_j} \right).$$

Similarly,

$$[\mathbf{B} \times (\nabla \times \mathbf{A})]_i = \sum_j B_j \left(\frac{\partial A_j}{\partial x_i} - \frac{\partial A_i}{\partial x_j} \right).$$

Further, we get for the last two terms,

$$[(\mathbf{A} \cdot \nabla)\mathbf{B}]_i = \sum_j A_j \frac{\partial B_i}{\partial x_j}$$

and

$$[(\mathbf{B} \cdot \nabla)\mathbf{A}]_i = \sum_j B_j \frac{\partial A_i}{\partial x_j}.$$

Putting all terms together, we get, for the ith component of the RHS,

$$\sum_j \left(A_j \frac{\partial B_j}{\partial x_i} + B_j \frac{\partial A_j}{\partial x_i} \right) = [\nabla(\mathbf{A} \cdot \mathbf{B})]_i. \qquad \square$$

Exercise   Prove Eq. (10.83).

Solution

$$\begin{aligned}
\nabla \cdot (\mathbf{A} \times \mathbf{B}) &= \frac{\partial}{\partial x_i}(\mathbf{A} \times \mathbf{B})_i = \frac{\partial}{\partial x_i}(\varepsilon_{ijk} A_j B_k) \\[2mm]
&= \varepsilon_{ijk} \frac{\partial A_j}{\partial x_i} B_k + \varepsilon_{ijk} \frac{\partial B_k}{\partial x_i} A_j \\[2mm]
&= (\nabla \times \mathbf{A})_k B_k - (\nabla \times \mathbf{B})_j A_j \\[2mm]
&= \mathbf{B} \cdot (\nabla \times \mathbf{A}) - \mathbf{A} \cdot (\nabla \times \mathbf{B}). \qquad (10.86)
\end{aligned}$$

Here are the rules for differentiating quotients,

$$\begin{aligned}
\nabla \left(\frac{f}{g} \right) &= \frac{g \nabla f - f \nabla g}{g^2} \\[2mm]
\nabla \cdot \left(\frac{\mathbf{A}}{g} \right) &= \frac{g(\nabla \cdot \mathbf{A}) - \mathbf{A} \cdot (\nabla g)}{g^2} \\[2mm]
\nabla \times \left(\frac{\mathbf{A}}{g} \right) &= \frac{g(\nabla \times \mathbf{A}) + \mathbf{A} \times (\nabla g)}{g^2} \qquad (10.87)
\end{aligned}$$

All the above rules for differentiating expressions of functions are valid for all differentiable functions, scalar or vector valued, as the case may be. Therefore, these rules can be treated as vector identities involving differential operators. You may try and prove all these identities using Levi-Civita symbols.

Second derivatives

Upto now we obtained rules to find different types of derivatives of expressions involving various types of functions. We shall now find rules to evaluate second derivatives obtained by combining different types of first derivatives, namely, the gradient, the divergence and the curl. Since ∇f is a vector for a scalar valued function f, we can take the *divergence* and the *curl* of it. We have,

(i) Divergence of the gradient: $\nabla^2 f \equiv \nabla \cdot (\nabla f)$.

(ii) Curl of gradient: $\nabla \times (\nabla f)$.
  The divergence $\nabla \cdot \mathbf{v}$ is a *scalar*, so we can take its *gradient*:

(iii) Gradient of divergence: $\nabla(\nabla \cdot \mathbf{v})$.
  The curl $\nabla \times \mathbf{v}$ is a *vector*, so we can take its *divergence* and *curl*:

(iv) Divergence of curl: $\nabla \cdot (\nabla \times \mathbf{v})$.

(v) Curl of a curl: $\nabla \times (\nabla \times \mathbf{v})$.

These are all the possibilities and we consider them one by one.

(i) The operator $\nabla^2 f$ defined above is called the Laplacian of f. We have,

$$\nabla^2 f \equiv \nabla \cdot (\nabla f) = \left(\hat{\mathbf{x}}\frac{\partial}{\partial x} + \hat{\mathbf{y}}\frac{\partial}{\partial y} + \hat{\mathbf{z}}\frac{\partial}{\partial z} \right) \cdot \left(\frac{\partial f}{\partial x}\hat{\mathbf{x}} + \frac{\partial f}{\partial y}\hat{\mathbf{y}} + \frac{\partial f}{\partial z}\hat{\mathbf{z}} \right)$$

$$= \frac{\partial^2 f}{\partial x^2} + \frac{\partial^2 f}{\partial y^2} + \frac{\partial^2 f}{\partial z^2}. \tag{10.88}$$

The Laplacian of a scalar valued function is a scalar.

Exercise   Show that the Laplacian of a scalar field $\phi(\mathbf{x})$ at a point is proportional to the difference between the value of ϕ at that point and the average value of ϕ at the surrounding points.

Solution   Let ϕ_0 be the value of ϕ at a point which we take to be the origin. Let $\phi(\pm\Delta x)$, $\phi(\pm\Delta y)$ and $\phi(\pm\Delta z)$ be the values at points $\pm\Delta x, \pm\Delta y, \pm\Delta z$ respectively. We can approximate the second order partial derivatives defining the Laplacian by the corresponding second order differences

$$\frac{\partial^2 \phi}{\partial x^2} = \frac{\phi(\Delta x) + \phi(-\Delta x) - 2\phi_0}{\Delta x^2}$$

$$\frac{\partial^2 \phi}{\partial y^2} = \frac{\phi(\Delta y) + \phi(-\Delta y) - 2\phi_0}{\Delta y^2}$$

$$\frac{\partial^2 \phi}{\partial z^2} = \frac{\phi(\Delta z) + \phi(-\Delta z) - 2\phi_0}{\Delta z^2}.$$

Taking $\Delta x = \Delta y = \Delta z = \Delta$ and then adding these ratios we get

$$\nabla^2 \phi = \frac{-6}{\Delta^2}\left[\phi_0 - \frac{1}{6}\phi(\Delta x) + \phi(-\Delta x) + \phi(\Delta y) + \phi(-\Delta y) + \phi(\Delta z) + \phi(-\Delta z)\right]$$

$$= \frac{-6}{\Delta^2}(\phi_0 - \phi_{\text{avg}}).$$

If the Laplacian at a point is negative then its value at that point exceeds average of its values at the surrounding neighbours. Since ϕ is a continuous and differentiable function, its values cannot differ drastically at nearby points. Thus, if $\nabla^2\phi < 0$ at a point, this point represents a local maximum of ϕ. On the other hand, if $\nabla^2\phi > 0$ at a point this point must be a local minimum of ϕ. Since negative divergence at a point corresponds to the inflow of the field into that point, $\nabla^2\phi < 0$ corresponds to the inflow of the field $\nabla\phi$ towards the point of maximum ϕ. $\nabla^2\phi > 0$ corresponds to a point of local minimum of ϕ and the field $\nabla\phi$ diverges out of this point. You can draw the maximum and a minimum (a peak and a valley) for a function of two variables and draw $\nabla\phi$ vectors perpendicular to the contours of constant ϕ values. Then you can varify the above statements with reference to these pictures. ☐

Exercise Explicitly calculate $\nabla^2\phi$ for $\phi = \frac{1}{r}$, $r \neq 0$ and show that it vanishes. ☐

We may occasionally encounter the Laplcian of a *vector*, $\nabla^2\mathbf{v}$ which is a vector quantity whose x-component is the Laplacian of $\mathbf{v}_x$ etc,[7]. We have,

$$\nabla^2\mathbf{v} \equiv (\nabla^2\mathbf{v}_x)\hat{\mathbf{x}} + (\nabla^2\mathbf{v}_y)\hat{\mathbf{y}} + (\nabla^2\mathbf{v}_z)\hat{\mathbf{z}}. \tag{10.89}$$

(ii) The curl of a gradient is always zero. That is,

$$\nabla \times (\nabla f) = \mathbf{0}. \tag{10.90}$$

Exercise Prove Eq. (10.90).

Solution We have,

$$[\nabla \times (\nabla f)]_i = \varepsilon_{ijk}\frac{\partial^2 f}{\partial x_j \partial x_k}.$$

---

[7] For curvilinear coordinates, where the unit vectors themselves depend on position, they too must be differentiated.

In this double sum, the pairs of terms like $\frac{\partial^2 f}{\partial x_1 \partial x_2}$ and $\frac{\partial^2 f}{\partial x_2 \partial x_1}$ occur with opposite signs and cancel[8] and all terms can be paired this way. Hence, the sum vanishes and we get

$$[\nabla \times (\nabla f)]_i = 0, \quad i = 1, 2, 3. \qquad \square$$

(iii) $\nabla(\nabla \cdot \mathbf{v})$ seldom occurs in physical applications. Note that $\nabla^2 \mathbf{v} \neq \nabla(\nabla \cdot \mathbf{v})$.

(iv) The divergence of a curl, like the curl of a gradient, is always zero.

$$\nabla \cdot (\nabla \times \mathbf{v}) = 0. \tag{10.91}$$

Exercise   Prove Eq. (10.91).

Solution

$$\nabla \cdot (\nabla \times \mathbf{v}) = \varepsilon_{ijk} \frac{\partial^2 v_k}{\partial x_i \partial x_j}.$$

In this triple sum, for a fixed value of k, two terms occur with interchanged values of indices i and j. These terms are identical but with opposite signs and hence cancel. All terms occur in such pairs so that the sum vanishes, thus proving Eq. (10.91). $\square$

(v) The curl of curl operator can be decomposed into the gradient of divergence and the vector Laplacian as follows.

$$\nabla \times (\nabla \times \mathbf{v}) = \nabla(\nabla \cdot \mathbf{v}) - \nabla^2 \mathbf{v}. \tag{10.92}$$

Exercise   Prove Eq. (10.92).

Solution

$$[\nabla \times (\nabla \times \mathbf{v})]_i = \varepsilon_{kij} \varepsilon_{klm} \frac{\partial^2 v_m}{\partial x_j \partial x_l}$$

Using

$$\varepsilon_{kij} \varepsilon_{klm} = \delta_{il} \delta_{jm} - \delta_{im} \delta_{jl}$$

this becomes

$$\frac{\partial}{\partial x_i} \left(\frac{\partial v_j}{\partial x_j} \right) - \frac{\partial^2 v_i}{\partial x_j^2} = [\nabla(\nabla \cdot \mathbf{v})]_i - [\nabla^2 \mathbf{v}]_i. \qquad \square$$

Note that Eq. (10.92) can be taken to be a coordinate free definition of $\nabla^2 \mathbf{v}$ in preference to Eq. (10.89) which depends on cartesian coordinates.

---

[8] We assume, of course, that the order of differentiation does not matter.

Exercise In what follows $\mathbf{r}$ denotes a position vector $r = |\mathbf{r}|$ is its magnitude, $\mathbf{A}(\mathbf{r})$ and $\mathbf{B}(\mathbf{r})$ are vector fields, $\phi(\mathbf{r})$ is a scalar field and $f(r)$ is a function of r. All fields and functions have continuous first derivatives. Using Levi-Civita symbols or otherwise, prove the following.

(i) $\nabla \times (\nabla \times \mathbf{A}) = \nabla(\nabla \cdot \mathbf{A}) - \nabla^2 \mathbf{A}$.

(ii) $\mathbf{A} \times (\nabla \times \mathbf{B}) = \nabla_B(\mathbf{A} \cdot \mathbf{B}) - (\mathbf{A} \cdot \nabla)\mathbf{B}$ where ∇_B operates on $\mathbf{B}$ only.

(iii) Given $\nabla \times \mathbf{A} = \mathbf{0} = \nabla \times \mathbf{B}$ show that $\nabla \cdot (\mathbf{A} \times \mathbf{B}) = 0$.

(iv) For constant $\mathbf{a}$ and $\mathbf{b}$ show that $\nabla \times [(\mathbf{a} \times \mathbf{r}) \times \mathbf{b}] = \mathbf{a} \times \mathbf{b}$.

(v) $\nabla \cdot \mathbf{r} = 3, \nabla \times \mathbf{r} = \mathbf{0}, \nabla(\mathbf{A} \cdot \mathbf{r}) = \mathbf{A}, (\mathbf{A} \cdot \nabla)\mathbf{r} = \mathbf{A}$.

(vi) $\nabla r^n = nr^{n-2}\mathbf{r}, \nabla \cdot \frac{f(r)\mathbf{r}}{r} = \frac{1}{r^2}\frac{d}{dr}(r^2 f)$.

We will use any one or more of these results in the sequel, as and when required.   □

Exercise A particle performs uniform circular motion on a circle of radius r and position vector $\mathbf{r}$. Show that (a) $\nabla \times \mathbf{v} = 2\omega$ and (b) $\nabla \cdot \mathbf{v} = 0$, where $\mathbf{v}$ is the linear velocity and ω is the (constant) rotational velocity of the particle.

Solution

(a) We know that for circular motion, $\mathbf{v} = \omega \times \mathbf{r}$. Therefore,

$$\nabla \times \mathbf{v} = \nabla \times (\omega \times \mathbf{r}) = \omega(\nabla \cdot \mathbf{r}) - \omega \cdot \nabla \mathbf{r}.$$

However, $\nabla \cdot \mathbf{r} = 3$ and $\omega \cdot \nabla \mathbf{r} = \omega$, which gives (a). Thus, we see that the curl operator transforms the velocity vector into a rotational velocity vector.

(b) $\nabla \cdot \mathbf{v} = \nabla \cdot (\omega \times \mathbf{r}) = \mathbf{r} \cdot \nabla \times \omega - \omega \cdot \nabla \times \mathbf{r} = 0$, since ω is a constant vector and $\nabla \times \mathbf{r} = \mathbf{0}$.   □

Thus, there are basically two types of second derivatives, the Laplacian, which is of fundamental importance and the gradient of divergence which we seldom encounter. Since the second derivatives suffice to deal with practically all the physical applications, going over to higher derivatives will reduce to an academic exercise without any physical motivation.

10.14 Differential Operators in Curvilinear Coordinates

A system of curvilinear coordinates, say (u, v, w), is specified via an invertible passive transformation $\mathbb{R}^3 \mapsto \mathbb{R}^3$:

$$(x, y, z) \mapsto (u(x, y, z), v(x, y, z), w(x, y, z)) \tag{10.93}$$

or via the inverse $\mathbb{R}^3 \mapsto \mathbb{R}^3$ transformation

$$(u, v, w) \mapsto (x(u, v, w), y(u, v, w), z(u, v, w)). \tag{10.94}$$

A system of curvilinear coordinates is said to be orthogonal if the coordinate surfaces or equivalently the coordinate lines or the unit vectors tangent to the coordinate lines at their point of intersection are mutually perpendicular (see Fig. 10.11). Note that there are different sets of coordinate surfaces, coordinate lines and the orthogonal basis vectors $\hat{\mathbf{u}}, \hat{\mathbf{v}}, \hat{\mathbf{w}}$ at different points in space. The transformations in Eqs (10.93), (10.94) are assumed to be C^1, that is, having continuous partial derivatives at all points in some region of space, as well as invertible everywhere in that region, that is, having a non-zero Jacobian determinant at all points in that region. Such transformations between two sets of coordinates are called *admissible* coordinate transformations defined over a given region of space. Just to refresh our memory, we recall the definitions of the coordinate lines and coordinate surfaces. Given any point, one can draw a curve passing through the point in such a way that only one of the three curvilinear coordinates changes along the curve while the values of the other two coordinates remain constant. For three curvilinear coordinates one can draw three such curves, all passing through the given point and mutually intersecting at right angles. Each is called a *coordinate curve* or a *coordinate line* and a surface passing through the given point on which a particular curvilinear coordinate has a constant value is called a *coordinate surface.* The u-coordinate line, for example, is the curve of intersection of the v and the w coordinate surfaces. All this is depicted in Fig. 10.11.

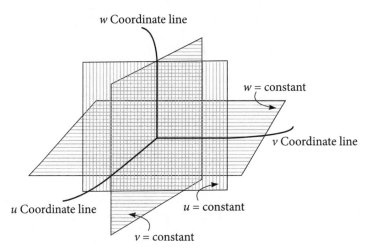

Fig. 10.11   The Network of coordinate lines and coordinate surfaces at any arbitary point, defining a curvilinear coordinate system

Let the equations for the coordinate curves at a point (u_0, v_0, w_0) be

$$\mathbf{x} = \mathbf{x}(u, v_0, w_0) \quad \mathbf{x} = \mathbf{x}(u_0, v, w_0) \quad \mathbf{x} = \mathbf{x}(u_0, v_0, w).$$

The tangents to the coordinate curves are given by the vectors

$$\frac{\partial \mathbf{x}(u, v_0, w_0)}{\partial u}, \frac{\partial \mathbf{x}(u_0, v, w_0)}{\partial v}, \frac{\partial \mathbf{x}(u_0, v_0, w)}{\partial w}$$

respectively. Orthogonality of these vectors requires that

$$\frac{\partial \mathbf{x}}{\partial u} \cdot \frac{\partial \mathbf{x}}{\partial v} = \frac{\partial \mathbf{x}}{\partial u} \cdot \frac{\partial \mathbf{x}}{\partial w} = \frac{\partial \mathbf{x}}{\partial v} \cdot \frac{\partial \mathbf{x}}{\partial w} = 0.$$

We are interested in the differential displacement $d\mathbf{x}$ as we go from $\mathbf{x}(u,v,w)$ to $\mathbf{x}(u + du, v + dv, w + dw)$. We have, in terms of the corresponding Jacobian matrix,

$$d\mathbf{x} = \begin{bmatrix} \frac{\partial s_1}{\partial u} & \frac{\partial s_1}{\partial v} & \frac{\partial s_1}{\partial w} \\ \frac{\partial s_2}{\partial u} & \frac{\partial s_2}{\partial v} & \frac{\partial s_2}{\partial w} \\ \frac{\partial s_3}{\partial u} & \frac{\partial s_3}{\partial v} & \frac{\partial s_3}{\partial w} \end{bmatrix} \begin{bmatrix} du \\ dv \\ dw \end{bmatrix} = \frac{\partial \mathbf{x}}{\partial u} du + \frac{\partial \mathbf{x}}{\partial u} dv + \frac{\partial \mathbf{x}}{\partial w} dw = \mathbf{x}_u du + \mathbf{x}_v dv + \mathbf{x}_w dw.$$

$$(10.95)$$

where $s_{1,2,3}(u,v,w) = \mathbf{x}(u,v,w) \cdot \{\hat{\mathbf{u}}, \hat{\mathbf{v}}, \hat{\mathbf{w}}\}$ are the components of $\mathbf{x}$ in the $\hat{\mathbf{u}}, \hat{\mathbf{v}}, \hat{\mathbf{w}}$ mutually orthogonal directions. This defines the line element $ds = |d\mathbf{x}|$ via

$$ds^2 = d\mathbf{x} \cdot d\mathbf{x} = \mathbf{x}_u \cdot \mathbf{x}_u du^2 + \mathbf{x}_v \cdot \mathbf{x}_v dv^2 + \mathbf{x}_w \cdot \mathbf{x}_w dw^2$$

$$= h_1^2 du^2 + h_2^2 dv^2 + h_3^2 dw^2. \qquad (10.96)$$

The parameters h_1, h_2, h_3 are the analogues of the Gaussian fundamental quantities E, F, G of a surface, we derived before. They relate the differential displacements along the $\hat{\mathbf{u}}, \hat{\mathbf{v}}, \hat{\mathbf{w}}$ directions as a result of the displacement $d\mathbf{x}$ to the diferentials du, dv, dw via

$$d\mathbf{x} = ds_1 \hat{\mathbf{u}} + ds_2 \hat{\mathbf{v}} + ds_3 \hat{\mathbf{w}} = h_1 du \hat{\mathbf{u}} + h_2 dv \hat{\mathbf{v}} + h_3 dw \hat{\mathbf{w}}.$$

Thus, the volume of the rectangular parallelepiped with sides ds_1, ds_2, ds_3 is given by

$$dV = ds_1 ds_2 ds_3 = h_1 h_2 h_3 du dv dw.$$

The product $h_1 h_2 h_3$ ensures that the the last term has the dimension of volume; as the curvilinear coordinates can be dimensionless quantities like angles.

The u coordinate surface passing through the point (u_0, v_0, w_0) is the collection of points (x, y, z) satisfying $u(x, y, z) = u_0$ and similarly, the v and w coordinate surfaces are given by $v(x, y, z) = v_0$ and $w(x, y, z) = w_0$, where (x, y, z) are the Cartesian coordinates with respect to some rectangular Cartesian coordinate system. We can vary the point (u_0, v_0, w_0) over the region for which the curvilinear coordinate transformations, Eqs (10.93), (10.94), are defined. Therefore, we can replace u_0, v_0, w_0 in the equations defining the coordinate surfaces by u, v, w and say that a particular triad of coordinate surfaces emerges when particular values of u, v and w are substituted on the RHS of these equations. Thus, we write, for the equations defining the coordinate surfaces

$$u = u(x, y, z) \quad v = v(x, y, z) \quad w = w(x, y, z).$$

The normals to the coordinate surfaces are given by $\nabla u, \nabla v, \nabla w$ (see section 10.8) which, owing to orthogonality, must satisfy

$$0 = \nabla u \cdot \nabla v = \nabla u \cdot \nabla w = \nabla v \cdot \nabla w.$$

The vectors normal to the coordinate surfaces are tangent to the corresponding coordinate curves so that we can *define* the fundamental triad for the curvilinear coordinates as

$$\hat{\mathbf{u}} = \frac{\nabla u}{|\nabla u|} \quad \hat{\mathbf{v}} = \frac{\nabla v}{|\nabla v|} \quad \hat{\mathbf{w}} = \frac{\nabla w}{|\nabla w|}. \tag{10.97}$$

Let $d\mathbf{s}_1 = ds_1\hat{\mathbf{u}}$, $d\mathbf{s}_2 = ds_2\hat{\mathbf{v}}$, $d\mathbf{s}_3 = ds_3\hat{\mathbf{w}}$ be the differential displacement along the $\hat{\mathbf{u}}, \hat{\mathbf{v}}, \hat{\mathbf{w}}$ directions. Since $\nabla u, \nabla v, \nabla w$ have the same values in all the orthonormal basis triads and since $\nabla u, d\mathbf{s}_1$, $\nabla v, d\mathbf{s}_2$ and $\nabla w, d\mathbf{s}_3$ are the pairs of parallel vectors, we can write,

$$du = \nabla u \cdot d\mathbf{s}_1 = |\nabla u||d\mathbf{s}_1|,$$

$$dv = \nabla v \cdot d\mathbf{s}_2 = |\nabla v||d\mathbf{s}_2|,$$

$$dw = \nabla w \cdot d\mathbf{s}_3 = |\nabla w||d\mathbf{s}_3|. \tag{10.98}$$

This gives,

$$ds^2 = ds_1^2 + ds_2^2 + ds_3^2 = \frac{du^2}{|\nabla u|^2} + \frac{dv^2}{|\nabla v|^2} + \frac{dw^2}{|\nabla w|^2}. \tag{10.99}$$

Comparing equations Eqs (10.96) and (10.99) we get

$$h_1 = \frac{1}{|\nabla u|} = \sqrt{\mathbf{x}_u \cdot \mathbf{x}_u} \text{ impling } \hat{\mathbf{u}} = h_1 \nabla u,$$

$$h_2 = \frac{1}{|\nabla v|} = \sqrt{\mathbf{x}_v \cdot \mathbf{x}_v} \text{ impling } \hat{\mathbf{v}} = h_2 \nabla v,$$

$$h_3 = \frac{1}{|\nabla w|} = \sqrt{\mathbf{x}_w \cdot \mathbf{x}_w} \text{ impling } \hat{\mathbf{w}} = h_3 \nabla w. \tag{10.100}$$

Example For spherical polar coordinates we identify $u = r$, $v = \theta$ and $w = \phi$, where

$$r = \sqrt{x^2 + y^2 + z^2}, \ \theta = \cos^{-1}\left(\frac{z}{\sqrt{x^2 + y^2 + z^2}}\right) \text{ and } \phi = \tan^{-1}\left(\frac{y}{x}\right).$$

This gives $h_1^{-1} = |\nabla r| = 1$, $h_2^{-1} = |\nabla \theta| = r^{-1}$ and $h_3^{-1} = |\nabla \phi| = (r \sin \theta)^{-1}$. Therefore,

$$ds^2 = h_1^2 dr^2 + h_2^2 d\theta^2 + h_3^2 d\phi^2 = dr^2 + r^2 d\theta^2 + r^2 \sin^2 \theta d\phi^2.$$

Also, the fundamental triad is,

$$\hat{\mathbf{u}} = \hat{\mathbf{r}}, \quad \hat{\mathbf{v}} = \hat{\theta}, \quad \hat{\mathbf{w}} = \hat{\phi}.$$

We can also invert the transformation to get

$$x = r \sin \theta \cos \phi \quad y = r \sin \theta \sin \phi \quad z = r \cos \theta.$$

This gives (Exercise),

$$h_1 = \sqrt{\left(\frac{dx}{dr}\right)^2 + \left(\frac{dy}{dr}\right)^2 + \left(\frac{dz}{dr}\right)^2} = 1,$$

$$h_2 = \sqrt{\left(\frac{dx}{d\theta}\right)^2 + \left(\frac{dy}{d\theta}\right)^2 + \left(\frac{dz}{d\theta}\right)^2} = r,$$

$$h_3 = \sqrt{\left(\frac{dx}{d\phi}\right)^2 + \left(\frac{dy}{d\phi}\right)^2 + \left(\frac{dz}{d\phi}\right)^2} = r \sin \theta. \tag{10.101}$$

which are identical to those already obtained from forward transformations.

The gradient of a scalar valued function $\phi(u,v,w)$ with respect to the Cartesian coordinates x, y, z can be obtained by applying chain rule:

$$\nabla \phi = \frac{\partial \phi}{\partial u} \nabla u + \frac{\partial \phi}{\partial v} \nabla v + \frac{\partial \phi}{\partial w} \nabla w$$

$$= \left(\frac{1}{h_1} \frac{\partial \phi}{\partial u}\right) \hat{\mathbf{u}} + \left(\frac{1}{h_2} \frac{\partial \phi}{\partial v}\right) \hat{\mathbf{v}} + \left(\frac{1}{h_3} \frac{\partial \phi}{\partial w}\right) \hat{\mathbf{w}}, \tag{10.102}$$

where we have used Eq. (10.100).

Our next job is to express the divergence $\nabla \cdot \mathbf{f}$ of a vector field $\mathbf{f}$ exclusively in terms of the derivatives with respect to the curvilinear coordinates u, v, w. We can do this, in principle, by a systematic application of the chain rule, but that will make us go through a lengthy algebra which only masochists can enjoy. There is a short cut, where we use the fact that the flux of a vector field through a differential volume dV is given by $\nabla \cdot \mathbf{f} dV$. In order to get hold of this quantity, we need to know how to represent the area of a piece of a surface by a vector. As shown in Fig. 10.12, an element of area da is represented by the vector $d\mathbf{a}$ given by

$$d\mathbf{a} = \hat{\mathbf{n}} da = da_x \hat{\mathbf{i}} + da_y \hat{\mathbf{j}} + da_z \hat{\mathbf{k}} \tag{10.103}$$

where $\hat{\mathbf{n}}$ is the unit outward normal to the surface, defined via its direction cosines

$$\hat{\mathbf{n}} = \cos \alpha \hat{\mathbf{i}} + \cos \beta \hat{\mathbf{j}} + \cos \gamma \hat{\mathbf{k}}. \tag{10.104}$$

Therefore, the components of $d\mathbf{a}$ are given by

$$da_x = da \cos \alpha, \quad da_y = da \cos \beta \quad da_z = da \cos \gamma.$$

In particular, $\mathbf{x} \cdot d\mathbf{a} = |\mathbf{x}| da \cos \theta$ where θ is the angle between $\hat{\mathbf{n}}$ and $\mathbf{x}$. If $\theta = 0$ or $\theta = \pi$ then $\mathbf{x} \cdot d\mathbf{a} = \pm|\mathbf{x}|da$. This situation arises when the surface is perpendicular to $\mathbf{x}$, that is, the area of the projection of the surface element on the plane perpendicular to $\mathbf{x}$ is the same as da. The flux of $\mathbf{f}$ through an element of area da is $\mathbf{f} \cdot d\mathbf{a}$.

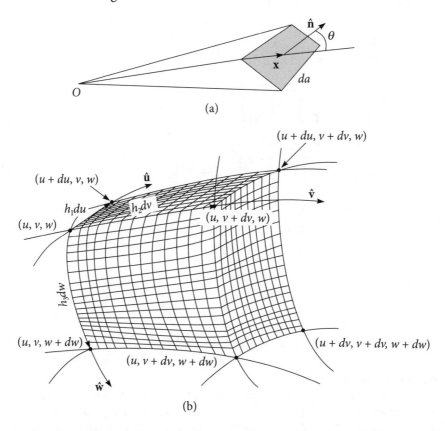

(a)

(b)

Fig. 10.12 (a) Evaluating $\mathbf{x} \cdot d\mathbf{a}$ (b) Flux through the opposite faces of a volume element

Let us now consider a differential volume of the shape of a rectangular parallelepiped with sides ds_1, ds_2, ds_3 defined above so that its volume is $dV = ds_1 ds_2 ds_3 = h_1 h_2 h_3 \, du dv dw$. Let us assume that the pairs $-\hat{\mathbf{u}}, \hat{\mathbf{u}}$ be the outward normals to the front and the back sides, $-\hat{\mathbf{v}}, \hat{\mathbf{v}}$ be the outward normals to the left and the right sides and $-\hat{\mathbf{w}}, \hat{\mathbf{w}}$ be the outward normals to the bottom and the top sides of the box. Then for the front face, $d\mathbf{a} = -h_2 h_3 dv dw \hat{\mathbf{u}}$ and $\mathbf{f} \cdot d\mathbf{a} = -(h_2 h_3 f_1) dv dw$, where $f_{1,2,3}$ are the components of $\mathbf{f}$

along $\hat{\mathbf{u}}, \hat{\mathbf{v}}, \hat{\mathbf{w}}$ respectively and the product $h_2 h_3 f_1$ is to be evaluated at u. On the back face, product $h_2 h_3 f_1$ is to be evaluated at $u + du$ so that $\mathbf{f} \cdot d\mathbf{a} = (h_2 h_3 f_1 + \frac{\partial}{\partial u}(h_2 h_3 f_1) \, du) dv dw$. Therefore, the net flux through the front and back pair of faces is

$$\left[\frac{\partial}{\partial u}(h_2 h_3 f_1)\right] du dv dw = \frac{1}{h_1 h_2 h_3}\frac{\partial}{\partial u}(h_2 h_3 f_1) dV.$$

In the same way, the right and the left sides give

$$\frac{1}{h_1 h_2 h_3}\frac{\partial}{\partial v}(h_1 h_3 f_2) dV$$

and the bottom and the top sides contribute

$$\frac{1}{h_1 h_2 h_3}\frac{\partial}{\partial w}(h_1 h_2 f_3) dV.$$

Thus, the total flux through the box is given by

$$(\nabla \cdot \mathbf{f}) dV = \frac{1}{h_1 h_2 h_3}\left[\frac{\partial}{\partial u}(h_2 h_3 f_1) + \frac{\partial}{\partial v}(h_1 h_3 f_2) + \frac{\partial}{\partial w}(h_1 h_2 f_3)\right] dV$$

This gives

$$\nabla \cdot \mathbf{f} = \frac{1}{h_1 h_2 h_3}\left[\frac{\partial}{\partial u}(h_2 h_3 f_1) + \frac{\partial}{\partial v}(h_3 h_1 f_2) + \frac{\partial}{\partial w}(h_1 h_2 f_3)\right]. \tag{10.105}$$

Combining Eq. (10.105) with Eq. (10.102) we get, for the Laplacian operator,

$$\nabla^2 \phi = \nabla \cdot \nabla \phi = \frac{1}{h_1 h_2 h_3}\left[\frac{\partial}{\partial u}\left(\frac{h_2 h_3}{h_1}\frac{\partial \phi}{\partial u}\right) + \frac{\partial}{\partial v}\left(\frac{h_3 h_1}{h_2}\frac{\partial \phi}{\partial v}\right) + \frac{\partial}{\partial w}\left(\frac{h_1 h_2}{h_3}\frac{\partial \phi}{\partial w}\right)\right]. \tag{10.106}$$

Our last task in this subsection is to express the curl $\nabla \times \mathbf{f}$ of a vector field $\mathbf{f}$ in terms of the derivatives with respect to the curvilinear coordinates u, v, w. The principle we follow for this is

Circulation of $\mathbf{f}$ around a loop enclosing an infinitesimal area $d\mathbf{a} = (\nabla \times \mathbf{f}) \cdot d\mathbf{a}$.

The sense of circulation is given by that which makes a right handed screw advance in the direction of $d\mathbf{a}$. The required circulation can be explicitly calculated for an infinitesimal loop of rectangular shape. For each side of the rectangle, we have to find the scalar product of $\mathbf{f}$ with the vector along the side and in the direction consistent with the sense of circulation. In the first place, the surface enclosed by an infinitesimal loop can be taken to be a plane. Consider such a rectangular loop in the $\hat{\mathbf{u}}, \hat{\mathbf{v}}$ plane, with $\hat{\mathbf{w}}$ normal to it (see Fig. 10.13). From Fig. 10.13 and $\hat{\mathbf{w}}$ pointing out of the page, it is clear that the sense of circulation which makes a right handed screw advance in $\hat{\mathbf{w}}$ direction is counterclockwise, as shown. The vector on the side along $\hat{\mathbf{u}}$ is $d\mathbf{s}_1 = h_1 du \hat{\mathbf{u}}$ that on the side along $\hat{\mathbf{v}}$ is $d\mathbf{s}_2 = h_2 dv \hat{\mathbf{v}}$ and area

$$da = h_1 h_2 du dv \hat{\mathbf{w}}.$$

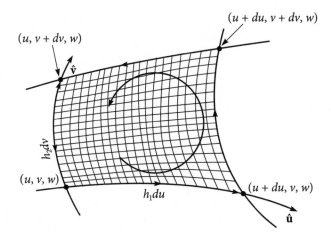

Fig. 10.13   Circulation around a loop

Along the bottom side (along $\hat{\mathbf{u}}$) the contribution of $\mathbf{f}$ to circulation is

$$\mathbf{f} \cdot d\mathbf{s}_1 = h_1 f_1 du$$

Along the top side, the sign is reversed and $h_1 f_1$ is evaluated at $v + dv$ rather than v. Both sides together give

$$\left[-(h_1 f_1)\Big|_{v+dv} + (h_1 f_1)\Big|_v \right] du = -\left[\frac{\partial}{\partial v}(h_1 f_1) \right] du dv.$$

Similarly, the right and the left sides yield

$$\left[\frac{\partial}{\partial u}(h_2 f_2) \right] du dv.$$

So, the total circulation is

$$\left[\frac{\partial}{\partial u}(h_2 f_2) - \frac{\partial}{\partial v}(h_1 f_1) \right] du dv = \frac{1}{h_1 h_2} \left[\frac{\partial}{\partial u}(h_2 f_2) - \frac{\partial}{\partial v}(h_1 f_1) \right] \hat{\mathbf{w}} \cdot d\mathbf{a}.$$

The coefficient of $d\mathbf{a}$ serves to define the w component of the curl. Constructing the u and v components in the same way, we get

$$\nabla \times \mathbf{f} = \frac{1}{h_2 h_3}\left[\frac{\partial}{\partial v}(h_3 f_3) - \frac{\partial}{\partial w}(h_2 f_2)\right]\hat{\mathbf{u}} + \frac{1}{h_1 h_3}\left[\frac{\partial}{\partial w}(h_1 f_1) - \frac{\partial}{\partial u}(h_3 f_3)\right]\hat{\mathbf{v}}$$

$$+ \frac{1}{h_1 h_2}\left[\frac{\partial}{\partial u}(h_2 f_2) - \frac{\partial}{\partial v}(h_1 f_1)\right]\hat{\mathbf{w}}. \tag{10.107}$$

This expression for $\nabla \times \mathbf{f}$ can be written in a compact determinantal form as

$$\nabla \times \mathbf{f} = \frac{1}{h_1 h_2 h_3}\begin{vmatrix} h_1\hat{\mathbf{u}} & h_2\hat{\mathbf{v}} & h_3\hat{\mathbf{w}} \\ \frac{\partial}{\partial u} & \frac{\partial}{\partial v} & \frac{\partial}{\partial w} \\ h_1 f_1 & h_2 f_2 & h_3 f_3 \end{vmatrix}. \tag{10.108}$$

Exercise Express the vector derivatives, that is, gradient, divergence, curl and Laplacian in terms of (a) spherical polar and (b) cylindrical coordinates for a scalar field $u(\mathbf{x})$ and a vector field $\mathbf{v}(\mathbf{x})$.

Answer

(a) Gradient:

$$\nabla u = \frac{\partial u}{\partial r}\hat{\mathbf{r}} + \frac{1}{r}\frac{\partial u}{\partial \theta}\hat{\theta} + \frac{1}{r\sin\theta}\frac{\partial u}{\partial \phi}\hat{\phi}.$$

Divergence:

$$\nabla \cdot \mathbf{v} = \frac{1}{r^2}\frac{\partial}{\partial r}(r^2 v_r) + \frac{1}{r\sin\theta}\frac{\partial}{\partial \theta}(\sin\theta v_\theta) + \frac{1}{r\sin\theta}\frac{\partial v_\phi}{\partial \phi}.$$

Curl:

$$\nabla \times \mathbf{v} = \frac{1}{r\sin\theta}\left[\frac{\partial}{\partial \theta}(\sin\theta v_\phi) - \frac{\partial v_\theta}{\partial \phi}\right]\hat{\mathbf{r}} + \frac{1}{r}\left[\frac{1}{\sin\theta}\frac{\partial v_r}{\partial \phi} - \frac{\partial}{\partial r}(rv_\phi)\right]$$

$$\hat{\theta} + \frac{1}{r}\left[\frac{\partial}{\partial r}(rv_\theta) - \frac{\partial v_r}{\partial \theta}\right]\hat{\phi}.$$

Laplacian:

$$\nabla^2 u = \frac{1}{r^2}\frac{\partial}{\partial r}\left(r^2\frac{\partial u}{\partial r}\right) + \frac{1}{r^2\sin\theta}\frac{\partial}{\partial \theta}\left(\sin\theta\frac{\partial u}{\partial \theta}\right) + \frac{1}{r^2\sin^2\theta}\frac{\partial^2 u}{\partial \phi^2}.$$

(b) Gradient:

$$\nabla u = \frac{\partial u}{\partial \rho}\hat{\rho} + \frac{1}{\rho}\frac{\partial u}{\partial \phi}\hat{\phi} + \frac{\partial u}{\partial z}\hat{\mathbf{z}}.$$

Divergence:

$$\nabla \cdot \mathbf{v} = \frac{1}{\rho} \frac{\partial}{\partial \rho}(\rho v_\rho) + \frac{1}{\rho} \frac{\partial v_\phi}{\partial \phi} + \frac{\partial v_z}{\partial z}.$$

Curl:

$$\nabla \times \mathbf{v} = \left(\frac{1}{\rho} \frac{\partial v_z}{\partial \phi} - \frac{\partial v_\phi}{\partial z} \right) \hat{\rho} + \left(\frac{\partial v_\rho}{\partial z} - \frac{\partial v_z}{\partial \rho} \right) \hat{\phi} + \frac{1}{\rho} \left(\frac{\partial}{\partial \rho}(\rho v_\phi) - \frac{\partial v_\rho}{\partial \phi} \right) \hat{z}.$$

Laplacian:

$$\nabla^2 u = \frac{1}{\rho} \frac{\partial}{\partial \rho} \left(\rho \frac{\partial u}{\partial \rho} \right) + \frac{1}{\rho^2} \frac{\partial^2 u}{\partial \phi^2} + \frac{\partial^2 u}{\partial z^2}.$$ □

11

Vector Integration

In this chapter we learn how to integrate a vector field, or a vector valued function $\mathbf{f}(\mathbf{x})$, over $\mathbf{x}$.

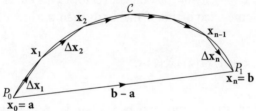

Fig. 11.1   Defining the line integral

We are interested in three possibilities. First, the variable of integration, $\mathbf{x}$, can vary over a continuous region $\mathcal{R}$ of volume V in space. Second, $\mathbf{x}$ is confined to vary over a piece of a smooth surface, that is, a surface parameterized by $\mathbf{x}(u,v)$ which has continuous partial derivatives $\frac{\partial \mathbf{x}}{\partial u}$ and $\frac{\partial \mathbf{x}}{\partial v}$. Third, $\mathbf{x}$ is constrained to vary over a piece of a smooth curve, parameterized, say by $\mathbf{x}(t)$, which is a continuously differentiable function of t. The first option is called a *volume or a triple integral*, the second option is called a *surface integral* and the last option is called a *line integral*. We learn about these integrals one by one, starting with the line integral.

11.1   Line Integrals and Potential Functions

Consider a piece of smooth curve in space, joining points P_0 and P_1 as shown in Fig. 11.1. We mark out points $\mathbf{x}_0(\equiv P_0), \mathbf{x}_1, \mathbf{x}_2, \ldots, \mathbf{x}_n(\equiv P_1)$ on this piece of curve and define $\Delta \mathbf{x}_k = \mathbf{x}_k - \mathbf{x}_{k-1}$, $k = 1, 2, \ldots, n$ (Fig. 11.1). Let $\mathbf{f}(\mathbf{x}_k)$, $k = 1 \ldots, n$ be the values of the field at these points. Then, the line integral of $\mathbf{f}(\mathbf{x})$ on this curve is defined as

$$\int_{P_0}^{P_1} \mathbf{f}(\mathbf{x}) \cdot d\mathbf{x} = \lim_{n \to \infty} \sum_{k=1}^{n} \mathbf{f}(\mathbf{x}_k) \cdot \Delta \mathbf{x}_k \tag{11.1}$$

In the limit as $n \to \infty$ the vectors $\Delta \mathbf{x}_k$ become tangent to the curve, so we are projecting the field values $\mathbf{f}(\mathbf{x}_k)$ along the tangent at that point to the curve summing the corresponding products along the curve. Thus, the value of the line integral is influenced by both the field as well as the curve along which the integral is taken. Later, we will obtain conditions under which the value of a line integral depends only on the field values at the end points and not on the curve joining them.

The line integral in Eq. (11.1) can be transformed using the fact that the curve is parameterized by a continuously differentiable function $\mathbf{x}(t)$. Let $\mathbf{x}_0 = \mathbf{x}(T_1)$ and $\mathbf{x}_n = \mathbf{x}(T_2)$ correspond to the end points P_0 and P_1 respectively. We choose values $t_0 = T_1, t_1, t_2, \ldots, t_n = T_2$ in the closed interval $[T_1, T_2]$ and let $\mathbf{x}_k = \mathbf{x}(t_k)$. We define $\Delta \mathbf{x}_k = \Delta \mathbf{x}(t_k) = \mathbf{x}(t_k) - \mathbf{x}(t_{k-1})$ and $\Delta t_k = t_k - t_{k-1}$. Then the line integral in Eq. (11.1) gets transformed to

$$\int_{T_1}^{T_2} \mathbf{f}(\mathbf{x}(t)) \cdot \dot{\mathbf{x}}(t)dt = \lim_{n \to \infty} \sum_{k=1}^{n} \mathbf{f}(\mathbf{x}(t_k)) \cdot \left(\frac{\Delta \mathbf{x}(t_k)}{\Delta t_k} \right) \Delta t_k \qquad (11.2)$$

where $\dot{\mathbf{x}}(t) = \frac{d\mathbf{x}(t)}{dt}$ is the velocity or the tangent vector to the curve at the point $\mathbf{x}(t)$. If we resolve the field along some fixed orthonormal basis then the line integral becomes

$$\sum_{i=1}^{3} \int_{T_1}^{T_2} f_i(x_1(t), x_2(t), x_3(t)) \dot{x}_i(t) dt \qquad (11.3)$$

where $f_{1,2,3}$ and $x_{1,2,3}$ are the components of $\mathbf{f}(\mathbf{x})$ and $\mathbf{x}$ respectively with respect to the fixed orthonormal basis. In particular, for a scalar valued function $f(\mathbf{x})$ the line integral becomes

$$\int_{T_1}^{T_2} f(x_1(t), x_2(t), x_3(t)) dt \qquad (11.4)$$

where $\mathbf{x}(t) \equiv (x_2(t), x_2(t), x_3(t))$ is the parametric description of the curve.

Exercise   Let the position vectors of the points P_0 and P_1 be $\mathbf{a}$ and $\mathbf{b}$ respectively. Find $\int_{P_0}^{P_1} d\mathbf{x}$.

Solution   Notice that no curve joining P_0 and P_1 is specified. In fact it is not necessary. Whichever way we choose a curve joining P_0 and P_1 and construct the set $\{\Delta \mathbf{x}_i\}$, all the vectors $\Delta \mathbf{x}_i$ add up to the vector $\mathbf{b} - \mathbf{a}$ (see Fig. 11.1). The integral is

$$\int_{P_0}^{P_1} d\mathbf{x} = \mathbf{b} - \mathbf{a},$$

whose value depends only on the end points and not on the path connecting them.   □

A piece of a curve of finite length, parameterized by a continuously differentiable function $\mathbf{x}(t)$ is called a smooth arc. We assume that the arc is oriented such that increasing t makes the corresponding point on the curve move *from P_0 towards P_1*. Such an arc is said to be positively oriented. If the orientation is reverse, the arc is said to be negatively oriented. We call such an arc a smooth oriented arc. If we denote by Γ $(-\Gamma)$ a positively (negatively) oriented arc, then the corresponding line integrals change sign:

$$\int_\Gamma \mathbf{f} \cdot d\mathbf{x} = \int_{P_0}^{P_1} \mathbf{f} \cdot d\mathbf{x} = -\int_{P_1}^{P_0} \mathbf{f} \cdot d\mathbf{x} = -\int_{-\Gamma} \mathbf{f} \cdot d\mathbf{x}.$$

The curve C over which we want to integrate a vector field $\mathbf{f}(\mathbf{x})$ may consist of many smooth oriented arcs $C_1, C_2, \ldots C_N$ joined at their end points where their derivatives may not match, so that the whole path can be parameterized by continuous functions with finite jump discontinuities in the derivative at finite number of points where the smooth arcs join. In such a case we can write

$$\int_C \mathbf{f}(\mathbf{x}) \cdot d\mathbf{x} = \int_{C_1} \mathbf{f}(\mathbf{x}) \cdot d\mathbf{x} + \int_{C_2} \mathbf{f}(\mathbf{x}) \cdot d\mathbf{x} + \cdots + \int_{C_N} \mathbf{f}(\mathbf{x}) \cdot d\mathbf{x}. \tag{11.5}$$

Another possibility is that C is a closed curve. We assume that the curve is oriented counterclockwise as the parameter t increases.

Exercise   Evaluate the integral in Eq. (11.2) for the planar field $\mathbf{f}(\mathbf{x}) = -y\hat{\mathbf{i}} - xy\hat{\mathbf{j}}$ on the circular arc C shown in Fig. 11.2 from P_0 to P_1.

Solution   We parameterize C by $\mathbf{x}(t) = \cos t\hat{\mathbf{i}} + \sin t\hat{\mathbf{j}}, \ 0 \le t \le \pi/2$. Therefore,

$$\mathbf{f}(\mathbf{x}(t)) = -\sin t\hat{\mathbf{i}} - \cos t \sin t\hat{\mathbf{j}}.$$

Differentiating $\mathbf{x}(t)$ we get $\dot{\mathbf{x}}(t) = -\sin t\hat{\mathbf{i}} + \cos t\hat{\mathbf{j}}$. Therefore the integral becomes

$$\int_{T_1}^{T_2} \mathbf{f}(\mathbf{x}(t)) \cdot \dot{\mathbf{x}}(t) dt = \int_0^{\pi/2} (\sin^2 t - \cos^2 t \sin t) dt = \frac{\pi}{4} - \frac{1}{3} = 0.4521. \qquad \square$$

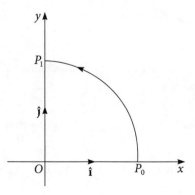

Fig. 11.2 $\mathbf{x}(t) = \cos t\hat{\mathbf{i}} + \sin t\hat{\mathbf{j}}$

Exercise   Evaluate the integral in Eq. (11.2) for the field $\mathbf{f}(\mathbf{x}) = z\hat{\mathbf{i}} + x\hat{\mathbf{j}} + y\hat{\mathbf{k}}$ on the helix C shown in Fig. 11.3,

$$\mathbf{x}(t) = \cos t\hat{\mathbf{i}} + \sin t\hat{\mathbf{j}} + 3t\hat{\mathbf{k}} \quad 0 \le t \le 2\pi$$

from P_0 to P_1.

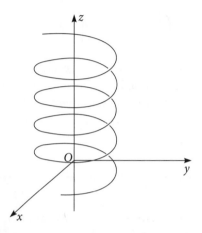

Fig. 11.3   A circular helix

Solution $\mathbf{f}(\mathbf{x}(t)) \cdot \dot{\mathbf{x}}(t) = -3t\sin t + \cos^2 t + 3\sin t$ Hence the required integral is

$$\int_0^{2\pi} (-3t\sin t + \cos^2 t + 3\sin t)dt = 7\pi \approx 21.99. \qquad \Box$$

Exercise   Find the work done by the electrostatic field due to a point charge q on a test charge as it traverses the paths shown in Fig. 11.4(a) and (b).

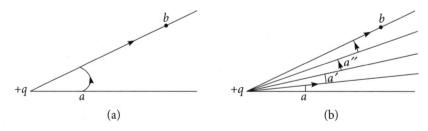

(a)   (b)

Fig. 11.4   In carrying a test charge from a to b the same work is done along either path

Hint $\mathbf{E} = \frac{1}{4\pi\epsilon_0}\frac{q}{r^2}\hat{\mathbf{r}}$ where r is the radial distance of the test charge from the source q. Work done along the circular arcs is zero.

Answer $W = -\int_a^b \mathbf{E} \cdot d\mathbf{s} = \dfrac{q}{4\pi\epsilon_0}\left(\dfrac{1}{r_a} - \dfrac{1}{r_b}\right)$ for both the paths.   □

Exercise   For the field $\mathbf{f}(\mathbf{x}) = xy\hat{\mathbf{i}} + (x^2 + y^2)\hat{\mathbf{j}}$ find $\int_\Gamma \mathbf{f}(\mathbf{x}) \cdot d\mathbf{x}$ where Γ is

(i) The arc $y = x^2 - 4$ from $(2,0)$ to $(5,21)$ and

(ii) The x-axis from $x = 2$ to $x = 5$ and then the line $x = 5$ from $y = 0$ to $y = 21$.

Solution $\displaystyle\int_\Gamma \mathbf{f}(\mathbf{x}) \cdot d\mathbf{x} = \int_\Gamma [xy\,dx + (x^2 + y^2)dy].$

(i) Along Γ $y = x^2 - 4$ or $x^2 = y + 4$. We substitute for y in the first term and for x in the second term of the integrand to get

$$\int_\Gamma \mathbf{f}(\mathbf{x}) \cdot d\mathbf{x} = \int_2^5 (x^3 - 4x)dx + \int_0^{21} (y^2 + y + 4)dy = 3501.75$$

(ii) Along the x axis $y = 0 = dy$ and along the vertical line $x = 5$ and $dx = 0$. This gives

$$\int_\Gamma \mathbf{f}(\mathbf{x}) \cdot d\mathbf{x} = \int_0^{21} (25 + y^2)dy = 3612.$$

We see that two values do not agree, so that the integral depends on the path. Thus, as explained below, the field is not conservative.   □

Sometimes we may have to evaluate the line integral separately on different parts of the given curve, as the following exercise shows.

Exercise   Evaluate $\int_\Gamma \mathbf{f} \cdot d\mathbf{x}$, where $\mathbf{f} = x\hat{\mathbf{j}} - y\hat{\mathbf{i}}$ and Γ is the unit circle about the origin.

Solution   We note that $\mathbf{f} \cdot d\mathbf{x} = x\,dy - y\,dx$. We can parameterize the unit circle by x as $y^2 = 1 - x^2$, but then y is not a single valued function of x. We can circumvent this by viewing the curve as made up of two parts (see Fig. 11.5), Γ_1 and Γ_2 where Γ_1 is the upper semi-circle and Γ_2 the lower, arrows indicating the positive direction along Γ as shown in Fig. 11.5.
   On Γ_1:

$$y = \sqrt{1 - x^2}, \quad dy = \frac{-x\,dx}{\sqrt{1 - x^2}}$$

and
   on Γ_2:

$$y = -\sqrt{1 - x^2}, \quad dy = \frac{x\,dx}{\sqrt{1 - x^2}}.$$

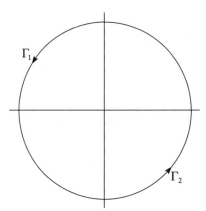

Fig. 11.5   Line integral over a unit circle

Therefore, the required integral is

$$
\int_{\Gamma} \mathbf{f} \cdot d\mathbf{x} \;=\; \int_{\Gamma_1} \frac{-x^2}{\sqrt{1-x^2}} dx - \int_{\Gamma_1} \sqrt{1-x^2}\, dx + \int_{\Gamma_2} \frac{x^2}{\sqrt{1-x^2}} dx + \int_{\Gamma_2} \sqrt{1-x^2}\, dx
$$

$$
\;=\; \int_{1}^{-1} \left(\frac{-x^2}{\sqrt{1-x^2}} - \sqrt{1-x^2} \right) dx + \int_{-1}^{1} \left(\frac{x^2}{\sqrt{1-x^2}} + \sqrt{1-x^2} \right) dx
$$

$$
\;=\; 2\pi. \qquad\qquad\qquad\qquad\qquad\qquad\qquad\qquad\qquad\qquad\qquad \Box
$$

The following three rules for evaluation of line integrals can be easily checked.

(i) $\int_{\mathcal{C}} (k\mathbf{f}) \cdot d\mathbf{x} = k \int_{\mathcal{C}} \mathbf{f} \cdot d\mathbf{x}$. where k is a (scalar) constant.

(ii) For two vector fields $\mathbf{f}$ and $\mathbf{g}$

$$
\int_{\mathcal{C}} (\mathbf{f} + \mathbf{g}) \cdot d\mathbf{x} = \int_{\mathcal{C}} \mathbf{f} \cdot d\mathbf{x} + \int_{\mathcal{C}} \mathbf{g} \cdot d\mathbf{x}.
$$

(iii) Any two parameterizations of $\mathcal{C}$ giving the same orientation on $\mathcal{C}$ yield the same value of the line integral Eq. (11.1).

Exercise   Prove rule (iii).

Solution   Let the curve $\mathcal{C}$ be parameterized by $\mathbf{x}(t)$, $a \leq t \leq b$ and also by $\mathbf{x}^*(t^*)$, $a^* \leq t^* \leq b^*$ and let these be related by $t = \phi(t^*)$. We are given that $\frac{dt}{dt^*} > 0$. Thus, $\mathbf{x}(t) = \mathbf{x}(\phi(t^*)) = \mathbf{x}^*(t^*)$ and $dt = (dt/dt^*)dt^*$. Therefore, the line integral over $\mathcal{C}$ can be written

$$
\int_{\mathcal{C}} \mathbf{f}(\mathbf{x}^*) \cdot d\mathbf{x}^* = \int_{a^*}^{b^*} \mathbf{f}(\mathbf{x}(\phi(t^*))) \cdot \frac{d\mathbf{x}}{dt} \frac{dt}{dt^*} dt^* = \int_{a}^{b} \mathbf{f}(\mathbf{x}(t)) \cdot \frac{d\mathbf{x}}{dt} dt = \int_{\mathcal{C}} \mathbf{f}(\mathbf{x}) \cdot d\mathbf{x}.
$$

Note that $\mathbf{f}(\mathbf{x}(t))$ and $\mathbf{f}(\mathbf{x}(\phi(t^*)))$ are different functions of their arguments but their values match at t and t^* satisfying $t = \phi(t^*)$, both corresponding to the same point P on the curve of integration. □

We now give two results often used while evaluating line integrals. Let $\{\hat{\mathbf{i}}, \hat{\mathbf{j}}, \hat{\mathbf{k}}\}$ be an orthonormal basis and $\{x, y, z\}$ be the corresponding Cartesian coordinate system. Let a vector field $\mathbf{f}(\mathbf{x})$ have components $f_{1,2,3}(\mathbf{x})$ along $\hat{\mathbf{i}}, \hat{\mathbf{j}}, \hat{\mathbf{k}}$ respectively and let Γ be some smooth curve in space.

(i) We can write

$$\int_\Gamma \mathbf{f}(\mathbf{x}) \cdot d\mathbf{x} = \int_\Gamma (f_1(\mathbf{x})\hat{\mathbf{i}} + f_2(\mathbf{x})\hat{\mathbf{j}} + f_3(\mathbf{x})\hat{\mathbf{k}}) \cdot (dx\hat{\mathbf{i}} + dy\hat{\mathbf{j}} + dz\hat{\mathbf{k}})$$

$$= \int_\Gamma f_1(\mathbf{x})dx + \int_\Gamma f_2(\mathbf{x})dy + \int_\Gamma f_3(\mathbf{x})dz \qquad (11.6)$$

where we have used the orthonormality of the basis. Thus, a line integral over a vector field along a curve Γ is the sum of the line integrals over the components of the field along Γ.

Exercise   Integrate the field

$$\mathbf{f}(\mathbf{x}) = x^2 y^2 \hat{\mathbf{i}} + y\hat{\mathbf{j}} + zy\hat{\mathbf{k}}$$

along the curve $y^2 = 4x$ from $(0, 0)$ to $(4, 4)$.

Solution   Note that the curve is on the xy plane and $z = 0 = dz$ along the curve. We have,

$$\int_\Gamma \mathbf{f}(\mathbf{x}) \cdot d\mathbf{x} = \int_\Gamma (x^2 y^2 \hat{\mathbf{i}} + y\hat{\mathbf{j}}) \cdot (dx\hat{\mathbf{i}} + dy\hat{\mathbf{j}})$$

$$= \int_\Gamma x^2 y^2 dx + \int_\Gamma y\, dy$$

Along the curve, $y^2 = 4x$ so that

$$\int_\Gamma x^2 y^2 dx = \int_0^4 4x^3 dx = 256$$

and

$$\int_0^4 y\, dy = 8.$$

Therefore,

$$\int_{\Gamma} \mathbf{f}(\mathbf{x}) \cdot d\mathbf{x} = 264. \qquad \qquad \square$$

(ii) Now let Γ be a smooth and simple closed curve oriented positively, that is, counterclockwise. Let $\Gamma_1, \Gamma_2, \Gamma_3$ be the projections of Γ on xy, yz and zx planes respectively, all oriented positively. Thus, in Fig. 11.6, Γ is the oriented curve $ABCA$, Γ_1 is oriented as $OABO$, Γ_2 as $OBCO$ and Γ_3 as $OCAO$. We have,

$$\int_{\Gamma_1} \mathbf{f} \cdot d\mathbf{x} + \int_{\Gamma_2} \mathbf{f} \cdot d\mathbf{x} + \int_{\Gamma_3} \mathbf{f} \cdot d\mathbf{x} = \int_{AB,BO,OA} \mathbf{f} \cdot d\mathbf{x} + \int_{BC,CO,OB} \mathbf{f} \cdot d\mathbf{x} + \int_{CA,AO,OC} \mathbf{f} \cdot d\mathbf{x}$$

$$= \int_{AB} \mathbf{f} \cdot d\mathbf{x} + \int_{BC} \mathbf{f} \cdot d\mathbf{x} + \int_{CA} \mathbf{f} \cdot d\mathbf{x}$$

$$= \int_{\Gamma} \mathbf{f} \cdot d\mathbf{x} \qquad \qquad (11.7)$$

because all integrals except those on the arcs of Γ cancel as each of them is traversed twice in opposite directions (see Fig. 11.6). Equation (11.7) is always valid whenever Γ is a simple closed curve.

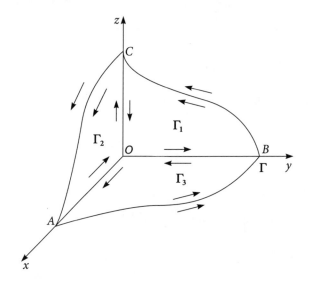

Fig. 11.6   Line integral around a simple closed curve as the sum of the line integrals over its projections on the coordinate planes

These two observations come in handy while evaluating line integrals.

From Eq. (11.2) and the exercises following it, we see that after substituting the parameterization $\mathbf{x}(t)$ in the integrand of a line integral, it becomes a scalar valued function of a scalar variable t, say $f(t)$. Let a point P on the curve of integration correspond to the parameter value t. We can define a function $F(P) = F(t)$, as a scalar valued function of a scalar variable t, by the indefinite integral

$$F(P) = F(t) = \int_{T_0}^{t} f(t)dt = \int_{T_0}^{t} \mathbf{f}(\mathbf{x}(t)) \cdot \dot{\mathbf{x}}(t)dt,$$

This gives,

$$dF(t) = \frac{dF}{dt}dt = \left(f_1(\mathbf{x}(t))\frac{dx}{dt} + f_2(\mathbf{x}(t))\frac{dy}{dt} + f_3(\mathbf{x}(t))\frac{dz}{dt}\right)dt. \tag{11.8}$$

where $f_{1,2,3}(\mathbf{x}(t))$ are the components of $\mathbf{f}(\mathbf{x}(t))$ at the point P corresponding to t on the curve joining P_0 and P_1 along which the line integral is evaluated. Thus, for any two points P and P' on the curve of integration we can write, by elementary integration,

$$\int_{P}^{P'} dF = F(P') - F(P) = F(t') - F(t). \tag{11.9}$$

where t' and t are the parameter values corresponding to P' and P respectively. Here, we assume that $t' > t$ so that the sense of traversal *from P to P'* gives the orientation of the curve of integration.

We emphasize that the differential $dF(t)$ is that of a scalar valued function of a single scalar variable t. Function $F(t)$ depends on the parameterization $\mathbf{x}(t)$ and hence on the curve joining P_0 and P_1 along which the integration is carried out. Therefore, the value of the integral essentially depends on the curve of integration. Equations (11.8), (11.9) are completely general and every line integral can be expressed as in Eq. (11.9).

Taking cue from the above observations we can define what is called a *Linear Differential Form* at *all points in the domain of the field* $\mathbf{f}(\mathbf{x})$ (and not necessarily along some curve) as

$$L = A(\mathbf{x})dx + B(\mathbf{x})dy + C(\mathbf{x})dz = \mathbf{f}(\mathbf{x}) \cdot d\mathbf{x} \tag{11.10}$$

where $A(\mathbf{x}), B(\mathbf{x}), C(\mathbf{x})$ are the scalar valued functions giving components of $\mathbf{f}(\mathbf{x})$ in all of its domain. This is called a Linear Differential Form because of its linear dependence on the differentials dx, dy, dz while their coefficients are functions of $\mathbf{x}$. The advantage of introducing the differential form L is that along a curve parameterized say by t, it naturally reduces to the differential of a scalar valued function. Thus, every line integral along a curve joining two points say P_0 and P has the form

$$F(P) = \int_{P_0}^{P} L = \int_{T_0}^{t} \left(A(\mathbf{x}(t))\frac{dx}{dt} + B(\mathbf{x}(t))\frac{dy}{dt} + C(\mathbf{x}(t))\frac{dz}{dt}\right)dt = F(t) \tag{11.11}$$

We will assume that the functions $A(\mathbf{x}), B(\mathbf{x}), C(\mathbf{x})$ are C^1, that is, they have continuous first derivatives throughout the domain of the field $\mathbf{f}(\mathbf{x})$.

We are interested in finding out the class of fields, the value of whose line integral depends only on the end points irrespective of the curve joining the end points used to evaluate the integral. This happens when the field is conservative, that is, the field is the gradient of a potential $\phi(\mathbf{x})$ so that

$$\mathbf{f}(\mathbf{x}) = \nabla\phi(\mathbf{x})$$

at all points at which $\mathbf{f}(\mathbf{x})$ is defined. Then using Eq. (10.27) we can write

$$\int_C \mathbf{f}(\mathbf{x}) \cdot d\mathbf{x} = \int_{T_1}^{T_2} \nabla\phi(\mathbf{x}(t)) \cdot \dot{\mathbf{x}}(t) dt = \int_{T_1}^{T_2} \frac{d\phi}{dt} dt = \phi(\mathbf{x}(t)) \Big|_{T_1}^{T_2} = \phi(P_1) - \phi(P_0).$$

Thus, if the field is the gradient of a potential, then its line integral depends only on the values of the potential at the end points, independent of the curve joining the end points.

It turns out that the reverse implication is also true. That is, a vector field whose line integral over a smooth arc joining any two points in its domain depends only on its end points then it must be conservative, that is, it must be the gradient of some scalar field $\phi(\mathbf{x})$. A vector field being the gradient of some scalar field is equivalent to its linear form being a perfect differential, that is, there is a scalar valued function $\phi(\mathbf{x})$ satisfying

$$L = \mathbf{f} \cdot d\mathbf{x} = \nabla\phi(\mathbf{x}) \cdot d\mathbf{x} = \frac{\partial\phi(\mathbf{x})}{\partial x} dx + \frac{\partial\phi(\mathbf{x})}{\partial y} dy + \frac{\partial\phi(\mathbf{x})}{\partial z} dz = d\phi. \qquad (11.12)$$

Note that we require this equation to be valid at every point in the domain of $\mathbf{f}$ and not only at the points on some curve in the domain. The RHS of Eq. (11.12) is easily recognized as the differential $d\phi$ of the scalar valued function ϕ. Now assume that the line integral of $\mathbf{f}$ over some smooth oriented arc Γ depends only on the end points of Γ. We want to show that there is a scalar function $\phi(\mathbf{x})$ defined on the domain of $\mathbf{f}$ such that $d\phi = L$ where $L = A(\mathbf{x})dx + B(\mathbf{x})dy + C(\mathbf{x})dz$ is the linear differential form giving the integrand of the line integral. Without losing generality we can assume that any two points in the domain can be connected by a smooth oriented arc. We fix a point P_0 in the domain and define the function $\phi(\mathbf{x}) = \phi(P)$ at any point P as the value of the line integral over any smooth oriented (from P_0 to P) curve joining P_0 and P. To get the partial derivatives of ϕ consider any point $(x, y, z) \equiv P$ and a smooth oriented curve, say Γ, joining P_0 and P. Since the domain is an open set, all points $(x + \Delta x, y, z) = P'$ are in the domain, provided $|\Delta x|$ is sufficiently small. Let γ be the oriented straight line segment joining P and P' (see Fig. 11.7). We can arrange, without losing generality, that the curve $\Gamma + \gamma$ is a simple oriented polygonal arc without any knots and overlaps with initial point P_0 and final point P'. It follows, then, by Eq. (11.5) that

$$\phi(x + \Delta x, y, z) - \phi(x, y, z) = \phi(P') - \phi(P) = \int_{\Gamma+\gamma} L - \int_{\Gamma} L = \int_{\gamma} L$$

$$= \int_x^{x+\Delta x} A(t, y, z) dt = A(x, y, z)\Delta x \qquad (11.13)$$

Dividing by Δx and passing to the limit as $\Delta x \to 0$ we find that

$$\frac{\partial \phi}{\partial x} = A$$

and similarly, $\frac{\partial \phi}{\partial y} = B$ and $\frac{\partial \phi}{\partial z} = C$. This shows that $d\phi = L$ as we wanted.

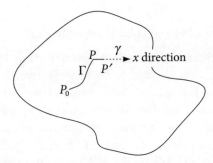

Fig. 11.7　Illustrating Eq. (11.13)

Exercise　Show that a vector field is conservative, if and only if its line integral over every closed loop is zero.　☐

We have proved that the conservative property of a vector field and dependence of its line integral only on the end points of the curve of integration are equivalent. However, this result is not of much practical value unless we find out some independent criteria to determine whether a given vector field is conservative or not. Equivalently, we have to find out whether a given differential form L is a perfect differential or not, that is, whether there is a function $\phi(\mathbf{x})$ satisfying $L = \nabla \phi \cdot d\mathbf{x}$.

The necessary condition for a vector field to be conservative is that its curl vanishes everywhere in its domain. Since the field is given to be conservative, we have,

$$\nabla \times \mathbf{f}(\mathbf{x}) = \nabla \times \nabla \phi(\mathbf{x}) = \mathbf{0} \tag{11.14}$$

for all $\mathbf{x}$ in the domain of $\mathbf{f}(\mathbf{x})$ because we have shown before that the curl of a gradient is always zero (see Eq. (10.90)). It is useful to state this necessary condition in terms of the linear differential form which, for a conservative field, ought to be a perfect differential:

$$L = A(\mathbf{x})dx + B(\mathbf{x})dy + C(\mathbf{x})dz = \nabla \phi(\mathbf{x}) \cdot d\mathbf{x} = \frac{\partial \phi}{\partial x}dx + \frac{\partial \phi}{\partial y}dy + \frac{\partial \phi}{\partial z}dz,$$

which means,

$$A = \frac{\partial \phi}{\partial x}, \quad B = \frac{\partial \phi}{\partial y} \quad C = \frac{\partial \phi}{\partial z}.$$

Suitably differentiating both sides of these equations and assuming that the order of differentiation does not matter, we get the following necessary conditions for a vector field to be conservative.

$$B_z - C_y = \frac{\partial B}{\partial z} - \frac{\partial C}{\partial y} = 0, \ \ C_x - A_z = \frac{\partial C}{\partial x} - \frac{\partial A}{\partial z} = 0, \ \ A_y - B_x = \frac{\partial A}{\partial y} - \frac{\partial B}{\partial x} = 0.$$

(11.15)

Exercise   Show that Eqs (11.14) and (11.15) are equivalent.   □

Now the question is whether the condition given by Eq. (11.14) or equivalently by Eq. (11.15) is sufficient for a vector field to be conservative. That is, given that a vector field satisfies Eq. (11.14) or Eq. (11.15), is it conservative? It turns out that unless the domain of definition of the field (or the corresponding differential form) is simply connected (to be explained below) all the line integrals of the field (or the differential form) are not independent of path (or are not zero over every closed path) in the domain, even if the field satisfies Eq. (11.14) or Eq. (11.15) in its domain. Simple connectivity means that a smooth curve joining any two points in the domain can be continuously deformed within the domain to coincide with any other smooth curve with the same end points. Equivalently, every simple closed curve in a simply connected domain can be continuously shrunk to any one of its interior points always staying within the domain. This is not possible if the domain has 'holes' in it, that is, if the field is not defined in some region within the domain. Thus, domains with holes are not simply connected.

Before finding out in detail what is meant by a connected or a simply connected set of points in space, we give an example to show that the conditions Eq. (11.15) are not by themselves sufficient to ensure the path independence of $\int L$, that is, to ensure that $\int L$ taken over every closed curve is zero. Consider the differential

$$L = \frac{x\,dy - y\,dx}{x^2 + y^2}$$

with the coefficients

$$A = \frac{-y}{x^2 + y^2}, \ \ B = \frac{x}{x^2 + y^2}, \ \ C = 0,$$

which are defined except for points on the z-axis ($x = y = 0$). Thus, the domain of definition of this differential form, or the corresponding field, is all space except z-axis. We show below that this differential form satisfies Eq. (11.15) and is a perfect differential but there exists a class of simple closed curves in its domain such that the integral of this differential form around such a curve does not vanish. In order to see that this is a perfect differential, we introduce the polar angle θ of a point $P(x, y, z)$ by

$$\cos\theta = \frac{x}{\sqrt{x^2 + y^2}}, \ \ \sin\theta = \frac{y}{\sqrt{x^2 + y^2}}$$

that is, the angle formed with the x,z-plane by the plane through P and passing through the z-axis. Then,

$$d\theta = d\, \tan^{-1} \frac{y}{x} = L,$$

so that L is represented as the total differential of the function $u = \theta$. We get

$$\int_C L = \int_0^{2\pi} d\theta = 2\pi \neq 0$$

with C as any closed loop in the x,y-plane surrounding the z-axis oriented positively with respect to θ. Thus, $\int L \neq 0$ over a closed loop in the domain even if L is a perfect differential there. The problem is that the inverse trigonometric functions are not single valued: They determine the values of θ only within the integral multiples of 2π. This fact is connected with the closed curve C of integration via

$$\int_C L = \int_C d\theta = \theta + 2n\pi$$

where n is the number of times the closed curve of integration winds around the z axis: Each winding adds up 2π on the RHS of the above equation (see Fig. 11.8).

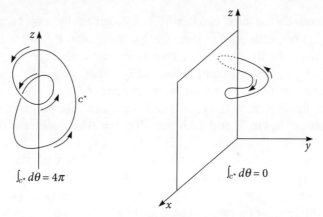

$$\int_{c^*} d\theta = 4\pi \qquad\qquad \int_{c^*} d\theta = 0$$

Fig. 11.8   Each winding of the curve of integration around the z axis adds 2π to its value

Therefore, *the value of $\int_{P_0}^{P} d\theta$ taken for two different paths with end points P_0, P is the same only if going along one path from P_0 to P and returning along the other path to P_0 we go zero times around the z-axis.* We can avoid any path going around the z-axis by avoiding all paths crossing the half plane $y = 0$, $x \leq 0$, that is, we remove this half plane from the region $\mathcal{R}$ over which the field is defined. To every point on the allowed path we can assign a unique value of θ with $-\pi < \theta < \pi$. Therefore, the integral $\int_{P_0}^{P} d\theta$ has a unique value $\theta(P) - \theta(P_0)$, which does not depend on a particular path. Similarly, the integral over a closed path in this region has value zero.

Simply connected sets

An open set $\mathcal{R}$ in space is said to be *connected* if every pair P_0, P_1 of distinct points in it can be connected by a smooth arc wholly within $\mathcal{R}$. Such an arc is parameterized by a triplet of continuously differentiable functions $(x(t), y(t), z(t))$, $0 \leq t \leq 1$; the point $P(t) = (x(t), y(t), z(t))$ lies in $\mathcal{R}$ for all t, coincides with P_0 for $t = 0$ and with P_1 for $t = 1$. Obviously, in a connected set, any two points can also be joined by a path comprising a string of smooth arcs joined at their end points.

Examples of connected sets are the *convex* sets $\mathcal{R}$ any two of whose points P' and P'' can be joined by a line segment in $\mathcal{R}$. The corresponding linear paths joining $P'(x', y', z')$ and $P''(x'', y'', z'')$ are simply the triple of linear functions

$$x(t) = (1-t)x' + tx'' \quad y(t) = (1-t)y' + ty'' \quad z(t) = (1-t)z' + tz''$$

for $0 \leq t \leq 1$.

Examples of convex sets are solid spheres or cubes. Examples of connected but not convex sets are solid torus, a spherical shell (space between two concentric spheres) and the outside of a sphere or cylinder. A set $\mathcal{R}$ which is not connected consists of connected subsets called the components of $\mathcal{R}$. Examples of disconnected sets are the set of points *not* belonging to a spherical shell, or a set of points none of whose coordinates are integers.

Now let $\mathcal{C}_0$ and $\mathcal{C}_1$ be any two paths in $\mathcal{R}$, given by $(x_0(t), y_0(t), z_0(t))$ and $(x_1(t), y_1(t), z_1(t))$ respectively. Let their end points P' and P'', corresponding to $t = 0$ and $t = 1$ respectively, be the same. The connected set $\mathcal{R}$ is *simply connected*, if we can deform $\mathcal{C}_0$ into $\mathcal{C}_1$ by means of a continuous family of paths $\mathcal{C}_\lambda$ with common end points P', P''. This means that there exist continuous functions $(x(t, \lambda), y(t, \lambda), z(t, \lambda))$ of the two variables t, λ for $0 \leq t \leq 1$, $0 \leq \lambda \leq 1$ such that the point $P(t, \lambda) = (x(t, \lambda), y(t, \lambda), z(t, \lambda))$ always lies in $\mathcal{R}$ and such that $P(t, \lambda = 0)$ coincides with $P(t) = (x_0(t), y_0(t), z_0(t))$, $P(t, \lambda = 1)$ coincides with $P(t) = (x_1(t), y_1(t), z_1(t))$, $P(t = 0, \lambda)$ coincides with P' and $P(t = 1, \lambda)$ coincides with P''. For each fixed λ the functions $(x(t, \lambda), y(t, \lambda), z(t, \lambda))$ determine a path $\mathcal{C}_\lambda$ in $\mathcal{R}$ that joins the end points P' and P''. As λ varies from 0 to 1, the path $\mathcal{C}_\lambda$ changes continuously from $\mathcal{C}_0$ to $\mathcal{C}_1$. This defines the "continuous deformation" of $\mathcal{C}_0$ into $\mathcal{C}_1$ (see Fig. 11.9).

As can be easily seen, convex sets are simply connected. The family of curves $\mathcal{C}_\lambda$ continuously deforming $\mathcal{C}_0$ to $\mathcal{C}_1$, all curves with common end points P', P'', is given by

$$x(t, \lambda) = (1 - \lambda)x_0(t) + \lambda x_1(t),$$

$$y(t, \lambda) = (1 - \lambda)y_0(t) + \lambda y_1(t),$$

$$z(t, \lambda) = (1 - \lambda)z_0(t) + \lambda z_1(t).$$

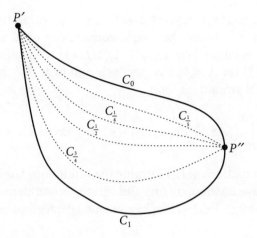

Fig. 11.9   Illustration of a simply connected domain

Thus, C_λ is obtained by joining the points of C_0 and C_1 that belong to the same t by a line segment and taking the point that divides the segment in the ratio $\frac{\lambda}{1-\lambda}$. The points obtained in this way all lie in $\mathcal{R}$ because of its convexity. A different type of simply connected set is given by a spherical shell. A region $\mathcal{R}$ in space obtained after removing the z-axis is not simply connected because the two semicircular paths

$$x = \cos \pi t, \; y = \sin \pi t, \; z = 0; \;\; 0 \le t \le 1$$

and

$$x = \cos \pi t, \; y = -\sin \pi t, \; z = 0; \;\; 0 \le t \le 1$$

have the same end points but cannot be deformed into each other without crossing the z-axis.

We shall now prove the following theorem:

If the coefficients of the differential form corresponding to the field $\mathbf{f}$ given by

$$L = \mathbf{f}(\mathbf{x}) \cdot d\mathbf{x} = A(\mathbf{x})dx + B(\mathbf{x})dy + C(\mathbf{x})dz$$

have continuous first derivatives in a simply connected domain $\mathcal{R}$ and satisfy conditions Eq. (11.15), namely,

$$B_z - C_y = 0, \; C_x - A_z = 0, \; A_y - B_x = 0,$$

then L is the total (perfect) differential of a function ϕ in $\mathcal{R}$:

$$A = \phi_x, \; B = \phi_y \; C = \phi_z.$$

It is enough to prove that $\int_{P'}^{P''} L$ over any simple polygonal arc joining P' and P'' has a value that depends only on P' and P''. We represent two oriented arcs C_0 and C_1 parametrically by $(x_0(t), y_0(t), z_0(t))$ and $(x_1(t), y_1(t), z_1(t))$, $0 \leq t \leq 1$ respectively with $t = 0$ yielding P' and $t = 1$ yielding P''. Using the simple connectivity of $\mathcal{R}$ we can imbed paths $\mathcal{C}_0$ and $\mathcal{C}_1$ into a continuous family $(x(t, \lambda), y(t, \lambda), z(t, \lambda))$ reducing to $(x_0(t), y_0(t), z_0(t))$ and $(x_1(t), y_1(t), z_1(t))$ for $\lambda = 0, 1$ respectively and to P', P'' for $t = 0, 1$ respectively. We have, for the integral around the loop,

$$\int_{\mathcal{C}_1} L - \int_{\mathcal{C}_0} L = \int_0^1 [(Ax_t + By_t + Cz_t)\big|_{\lambda=1} - (Ax_t + By_t + Cz_t)\big|_{\lambda=0}]dt,$$

where (x, y, z) are the functions of t, λ forming the continuous family of paths. We assume that these functions have continuous first and mixed second derivatives with respect to t and λ for $0 \leq t \leq 1$ and $0 \leq \lambda \leq 1$. Then by elementary integration,

$$\int_{\mathcal{C}_1} L - \int_{\mathcal{C}_0} L = \int_0^1 dt \int_0^1 (Ax_t + By_t + Cz_t)_\lambda d\lambda.$$

Now, using the chain rule and the conditions Eq. (11.15) we get the identity

$$(Ax_t + By_t + Cz_t)_\lambda = Ax_{\lambda t} + By_{\lambda t} + Cz_{\lambda t} + A_x x_\lambda x_t + A_y y_\lambda x_t + A_z z_\lambda x_t$$

$$+ B_x x_\lambda y_t + B_y y_\lambda y_t + B_z z_\lambda y_t + C_x x_\lambda z_t + C_y y_\lambda z_t + C_z z_\lambda z_t$$

$$= (Ax_\lambda + By_\lambda + Cz_\lambda)_t \tag{11.16}$$

Interchanging orders of integration we find

$$\int_{\mathcal{C}_1} L - \int_{\mathcal{C}_0} L = \int_0^1 d\lambda \int_0^1 (Ax_\lambda + By_\lambda + Cz_\lambda)_t dt = 0,$$

since $x_\lambda, y_\lambda, z_\lambda$ vanish for $t = 0, 1$ because the end points are independent of λ. This completes the proof.

We see the important part played by the assumption that the region $\mathcal{R}$ is simply connected: It enables us to convert the difference of the line integrals into a double integral over some intermediate region. The above proof can be extended to the case where the intermediate paths are continuous but may not be differentiable with respect to λ and also to the case where $\mathcal{C}_0$ and $\mathcal{C}_1$ are only sectionally smooth, that is, polygonal arcs.

Exercise   Find out whether the field $\mathbf{f}(\mathbf{x}) = e^{xy}\hat{\mathbf{i}} + e^{x+y}\hat{\mathbf{j}}$ is conservative.

Solution   The coefficients in the linear form are $A(x, y) = e^{xy}$ and $B(x, y) = e^{x+y}$ and conditions Eq. (11.15) reduce to $\frac{\partial A}{\partial y} = \frac{\partial B}{\partial x}$. Evaluating both sides we see that they are not equal. Hence, the field is not conservative. $\square$

Exercise   Find whether the following fields are conservative.

(i) $\mathbf{f}(\mathbf{x}) = \cos y \hat{\mathbf{i}} - x \sin y \hat{\mathbf{j}} - \cos z \hat{\mathbf{k}}$.

(ii) $\mathbf{f}(\mathbf{x}) = xy\hat{\mathbf{i}} + (x^2 + y^2)\hat{\mathbf{j}}$.

(iii) $\mathbf{f}(\mathbf{x}) = (x^2 - y^2)\hat{\mathbf{i}} + xy\hat{\mathbf{j}}$.

Hint   Directly evaluate $\nabla \times \mathbf{f}$.   ☐

Exercise   Let the field be $\mathbf{f}(\mathbf{x}) = 2xy\hat{\mathbf{i}} + (x^2 + 3y^2)\hat{\mathbf{j}}$. Find whether the field is conservative and if it is, find the potential function.

Solution   Evaluating A_y and B_x we find that they are equal, so the potential function say $\phi(x,y)$ may exist. To find it, we first evaluate the integral $\int A(x,y) \, dx = \int \frac{\partial \phi}{\partial x} dx = \int 2xy \, dx$ keeping y constant to get $x^2 y$ for the indefinite integral. We must now find a function $u(y)$ such that

$$\frac{\partial}{\partial y}(x^2 y + u(y)) = x^2 + 3y^2.$$

Differentiating and simplifying, this equation leads to

$$\frac{du}{dy} = 3y^2.$$

Integrating, we find $u(y) = y^3$. This gives, for the potential function,

$$\phi(x,y) = x^2 y + y^3.$$ ☐

Exercise   Show that $\mathbf{f}(\mathbf{x}) = (\sin y + z)\hat{\mathbf{i}} - (x\cos y - z)\hat{\mathbf{j}} - (x - y)\hat{\mathbf{k}}$ is conservative and find the function ϕ such that $\mathbf{f}(\mathbf{x}) = \nabla\phi$.

Solution   We check that $\nabla \times \mathbf{f} = \mathbf{0}$ so that this field is conservative.
   To find a potential ϕ we equate the components of $\mathbf{f} = \nabla\phi$. We get

(i) $f_x = \frac{\partial \phi}{\partial x} = \sin y + z$,

(ii) $f_y = \frac{\partial \phi}{\partial y} = x\cos y - z$,

(iii) $f_z = \frac{\partial \phi}{\partial z} = x - y$.

   Integrating f_x, f_y, f_z with respect to x, y, z respectively, we obtain

(iv) $\phi = x\sin y + xz + f(y,z)$,

(v) $\phi = x\sin y - yz + g(x,z)$,

(vi) $\phi = xz - yz + h(x,y)$.

Since the derivatives are partial derivatives, the "constants" of integration are functions of variables which are not integrated over. Note that (iv),(v),(vi) each represent ϕ. Therefore, $f(y,z)$ must occur in (v). The only possibility is to identify $f(y,z)$ with $-yz$ plus some function of z but not involving x. By (vi) we see that $f(y,z)$ must simply be $-yz + C$ where C is a constant. Thus,

$$\phi = x\sin y + xz - yz + C. \qquad\qquad \square$$

Exercise   Let $\mathbf{f}(\mathbf{x}) = x^2\hat{\mathbf{i}} + xy\hat{\mathbf{j}}$. and let the path C consist of the segment of the parabola $y = x^2$ between $(0,0)$ and $(1,1)$ (C_1) and the line segment from $(1,1)$ to $(0,0)$ (C_2) (see Fig. 11.10). Find $\int_C \mathbf{f}(\mathbf{x}) \cdot d\mathbf{x}$.

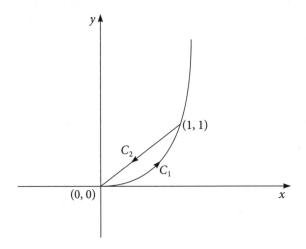

Fig. 11.10   The closed loop for integration

Hint   Parameterize C_1 by $\mathbf{x}(t) = t\hat{\mathbf{i}} + t^2\hat{\mathbf{j}}$ and C_2 by $\mathbf{x}(t) = (1-t)\hat{\mathbf{i}} + (1-t)\hat{\mathbf{j}}$. Evaluate the integral separately on C_1 and C_2 and add.

Answer $\displaystyle\int_C \mathbf{f}(\mathbf{x}) \cdot d\mathbf{x} = \frac{1}{15}$. Thus, the field is not conservative. $\square$

Exercise   Find the potential function for the centrifugal force field $\mathbf{f}(\mathbf{r}) = m(\boldsymbol{\omega} \times \mathbf{r}) \times \boldsymbol{\omega}$ where $\boldsymbol{\omega}$ is the rotational velocity of a frame rotating with respect to an inertial frame.

Solution   The required potential is $\frac{1}{2}m(\boldsymbol{\omega} \times \mathbf{r}) \cdot (\boldsymbol{\omega} \times \mathbf{r}) = \frac{1}{2}m|\boldsymbol{\omega} \times \mathbf{r}|^2$ which can be seen as follows. Using identity II we get,

$$\frac{1}{2}m\nabla((\boldsymbol{\omega} \times \mathbf{r}) \cdot (\boldsymbol{\omega} \times \mathbf{r})) = \frac{1}{2}m\nabla(\omega^2 r^2 - (\boldsymbol{\omega} \cdot \mathbf{r})^2) = m(\omega^2 \mathbf{r} - (\boldsymbol{\omega} \cdot \mathbf{r})\boldsymbol{\omega})$$

which, using identity I reduces to

$$\frac{1}{2}m\nabla((\omega \times \mathbf{r}) \cdot (\omega \times \mathbf{r})) = m\omega \times (\mathbf{r} \times \omega) = m(\omega \times \mathbf{r}) \times \omega. \qquad \square$$

In general, a vector field is produced by given sources and the relation between the fields and their sources is formulated in terms of a system of differential equations in which the sources are given and the fields are the solutions of these differential equations. The most celebrated examples are the Maxwell's equations giving electric and magnetic fields produced by the given distributions of charges and currents and the Navier–Stokes equations giving velocity field of an imperfect fluid for given distribution of pressure, viscosity, shear, external forces etc. For the conservative fields these differential equations can be transformed into equations for the potential, which are easier to handle, as they deal with scalar fields. For example, the equation for the electrostatic field $\nabla \cdot \mathbf{E} = \rho/\epsilon_0$ gets transformed to Poisson's equation $\nabla^2 \phi = -\rho/\epsilon_0$ where ϕ is the electrostatic potential satisfying $\mathbf{E} = -\nabla\phi$.

11.1.1   Curl of a vector field and the line integral

We express the curl of a vector field $\mathbf{f}(\mathbf{x})$ in terms of its line integral over a simple closed curve Γ in a plane with unit normal $\hat{\mathbf{n}}$. Let S be the (planar) area enclosed by Γ and P be a point interior to or on Γ. We define a number G_n by

$$G_n = \lim_{\Gamma \to P} \frac{1}{S} \int_\Gamma \mathbf{f}(\mathbf{x}) \cdot d\mathbf{x}$$

where the integration is taken in the positive (counterclockwise) sense. Note that, in general, this integral depends on the direction $\hat{\mathbf{n}}$ because if we change $\hat{\mathbf{n}}$ (by rotating the plane say) the integrand and hence the integral will change. The limit $\Gamma \to P$ requires that every point of Γ approaches P. If this limit exists, then G_n is independent of Γ. As we show below, if Γ is a planar curve and $\mathbf{f}(\mathbf{x})$ has Taylor series expansion around P, then the limit exists and is independent of Γ.

We choose the origin at P and let a point on Γ have position vector $\mathbf{x}$ relative to the origin at P. We expand $\mathbf{f}(\mathbf{x})$ around P that is, around $\mathbf{0}$. We get

$$\mathbf{f}(\mathbf{x}) = \mathbf{f}(0) + \mathbf{x} \cdot \nabla \mathbf{f}(0) + \mathbf{R}, \qquad (11.17)$$

where $\mathbf{R}$ is the remainder containing all the second and higher order terms $(\mathbf{x} \cdot \nabla)^2 \cdots$ (see Eq. (10.22)). We set up a rectangular Cartesian coordinate system (ξ, η, ζ) with its origin at P such that (ξ, η) plane contains Γ (see Fig. 11.11). The vector $\mathbf{x}$ has the components (ξ, η, ζ) and let the components of $\mathbf{f}(\mathbf{x})$ be $f_\xi(\mathbf{x}), f_\eta(\mathbf{x}), f_\zeta(\mathbf{x})$. This gives

$$\mathbf{x} \cdot \nabla f_\xi(\mathbf{x}) = \xi \frac{\partial f_\xi}{\partial \xi} + \eta \frac{\partial f_\xi}{\partial \eta} + \zeta \frac{\partial f_\xi}{\partial \zeta}$$

and similarly for $\mathbf{x} \cdot \nabla f_\eta(\mathbf{x})$ and $\mathbf{x} \cdot \nabla f_\zeta(\mathbf{x})$. Then,

$$\mathbf{x} \cdot \nabla \mathbf{f} = \begin{bmatrix} \mathbf{x} \cdot \nabla f_\xi(\mathbf{x}) \\ \mathbf{x} \cdot \nabla f_\eta(\mathbf{x}) \\ \mathbf{x} \cdot \nabla f_\zeta(\mathbf{x}) \end{bmatrix} = \begin{bmatrix} \xi \frac{\partial f_\xi}{\partial \xi} + \eta \frac{\partial f_\xi}{\partial \eta} + \zeta \frac{\partial f_\xi}{\partial \zeta} \\ \xi \frac{\partial f_\eta}{\partial \xi} + \eta \frac{\partial f_\eta}{\partial \eta} + \zeta \frac{\partial f_\eta}{\partial \zeta} \\ \xi \frac{\partial f_\zeta}{\partial \xi} + \eta \frac{\partial f_\zeta}{\partial \eta} + \zeta \frac{\partial f_\zeta}{\partial \zeta} \end{bmatrix}$$

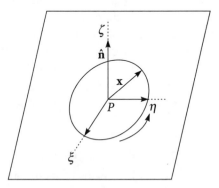

Fig. 11.11   The geometry of Eq. (11.17)

where all the partial derivatives are evaluated at the origin. Along Γ, $d\mathbf{x} \equiv (d\xi, d\eta, 0)$ so that

$$(\mathbf{x} \cdot \nabla \mathbf{f}) \cdot d\mathbf{x} = \left(\xi \frac{\partial f_\xi}{\partial \xi} + \eta \frac{\partial f_\xi}{\partial \eta} \right) d\xi + \left(\xi \frac{\partial f_\eta}{\partial \xi} + \eta \frac{\partial f_\eta}{\partial \eta} \right) d\eta.$$

Therefore, dotting Eq. (11.17) with $d\mathbf{x}$ we get

$$\mathbf{f}(\mathbf{x}) \cdot d\mathbf{x} = \mathbf{f}(\mathbf{0}) \cdot d\mathbf{x} + \left(\xi \frac{\partial f_\xi}{\partial \xi} + \eta \frac{\partial f_\xi}{\partial \eta} \right) d\xi + \left(\xi \frac{\partial f_\eta}{\partial \xi} + \eta \frac{\partial f_\eta}{\partial \eta} \right) d\eta + \mathbf{R} \cdot d\mathbf{x}.$$

Integrating along Γ we get

$$\int_\Gamma \mathbf{f}(\mathbf{x}) \cdot d\mathbf{x} = \mathbf{f}(\mathbf{0}) \cdot \int_\Gamma d\mathbf{x} + \frac{\partial f_\xi}{\partial \xi} \int_\Gamma \xi d\xi + \frac{\partial f_\xi}{\partial \eta} \int_\Gamma \eta d\xi$$

$$+ \frac{\partial f_\eta}{\partial \xi} \int_\Gamma \xi d\eta + \frac{\partial f_\eta}{\partial \eta} \int_\Gamma \eta d\eta + \int_\Gamma \mathbf{R} \cdot d\mathbf{x}. \tag{11.18}$$

Exercise   Show that

$$\int_\Gamma d\mathbf{x} = \mathbf{0}$$

$$\int_\Gamma \xi \, d\xi = 0 = -\int_\Gamma \eta \, d\xi$$

and

$$\int_\Gamma \xi \, d\eta = -\int_\Gamma \eta \, d\xi = S$$

where S is the area enclosed by Γ. □

Thus, Eq. (11.18) reduces to (Fig. 11.11)

$$\frac{1}{S}\int_\Gamma \mathbf{f}(\mathbf{x}) \cdot d\mathbf{x} = \left(\frac{\partial f_\eta}{\partial \xi} - \frac{\partial f_\xi}{\partial \eta}\right) + \frac{1}{S}\int_\Gamma \mathbf{R} \cdot d\mathbf{x}. \tag{11.19}$$

In the last term the integral is of the order of $|\mathbf{x}|^3$ as $\mathbf{R}$ is of the order of $|\mathbf{x}|^2$. Therefore, the last term is of the order of $|\mathbf{x}|$ and vanishes in the limit $\Gamma \to P$ or $|\mathbf{x}| \to 0$. Therefore,

$$G_n = \lim_{\Gamma \to P} \frac{1}{S}\int_\Gamma \mathbf{f}(\mathbf{x}) \cdot d\mathbf{x} = \frac{\partial f_\eta}{\partial \xi} - \frac{\partial f_\xi}{\partial \eta}$$

This limit depends only on the derivatives of $\mathbf{f}$ evaluated at P and is independent of Γ.

Now let Γ be a planar curve in a plane defined by the normal direction $\hat{\mathbf{n}}$ and let $\Gamma_1, \Gamma_2, \Gamma_3$ be the projections of Γ on the xy, yz, zx planes of the coordinate system corresponding to an orthonormal basis $(\hat{\mathbf{i}}, \hat{\mathbf{j}}, \hat{\mathbf{k}})$. We know that (see Eq. (11.11)),

$$\int_\Gamma \mathbf{f} \cdot d\mathbf{x} = \int_{\Gamma_1} \mathbf{f} \cdot d\mathbf{x} + \int_{\Gamma_2} \mathbf{f} \cdot d\mathbf{x} + \int_{\Gamma_3} \mathbf{f} \cdot d\mathbf{x}.$$

The areas of projections are given by

$$S_1 = S\hat{\mathbf{i}} \cdot \hat{\mathbf{n}} \quad S_2 = S\hat{\mathbf{j}} \cdot \hat{\mathbf{n}} \quad S_3 = S\hat{\mathbf{k}} \cdot \hat{\mathbf{n}}$$

where $\hat{\mathbf{i}} \cdot \hat{\mathbf{n}}$ etc are the direction cosines of $\hat{\mathbf{n}}$. Hence,

$$\frac{1}{S}\int_\Gamma \mathbf{f}(\mathbf{x}) \cdot d\mathbf{x} = \frac{\hat{\mathbf{i}} \cdot \hat{\mathbf{n}}}{S_1}\int_{\Gamma_1} \mathbf{f}(\mathbf{x}) \cdot d\mathbf{x} + \frac{\hat{\mathbf{j}} \cdot \hat{\mathbf{n}}}{S_2}\int_{\Gamma_2} \mathbf{f}(\mathbf{x}) \cdot d\mathbf{x} + \frac{\hat{\mathbf{k}} \cdot \hat{\mathbf{n}}}{S_3}\int_{\Gamma_3} \mathbf{f}(\mathbf{x}) \cdot d\mathbf{x}.$$

In the limit as $\Gamma \to P$ we get,

$$G_n = \mathbf{G}' \cdot \hat{\mathbf{n}}$$

where

$$\mathbf{G}' = G_1'\hat{\mathbf{i}} + G_2'\hat{\mathbf{j}} + G_3'\hat{\mathbf{k}}$$

and

$$G_i' = \lim_{\Gamma_i \to P} \frac{1}{S_i} \int_{\Gamma_i} \mathbf{f}(\mathbf{x}) \cdot d\mathbf{x} \quad i = 1, 2, 3.$$

For the components of $\mathbf{G}'$ we get

$$G_1' = \lim_{\Gamma_1 \to P} \frac{1}{S_1} \int_{\Gamma_1} \mathbf{f}(\mathbf{x}) \cdot d\mathbf{x} = \frac{\partial f_z}{\partial y} - \frac{\partial f_y}{\partial z}$$

$$G_2' = \lim_{\Gamma_2 \to P} \frac{1}{S_2} \int_{\Gamma_2} \mathbf{f}(\mathbf{x}) \cdot d\mathbf{x} = \frac{\partial f_x}{\partial z} - \frac{\partial f_z}{\partial x}$$

$$G_3' = \lim_{\Gamma_3 \to P} \frac{1}{S_3} \int_{\Gamma_3} \mathbf{f}(\mathbf{x}) \cdot d\mathbf{x} = \frac{\partial f_y}{\partial x} - \frac{\partial f_x}{\partial y}.$$

We immediately identify $\mathbf{G}'$ with curl $\mathbf{f}$ or $\nabla \times \mathbf{f}$. Thus, the curl of a vector field that can be Taylor expanded around a point P can be approximated by its line integral around a simple closed curve Γ surrounding the point P. The approximation gets better as the size of Γ gets smaller but the quantitative estimate of the error will involve the field.

11.2   Applications of the Potential Functions

In this section we deal with the potential functions appearing in real life situations.[1]

We obtain the gravitational field and the gravitational potential of a continuous body of an arbitrary shape at a given point in space. From this, we obtain the internal and external gravitational potential of a spherically symmetric body. We get the multipole expansion of the potential and the field of a body with arbitrary shape upto the first term corresponding to the deviation from sphericity. We do the same, upto third order term for an axially symmetric body.

Gravitational field due to a single particle of mass m_1 at $\mathbf{x}_1 = \mathbf{x}_1(t)$ at a point $\mathbf{x}$ in space is given by

$$\mathbf{g}_1(\mathbf{x}, t) = -Gm_1 \frac{\mathbf{x} - \mathbf{x}_1(t)}{|\mathbf{x} - \mathbf{x}_1(t)|^3}. \tag{11.20}$$

The particle at $\mathbf{x}_1 = \mathbf{x}_1(t)$ is called the source of the field and the mass m_1 is the source strength. The field $\mathbf{g}_1$ is a map (actually a one parameter family) assigning a definite vector $\mathbf{g}_1(\mathbf{x}, t)$ to every point $\mathbf{x}$ in space, at a given instant of time. Note that the time dependence is solely due to the motion of the source.

---

[1] Both these applications are treated in [10] using geometric algebra.

If a particle of mass m is placed at a point $\mathbf{x}$ in the gravitational field $\mathbf{g}_1$, we say that the field exerts a force

$$\mathbf{f}_1 = \mathbf{f}(\mathbf{x}, t) = m\mathbf{g}_1(\mathbf{x}, t). \tag{11.21}$$

Equation (11.21) is mathematically same as Newton's force law. However, if we impart physical reality to the field concept, it would mean that particles interact with each other via their force fields rather than acting directly by exerting forces on one another in accordance with Newton's law. The gravitational field is regarded as a real physical entity pervading all space surrounding its source and acting on any matter that is present. The field concept also has a formal mathematical advantage. It enables us to separate gravitational interactions into two parts, namely (a) production of gravitational fields by extended sources and (b) the effect of a given gravitational field on given bodies. We are concerned here with the production of fields.

The single paticle gravitational field, Eq. (11.20), can be derived from the gravitational potential

$$\phi_1(\mathbf{x}, t) = \frac{-Gm_1}{|\mathbf{x} - \mathbf{x}_1(t)|}, \tag{11.22}$$

by differentiation, giving

$$\mathbf{g}_1(\mathbf{x}, t) = -\nabla_\mathbf{x}\phi_1(\mathbf{x}, t), \tag{11.23}$$

where $\nabla_\mathbf{x}$ is the derivative (gradient) with respect to the field variable $\mathbf{x}$. Henceforth, we leave suffix $\mathbf{x}$ to be understood. The gravitational potential energy of a particle with mass m at $\mathbf{x}$ is given by

$$V_1(\mathbf{x}, t) = m\phi_1(\mathbf{x}, t) = \frac{-Gmm_1}{|\mathbf{x} - \mathbf{x}_1(t)|}. \tag{11.24}$$

It is important to clearly distinguish between potential and potential energy. Latter is the shared energy of two interacting objects, while former is characteristic of a single object namely its source.

The gravitational field $\mathbf{g}(\mathbf{x}, t)$ of a N particle system is given by the superposition of fields

$$\mathbf{g}(\mathbf{x}, t) = \sum_{k=1}^{N} \mathbf{g}_k(\mathbf{x}, t) = -G\sum_{k=1}^{N} m_k\frac{\mathbf{x} - \mathbf{x}_k(t)}{|\mathbf{x} - \mathbf{x}_k(t)|^3}. \tag{11.25}$$

A particle of mass m at $\mathbf{x}$ experiences a force

$$\mathbf{f} = m\mathbf{g} = \sum_k m\mathbf{g}_k = \sum_k \mathbf{f}_k \tag{11.26}$$

due to field in Eq. (11.25) which is consistent with the law of superposition of forces. This field can be derived from a potential; thus

$$\mathbf{g}(\mathbf{x}, t) = -\nabla \phi(\mathbf{x}, t) \tag{11.27}$$

where

$$\phi(\mathbf{x}, t) = \sum_k \phi_k(\mathbf{x}, t) = -G \sum_k \frac{m_k}{|\mathbf{x} - \mathbf{x}_k(t)|}. \tag{11.28}$$

The potential energy of a particle in a field is given by

$$V(\mathbf{x}, t) = m\phi(\mathbf{x}, t). \tag{11.29}$$

Note that this does not include the potential energy of interaction between the particles producing the field. The internal energy can be ignored as long as we are concerned only with the influence of the system on external objects.

The gravitational field of a continuous body is obtained from that of a system of N particles via the following limiting process. We divide the body into small parts which can be regarded as particulate and in the limit of infinitely small subdivision the sum in Eq. (11.25) becomes the integral,

$$\mathbf{g}(\mathbf{x}, t) = -G \int dm' \frac{\mathbf{x} - \mathbf{x}'(t)}{|\mathbf{x} - \mathbf{x}'(t)|^3} \tag{11.30}$$

where $dm' = dm(\mathbf{x}', t)$ is the mass given by the differential of the mass distribution $m(\mathbf{x}', t)$, supposed to be known. In other words, this is the mass of a small enough corpuscle at point $\mathbf{x}'$ at time t. Similar limiting process for Eq. (11.28) gives us the gravitational potential of a continuous body

$$\phi(\mathbf{x}, t) = -G \int \frac{dm'}{|\mathbf{x} - \mathbf{x}'(t)|}. \tag{11.31}$$

Henceforth we shall not write the time dependence explicitly.

Equation (11.27) applies with $\phi(\mathbf{x}, t)$ given by Eq. (11.31) so that we find the field $\mathbf{g}$ by differentiating Eq. (11.31).

For a spherically symmetric mass distribution, the integral in Eq. (11.31) can be easily evaluated. We place the origin at body's centre of mass and denote the position vectors with respect to the centre of mass by $\mathbf{r}$ and $\mathbf{r}'$ instead of $\mathbf{x}$ and $\mathbf{x}'$ which we use in the case of an external inertial frame (see Fig. 11.12).

A spherically symmetric mass density is a function of radial distance alone. Thus,

$$dm' = \rho(r')r'^2 dr' d\Omega \tag{11.32}$$

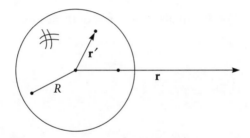

Fig. 11.12   A spherically symmetric mass distribution

where $d\Omega = \sin\theta\, d\theta\, d\phi$ is the element of solid angle. Thus,

$$\phi(\mathbf{r}) = -G \int \frac{dm'}{|\mathbf{r}-\mathbf{r}'|} = -G \int \rho(r')r'^2 dr' \int \frac{d\Omega}{|\mathbf{r}-\mathbf{r}'|}.$$

For $r > r'$, (field point external to the body), we can easily evaluate the integral

$$\int \frac{d\Omega}{|\mathbf{r}-\mathbf{r}'|} = 2\pi \int_0^\pi \frac{\sin\theta\, d\theta}{[r^2 + r'^2 - 2rr'\cos\theta]^{\frac{1}{2}}} = \frac{4\pi}{r} \tag{11.33}$$

and the remaining integral simply gives the total mass of the body

$$M = \int dm' = 4\pi \int_0^R \rho(r')r'^2 dr'.$$

Therefore, the external gravitational potential of a spherically symmetric body is given by

$$\phi(\mathbf{r}) = -G \int \frac{dm'}{|\mathbf{r}-\mathbf{r}'|} = -\frac{GM}{r}. \tag{11.34}$$

This is just the potential of a point particle with mass M (= mass of the body) placed at the centre of mass of the spherically symmetric body. Obviously, the gravitational field of a spherically symmetric body $(\mathbf{g} = -\nabla\phi)$ is also the same as the particle with mass M placed at its centre. Since many celestial bodies are nearly spherically symmetric, this is an excellent first approximation to their gravitational fields. Indeed, in many cases it is sufficient to apply Eq. (11.34).

To get a more accurate description of gravitational fields produced by non-spherical bodies, we employ perturbation methods which enable us to systematically evaluate the effects of deviations from spherical symmetry. The basic idea is to expand the potential of a given body in Taylor series about its centre of mass. Obviously, we need a series expansion for the scalar valued function $\frac{1}{|\mathbf{r}-\mathbf{r}'|}$. For $r > r'$ we have the following well known result, which we derive at the end.

$$\frac{1}{|\mathbf{r}-\mathbf{r}'|} = \frac{1}{r}\left\{1 + \sum_{n=1}^\infty \left(\frac{r'}{r}\right)^n P_n(\hat{\mathbf{r}}\cdot\hat{\mathbf{r}}')\right\}, \tag{11.35}$$

where P_n are the Legender polynomials. A first few of these are

$$P_1(\hat{\mathbf{r}} \cdot \hat{\mathbf{r}}') = \hat{\mathbf{r}} \cdot \hat{\mathbf{r}}'$$

$$P_2(\hat{\mathbf{r}} \cdot \hat{\mathbf{r}}') = \frac{1}{2}(3(\hat{\mathbf{r}} \cdot \hat{\mathbf{r}}')^2 - 1)$$

$$P_3(\hat{\mathbf{r}} \cdot \hat{\mathbf{r}}') = \frac{1}{2}(5(\hat{\mathbf{r}} \cdot \hat{\mathbf{r}}')^3 - 3(\hat{\mathbf{r}} \cdot \hat{\mathbf{r}}')). \tag{11.36}$$

A variant of Eq. (11.35) is

$$\frac{1}{|\mathbf{r} - \mathbf{r}'|} = \frac{1}{r}\left\{1 + \sum_{n=1}^{\infty} r^{-2n} P_n(\mathbf{r} \cdot \mathbf{r}')\right\}, \tag{11.37}$$

where a first few $P_n(\mathbf{r} \cdot \mathbf{r}')$ are

$$P_1(\mathbf{r} \cdot \mathbf{r}') = \mathbf{r} \cdot \mathbf{r}'$$

$$P_2(\mathbf{r} \cdot \mathbf{r}') = \frac{1}{2}(3(\mathbf{r} \cdot \mathbf{r}')^2 - r^2 r'^2)$$

$$P_3(\mathbf{r} \cdot \mathbf{r}') = \frac{1}{2}(5(\mathbf{r} \cdot \mathbf{r}')^3 - 3r^2 r'^2 \mathbf{r} \cdot \mathbf{r}'). \tag{11.38}$$

It is clear from Eq. (11.35) that the magnitude of the nth term in the expansion is of the order of $(\frac{r'}{r})^n$ so the series converges rapidly at a distance r which is large compared to the dimensions of the body. Series (11.37) gives a series for the potential

$$\phi(\mathbf{r}) = -\frac{G}{r}\left\{M + \frac{1}{r^2}\int P_1(\mathbf{r} \cdot \mathbf{r}')dm' + \frac{1}{r^4}\int P_2(\mathbf{r} \cdot \mathbf{r}')dm' + \cdots\right\}$$

By Eq. (11.38)

$$\int P_1(\mathbf{r} \cdot \mathbf{r}')dm' = \mathbf{r} \cdot \left[\int \mathbf{r}'dm'\right] = \mathbf{r} \cdot [\mathbf{0}] = 0.$$

Here, $\int \mathbf{r}'dm'$ gives the position vector of the centre of mass which vanishes because the centre of mass is at the origin.

It is convenient to express the next term in the expansion (involving $P_2(\mathbf{r} \cdot \mathbf{r}')$) in terms of the inertia operator $\mathscr{I} : \mathbb{R}^3 \longmapsto \mathbb{R}^3$ or the moment of inertia tensor of the body, defined by, (Remember that $\mathscr{I}\mathbf{r} \in \mathbb{R}^3$ is a vector),

$$\mathscr{I}\mathbf{r} = \int dm'\mathbf{r}' \times (\mathbf{r} \times \mathbf{r}') = \int dm'(r'^2\mathbf{r} - (\mathbf{r}' \cdot \mathbf{r})\mathbf{r}'). \tag{11.39}$$

The trace of the inertia tensor is given by

$$Tr \, \mathscr{I} = 2 \int dm' \, r'^2 = I_1 + I_2 + I_3, \tag{11.40}$$

where I_1, I_2, I_3 are the principal moments of inertia.

Exercise Prove Eq. (11.40).

Solution We set up the matrix representing the inertia operator in an orthonormal basis $\{\sigma_1, s_2, s_3\}$ with elements $I_{ij} = \hat{\sigma}_i \cdot \mathscr{I} \hat{\sigma}_j$. Then, its trace is given by the sum of its diagonal elements. From Eq. (11.39) we get, suppressing primes,

$$\sum_{i=1}^{3} \hat{\sigma}_i \cdot \mathscr{I} \hat{\sigma}_i = \int dm \sum_{i=1}^{3} (r^2 - r_i^2) = 2 \int dm r^2 = I_1 + I_2 + I_3,$$

where I_1, I_2, I_3 are the principal moments of inertia which are the eigenvalues of the inertia operator. The last equality follows because the trace is seen to be independent of the basis used to compute it. $\square$

Therefore,

$$\int P_2(\mathbf{r} \cdot \mathbf{r}') dm' = \int dm' \frac{1}{2} (3(\mathbf{r} \cdot \mathbf{r}')^2 - r^2 r'^2) = \frac{1}{2} [r^2 Tr \, \mathscr{I} - 3\mathbf{r} \cdot \mathscr{I} \mathbf{r}] = \frac{1}{2} \mathbf{r} \cdot \mathcal{Q} \mathbf{r}, \tag{11.41}$$

which defines a symmetric tensor

$$\mathcal{Q} \mathbf{r} = \mathbf{r} Tr \, \mathscr{I} - 3 \mathscr{I} \mathbf{r}. \tag{11.42}$$

Exercise Show that the tensor $\mathcal{Q}$ is symmetric.

Solution We first show that the MI operator $\mathscr{I}$ is symmetric. We have, suppressing primes,

$$\mathscr{I}_{ij} = \sigma_i \cdot \mathscr{I} \sigma_j = \int dm(r^2 \delta_{ij} - r_i r_j) = \sigma_j \cdot \mathscr{I} \sigma_i = \mathscr{I}_{ji}.$$

This gives,

$$\mathcal{Q}_{ij} = \hat{\sigma}_i \cdot \mathcal{Q} \hat{\sigma}_j = \hat{\sigma}_i \cdot \hat{\sigma}_j Tr \mathscr{I} - 3\hat{\sigma}_i \cdot \mathscr{I} \hat{\sigma}_j = \mathcal{Q}_{ji}. \qquad \square$$

Following the well known terminology from electromagnetic theory, we call $\mathcal{Q}$ the gravitational quadrupole tensor. (Again, remember that LHS of Eq. (11.42) is a vector in $\mathbb{R}^3$.)

Now the expanded potential is

$$\phi(\mathbf{r}) = -\frac{G}{r}\left\{M + \frac{1}{2}\frac{\mathbf{r}\cdot\mathcal{Q}\mathbf{r}}{r^4} + \cdots\right\}. \tag{11.43}$$

This is called a harmonic or multipole expansion of the potential. The quadrupole term describes the first non-zero correction to the potential of a spherically symmetric body. The gravitational field $(\mathbf{g} = -\nabla\phi)$ can be obtained from Eq. (11.43) with the help of

$$\nabla\left(\frac{1}{2}\mathbf{r}\cdot\mathcal{Q}\mathbf{r}\right) = \mathcal{Q}\mathbf{r},$$

$$\nabla r^n = nr^{n-1}\hat{\mathbf{r}}.$$

Thus,

$$\mathbf{g}(\mathbf{r}) = -\frac{G}{r^2}\left\{M\hat{\mathbf{r}} - \frac{1}{r^2}\left(\mathcal{Q}\hat{\mathbf{r}} - \frac{5}{2}(\hat{\mathbf{r}}\cdot\mathcal{Q}\hat{\mathbf{r}})\hat{\mathbf{r}}\right) + \cdots\right\}. \tag{11.44}$$

Exercise   Derive Eq. (11.44).   □

This expression for the gravitational field holds for a body with arbitrary shape and density distribution.

The moment of inertia tensor for an axially symmetric body can be put in the form

$$\mathscr{I}\mathbf{r} = I_1\mathbf{r} + (I_3 - I_1)(\mathbf{r}\cdot\hat{\mathbf{u}})\hat{\mathbf{u}}, \tag{11.45}$$

where $I_1 = I_2$ is the moment of inertia about any axis in the plane normal to the symmetry axis and passing through the centre of mass, called equatorial moment of inertia, I_3 is the moment of inertia about the symmetry axis, or the so called polar moment of inertia. $\hat{\mathbf{u}}$ is the direction of the symmetry axis.

Exercise   Prove Eq. (11.45).

Solution   Let $\{\hat{\sigma}_1, \hat{\sigma}_2, \hat{\mathbf{u}}\}$ be the eigenbasis of the inertia operator of the axially symmetric body and let $\mathbf{r} = r_1\hat{\sigma}_1 + r_2\hat{\sigma}_2 + r_3\hat{\mathbf{u}}$ be a position vector. Due to symmetry about the axis given by $\hat{\mathbf{u}}$, the eigenvalues corresponding to $\{\hat{\sigma}_1, \hat{\sigma}_2\}$ must be equal, giving the eigenvalues to be I_1, I_1, I_3. We get

$$\begin{aligned}
\mathscr{I}\mathbf{r} &= I_1(r_1\hat{\sigma}_1 + r_2\hat{\sigma}_2) + I_3 r_3\hat{\mathbf{u}} \\[2mm]
&= I_1\mathbf{r} + I_3 r_3\hat{\mathbf{u}} - I_1 r_3\hat{\mathbf{u}} \\[2mm]
&= I_1\mathbf{r} + (I_3 - I_1)(\mathbf{r}\cdot\hat{\mathbf{u}})\hat{\mathbf{u}}.
\end{aligned}$$

□

Then Eqs (11.42) and (11.40) give,

$$Q\mathbf{r} = (I_3 - I_1)(\mathbf{r} - 3(\mathbf{r} \cdot \hat{\mathbf{u}})\hat{\mathbf{u}}).$$ (11.46)

From Eq. (11.44), then, the gravitational field of an axially symmetric body is

$$\mathbf{g}(\mathbf{r}) = -\frac{MG}{r^2}\left\{\hat{\mathbf{r}} + \frac{3}{2}J_2\left(\frac{R}{r}\right)^2 [1 - 5(\hat{\mathbf{r}} \cdot \hat{\mathbf{u}})^2\,\hat{\mathbf{r}} + 2\hat{\mathbf{r}} \cdot \hat{\mathbf{u}}\,\hat{\mathbf{u}}] + \cdots\right\}.$$ (11.47)

where R is the equatorial radius of the body and J_2 is defined as

$$J_2 = \frac{I_3 - I_1}{MR^2}.$$ (11.48)

The constant J_2 is a dimensionless measure of the oblateness of the body and the factor $\left(\frac{R}{r}\right)^2$ in Eq. (11.47) measures the rate at which the oblateness effect (on the field) falls off with distance.

For an axially symmetric body, the effect of harmonics higher than the quadrupole are rather simply found, because the series Eq. (11.35) (or Eq. (11.37)) integrates to a harmonic expansion for the potential, giving,

$$\phi(\mathbf{r}) = -\frac{GM}{r}\left\{1 - \sum_{n=2}^{\infty} J_n\left(\frac{R}{r}\right)^n P_n(\hat{\mathbf{r}} \cdot \hat{\mathbf{u}})\right\},$$ (11.49)

where J_n are the dimensionless constant coefficients. As stated above, J_2 measures the oblateness of the body and is related to the moment of inertia via Eq. (11.48). The constant J_3 measures the extent to which the body is "pearshaped", (i.e., the southern hemisphere fatter than the northern hemisphere). The advantage of Eq. (11.49) is that it can be immediately written down once the axial symmetry is assumed and the constants J_n can be determined empirically, in particular, by fitting Eq. (11.49) to data on orbiting satellites. For the earth,

$$J_2 = 1.083 \times 10^{-3}, \ J_3 = -2.5 \times 10^{-6}, \ J_4 = -1.6 \times 10^{-6}, \ J_5 = -0.2 \times 10^{-6}.$$

Clearly the quadrupole harmonic strongly dominates. The contributions of the harmonics decrease with n because of the factor $\left(\frac{R}{r}\right)^n$ in Eq. (11.49). Since J_n are dimensionless, comparison of J_n values for different planets can be used to quantitatively compare the shapes of planets.

Using the directional derivative

$$\hat{\mathbf{u}} \cdot \nabla \hat{\mathbf{r}} = \frac{\hat{\mathbf{u}} - (\hat{\mathbf{u}} \cdot \hat{\mathbf{r}})\hat{\mathbf{r}}}{r},$$ (11.50)

we can differentiate the term $(n = 3)$ in Eq. (11.49) to get its contribution to the gravitational field as

$$\mathbf{g}_3(\mathbf{r}) = -\frac{GM}{r^3}\left\{\frac{5}{2}J_3\left(\frac{R}{r}\right)^3\left[\left(-7(\hat{\mathbf{r}}\cdot\hat{\mathbf{u}})^3 + 3\hat{\mathbf{r}}\cdot\hat{\mathbf{u}}\right)\mathbf{r} + \left(3(\hat{\mathbf{r}}\cdot\hat{\mathbf{u}})^2 - \frac{3}{5}\right)\mathbf{u}\right],\right. \tag{11.51}$$

where $\mathbf{u} = r\hat{\mathbf{u}}$. The contribution of the term with $n = 2$ is already obtained in Eq. (11.47).

Differentiating, in this way, term by term in Eq. (11.49), we can express the gravitational field of a axially symmetric body as

$$\mathbf{g}(\mathbf{r}) = -\frac{GM}{r^3}\left\{\mathbf{r} + \sum_{n=2}^{\infty}\mathbf{g}_n(\mathbf{r})\right\}. \tag{11.52}$$

Finally, we establish Eq. (11.35). We have, using law of cosines, (see Fig. 11.13)

$$|\mathbf{r} - \mathbf{r}'|^2 = r^2 + r'^2 - 2rr'(\hat{\mathbf{r}}\cdot\hat{\mathbf{r}}')$$

$$= r^2\left(1 + \left(\frac{r'}{r}\right)^2 - 2\left(\frac{r'}{r}\right)\hat{\mathbf{r}}\cdot\hat{\mathbf{r}}'\right)$$

or,

$$|\mathbf{r} - \mathbf{r}'| = r\sqrt{1 + \epsilon},$$

where

$$\epsilon = \left(\frac{r'}{r}\right)\left(\frac{r'}{r} - 2\hat{\mathbf{r}}\cdot\hat{\mathbf{r}}'\right). \tag{11.53}$$

As long as $r > r'$, $\epsilon < 1$, so that we can use binomial expansion to get

$$\frac{1}{|\mathbf{r} - \mathbf{r}'|} = \frac{1}{r}(1 + \epsilon)^{-\frac{1}{2}} = \frac{1}{r}\left(1 - \frac{1}{2}\epsilon + \frac{3}{8}\epsilon^2 - \frac{5}{16}\epsilon^3 + \cdots\right). \tag{11.54}$$

Putting Eq. (11.53) in Eq. (11.54) and collecting the coefficients of different powers of $\left(\frac{r'}{r}\right)$ we get Eq. (11.35).

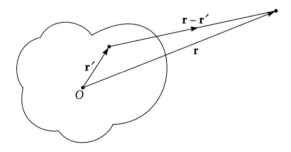

Fig. 11.13   Variables in the multipole expansion

Exercise Develop the multipole expansion for the electrostatic potential at **r** due to an arbitrary localized charge distribution, in powers of $\frac{1}{r}$. This is analogous to the above development of multipole expansion for the gravitational potential of an arbitrary localized mass distribution. Give the geometric interpretation of the of the terms proportional to $\frac{1}{r^2}, \frac{1}{r^3}, \frac{1}{r^4}$. Compare these two cases. (Consult ref [9]).   □

We shall now obtain the equation to the surface of the earth by assuming it to be an equipotential for the effective gravitational potential

$$\Phi(\mathbf{r}) = V(\mathbf{r}) - \frac{1}{2}(\mathbf{\Omega} \times \mathbf{r})^2, \tag{11.55}$$

where $V(\mathbf{r})$ is the true gravitational potential at the earth's surface and the last term is the centrifugal potential. We do this by expressing $\Phi(\mathbf{r})$ in terms of the ellipticity parameter for the earth given by

$$\epsilon = \frac{a-c}{c},$$

a, c being the equatorial and polar radii of the earth respectively. We show that the resulting shape of the earth is an approximate oblate spheroid. We differentiate the geopotential $\Phi(\mathbf{r})$ to express the equatorial and polar gravitational accelerations, g_e and g_p respectively, in terms of the ellipticity parameter ϵ. We use the observed values of g_e and g_p namely,

$$g_e = 978.039 \text{ cm}/\text{sec}^2$$

$$g_p = 983.217 \text{ cm}/\text{sec}^2$$

to estimate the ellipticity parameter ϵ.

Earth's shape is all important for cartography and has a role in many geophysical phenomena. It is intimately connected with the rotation of the earth as we shall see. In fact the basic idea is that earth's shape originated from the cooling of a spinning molten mass to form a solid crust. Another 'shape forming agency' is the oscillating tides due to other astronomical bodies like the moon and the sun. However, this effect is of higher order of smallness to be included in more refined models.

For our purpose, we model the earth as a spinning fluid, held together in steady state by the gravitational field (see Fig. 11.14).

In a geocentric frame spinning with the earth, the fluid is at rest with the effective gravitational potential given by Eq. (11.55). The gravitational field

$$\mathbf{g} = -\nabla\Phi \tag{11.56}$$

must be normal to the surface. If it had a tangential component, it will make the fluid flow on the surface. This means that the surface of the earth is an equipotential surface defined by

$$\Phi(\mathbf{r}) = \Phi_0, \tag{11.57}$$

where Φ_0 is the constant to be determined.

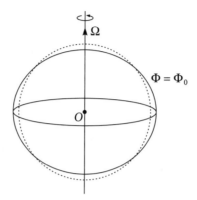

Fig. 11.14   Earth's rotation affected its shape in its formative stage

Due to axial symmetry in the problem, earth's gravitational potential V can be described by the Legendre expansion Eq. (11.49). Therefore, to the second order, earth's shape is given explicitly by the equation

$$\Phi(\mathbf{r}) = -\frac{GM_\oplus}{r}\left\{1 - \frac{1}{2}J_2\left(\frac{a}{r}\right)^2\left[3(\hat{\mathbf{r}}\cdot\hat{\mathbf{u}})^2 - 1\right]\right\} - \frac{1}{2}\Omega^2 r^2\left[1 - (\hat{\mathbf{r}}\cdot\hat{\mathbf{u}})^2\right] = \Phi_0, \tag{11.58}$$

where $\hat{\mathbf{u}} = \hat{\boldsymbol{\Omega}}$ specifies the rotation axis, a is the equatorial radius of the earth and we have used identity II. The surface described by this equation is called *geoid*. Its deviation from the sphere is characterized by the so called ellipticity (or flattening) parameter ϵ defined by

$$\epsilon = \frac{a-c}{c}, \tag{11.59}$$

with c as the earth's polar radius. To evaluate the constant Φ_0 in Eq. (11.57) we set $r = c$ and $\hat{\mathbf{r}}\cdot\hat{\mathbf{u}} = 1$ in Eq. (11.58) giving

$$\Phi_0 = -\frac{GM_\oplus}{c}\left\{1 - \frac{J_2 a^2}{c^2}\right\}. \tag{11.60}$$

To express the ellipticity parameter ϵ in terms of other parameters we set $r = a$ and $\hat{\mathbf{r}}\cdot\hat{\mathbf{u}} = 0$ in Eq. (11.58) to get

$$-\frac{GM_\oplus}{a}\left\{1 + \frac{1}{2}J_2\right\} - \frac{1}{2}\Omega^2 a^2 = -\frac{GM_\oplus}{a}\left\{1 - \frac{J_2 a^2}{c^2}\right\}(1+\epsilon), \tag{11.61}$$

where we have used $\frac{a}{c} = 1 + \epsilon$ and Eq. (11.60). Since ϵ and J_2 are known to be small quantities, it suffices to solve this equation for ϵ to the first order, so that

$$\epsilon = \frac{3}{2}J_2 + \frac{1}{2}\beta, \tag{11.62}$$

where

$$\beta = \frac{\Omega^2 a^3}{GM_\oplus} = \frac{\Omega^2 a}{GM_\oplus/a^2} \tag{11.63}$$

is the ratio of the centripetal to the gravitational acceleration at the equator.

The potential $\Phi(\mathbf{r})$ can now be expressed in terms of ϵ and β,

$$\Phi(\mathbf{r}) = -\frac{GM_\oplus}{r}\left\{1 + (\epsilon - \frac{1}{2}\beta)\left(\frac{a}{r}\right)^3\left[\frac{1}{3} - (\hat{\mathbf{r}}\cdot\hat{\mathbf{u}})^2\right] + \frac{1}{2}\beta\left(\frac{r}{a}\right)^3\left[1 - (\hat{\mathbf{r}}\cdot\hat{\mathbf{u}})^2\right]\right\}. \tag{11.64}$$

To get the equation for the geoid, to the first order in ϵ, we approximate $\left(\frac{a}{r}\right)$ in Eq. (11.64) by $\frac{a}{c} = 1 + \epsilon$, use binomial theorem and simplify Eq. (11.64) keeping only the first order terms. We then equate the resulting expression to that for Φ_0 obtained by expressing the LHS of Eq. (11.61) in terms of ϵ and β, namely,

$$\Phi_0 = -\frac{GM_\oplus}{a}\left\{1 + \frac{1}{3}(\epsilon + \beta)\right\}. \tag{11.65}$$

This gives the equation for the geoid, to the first order in the ellipticity parameter ϵ as

$$r = a(1 - \epsilon(\hat{\mathbf{r}}\cdot\hat{\mathbf{u}})^2). \tag{11.66}$$

That this is an equation to an approximate oblate spheroid can be seen by approximating the equation to the oblate spheroid

$$1 = \frac{(\mathbf{r}\cdot\hat{\mathbf{u}})^2}{c^2} + \frac{(\mathbf{r}\times\hat{\mathbf{u}})^2}{b^2} = \frac{r^2}{b^2}\left[1 + \left(\frac{b^2 - c^2}{c^2}\right)(\hat{\mathbf{r}}\cdot\hat{\mathbf{u}})^2\right] \tag{11.67}$$

for small $\frac{b-c}{c} \equiv \epsilon'$ as

$$r \approx \frac{b}{[1 + 2\epsilon'(\hat{\mathbf{r}}\cdot\hat{\mathbf{u}})^2]^{\frac{1}{2}}} \approx b\left[1 - \epsilon'(\hat{\mathbf{r}}\cdot\hat{\mathbf{u}})^2\right]. \tag{11.68}$$

To get the accelerations g_e and g_p, we have to differentiate $\Phi(\mathbf{r})$ as in Eq. (11.56). We do it using explicit coordinate system on earth, for its geometric visualization. In terms of coordinates (r, λ), λ being the latitude, $\Phi(r, \lambda)$ can be written as (see Eq. (11.58))

$$\Phi(r,\lambda) = -\frac{GM_\oplus}{r} + \frac{GM_\oplus a^2}{2r^3}J_2(3\sin^2\lambda - 1) - \frac{1}{2}\Omega^2 r^2 \cos^2\lambda. \tag{11.69}$$

and the magnitude of the acceleration g is given by

$$g = -\left[\left(\frac{\partial\Phi}{\partial r}\right)^2 + \left(\frac{1}{r}\frac{\partial\Phi}{\partial\lambda}\right)^2\right]^{\frac{1}{2}}. \tag{11.70}$$

Due to the smallness of ϵ, $\mathbf{g}$ is almost normal to the spherical earth, although it is strictly normal to the geoid. Thus, $\mathbf{g}$ deviates from the radial direction (which defines (λ)) only by a small angle of the order of ϵ. Therefore, $\left(\frac{\partial\Phi}{\partial\lambda}\right) \approx \epsilon$, making the second term in Eq. (11.70) of the order of ϵ^2 and hence negligible. Therefore,

$$-g = \frac{\partial\Phi}{\partial r} = \frac{GM_\oplus}{r^2} - \frac{3}{2}\frac{GM_\oplus a^2}{r^4}J_2(3\sin^2\lambda - 1) - \Omega^2 r(1 - \sin^2\lambda). \tag{11.71}$$

From Eq. (11.66) we substitute the value of r on the geoid at arbitrary latitude λ

$$r = a\left(1 - \epsilon\sin^2\lambda\right) \tag{11.72}$$

in Eq. (11.71) and use the binomial expansion

$$\left(1 - \epsilon\sin^2\lambda\right)^{-n} = \left(1 + n\epsilon\sin^2\lambda\cdots\right). \tag{11.73}$$

Neglecting the products of small quantities and higher orders in ϵ, we get

$$-g = \frac{GM_\oplus}{a^2}\left(1 + 2\epsilon\sin^2\lambda\right) - \frac{3}{2}\frac{GM_\oplus}{a^2}J_2\left(3\sin^2\lambda - 1\right) - \Omega^2 a\left(1 - \sin^2\lambda\right). \tag{11.74}$$

Putting $\lambda = 0$ in Eq. (3.20) we get the value of the equatorial gravity

$$g_e = -\frac{GM_\oplus}{a^2}\left(1 + \frac{3}{2}J_2 - \beta\right) = \frac{GM_\oplus}{a^2}\left(1 + \epsilon - \frac{3}{2}\beta\right). \tag{11.75}$$

Similarly, putting $\lambda = \frac{\pi}{2}$ in Eq. (2.20) we get the value at the poles

$$g_p = \frac{GM_\oplus}{a^2}(1 + \beta). \tag{11.76}$$

Using the given experimental values of g_e and g_p and the known values of a and Ω we can solve the simultaneous Eqs (11.75) and (11.76) to get

$$\epsilon = 0.003376; \beta = 0.003468 \tag{11.77}$$

We can substitute these values of ϵ and β in Eq. (11.62) to get the value of J_2 which agrees with the value of J_2 mentioned above, which was obtained using satellite data, within one percent. This gives us a check on the internal consistency of the theory.

The shape of the earth given by the geoid Eq. (11.66) agrees with measurements of sea level to within a few meters. However, radar ranging to measure the height of the ocean is accurate to a fraction of a meter. This shows the need to develop more refined models for the shape of the earth. The principal deviation from the geoid is an excessive bulge around the equator. This is attributed to a retardation of the rotating earth over past million years. For a detailed exposition of the physics of the earth, the reader may consult ref [16] and [24].

11.3   Area Integral

We already know that the magnitude of a vector product like $\mathbf{x}_1 \times \mathbf{x}_2$ equals the area of the parallelogram with $\mathbf{x}_1$ and $\mathbf{x}_2$ as its adjacent sides and its direction is that in which a right handed screw advances when rotated in the sense of $\mathbf{x}_1$ rotating towards $\mathbf{x}_2$. If $\hat{\mathbf{n}}$ is the unit vector in the direction of $\mathbf{x}_1 \times \mathbf{x}_2$ then the area vector representing the area of the corresponding parallelogram is defined to be

$$\mathbf{a} = \pm|\mathbf{x}_1 \times \mathbf{x}_2|\hat{\mathbf{n}}, \tag{11.78}$$

where the $+$ sign applies if the rotation of $\mathbf{x}_1$ towards $\mathbf{x}_2$ is counterclockwise and $-$ sign applies if it is clockwise. This definition of the area vector suggests the following construction of an area integral:

$$\mathbf{A} = \frac{1}{2}\int_{\mathbf{a}}^{\mathbf{b}} \mathbf{x} \times d\mathbf{x} = \frac{1}{2}\lim_{n\to\infty}\sum_{k=1}^{n} \mathbf{x}_k \times \Delta\mathbf{x}_k \tag{11.79}$$

with $\sum_{k=1}^{n} \Delta\mathbf{x}_k = \mathbf{b} - \mathbf{a}$. Note that this is totally a vector relation in which differential area vectors are added to give the resulting area vector in the limit as $|\Delta\mathbf{x}| \to 0$. If n is large enough, we can approximate this area integral by the sum

$$\mathbf{A} \approx \frac{1}{2}\sum_{k=1}^{n} \mathbf{x}_k \times \Delta\mathbf{x}_k$$

$$= \frac{1}{2}\mathbf{x}_0 \times \mathbf{x}_1 + \frac{1}{2}\mathbf{x}_1 \times \mathbf{x}_2 + \cdots + \frac{1}{2}\mathbf{x}_{n-1} \times \mathbf{x}_n. \tag{11.80}$$

As depicted in Fig. 11.15, each term in this sum is the area vector of a triangle with one vertex at the origin. The magnitude of the kth term approximates the area swept out by the line segment represented by the vector variable $\mathbf{x}$ as its tip moves continuously along the curve joining $\mathbf{a}$ and $\mathbf{b}$ from $\mathbf{x}_{k-1}$ to $\mathbf{x}_k$ with its tail at the origin, while the direction of the corresponding area vector is consistent with the sense of rotation of $\mathbf{x}$ from $\mathbf{x}_{k-1}$ to $\mathbf{x}_k$. Thus, the sum in Eq. (11.80) approximates the area vector corresponding to the area swept out as the variable $\mathbf{x}$ moves from $\mathbf{a}$ to $\mathbf{b}$. Thus, the integral Eq. (11.79) is the area vector for the total area swept out by the vector variable $\mathbf{x}$ as it moves continuously along the curve from $\mathbf{a}$ to $\mathbf{b}$. Thus, the value of the area integral Eq. (11.79) is not path independent as the area swept out depends on the path from $\mathbf{a}$ to $\mathbf{b}$.

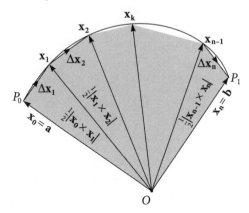

Fig. 11.15   Area integral

If the curve is represented by the parametric equation $\mathbf{x} = \mathbf{x}(t)$, with $\mathbf{x}(0) = \mathbf{a}$, then the corresponding area vector can be obtained as a parametric function $\mathbf{A} = \mathbf{A}(t)$ as

$$\mathbf{A}(t) = \frac{1}{2}\int_{\mathbf{x}(0)}^{\mathbf{x}(t)} \mathbf{x} \times d\mathbf{x} = \frac{1}{2}\int_0^t \mathbf{x} \times \dot{\mathbf{x}}\,dt \ \text{ with } \mathbf{x} \text{ and } \dot{\mathbf{x}} \text{ both functions at } t. \quad (11.81)$$

Differentiating with respect to the upper limit of the integral, we get,

$$\dot{\mathbf{A}} = \frac{1}{2}\mathbf{x} \times \dot{\mathbf{x}}, \qquad\qquad (11.82)$$

expressing the rate at which the area is swept out. This rate depends on the choice of the parameterization $\mathbf{x} = \mathbf{x}(t)$, although the total area swept out depends only on the curve.

If we integrate along a closed curve $\mathcal{C}$ in a plane, enclosing the origin, (see Fig. 11.16), then the integral

$$\mathbf{A} = \frac{1}{2}\int_{\mathcal{C}} \mathbf{x} \times d\mathbf{x} \qquad\qquad (11.83)$$

gives the area vector of the area enclosed by the curve $\mathcal{C}$. This is evident by applying the approximation of the integral by the areas of triangles as expressed by Eq. (11.80), with $\mathbf{x}_0 = \mathbf{x}_n$. The sign of the area vector $\mathbf{A}$ is positive if the curve $\mathcal{C}$ has counterclockwise orientation (as in Fig. 11.16(a)), or is negative if $\mathcal{C}$ has clockwise orientation. For the situation in Fig. 11.16(a) we get,

$$\frac{1}{2}\mathbf{x} \times d\mathbf{x} = \frac{1}{2}|\mathbf{x} \times d\mathbf{x}|\hat{\mathbf{n}}$$

for the kth element of the area, hence from Eq. (11.83),

$$|\mathbf{A}| = \frac{1}{2} \int_{\mathcal{C}} |\mathbf{x} \times d\mathbf{x}|. \tag{11.84}$$

We emphasize that Eq. (11.84) follows from Eq. (11.83) only when all coplanar elements of area have the same orientation. as in Fig. 11.16(a). This condition is not met if the curve $\mathcal{C}$ is self-intersecting or does not enclose the origin.

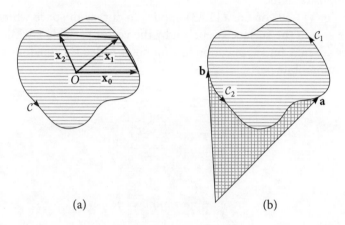

(a)   (b)

Fig. 11.16   Area swept out by radius vector along a closed curve.   Cross-hatched region is swept out twice in opposite directions, so its area is zero.

The area integral Eq. (11.83) is independent of the origin although the values of the vector variable $\mathbf{x}$ depends on the origin. To see this, displace the origin inside the curve $\mathcal{C}$ in Fig. 11.16(a) to a place outside the curve as shown in Fig. 11.16(b). Choosing the points $\mathbf{a}$ and $\mathbf{b}$ on $\mathcal{C}$ we separate $\mathcal{C}$ into two pieces $\mathcal{C}_1$ and $\mathcal{C}_2$, so the area integral becomes

$$\mathbf{A} = \frac{1}{2} \int_{\mathcal{C}} \mathbf{x} \times d\mathbf{x} = \frac{1}{2} \int_{\mathcal{C}_1} \mathbf{x} \times d\mathbf{x} + \frac{1}{2} \int_{\mathcal{C}_2} \mathbf{x} \times d\mathbf{x}.$$

Referring to Fig. 11.6(b) we see that the coordinate vector sweeps over the region inside $\mathcal{C}$ once as it goes between $\mathbf{a}$ and $\mathbf{b}$ along $\mathcal{C}$, but it sweeps over the meshed region to the left of $\mathcal{C}_2$ twice, once as it traverses $\mathcal{C}_2$ and again as it traverses $\mathcal{C}_1$ and since the sweeps over the latter region are in opposite directions their contributions to the integral have same magnitude but opposite signs, and hence cancel. We are thus left with the area vector corresponding to $\mathcal{C}$ as claimed.

For a general proof that the closed area integral is independent of the origin, we displace the origin by a vector $\mathbf{c}$ by making the change of variables $\mathbf{x} \to \mathbf{x}' = \mathbf{x} - \mathbf{c}$. Then,

$$\int_{\mathcal{C}} \mathbf{x}' \times d\mathbf{x}' = \int_{\mathcal{C}} (\mathbf{x} - \mathbf{c}) \times d\mathbf{x} = \int_{\mathcal{C}} \mathbf{x} \times d\mathbf{x} - \mathbf{c} \times \int_{\mathcal{C}} d\mathbf{x}.$$

However, the last term vanishes because $\int_C d\mathbf{x} = \mathbf{0}$, so the independence of origin of the area integral is proved. Note that the cancellation of the parts of the integral proving its independence of the origin remains valid even if the origin is chosen out of the plane containing the curve **c**. Thus, the value of the area integral over a closed plane curve is invariant of the origin, even if the origin is taken out of the plane containing the curve.

The area integral of a closed planar curve can be evaluated to give the area enclosed by an self-intersecting plane curve such as the one shown in Fig. 11.17. The sign of the area integral for subregions are indicated in the figure, with zero for subregions which are swept out twice with opposite signs.

The integral Eq. (11.79) or Eq. (11.83) applies to curves in space which do not lie in plane, giving the area of the surface swept out by the vector variable **x** while traversing the curve. Such integrals may find application in Computer Aided Design, for example, applied to the design of automobile parts.

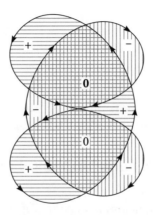

Fig. 11.17 Directed area of a self-intersecting closed plane curve. Vertical and horizontal lines denote areas with opposite orientation, so cross-hatched region has zero area.

11.4 Multiple Integrals

In this section we learn about multiple integrals, specifically about double and triple integrals. A double integral is the integral over a scalar valued function $f(\mathbf{x})$ where **x** is a 2-D vector varying over some connected finite region in a plane. Equivalently, we integrate a function of two scalar variables (x, y) where $x\hat{\mathbf{i}} + y\hat{\mathbf{j}}$ span some connected region on a plane. The coordinates (x, y) of the vector variable **x** range over the area of the region of integration. A triple or a volume integral is an integral of a scalar valued function $f(\mathbf{x})$, with **x** spanning a finite connected region in space, or over a function of three scalar variables say $f(x, y, z)$ where $x\hat{\mathbf{i}} + y\hat{\mathbf{j}} + z\hat{\mathbf{k}}$ spans some finite connected region in space. The coordinates (x, y, z) of the variable **x** range over the volume V of the region of integration. The corresponding integrals on a disconnected region is the sum of the integrals on its connected components. We will generally express multiple integrals as integrals over the functions of three scalar variables. In order to express multiple integrals fully in terms of vectors and vector algebra, we have to take recourse to geometric algebra and geometric calculus[10, 11, 7]. [2]

11.4.1 Area of a planar region: Jordan measure

Our aim is to get a quantitative measure of the area of a planar region S.

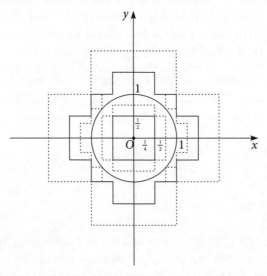

Fig. 11.18   Interior and exterior approximations to the area of the unit disc $|\mathbf{x}| \leq 1$ for $n = 0, 1, 2$ where $A_0^- = 0, A_1^- = 1, A_2^- = 2, A_2^+ = 4.25, A_1^+ = 6, A_0^+ = 12$

We divide the plane into squares by first drawing x, y axes and then drawing the sequences of parallel lines to x and y axis respectively at a separation of one unit of length. The coordinates of the points of intersection of this mesh are $x = 0, \pm 1, \pm 2, \ldots$ and $y = 0, \pm 1, \pm 2, \ldots$. This mesh covers the whole plane by closed unit squares without a gap or overlap. Also, the interiors of any two squares of this mesh are disjoint. Let $A_0^+(S)$ be the number of squares having points in common with S and $A_0^-(S)$ be the number of squares totally contained in S. Note that $A_0^+(S)$ and $A_0^-(S)$ also give the areas of figures formed by these squares because the area of a single square is unity. Next, divide each square into four equal squares of side $\frac{1}{2}$ and area $\frac{1}{4}$. Let $A_1^+(S)$ be the area covered by the number of such squares (each of area $2^{-1} \times 2^{-1} = 2^{-2}$) overlapping S and $A_1^-(S)$ be the area covered by the number of such squares contained in S. Since the area of individual squares is now reduced by a factor of 2^{-2}, one or more such smaller squares may get accommodated in the interior portion of S lying between the boundary of the figure corresponding to $A_0^-(S)$ and the boundary of S. This increases the interior area covered

---

[2]Calculus with functions of three variables is called calculus of three variables. Calculus of three variables and vector calculus are two sides of the same coin. Former is carried out in $\mathbb{R}^3$ while the latter is carried out in $\mathscr{E}_3$.

by the smaller squares in comparison to that covered by the larger squares. On the other hand, a larger square, overlapping S but not contained in S, when divided into four smaller squares of equal area will generate one or more smaller squares with no overlap with S at all, thus reducing the area of the figure corresponding to $A_0^+(S)$. Thus, we see that,

$$A_0^-(S) \leq A_1^-(S)$$

and

$$A_0^+(S) \geq A_1^+(S). \tag{11.85}$$

We iterate this process n times each time dividing the square in the previous iterate by $\frac{1}{2}$ to get each square of side 2^{-n} and area 2^{-2n}. Reiterating exactly the same argument which led to inequalities Eq. (11.85), we get, at nth step, (see Fig. 11.18)

$$A_{n-1}^-(S) \leq A_n^-(S)$$

and

$$A_{n-1}^+(S) \geq A_n^+(S). \tag{11.86}$$

It is clear that the values $A_n^+(S)$ form a monotonically decreasing and bounded sequence converging to a value $A^+(S)$, while $A_n^-(S)$ increase monotonically and converge to a value $A^-(S)$. The value $A^-(S)$ represents the *inner area*, the closest we can approximate the area of S from below by congruent squares contained in S while the *outer area* gives the least upper bound obtained by covering S by congruent squares. If both these values are the same, we say that S is Jordan measurable and call the common value $A^+(S) = A^-(S) = A(S)$ the content or the Jordan measure of S. We express the fact that S is Jordan measurable by saying that S has an area $A(S)$.

The difference $A_n^+(S) - A_n^-(S)$ gives the total area of squares after nth iteration that overlap with S, however, are not completely contained in S. All these squares contain boundary points of S so that

$$A_n^+(S) - A_n^-(S) \leq A_n^+(\partial S),$$

where ∂S is the boundary of S. If the boundary of S has zero area, then we find that

$$A^+(S) - A^-(S) = \lim_{n \to \infty} [A_n^+(S) - A_n^-(S)] = \lim_{n \to \infty} A_n^+(\partial S) = 0,$$

which means $A^+(S) = A^-(S) = A(S)$, that is, S has area $A(S)$. Thus, S has an area if its boundary ∂S has zero area. We can also show that if S has an area then $A^+(\partial S) = 0$.

The criterion $A^+(\partial S) = 0$ is sufficient to show that most of the planar regions we encounter in practice have definite area. This is certainly true if ∂S consists of a finite number of arcs described by a function $f(x)$ or $g(y)$ with f or g continuous over a finite closed interval. The uniform continuity[3] of continuous functions over bounded closed interval immediately shows us that these arcs can be covered by a finite number of rectangles of arbitrarily small area say ϵ^2. Therefore,

$$A^+(\partial S) \le n\epsilon^2$$

with n finite and ϵ arbitrarily small we must have $A^+(\partial S) = 0$.

Given two Jordan measurable planar sets S and T with areas $A(S)$ and $A(T)$ the sets $S \cup T$ and $S \cap T$ are also Jordan measurable and

$$A(S \cup T) = A(S) + A(T) - A(S \cap T).$$

If S and T are disjoint then

$$A(S \cup T) = A(S) + A(T).$$

For a finite number of disjoint Jordan measurable sets $S_1, \ldots, S_N$,

$$A(\cup_{i=1}^N S_i) = \sum_{i=1}^N A(S_i).$$

Everything, we have said above, about the areas of the planar sets carries over immediately to the volumes in three dimensions. In order to define the volume $V(S)$ of a bounded set S in 3-D space, we have to use subdivisions of space into cubes of sides 2^{-n}. The set S has a volume if its boundary can be covered by a finite number of these cubes with arbitrarily small total volume. This is true for all bounded sets S whose boundary consists of a finite number of surfaces each of which is represented by a continuous function $f(\mathbf{x})$, $\mathbf{x}$ varying over a closed planar set.

11.4.2   Double integral

We are now in a position to define the double integral of a function $f(\mathbf{x}) \equiv f(x,y)$.

Let a continuous function $f(\mathbf{x}) \equiv f(x,y)$ define the surface $z = f(x,y)$ over its Jordan measurable closed domain $\mathcal{R}$ in the x, y plane (see Fig. 11.19). For simplicity, we assume $z = f(x,y) \ge 0$ for all $(x,y) \in \mathcal{R}$. Consider the set S of points $\mathbf{x} \equiv (x,y,z)$ for which

$$(x,y) \in \mathcal{R} \; ; \; 0 \le z \le f(x,y).$$

The surfaces enclosing this set are (i)$z = f(x,y)$ (ii) $\mathcal{R}$ $(z = 0)$ and (iii) $(x,y) \in \partial\mathcal{R}$; $0 \le z \le f(x,y)$. We define the double integral by the volume $V(S)$ of the set S, which can be obtained as follows.

---

[3]Uniform continuity of $f(x)$ means that for every $\varepsilon > 0$, there is a $\Delta > 0$ such that $d(x_1, x_2) < \Delta$ implies $d(f(x_1), f(x_2)) < \varepsilon$ for *every* (x_1, x_2). This means that a finite arc given by $f(x)$ can be covered by a finite, say n, number of squares of size ε^2, for every $\varepsilon > 0$.

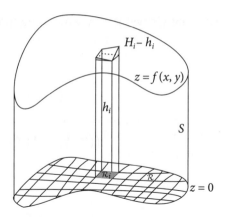

Fig. 11.19   Evaluation of a double integral

We divide $\mathcal{R}$ into non-overlapping Jordan measurable closed sets $\mathcal{R}_1,\ldots,\mathcal{R}_N$. Let h_i be the minimum and H_i be the maximum of $f(x,y)$ with $(x,y) \in \mathcal{R}_i$. The cylinder with height h_i and base $\mathcal{R}_i$ has the volume $h_i A(\mathcal{R}_i)$ where $A(\mathcal{R}_i)$ is the area of $\mathcal{R}_i$. These cylinders do not overlap. Similarly, the cylinders with height H_i and base $\mathcal{R}_i$ do not overlap and have the volume $H_i A(\mathcal{R}_i)$. It follows that

$$\sum_{i=1}^{N} h_i A(\mathcal{R}_i) \leq V(S) \leq \sum_{i=1}^{N} H_i A(\mathcal{R}_i). \tag{11.87}$$

The sums in this inequality are respectively called the lower sum and the upper sum. We now make the subdivision of $\mathcal{R}$ finer and finer, such that the number of subsets the number of subdivisions and the largest diameter of $\mathcal{R}_i$; $i = 1,\ldots,N$ tends to zero. The continuous function $f(x,y)$ is uniformly continuous in the closed and bounded set $\mathcal{R}$, so that the maximum difference $H_i - h_i$ tends to zero with the maximum diameter over the sets $\mathcal{R}_i$ of the subdivision. The differences over the upper and the lower sum also tend to zero, since,

$$\sum_{i=1}^{N} H_i A(\mathcal{R}_i) - \sum_{i=1}^{N} h_i A(\mathcal{R}_i) = \sum_{i=1}^{N} (H_i - h_i) A(\mathcal{R}_i)$$

$$\leq \left[\max_i (H_i - h_i)\right] \sum_{k=1}^{N} A(\mathcal{R}_k)$$

$$= \left[\max_i (H_i - h_i)\right] A(\mathcal{R}). \tag{11.88}$$

It follows from inequality Eq. (11.87) that the upper and lower sum both converge to the limit $V(S)$ as the number of subdivisions $N \to \infty$ or the largest diameter tends to zero.

We obtain the same limiting value if we take the value of the function $f(x_i, y_i)$ at a point $(x_i, y_i) \in \mathcal{R}_i$, instead of h_i or H_i. We call the limit $V(S)$ the double integral of f over the set $\mathcal{R}$ and write

$$V(S) = \int\int_{\mathcal{R}} f(x,y) d\mathcal{R}. \tag{11.89}$$

Suppose, we now lift the restriction $z = f(x,y) > 0$. Due to continuity of $f(x,y)$ the surface $(x,y) \in \mathcal{R}$; $z = f(x,y)$ may cut the x,y plane in some continuous curve and the set S defined above is divided into two (or more, but we assume two) sets, one above and the other below the x,y plane, each corresponding to two distinct parts, $\mathcal{R}^+$ and $\mathcal{R}^-$ of the domain $\mathcal{R}$. These are the set S^+ given by $(x,y) \in \mathcal{R}$; $z = f(x,y) > 0$ and the set S^- given by $(x,y) \in \mathcal{R}$; $z = f(x,y) < 0$. We define a new set $S^{\mp}$ by $(x,y) \in \mathcal{R}$; $z = -f(x,y) > 0$. Both these are the sets of points above the x,y plane so that

$$\int\int_{\mathcal{R}^+} f(x,y) d\mathcal{R} = V(S^+) \quad \text{and} \quad \int\int_{\mathcal{R}^-} (-f(x,y)) d\mathcal{R} = V(S^{\mp}) = V(S^-).$$

This means

$$\int\int_{\mathcal{R}} f(x,y) d\mathcal{R} = V(S^+) - V(S^-).$$

We can summarize as follows. Consider a closed and bounded set $\mathcal{R}$ with area $A(\mathcal{R}) = \Delta \mathcal{R}$ and a function $f(x,y)$ that is continuous everywhere in $\mathcal{R}$ including its boundary. We subdivide $\mathcal{R}$ into N non-overlapping Jordan measurable subsets $\mathcal{R}_1, \mathcal{R}_2, \ldots, \mathcal{R}_N$ with areas $\Delta \mathcal{R}_1, \Delta \mathcal{R}_2, \ldots, \Delta \mathcal{R}_N$. In $\mathcal{R}_i$ we choose an arbitrary point (x_i, y_i) where $f(x_i, y_i) = f_i$ and form the sum

$$V_N = \sum_{i=1}^{N} f_i A(\mathcal{R}_i).$$

Then, we have the theorem:

If the number N tends to infinity and simultaneously the greatest of the diameters of the subregions tends to zero, then V_N tends to a limit V. This limit is independent of the particular nature of the subdivision of $\mathcal{R}$ and of the choice of the point (x_i, y_i) in $\mathcal{R}_i$. We call the limit V the double integral of the function $f(x,y)$ over the region $\mathcal{R}$ and denote it by

$$\int\int_{\mathcal{R}} f(x,y) d\mathcal{R}.$$

Since $A(\partial \mathcal{R}) = 0$ we can choose all $\mathcal{R}_i$ to lie entirely in the interior of $\mathcal{R}$ having no points common with the boundary of $\mathcal{R}$.

We consider some specific subdivisions. In the simplest case, $\mathcal{R}$ is a rectangle $a \leq x \leq b$; $c \leq y \leq d$ and the subregions $\mathcal{R}_i$ are also rectangles obtained by dividing the x interval into n equal parts and the y interval into m equal parts having lengths

$$\Delta x = \frac{b-a}{n} \text{ and } \Delta y = \frac{d-c}{m}.$$

Let the points of subdivision be $x_0 = a, x_1, x_2, \ldots, x_n = b$ and $y_0 = c, y_1, y_2, \ldots, y_n = d$. We have $N = nm$. Every subregion is a rectangle with area $A(\mathcal{R}_i) = \Delta \mathcal{R}_i = \Delta x \Delta y$. For the point (x_i, y_i) we take any point in the corresponding rectangle $\mathcal{R}_i$ and then form the sum

$$\sum_i f(x_i, y_i) \Delta x \Delta y$$

over all the rectangles of the subdivision. If we now let both m and n simultaneously tend to infinity, the sum tends to the integral of the function f over the rectangle $\mathcal{R}$.

These rectangles can also be characterized by two suffixes μ and ν corresponding to the coordinates $x = a + \nu \Delta x$ and $y = c + \mu \Delta y$ of the lower left hand corner of the rectangle in question. Here, $0 \leq \nu \leq (n-1)$ and $0 \leq \mu \leq (m-1)$. With this identification of rectangles with suffixes ν and μ we may write the sum as the double sum

$$\sum_{\nu=0}^{n-1} \sum_{\mu=0}^{m-1} f(x_\nu, y_\mu) \Delta x \Delta y. \tag{11.90}$$

Even if $\mathcal{R}$ is not a rectangle, it is often convenient to subdivide it into rectangular subregions $\mathcal{R}_i$. We can superimpose a rectangular net given by

$$x = \nu h \quad (\nu = 0, \pm 1, \pm 2, \ldots),$$

$$y = \mu k \quad (\mu = 0, \pm 1, \pm 2, \ldots), \tag{11.91}$$

where h and k are numbers chosen conveniently. We call $\mathcal{R}_i$ the rectangles of the division that lie entirely within $\mathcal{R}$. $\mathcal{R}_i$ do not completely fill the region $\mathcal{R}$. However, as we have noted above, we can calculate the integral of the function f over $\mathcal{R}$ by summing only over interior rectangles and then passing to the limit. Whenever we use a rectangular grid with lines parallel to x and y axes we replace the in the integral differential $d\mathcal{R}$ by $dxdy$. Thus,

$$\int\int_{\mathcal{R}} f(x,y) d\mathcal{R} = \int\int_{\mathcal{R}} f(x,y) dxdy.$$

Further, the dummy variables of integration x, y can be replaced, in the integral, by any other pair of variables $(u, v), (\xi, \eta)$ etc.

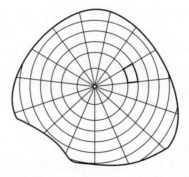

Fig. 11.20   Subdivision by polar coordinate net

The subdivision by the polar coordinate net (see Fig. 3.20) also finds frequent application. We subdivide the entire angle 2π into n parts $\Delta\theta = 2\pi/n$ and also choose a quantum Δr for the r coordinate. We draw the lines $\theta = \nu\Delta\theta \, (\nu = 0, 1, 2, \dots, n-1)$ through the origin and also the concentric circles $r_\mu = \mu\Delta r, (\mu = 0, 1, 2, \dots)$. We denote by $\mathcal{R}_i$ the patches formed by their intersection which lie entirely in the interior of $\mathcal{R}$, and the areas of $\mathcal{R}_i$ by $\Delta\mathcal{R}_i$. Then, the integral of the function $f(x,y)$ is given by the limit of the sum

$$\sum f(x_i, y_i)\Delta\mathcal{R}_i,$$

where (x_i, y_i) is a point chosen arbitrarily in $\mathcal{R}_i$ whose polar coordinates satisfy $x_i = r_i \cos\theta_i$ and $y_i = r_i \sin\theta_i$. By elementary geometry the area $\Delta\mathcal{R}_i$ given by

$$\Delta\mathcal{R}_i = \frac{1}{2}(r_{\mu+1}^2 - r_\mu^2)\Delta\theta = \frac{1}{2}(2\mu + 1)(\Delta r)^2\Delta\theta,$$

if we assume that $\mathcal{R}_i$ lies in the ring bounded by the circles with radia $\mu\Delta r$ and $(\mu+1)\Delta r$. Therefore, the required sum can be written as

$$\frac{1}{2}\sum_{\mu=0}^{n-1}\sum_{\nu=0}^{n-1} f(r_\mu\cos\theta_\nu, r_\mu\sin\theta_\nu)(2\mu+1)(\Delta r)^2\Delta\theta$$

and the double integral of f over $\mathcal{R}$ is obtained in the limit $n \to \infty$ (or equivalently $\Delta r \to 0$ and $\Delta\theta \to 0$) of this sum.

As an example, consider $f(x,y) = 1$ over some bounded region $\mathcal{R}$ in the x, y plane. Then, the double integral of $f(x,y)$ is given by the volume below the region $\mathcal{R}$ shifted vertically to the plane $z = 1$. This volume is given by $f(x,y) \cdot A(\mathcal{R}) = 1 \cdot A(\mathcal{R}) = A(\mathcal{R})$. Thus, we get the result

$$\iint_\mathcal{R} d\mathcal{R} = A(\mathcal{R}).$$

Our next example is the double integral of $f(x,y) = xy$ over the rectangle $a \leq x \leq b$; $c \leq y \leq d$, or, more generally, any function $f(x,y)$ that can be decomposed as a product of a function of x and a function of y in the form $f(x,y) = \phi(x)\psi(y)$. We use the same division of the rectangle as in Eq. (11.90) and the value of the function at the lower left hand corner of the sub-rectangle in the summand. The integral is then the limit of the sum

$$\Delta x \Delta y \sum_{\nu=0}^{n-1} \sum_{\mu=0}^{m-1} \phi(\nu \Delta x) \psi(\mu \Delta y),$$

which can be written as the product of two sums as

$$\sum_{\nu=0}^{n-1} \phi(\nu \Delta x) \Delta x \sum_{\mu=0}^{m-1} \psi(\mu \Delta y) \Delta y.$$

From the definition of the ordinary integral, as $\Delta x \to 0$ and $\Delta y \to 0$ these factors tend to the integrals of the corresponding functions over the respective intervals from a to b and from c to d. Thus, we get a general rule that the double integral of a function satisfying $f(x,y) = \phi(x)\psi(y)$ over a rectangle $a \leq x \leq b$; $c \leq y \leq d$ can be resolved into the product of two integrals

$$\int \int_{\mathcal{R}} f(x,y) dx dy = \int_a^b \phi(x) dx \cdot \int_c^d \psi(y) dy.$$

This rule and the summation rule (see below) yield the integral over any polynomial over a rectangle with sides parallel to the axes.

In our last example, we use a subdivision by a polar coordinate net. Let the region $\mathcal{R}$ be the unit disc centered at the origin, given by $x^2 + y^2 \leq 1$ and let

$$f(x,y) = \sqrt{1 - x^2 - y^2}.$$

The integral of f over $\mathcal{R}$ is simply the volume of a hemisphere of unit radius.

We construct the polar net as above. The subregion lying between the circles $r_\mu = \mu \Delta r$ and $r_{\mu+1} = (\mu + 1)\Delta r$ and between the lines $\theta = \nu \Delta \theta$ and $\theta = (\nu + 1)\Delta \theta$ makes the contribution

$$\frac{1}{2} \sqrt{1 - \left(\frac{r_{\mu+1} + r_\mu}{2} \right)^2} (r_{\mu+1}^2 - r_\mu^2) \Delta \theta = \rho_\mu \sqrt{1 - \rho_\mu^2} \, \Delta r \Delta \theta,$$

where we have taken the value of the function at an intermediate circle with the radius $\rho_\mu = (r_{\mu+1} + r_\mu)/2$. All subregions that lie in the same ring have the same contribution and since there are $n = 2\pi / \Delta \theta$ such regions the contribution of the whole ring is

$$2\pi\rho_\mu\sqrt{1-\rho_\mu^2}\,\Delta r.$$

The integral is therefore the limit of the sum

$$\sum_{\mu=0}^{m-1}2\pi\rho_\mu\sqrt{1-\rho_\mu^2}\,\Delta r.$$

This sum tends to the single integral

$$2\pi\int_0^1 r\sqrt{1-r^2}\,dr = -\frac{2\pi}{3}\sqrt{(1-r^2)^3}\,\Big|_0^1 = \frac{2\pi}{3}.$$

We therefore get

$$\int\int_{\mathcal{R}}\sqrt{1-x^2-y^2}\,d\mathcal{R} = \frac{2\pi}{3}$$

in agreement with the known formula for the volume of a sphere.

For double integrals, as for single integrals, the following fundamental rules apply. If c is a constant, then

$$\int\int_{\mathcal{R}} cf(x,y)\,d\mathcal{R} = c\int\int_{\mathcal{R}} f(x,y)\,d\mathcal{R}.$$

Further, the operation of integration is linear:

$$\int\int_{\mathcal{R}}[\phi(x,y)+\psi(x,y)]\,d\mathcal{R} = \int\int_{\mathcal{R}}\phi(x,y)\,d\mathcal{R} + \int\int_{\mathcal{R}}\psi(x,y)\,d\mathcal{R}.$$

If the region $\mathcal{R}$ consists of two subregions $\mathcal{R}_1$ and $\mathcal{R}_2$ such that $\mathcal{R}_1\cup\mathcal{R}_2=\mathcal{R}$ and $\mathcal{R}_1\cap\mathcal{R}_2\subset(\partial\mathcal{R}_1\cup\partial\mathcal{R}_2)$, then

$$\int\int_{\mathcal{R}} f(x,y)\,d\mathcal{R} = \int\int_{\mathcal{R}_1} f(x,y)\,d\mathcal{R}_1 + \int\int_{\mathcal{R}_2} f(x,y)\,d\mathcal{R}_2.$$

Thus, for the regions that are joined together, the corresponding integrals are added.

11.4.3 Integral estimates

The upper and lower bounds on the double integral can be seen quite easily under certain conditions.

If $f(x,y)\geq 0$ or $f(x,y)\leq 0$ in $\mathcal{R}$, then,

$$\int\int_{\mathcal{R}} f(x,y)\,d\mathcal{R} \geq 0,$$

or,

$$\int\int_{\mathcal{R}} f(x,y)d\mathcal{R} \leq 0.$$

From this we see that, if the inequality

$$f(x,y) \geq g(x,y)$$

holds everywhere in $\mathcal{R}$, then,

$$\int\int_{\mathcal{R}} f(x,y)d\mathcal{R} \geq \int\int_{\mathcal{R}} g(x,y)d\mathcal{R}.$$

From this it follows that

$$\int\int_{\mathcal{R}} f(x,y)d\mathcal{R} \leq \int\int_{\mathcal{R}} |f(x,y)|d\mathcal{R}$$

and

$$\int\int_{\mathcal{R}} f(x,y)d\mathcal{R} \geq -\int\int_{\mathcal{R}} |f(x,y)|d\mathcal{R}.$$

These two inequalities can be combined:

$$\left|\int\int_{\mathcal{R}} f(x,y)d\mathcal{R}\right| \leq \int\int_{\mathcal{R}} |f(x,y)|d\mathcal{R}.$$

If m is the greatest lower bound and M is the least upper bound of the function $f(x,y)$ in $\mathcal{R}$, and $\Delta\mathcal{R}$ is the area of $\mathcal{R}$, then,

$$m\Delta\mathcal{R} \leq \int\int_{\mathcal{R}} f(x,y)d\mathcal{R} \leq M\Delta\mathcal{R}.$$

The integral can then be expressed as

$$\int\int_{\mathcal{R}} f(x,y)d\mathcal{R} = \mu\Delta\mathcal{R}$$

with μ lying between m and M. The precise value of μ cannot be specified more exactly. This equation is called the mean value theorem in integral calculus. Generalizing, we can say that for an arbitrary positive continuous function $p(x,y)$ on $\mathcal{R}$,

$$\int\int_{\mathcal{R}} p(x,y)f(x,y)d\mathcal{R} = \mu\int\int_{\mathcal{R}} p(x,y)d\mathcal{R},$$

where μ is a number between the greatest and the lowest values of $f(x,y)$ on $\mathcal{R}$ that cannot be further specified.

We close by making the following two observations. The first is that a double integral on $\mathcal{R}$ *varies continuously with the function* to be integrated. This means, given two functions f and g satisfying

$$|f(x,y) - g(x,y)| < \epsilon, \quad (x,y) \in \mathcal{R},$$

where $\epsilon > 0$ is a fixed number, then the integrals $\int\int_{\mathcal{R}} f(x,y)d\mathcal{R}$ and $\int\int_{\mathcal{R}} g(x,y)d\mathcal{R}$ differ by less than $\epsilon \Delta \mathcal{R}$ where $\Delta \mathcal{R}$ is the area of $\mathcal{R}$, that is, by less than a number that goes to zero with ϵ. Similarly, we see that *the integral of a function varies continuously with the region.* Suppose that the region $\mathcal{R}_2$ is obtained from $\mathcal{R}_1$ by removing portions whose total area is less than $\epsilon > 0$ and $f(x,y)$ be a function continuous on both regions with $|f(x,y)| < M$ where M is a fixed number. The two integrals $\int\int_{\mathcal{R}_1} f(x,y)d\mathcal{R}$ and $\int\int_{\mathcal{R}_2} f(x,y)d\mathcal{R}$ then differ by less than $M\epsilon$, that is, by a number less than that tends to zero with ϵ. Both these observations follow from the fundamental rules stated above.

Thus, we see that an integral over a region $\mathcal{R}$ can be approximated as closely as we please by evaluating it over a subregion of $\mathcal{R}$ whose total area differs from the area of $\mathcal{R}$ by a sufficiently small amount. In a region $\mathcal{R}$ we can construct a polygon whose total area differs from that of $\mathcal{R}$ by as little an amount as we please. In particular, we can construct this polygon by piecing together rectangles whose sides are lines parallel to the axes.

11.4.4   Triple integrals

Whatever we have said about the integrals over a bounded, closed and connected region in the x,y plane gets carried over, without further complication or introduction of new ideas, to the integrals over a bounded, closed and connected region in the 3-D space called triple integrals. In order to treat the integral over a 3-D region $\mathcal{R}$, we need to subdivide $\mathcal{R}$ into closed non-overlapping Jordan measurable subregions $\mathcal{R}_1, \mathcal{R}_2, \ldots, \mathcal{R}_N$ that completely fill $\mathcal{R}$. If $f(\mathbf{x}) \equiv f(x,y,z)$ is a function that is continuous in the region $\mathcal{R}$ and if (x_i, y_i, z_i) is an arbitrary point in the region $\mathcal{R}_i$, we again form the sum

$$\sum_{i=1}^{N} f(x_i, y_i, z_i) \Delta \mathcal{R}_i,$$

where $\Delta \mathcal{R}_i$ is now the volume of the region $\mathcal{R}_i$. The sum may be taken over all regions $\mathcal{R}_i$, or, over those $\mathcal{R}_i$ which are interior to $\mathcal{R}$. If we now take the limit as $N \to \infty$ such that the largest of the diameters of $\mathcal{R}_i$ tends to zero, then the sum tends to a limiting value which is independent of the mode of subdivision or the choice of the intermediate points. We call this limit the integral of the function $f(x,y,z)$ over the region $\mathcal{R}$ and write it as

$$\int\int_{\mathcal{R}} f(x,y,z)d\mathcal{R}.$$

In particular, if the we subdivide into rectangular boxes with sides $\Delta x, \Delta y, \Delta z$ then the volumes of all the inner regions $\mathcal{R}_i$ have the same value $\Delta x \Delta y \Delta z$ and the corresponding integral is written as

$$\int \int \int_{\mathcal{R}} f(x,y,z) dx dy dz.$$

Apart from the changes in notation all that has been said about the double integral is valid for the triple integral.

11.4.5   Multiple integrals as successive single integrals

Evaluation of multiple integrals can be reduced to successive evaluation of single integrals. This allows us to employ all the standard techniques available to evaluate indefinite integrals of a function of a single variable.

Integrals over a rectangle

We first consider the case where the region of integration $\mathcal{R}$ is a rectangle $a \le x \le b$, $c \le y \le d$. We want to integrate a continuous function $f(x,y)$ over $\mathcal{R}$. The procedure to do this is given in the following theorem, which we state without proof.

To find $\int \int_{\mathcal{R}} f(x,y) dx dy$ we first regard y as constant and integrate $f(x,y)$ with respect to x between the limits a and b. The resulting integral,

$$\phi(y) = \int_a^b f(x,y) dx$$

is a function of y, which we integrate between the limits c and d to obtain the double integral. In symbols,

$$\int \int_{\mathcal{R}} f(x,y) dx dy = \int_c^d \phi(y) dy, \quad \phi(y) = \int_a^b f(x,y) dx,$$

or,

$$\int \int_{\mathcal{R}} f(x,y) dx dy = \int_c^d dy \int_a^b f(x,y) dx. \tag{11.92}$$

Since the roles of x and y are interchangeable, we have

$$\int \int_{\mathcal{R}} f(x,y) dx dy = \int_a^b dx \int_c^d f(x,y) dy. \tag{11.93}$$

Equations (11.92) and (11.93) together imply

$$\int_c^d dy \int_a^b f(x,y) dx = \int_a^b dx \int_c^d f(x,y) dy. \tag{11.94}$$

That is, in the repeated integration of a continuous function with constant limits of integration, the order of integration can be reversed. This facility of changing the order of integration is particularly useful in the explicit calculation of simple definite integrals for which no indefinite integral can be found.

Exercise   Evaluate $I = \displaystyle\int_0^\infty \frac{e^{-ax} - e^{-bx}}{x} \, dx$.

Solution   We can write

$$I = \lim_{T \to \infty} \int_0^T dx \int_a^b e^{-xy} \, dy,$$

from which we obtain by changing the order of integration

$$I = \lim_{T \to \infty} \int_a^b \frac{1 - e^{-Ty}}{y} \, dy = \log \frac{b}{a} - \lim_{T \to \infty} \int_a^b \frac{e^{-Ty}}{y} \, dy.$$

By virtue of the relation

$$\int_a^b \frac{e^{-Ty}}{y} \, dy = \int_{Ta}^{Tb} \frac{e^{-y}}{y} \, dy,$$

the second integral tends to zero as T increases, so that,

$$I = \int_0^\infty \frac{e^{-ax} - e^{-bx}}{x} \, dx = \log \frac{b}{a}. \qquad \qquad \square$$

Exercise   If $f(t)$ is a C^1 function of t except at countably many points for $t \geq 0$ and if the integral

$$\int_1^\infty \frac{f(t)}{t} \, dt$$

exists, then show that, for positive a and b,

$$I = \int_0^\infty \frac{f(ax) - f(bx)}{x} \, dx = f(0) \log \frac{b}{a}.$$

Hint   Write

$$I = \int_0^\infty dx \int_b^a f'(xy) \, dy$$

and change the order of integration. $\qquad \qquad \square$

We can resolve a double integral into a succession of single integrals even if the region of integration is not a rectangle. We first consider a convex region $\mathcal{R}$. A line parallel to x or y axis cuts the boundary of such a region in not more than two points unless it forms a part of the boundary (see Fig. 11.21). We can draw the so called *lines of support* giving the circumscribing rectangle as shown in Fig. 11.21., at $x = x_0, x = x_1, y = y_0, y = y_1$. As we move, for example, the line $x = x_0$ towards right, it cuts the boundary of $\mathcal{R}$ at two points whose y coordinates are functions of x say $\psi_1(x)$ and $\psi_2(x)$ as shown in Fig. 11.21.

Similarly, as we move the line $y = y_0$ upwards, it cuts the boundary of $\mathcal{R}$ at two points whose x coordinates are functions of y say $\phi_1(y)$ and $\phi_2(y)$ as shown in Fig. 11.21. Thus, if we want to integrate $f(x, y)$ over x for a fixed value of $y = y_c$ we must integrate between $\phi_1(y_c)$ and $\phi_2(y_c)$. Treating y as a parameter, then, the integral

$$\int_{\phi_1(y)}^{\phi_2(y)} f(x,y)dx$$

is a function of y and similarly, the integral

$$\int_{\psi_1(x)}^{\psi_2(x)} f(x,y)dy$$

is a function of the parameter x.

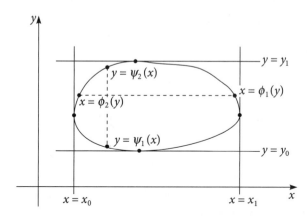

Fig. 11.21   General convex region of integration

The resolution of the double integral over $\mathcal{R}$ into repeated single integrals is then given by the equations

$$\int\int_{\mathcal{R}} f(x,y)d\mathcal{R} = \int_{y_0}^{y_1} dy \int_{\phi_1(y)}^{\phi_2(y)} f(x,y)dx$$

$$= \int_{x_0}^{x_1} dx \int_{\psi_1(x)}^{\psi_2(x)} f(x,y)dy. \tag{11.95}$$

The generalization to the case of non-convex region $\mathcal{R}$ (see Fig. 11.22) is straightforward. A line $x =$ constant may now intersect the boundary of $\mathcal{R}$ in more than two points giving rise to more than one segments over which we have to integrate $f(x,y)$ with respect to y. Each pair of the points of intersection of the line $x =$ constant gives rise to a pair of functions of x. By $\int f(x,y)dy$ we then mean the sum of the integrals of the function $f(x,y)$ for a fixed x, taken over all the intervals that the line $x =$ constant has in common with the closed region.

It is possible to evaluate the double integral by dividing $\mathcal{R}$ into subregions each corresponding to the fixed number of terms in such a sum. The integral over x ranges from x_0 to x_1 which are the circumscribing vertical lines for $\mathcal{R}$, that is, along the whole interval over which the region $\mathcal{R}$ lies.

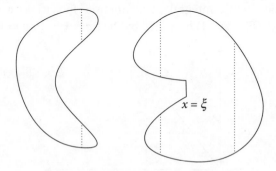

Fig. 11.22   Non-convex region of integration

Exercise   Express the double integral of a function $f(x,y)$ as a succession of single integrals in (a) the unit disc defined by $x^2 + y^2 \leq 1$ and (b) the circular ring between the circles $x^2 + y^2 = 1$ and $x^2 + y^2 = 4$.

Hint   See Fig. 11.23.

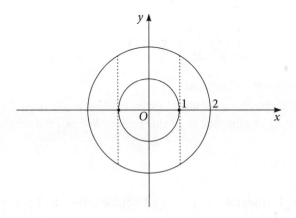

Fig. 11.23   Circular ring as a region of integration

Answer

(a) $\displaystyle\int\int_{\mathcal{R}} f(x,y)d\mathcal{R} = \int_{-1}^{+1} dx \int_{-\sqrt{1-x^2}}^{+\sqrt{1-x^2}} f(x,y)dy.$

(b) $\displaystyle\int\int_{\mathcal{R}} f(x,y)d\mathcal{R} = \int_{-2}^{-1} dx \int_{-\sqrt{4-x^2}}^{+\sqrt{4-x^2}} f(x,y)dy + \int_{1}^{2} dx \int_{-\sqrt{4-x^2}}^{+\sqrt{4-x^2}} f(x,y)dy$

$$+ \int_{-1}^{+1} dx \int_{-\sqrt{4-x^2}}^{+\sqrt{1-x^2}} f(x,y)dy + \int_{-1}^{+1} dx \int_{-\sqrt{1-x^2}}^{+\sqrt{4-x^2}} f(x,y)dy. \qquad \square \ (11.96)$$

Exercise   Express the double integral of a function $f(x,y)$ as a succession of single integrals over a triangle (Fig. 11.24) bounded by the lines $x = y$, $y = 0$ and $x = a$ $(a > 0)$.

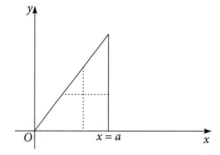

Fig. 11.24   Triangle as a region of integration

Answer

$$\int\int_{\mathcal{R}} f(x,y)d\mathcal{R} = \int_{0}^{a} dx \int_{0}^{x} f(x,y)dy$$

$$= \int_{0}^{a} dy \int_{y}^{a} f(x,y)dx. \qquad \square \ (11.97)$$

Extension to three dimensional regions

We first consider the rectangular region $\mathcal{R}$ given by $x_0 \le x \le x_1$; $y_0 \le y \le y_1$; $z_0 \le z \le z_1$ and a function $f(x,y,z)$ continuous in in this region. We can reduce the triple integral

$$V = \int\int\int_{\mathcal{R}} f(x,y,z)d\mathcal{R}$$

to a succession of single integrals or single and double integrals. For example,

$$\int\int\int_{\mathcal{R}} f(x,y,z)d\mathcal{R} = \int_{z_0}^{z_1} \int\int_{B} f(x,y,z)dxdy,$$

where

$$\int\int_{\mathcal{B}} f(x,y,z)dxdy$$

is the double integral taken over the rectangle described by $x_0 \le x \le x_1$; $y_0 \le y \le y_1$ evaluated at fixed z so that the double integral is a function of the parameter z. Either of the remaining coordinate x and y can be singled out in the same way.

The triple integral V can be evaluated as a succession of three single integrations. We may first consider the integration

$$\int_{z_0}^{z_1} f(x,y,z)dz,$$

x and y being fixed and then the integration

$$\int_{y_0}^{y_1} dy \int_{z_0}^{z_1} f(x,y,z)dz,$$

x being fixed. We finally obtain

$$V = \int_{x_0}^{x_1} dx \int_{y_0}^{y_1} dy \int_{z_0}^{z_1} f(x,y,z)dz.$$

In this repeated integral we could have carried out integration in any order, (say first with respect to x, then with respect to y and finally with respect to z) giving the same triple integral. Thus, we can conclude that a *repeated integral of a continuous function throughout a closed rectangular region is independent of the order of integration.*

Exercise   Express the triple integral of a function $f(x,y,z)$ continuous on the closed spherical region $x^2 + y^2 + z^2 \le 1$ in terms of repeated single integrals.

Answer

$$\int\int\int_{\mathcal{R}} f(x,y,z)dxdydz = \int_{-1}^{+1} dx \int_{-\sqrt{1-x^2}}^{+\sqrt{1-x^2}} dy \int_{-\sqrt{1-x^2-y^2}}^{+\sqrt{1-x^2-y^2}} f(x,y,z)dz. \qquad \square$$

Exercise   Find the mass of the right triangular pyramid of rectangular base sides a and height $3a/2$ with uniform density ρ (see Fig. 11.25).

Solution   Denoting the volume of the pyramid by V and its mass by M we know that $M = \rho V$. Thus, we have to find the volume of the pyramid given by the triple integral

$$\int\int\int_{\mathcal{P}} d\mathcal{P},$$

where $\mathcal{P}$ is the pyramidal region of integration. To evaluate this triple integral, we convert it to three repeated single integrals. We vary z from 0 to $3a/2$. For a fixed z, using similarity of triangles AOC and ADE (see Fig. 3.55) we find that y varies from 0 to $a - 2z/3$.

Now fixing both z and y and again using similarity of triangles which we leave for you to find, we see that x varies from 0 to $a - 2z/3 - y$. Thus we get,

$$M = \rho \int_0^{3a/2} dz \int_0^{a-(2z/3)} dy \int_0^{a-(2z/3)-y} dx$$

$$= \frac{1}{4} a^3 \rho. \qquad \qquad \Box$$

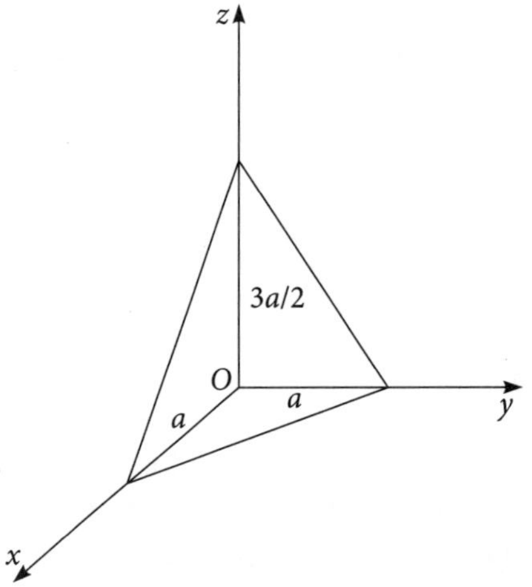

Fig. 11.25   The right triangular pyramid

11.4.6   Changing variables of integration

Introducing new variables of integration is the principal method of transforming and simplifying integrals. Here, we try and understand the general form of such a transformation. Apart from facilitating the evaluation of double and triple integrals, these transformations give us opportunity to apply the concept of integration in a wide variety of contexts.

Consider the double integral

$$\int\int_{\mathcal{R}} f(x,y) d\mathcal{R} = \int\int_{\mathcal{R}} f(x,y) dx dy$$

over a region $\mathcal{R}$ in the x, y plane. Let

$$x = \phi(u,v), \ y = \psi(u,v)$$

be a $1 - 1$ mapping of $\mathcal{R}$ onto the closed region $\tilde{\mathcal{R}}$ in the u, v plane. We assume that both ϕ and ψ are C^1 functions and their Jacobian determinant

$$D = \begin{vmatrix} \phi_u & \phi_v \\ \psi_u & \psi_v \end{vmatrix} = \phi_u \psi_v - \psi_u \phi_v$$

is never zero in $\mathcal{R}$. In other words, the functions $x = \phi(u, v)$ and $y = \psi(u, v)$ possess a unique inverse $u = g(x, y)$ and $v = h(x, y)$. Moreover, the two families of curves $u =$ constant and $v =$ constant form a net over the region $\mathcal{R}$. Each curve in the family $u =$ constant corresponds to a fixed value of u and is parameterized by v. We have,

$$\mathbf{x}(v) \equiv (\phi(u, v), \psi(u, v)) : u \text{ fixed, v is the parameter}$$

$$\mathbf{x}(u) \equiv (\phi(u, v), \psi(u, v)) : v \text{ fixed, u is the parameter.} \tag{11.98}$$

We can construct the mesh of curves on the x, y plane as follows. We first cover the u, v plane by the rectangular mesh of straight lines $u = v\Delta u$ and $v = \mu \Delta v$, $v, \mu = 0, \pm 1$, $\pm 2, \ldots$ and then map each of these curves on the x, y plane by $x = \phi(u, v)$, $y = \psi(u, v)$ giving the mesh on the x, y plane by the curves defined in Eq. (11.98). This mesh subdivides the region of integration $\mathcal{R}$ into subregions $\mathcal{R}_i$ which are not, in general, rectangular (see Fig. 11.16(b)). However, the subregions $\tilde{\mathcal{R}}_i$ into which the region $\tilde{\mathcal{R}}$ gets divided are rectangular (see Fig. 11.16(a)). To find the double integral, we have to find the area of the subregion $\mathcal{R}_i$, multiply by the value of the function f at a point in $\mathcal{R}_i$, sum this product over $\mathcal{R}_i$ lying entirely within $\mathcal{R}$ and then take the limit of this sum as $\Delta u \to 0$, $\Delta v \to 0$.

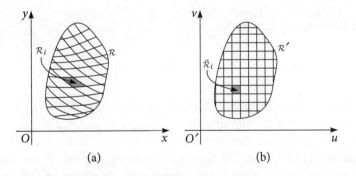

Fig. 11.26   Changing variables of integration (see text)

The way we have constructed the subregions $\mathcal{R}_i$ tells us that the curves defining its boundary are separated pairwise by the parameter values Δu and Δv. The coordinates of the vertices of $\tilde{\mathcal{R}}_i$ are $(u_v, v_\mu), (u_v + \Delta u, v_\mu), (u_v, v_\mu + \Delta v), (u_v + \Delta u, v_\mu + \Delta v)$ and the x, y coordinates of the vertices of $\mathcal{R}_i$ are obtained by mapping these coordinates by ϕ and ψ respectively. If $\mathcal{R}_i$ were a parallelogram joining these vertices, instead of being bounded by curves, then the area of $\mathcal{R}_i$ is given by the absolute value of the determinant (or the absolute value of the cross product of the corresponding vectors)

$$\begin{vmatrix} \phi(u_\nu + \Delta u, v_\mu) - \phi(u_\nu, v_\mu) & \phi(u_\nu, v_\mu + \Delta v) - \phi(u_\nu, v_\mu) \\ \psi(u_\nu + \Delta u, v_\mu) - \psi(u_\nu, v_\mu) & \psi(u_\nu, v_\mu + \Delta v) - \psi(u_\nu, v_\mu) \end{vmatrix}.$$

Since ϕ and ψ are C^1, we can approximate, for example, $\phi(u_\nu + \Delta u, v_\mu) - \phi(u_\nu, v_\mu)$ by $\phi_u(u_\nu, v_\mu)\Delta u \Delta v$ so that the area of $\mathcal{R}_i$ is approximated by the absolute value of

$$\begin{vmatrix} \phi_u(u_\nu, v_\mu) & \phi_v(u_\nu, v_\mu) \\ \psi_u(u_\nu, v_\mu) & \psi_v(u_\nu, v_\mu) \end{vmatrix} \Delta u \Delta v = \Delta u \Delta v D.$$

Thus, forming the required sum and passing to the limit as $\Delta u \rightarrow 0$, $\Delta v \rightarrow 0$, we obtain the expression for the double integral transformed to the new variables,

$$\int\int_{\tilde{\mathcal{R}}} f(\phi(u,v), \psi(u,v))|D| du dv.$$

We will not pause here to show that the area of $\mathcal{R}_i$ coincides with the corresponding parallelogram in limit $\Delta u \rightarrow 0$, $\Delta v \rightarrow 0$ and state the final result:

If the transformation $x = \phi(u,v); y = \psi(u,v)$ represents a continuous $1-1$ mapping of the closed Jordan measurable region $\mathcal{R}$ of the x, y plane to a region $\tilde{\mathcal{R}}$ of the u, v plane and if the functions ϕ and ψ are C^1 and their Jacobian

$$\frac{d(x,y)}{d(u,v)} = \phi_u \psi_v - \psi_u \phi_v$$

is everywhere different from zero, then

$$\int\int_{\mathcal{R}} f(x,y) dx dy = \int\int_{\tilde{\mathcal{R}}} f(\phi(u,v), \psi(u,v)) \left| \frac{d(x,y)}{d(u,v)} \right| du dv. \tag{11.99}$$

We may add that the transformation formula is valid even if the Jacobian determinant vanishes without reversing its sign at a finite number of isolated points in the region of integration. In this case we cut these points out of $\mathcal{R}$ by enclosing them in small circles of radius ρ. Equation (11.99) is valid for the remaining region. If we then let $\rho \rightarrow 0$ Eq. (11.99) continues to be valid for the region $\mathcal{R}$ by virtue of the continuity of all functions involved.

We can obtain the same result for the transformation of a triple integral over a three dimensional region $\mathcal{R}$ which can be stated as follows.

If a closed Jordan measurable region $\mathcal{R}$ of x, y, z space is mapped on a region $\tilde{\mathcal{R}}$ of u, v, w space by a $1-1$ transformation

$$x = x(u,v,w), y = y(u,v,w), z = z(u,v,w)$$

whose Jacobian determinant

$$\frac{d(x,y,z)}{d(u,v,w)}$$

is nowhere zero, then this transformation transforms the triple integral as

$$\iiint_{\mathcal{R}} f(x,y,z)dxdydz = \iiint_{\tilde{\mathcal{R}}} F(r,\theta,\phi) \left| \frac{d(x,y,z)}{d(u,v,w)} \right| dudvdw, \quad (11.100)$$

where $F(r,\theta,\phi) = f(x(u,v,w),y(u,v,w),z(u,v,w))$.

Exercise   Find the transformed double and triple integrals respectively (a) for $f(x,y)$ over a closed disc of radius R in the polar and (b) for $f(x,y,z)$ over a closed ball of radius R in the spherical polar coordinates.

Solution

(a) We have $x = r\cos\theta$ and $y = r\sin\theta$ which easily gives $\frac{\partial(x,y)}{\partial(r,\theta)} = r$ so that

$$\iint_{\mathcal{R}} f(x,y)dxdy = \iint_{\tilde{\mathcal{R}}} f(r\cos\theta, r\sin\theta)rdrd\theta.$$

The whole x,y plane is spanned by $0 \le r < \infty$ and $0 \le \theta < 2\pi$ so that for a given finite region, the integral on RHS can be replaced by

$$\int_0^R r \int_0^{2\pi} f(r\cos\theta, r\sin\theta)drd\theta.$$

(b) The transformation is

$$x = r\sin\theta\cos\phi, \quad y = r\sin\theta\sin\phi, \quad z = r\cos\theta$$

with $0 \le r < \infty$, $0 \le \theta \le \pi$ and $0 \le \phi < 2\pi$. We obtain for the Jacobian determinant,

$$\frac{d(x,y,z)}{d(r,\theta,\phi)} = \begin{vmatrix} \sin\theta\cos\phi & r\cos\theta\cos\phi & -r\sin\theta\sin\phi \\ \sin\theta\sin\phi & r\cos\theta\sin\phi & r\sin\theta\cos\phi \\ \cos\theta & -r\sin\theta & 0 \end{vmatrix} = r^2\sin\theta.$$

Thus, the required transformed integral is given by

$$\iiint_{\mathcal{R}} f(x,y,z)dxdydz = \int_0^R r^2 \int_0^\pi \sin\theta \int_0^{2\pi} F(r,\theta,\phi)drd\theta d\phi, \quad (11.101)$$

where $F(r,\theta,\phi) = f(r\sin\theta\cos\phi, r\sin\theta\sin\phi, r\cos\theta)$.

For the spherical polar coordinates, the Jacobian determinant vanishes at $r = 0$ or $\theta = 0, \pi$ corresponding to the origin and the whole of z-axis. However, there is no trouble for our formula, which can be seen to be valid in the whole space in the same way as we saw in the 2-D case, using the continuity of the functions involved.   □

Exercise   Find the transformed triple integral for $f(x,y,z)$ over the whole space, in the cylindrical coordinates ρ, θ, z related to cartesian coordinates by $x = \rho \cos \theta$, $y = \rho \sin \theta$, $z = z$, where $0 \leq \rho < \infty$, $0 \leq \theta < 2\pi$ and $-\infty < z < +\infty$.

Solution   We easily find that $\frac{d(x,y,z)}{d(\rho,\theta,z)} = \rho$. This gives

$$\iint\int_{\mathcal{R}} f(x,y,z)dxdydz = \int_0^\infty \rho \int_0^{2\pi} \int_{-\infty}^{+\infty} F(\rho,\theta,z)d\rho d\theta dz, \qquad (11.102)$$

where $F(\rho,\theta,z) = f(\rho \cos \theta, \rho \sin \theta, z)$.   □

11.4.7 Geometrical applications

We already know that the volume of a 3-D region $\mathcal{R}$ is given by the integral

$$\iint\int_{\mathcal{R}} dxdydz$$

over $\mathcal{R}$. Expressing this integral as $\int dz \int\int dxdy$ is consistent with the fact that the volume of a solid is known if we know the area of every planar cross section that is perpendicular to definite line, say the z-axis. The generic triple integral given above, representing the volume of a 3-D region, can be used to obtain closed form expressions for the volume of a 3-D region, in terms of its geometrical characteristics. Here, we do this to calculate the volumes of various solids.

To find the volume of ellipsoid of revolution we write its equation

$$\frac{x^2 + y^2}{a^2} + \frac{z^2}{b^2} = 1$$

in the form

$$z = \pm \frac{b}{a}\sqrt{a^2 - x^2 - y^2}.$$

The volume of half of the ellipsoid above the x, y plane is given by the double integral

$$V = \frac{b}{a} \int\int_{\mathcal{R}} \sqrt{a^2 - x^2 - y^2}dxdy$$

over the disc $\mathcal{R} = x^2 + y^2 \leq a^2$. Transforming to polar coordinates, the double integral becomes

$$\iint_{\tilde{\mathcal{R}}} r\sqrt{a^2 - r^2} \, dr d\theta,$$

where the region $\tilde{\mathcal{R}}$ is the rectangle $0 \leq \rho \leq a$, $0 \leq \theta \leq 2\pi$, so that resolving into single integrals we get, for half the volume V,

$$V = \frac{b}{a} \int_0^{2\pi} d\theta \int_0^a r\sqrt{a^2 - r^2} \, dr = 2\pi \frac{b}{a} \int_0^a r\sqrt{a^2 - r^2} \, dr,$$

giving the required volume,

$$V_e = 2V = \frac{4}{3}\pi a^2 b.$$

To find the volume of the general ellipsoid,

$$\frac{x^2}{a^2} + \frac{y^2}{b^2} + \frac{z^2}{c^2} = 1$$

we make the transformation

$$x = a\rho\cos\theta, \quad y = b\rho\sin\theta, \quad \frac{d(x,y)}{d(\rho,\theta)} = ab\rho$$

to get, for half the volume

$$V = c \iint_{\mathcal{R}} \sqrt{1 - \frac{x^2}{a^2} - \frac{y^2}{b^2}} \, dxdy = \iint_{\tilde{\mathcal{R}}} \rho\sqrt{1 - \rho^2} \, d\rho d\theta,$$

where the region $\tilde{\mathcal{R}}$ is the rectangle $0 \leq \rho \leq 1$, $0 \leq \theta \leq 2\pi$. Thus,

$$V = abc \int_0^{2\pi} d\theta \int_0^1 \rho\sqrt{1 - \rho^2} \, d\rho = \frac{2}{3}\pi abc.$$

Therefore, the full volume V_e is

$$V_e = 2V = \frac{4}{3}\pi abc.$$

Finally, we calculate the volume of the pyramid enclosed by the three coordinate planes and the plane $hx + ky + lz = 1$ where we assume that h, k, l are positive. This volume is given by

$$V = \frac{1}{l} \iint_{\mathcal{R}} (1 - hx - ky) \, dxdy,$$

where the region of integration is the triangle $0 \leq x \leq \frac{1}{h}$, $0 \leq y \leq \frac{(1-hx)}{k}$ in the x, y plane. Therefore,

$$V = \frac{1}{l} \int_0^{\frac{1}{h}} \int_0^{\frac{(1-hx)}{k}} (1 - hx - ky)dy.$$

Integration with respect to y gives $\dfrac{(1-hx)^2}{2k}$ and we integrate again by substituting $1 - hx = t$ to get

$$V = \frac{1}{6hkl}.$$

This agrees with the rule that the volume of a pyramid is one third of the product of its base area with its height. Note that, in the single crystal scenario, h, k, l are the reciprocals of the miller indices (which are positive integers with no common factors) of a crystal lattice plane, intersecting the crystal axes, with intercepts h, k, l.

In many instances, the volume triple integral is evaluated by converting it to a succession of single integrals over spherical polar or cylindrical coordinates. As a generic application, we calculate the volume of a solid of revolution obtained by rotating a curve $x = \phi(z)$ about the z-axis. We assume that the curve does not cross the z-axis and that the solid revolution is bounded above and below by the planes $z = $ constant. Therefore, the inequalities defining the solid are of the form $a \leq z \leq b$ and $0 \leq x^2 + y^2 \leq (\phi(z))^2$. In terms of the cylindrical coordinates

$$z, \ \rho = \sqrt{x^2 + y^2}, \ \theta = \cos^{-1} \frac{x}{\rho} = \sin^{-1} \frac{y}{\rho}$$

the volume triple integral becomes

$$\int \int \int_{\mathcal{R}} dxdydz = \int_a^b dz \int_0^{2\pi} d\theta \int_0^{\phi(z)} \rho d\rho.$$

This gives, after integration,

$$V = \pi \int_a^b \phi(z)^2 dz. \qquad (11.103)$$

This integral can be interpreted as the sum of the volumes of the discs of radii $\phi(z)$ and width Δz stacked together to fill the region of integration, in the limit $\Delta z \to 0$.

Next, let the region $\mathcal{R}$ contain the origin O of the spherical polar coordinate system (r, θ, ϕ) and let $r = f(\theta, \phi)$ be the surface defining the boundary of $\mathcal{R}$. Then, the volume of $\mathcal{R}$ is given by

$$V = \int_0^{2\pi} d\phi \int_0^{\pi} \sin\theta d\theta \int_0^{f(\theta,\phi)} r^2 dr.$$

Integrating with respect to r we get

$$V = \frac{1}{3} \int_0^{2\pi} d\phi \int_0^{\pi} f^3(\theta,\phi) \sin\theta d\theta. \tag{11.104}$$

If $\mathcal{R}$ was a closed spherical ball of radius R, so that $f(\theta,\phi) = R$ is constant, Eq. (11.104) yields the volume $\frac{4}{3}\pi R^3$.

Area of a curved surface

We wish to find an expression for the area of a curved surface by means of a double integral. We construct a polyhedron circumscribing the given surface such that each of its polygonal faces is tangent to the surface at one point, as follows.

We assume, that the surface is represented by a function $z = f(x,y)$ with continuous derivatives on a region $\mathcal{R}$ on the x,y plane. We subdivide $\mathcal{R}$ into n subregions $\mathcal{R}_\nu, \nu = 1, 2,\ldots,n$ with areas $\Delta\mathcal{R}_\nu, \nu = 1,2,\ldots,n$. In these subregions we choose points $(\xi_\nu,\eta_\nu), \nu = 1,2,\ldots,n$. At the point on the surface $x_\nu, y_\nu, \zeta_\nu = f(x_\nu,y_\nu)$, we construct the tangent plane to the surface and find the area of the portion of this plane lying above the region $\mathcal{R}_\nu$ (see Fig. 11.27). Let β_ν be the angle that the tangent plane

$$z - \zeta_\nu = f_x(\xi_\nu,\eta_\nu)(x - \xi_\nu) + f_y(\xi_\nu,\eta_\nu)(y - \eta_\nu)$$

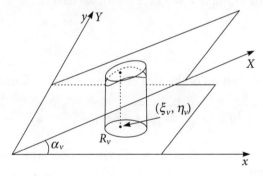

Fig. 11.27 Tangent plane to the surface

makes with the x,y plane and let $\Delta\tau_\nu$ be the area of the portion τ_ν of the tangent plane above $\mathcal{R}_\nu$. Then, the region $\mathcal{R}_\nu$ is the projection of τ_ν on the x,y plane. Therefore,

$$\Delta\mathcal{R}_\nu = \Delta\tau_\nu \cos\beta_\nu.$$

To get $\cos\beta_\nu$ note that β_ν is also the angle between the normals to the planes $\phi_1(\mathbf{x}) = z = 0$ and $\phi_2(\mathbf{x}) = (z - \zeta_\nu) - f_x(\xi_\nu,\eta_\nu)(x - \xi_\nu) - f_y(\xi_\nu,\eta_\nu)(y - \eta_\nu) = 0$ or between the gradients of $\phi_1(\mathbf{x})$ and $\phi_2(\mathbf{x})$. The vectors $\nabla\phi_1$ and $\nabla\phi_2$ are (001) and $(f_x(\xi_\nu,\eta_\nu)f_y(\xi_\nu,\eta_\nu)1)$ respectively. Evaluating their dot products by their components and by their magnitudes and equating these, we get $1 = |\nabla\phi_1| \, |\nabla\phi_2|\cos\beta_\nu = \sqrt{1 + f_x^2(\xi_\nu,\eta_\nu) + f_y^2(\xi_\nu,\eta_\nu)} \cos\beta_\nu$ or,

$$\cos \beta_\nu = \frac{1}{\sqrt{1 + f_x^2(\xi_\nu, \eta_\nu) + f_y^2(\xi_\nu, \eta_\nu)}}.$$

Therefore,

$$\Delta \tau_\nu = \sqrt{1 + f_x^2(\xi_\nu, \eta_\nu) + f_y^2(\xi_\nu, \eta_\nu)} \cdot \Delta R_\nu.$$

We form the sum of all these areas

$$\sum_{\nu=1}^{n} \Delta \tau_\nu$$

and let $n \to \infty$ and simultaneously the diameter of the largest subdivision tend to zero. This sum will then have the limit, independent of the way we subdivide $\mathcal{R}$,

$$A = \int \int_{\mathcal{R}} \sqrt{1 + f_x^2 + f_y^2} d\mathcal{R}. \tag{11.105}$$

We use this integral to define the area of the given surface. Note that if the surface happens to be a plane surface, for example $z = f(x, y) = 0$, we have

$$A = \int \int_{\mathcal{R}} d\mathcal{R},$$

which agrees with our definition of the area of a planar region. Sometimes we call

$$d\sigma = \sqrt{1 + f_x^2 + f_y^2} d\mathcal{R} = \sqrt{1 + f_x^2 + f_y^2} dx dy$$

the element of area of the surface $z = f(x, y)$. The area integral can be written symbolically in the form

$$A = \int \int_{\mathcal{R}} d\sigma.$$

Exercise   Evaluate the area of a spherical surface of radius R.

Solution   The equation to the hemispherical surface of radius R can be written in the $z = f(x, y)$ form as

$$z = \sqrt{R^2 - x^2 - y^2}.$$

We find

$$\frac{\partial z}{\partial x} = -\frac{x}{\sqrt{R^2 - x^2 - y^2}} \;;\; \frac{\partial z}{\partial y} = -\frac{y}{\sqrt{R^2 - x^2 - y^2}}.$$

The area of the full sphere is therefore given by the integral

$$A = 2R \int \int \frac{dxdy}{\sqrt{R^2 - x^2 - y^2}},$$

where the region of integration is the circle of radius R lying in the x, y plane with its origin at the center. Introducing polar coordinates and resolving into single integrals we get

$$A = 2R \int_0^{2\pi} d\theta \int_0^R \frac{rdr}{\sqrt{R^2 - r^2}} = 4\pi R \int_0^R \frac{rdr}{\sqrt{R^2 - r^2}} = 4\pi R^2,$$

where the last integral on the right can be easily evaluated by substituting $R^2 - r^2 = u^2$.   □

If the equation to the surface is given in the form $\phi(x, y, z) = 0$ then we get another expression for its area. Assuming this equation gives implicit dependence of z on independent variables x and y, and also that $\phi_z \neq 0$, we get

$$\frac{d\phi}{dx} = \frac{\partial \phi}{\partial x} + \frac{\partial \phi}{\partial z}\frac{\partial z}{\partial x} = 0; \text{ or, } f_x = \frac{\partial z}{\partial x} = -\frac{\phi_x}{\phi_z}.$$

Similarly,

$$f_y = \frac{\partial z}{\partial y} = -\frac{\phi_y}{\phi_z}.$$

These two relations at once give the expression

$$A = \int \int_{\mathcal{R}} \sqrt{\phi_x^2 + \phi_y^2 + \phi_z^2} \left|\frac{1}{\phi_z}\right| dxdy \tag{11.106}$$

for the area where the region $\mathcal{R}$ is again the projection of the surface on the x, y plane.

If, instead of $z = z(x, y)$, the surface was given by $x = x(y, z)$ then the expression for area would be

$$A = \int \int \sqrt{1 + x_y^2 + x_z^2} dy dz = \int \int \sqrt{\phi_x^2 + \phi_y^2 + \phi_z^2} \left|\frac{1}{\phi_x}\right| dy dz, \tag{11.107}$$

or, if the surface was given by $y = y(z, x)$ then the expression for area would be

$$A = \int \int \sqrt{1 + y_x^2 + y_z^2} \, dz dx = \int \int \sqrt{\phi_x^2 + \phi_y^2 + \phi_z^2} \; \left| \frac{1}{\phi_y} \right| dz dx. \qquad (11.108)$$

Equations (11.106), (11.107), (11.108) define the same area. To see this, apply the transformation

$$x = x(y, z), \; y = y,$$

where $x = x(y, z)$ is obtained by solving the equation $\phi(x, y, z) = 0$, to the integral in Eq. (11.106). The Jacobian determinant is

$$\frac{d(x, y)}{d(y, z)} = \frac{\phi_z}{\phi_x},$$

so that

$$\int \int_{\mathcal{R}} \sqrt{\phi_x^2 + \phi_y^2 + \phi_z^2} \; \left| \frac{1}{\phi_z} \right| dx dy = \int \int_{\tilde{\mathcal{R}}} \sqrt{\phi_x^2 + \phi_y^2 + \phi_z^2} \; \left| \frac{1}{\phi_x} \right| dy dz,$$

where $\tilde{\mathcal{R}}$ is the projection of the surface on the y, z plane.

We can get rid of any special assumption about the relation of the surface and the coordinate system, by representing the surface in the parametric form

$$x = \phi(u, v), \; y = \psi(u, v), \; z = \chi(u, v)$$

and expressing the area of the surface as an integral over the appropriate parameter domain. Then, a definite region in the (u, v) plane corresponds to the surface. Without going into the details we simply state the expression for the area of a surface in terms of its parametric description.

$$A = \int \int_{\mathcal{R}} \sqrt{(\phi_u \psi_v - \psi_u \phi_v)^2 + (\psi_u \chi_v - \chi_u \psi_v)^2 + (\chi_u \phi_v - \phi_u \chi_v)^2} \, du dv. \qquad (11.109)$$

Exercise   For a given surface parameterized by u, v show that

$$A = \int \int \sqrt{EG - F^2} \, du dv \qquad (11.110)$$

and that the element of area

$$d\sigma = \sqrt{EG - F^2} \, du dv,$$

where E, F, G are the coefficients of the line element given by Eqs (10.66), (10.67), (10.68).

Hint   A simple calculation shows

$$EG - F^2 = (\phi_u \psi_v - \psi_u \phi_v)^2 + (\psi_u \chi_v - \chi_u \psi_v)^2 + (\chi_u \phi_v - \phi_u \chi_v)^2. \qquad \square$$

Exercise   Using the parametric representation of a sphere of radius R via the spherical polar coordinates $\theta, \phi, 0 \le \theta \le \pi, \ 0 \le \phi \le 2\pi$, show that

$$d\sigma = R^2 \sin \theta d\theta d\phi$$

and hence show that the area of this sphere is $4\pi R^2$. $\qquad \square$

We can apply Eq. (11.110) to the surface of revolution formed by rotating the curve $z = \phi(x)$, cut off by the two planes $z = z_0$ and $z = z_1$, about the z-axis. Referring the surface to polar coordinates r, θ in the x, y plane as parameters, we get

$$x = r \cos \theta, \ \ y = r \sin \theta, \ \ z = \phi(\sqrt{x^2 + y^2}) = \phi(r).$$

Here, r coordinate of a point on the curve is the radius of the circle it traces out as it rotates about the z-axis. This gives

$$E = 1 + \phi'^2(r), \ \ F = 0, \ \ G = r^2$$

so that the area is given by

$$\int_0^{2\pi} d\theta \int_{r_0}^{r_1} r\sqrt{1 + \phi'^2(r)} dr = 2\pi \int_{r_0}^{r_1} r\sqrt{1 + \phi'^2(r)} dr.$$

Recognizing $\sqrt{1 + \phi'^2(r)} dr = ds$ where s is the arc length parameter of the curve $z = \phi(r)$ we can express the area of the surface of revolution in the form

$$2\pi \int_{s_0}^{s_1} r ds,$$

where r is the distance from the z-axis to the point on the rotating curve corresponding to s.

Exercise   Use the above integral with respect to the arc length parameter to calculate the surface area of the torus obtained by rotating the circle $(x - a)^2 + z^2 = r^2$ about the z-axis.

Solution   We introduce arc length as parameter, so that the distance u of a point on the circle from the z-axis is given by $u = a + r \cos(s/r)$. The area is, therefore,

$$2\pi \int_0^{2\pi r} u ds = 2\pi \int_0^{2\pi r} \left(a + r \cos \frac{s}{r}\right) ds = 2\pi a \cdot 2\pi r.$$

The area of the torus is therefore equal to the product of the circumference of the generating circle and the length of the path traced out by the center of the circle.   □

11.4.8   Physical applications of multiple integrals

Applications of multiple integrals to science and engineering are ubiquitous and are found in all parts of it and in all kinds of situations. An exposure to it can really be obtained through a wide verity of books and literature on various subjects and also while practising different professions. Here, we give a brief account of some applications to mechanics.

Consider a distribution of n particles with respect to a cartesian coordinate system, whose masses and positions are given by $m_\nu, (x_\nu, y_\nu, z_\nu)$, $\nu = 1, 2, \ldots, n$. Then, the moments of such a mass distribution with respect to x, y y, z and z, x planes are defined to be $T_z = \sum_{\nu=1}^{n} m_\nu z_\nu$, $T_x = \sum_{\nu=1}^{n} m_\nu x_\nu$ and $T_y = \sum_{\nu=1}^{n} m_\nu y_\nu$ respectively. When we deal with a continuous distribution of mass with density $\mu(x, y, z)$ in a region $\mathcal{R}$ in space or a surface S or a curve γ, going through the same limiting process as we did while defining multiple integrals, The corresponding moments go over to

$$T_x = \iiint_{\mathcal{R}} \mu x \, dx \, dy \, dz, \quad T_y = \iiint_{\mathcal{R}} \mu y \, dx \, dy \, dz, \quad T_z = \iiint_{\mathcal{R}} \mu z \, dx \, dy \, dz, \quad (11.111)$$

and we call these the *moments of a volume distribution*.

If the mass is continuously distributed over a surface S given by $x = \phi(u, v)$, $y = \psi(u, v)$, $z = \chi(u, v)$ with density $\mu(u, v)$, we define the moments of the surface distribution by expressions

$$T_x = \iint_S \mu x \, d\sigma = \iint_R \mu x \sqrt{EG - F^2} \, du \, dv,$$

$$T_y = \iint_S \mu y \, d\sigma = \iint_R \mu y \sqrt{EG - F^2} \, du \, dv,$$

$$T_z = \iint_S \mu z \, d\sigma = \iint_R \mu z \sqrt{EG - F^2} \, du \, dv. \quad (11.112)$$

Finally, the moments of a curve $x(s), y(s), z(s)$ in space with mass density $\mu(s)$ are defined by

$$T_x = \int_{s_0}^{s_1} \mu x \, ds, \quad T_y = \int_{s_0}^{s_1} \mu y \, ds, \quad T_z = \int_{s_0}^{s_1} \mu z \, ds,$$

where s denotes the arc length.

The *center of mass* of a continuous mass distribution over a region $\mathcal{R}$, with total mass M, is defined as the point with coordinates

$$\xi = \frac{T_x}{M}, \quad \eta = \frac{T_y}{M}, \quad \zeta = \frac{T_z}{M}. \quad (11.113)$$

That is, the center of mass has the coordinates, $\{\xi, \eta, \zeta\} = \frac{1}{M} \int \int \int_{\mathcal{R}} \mu\{x, y, z\} dx dy dz$ where $M = \int \int \int_{\mathcal{R}} \mu dx dy dz$.

If the mass distribution is homogeneous, that is, $\mu = constant$ the center of mass of the region is called its *centroid*. The centroid is clearly independent of the choice of the constant positive value of the mass density. Thus, the centroid becomes a geometrical concept associated only with the shape of the region $\mathcal{R}$, independent of the mass distribution.

Exercise   Find the center of mass of a homogeneous hemispherical region $\mathcal{H}$ with mass density 1.

Solution   The region is given by $x^2 + y^2 + z^2 \leq 1$; $z \geq 0$. The two moments T_x and T_y are zero as the respective integrations with respect to x and y vanish. For

$$T_z = \int \int \int_{\mathcal{H}} z dx dy dz,$$

we introduce cylindrical coordinates (r, θ, z) via the equations

$$z = z, \quad x = r\cos\theta, \quad y = r\sin\theta$$

to get

$$T_z = \int_0^1 z dz \int_0^{\sqrt{1-z^2}} r dr \int_0^{2\pi} d\theta = 2\pi \int_0^1 \frac{1-z^2}{2} z dz = \frac{\pi}{4}.$$

Since the total mass is $\frac{2\pi}{3}$, the coordinates of the center of mass are $(0, 0, \frac{3}{8})$.   □

Exercise   Find the center of mass of a hemispherical surface of unit radius over which a mass of unit density is uniformly distributed.

Solution   For the parametric representation

$$x = \sin\theta \cos\phi, \quad y = \sin\theta \sin\phi \quad z = \cos\theta$$

we get, for the surface element,

$$d\sigma = \sqrt{EG - F^2} d\theta d\phi = \sin\theta d\theta d\phi.$$

This leads to $T_x = 0 = T_y$ because these involve integrating $\cos\phi$ and $\sin\phi$ over a single period and

$$T_z = \int_0^{\pi/2} \sin\theta \cos\theta d\theta \int_0^{2\pi} d\phi = \pi.$$

Since the total mass is 2π we see that the coordinates of the center of mass are $(0, 0, \frac{1}{2})$.   □

Moment of inertia

The *moment of inertia* plays the role of mass for the rotational motion of a rigid body. The kinetic energy of a body rotating uniformly about an axis equals the product of the square of the rotational velocity and the moment of inertia. The moment of inertia of a continuous mass distribution with density $\mu(\mathbf{x}) = \mu(x, y, z)$ over a region $\mathcal{R}$ with respect to the x-axis is given by

$$\mathscr{I}_x = \int \int \int_{\mathcal{R}} \mu(y^2 + z^2) dx dy dz.$$

This is simply integrating over the distance of every point (x, y, z) in $\mathcal{R}$ from the x-axis multiplied by the mass density $\mu(x, y, z)$. The moments of inertia about the other two axes are defined similarly. The moment of inertia about a point, say the origin is defined to be

$$\int \int \int_{\mathcal{R}} \mu(x^2 + y^2 + z^2) dx dy dz$$

and the moment of inertia with respect to a plane say the y, z plane is

$$\int \int \int_{\mathcal{R}} \mu x^2 dx dy dz.$$

A complete description of the arbitrary rotational motion of a rigid body requires the so called *products of inertia*

$$\mathscr{I}_{xy} = -\int \int \int_{\mathcal{R}} \mu xy \, dx dy dz = \mathscr{I}_{yx},$$

$$\mathscr{I}_{yz} = -\int \int \int_{\mathcal{R}} \mu yz \, dx dy dz = \mathscr{I}_{zy},$$

$$\mathscr{I}_{zx} = -\int \int \int_{\mathcal{R}} \mu zx \, dx dy dz = \mathscr{I}_{xz}. \tag{11.114}$$

The three quantities $\mathscr{I}_x, \mathscr{I}_y, \mathscr{I}_z$ and the six products of inertia are sufficient to describe arbitrary rotational motion of a rigid body. These nine quantities, written as a symmetric matrix, are collectively called the *moment of inertia tensor*. The mutually perpendicular axes with respect to which the moment of inertia tensor becomes diagonal are called the principal axes. Generally, these are determined by the symmetry elements of the rigid body.

The moment of inertia with respect to an axis parallel to x-axis and passing through the point (ξ, η, ζ), is given by the expression

$$\int \int \int_{\mathcal{R}} \mu[(y - \eta)^2 + (z - \zeta)^2] dx dy dz,$$

obtained by shifting the origin to (ξ, η, ζ).

If we let (ξ, η, ζ) be the coordinates of the center of mass and use Eq. (11.113) for the coordinates of the center of mass, we immediately get

$$\iiint_R \mu(y^2 + z^2)\,dx\,dy\,dz$$

$$= \iiint_R \mu[(y-\eta)^2 + (z-\zeta)^2]\,dx\,dy\,dz + (\eta^2 + \zeta^2)\iiint_R \mu\,dx\,dy\,dz.$$

Since any arbitrary axis of rotation can be chosen to be the x-axis, the result we have got can be expressed as follows.

The moment of inertia of a rigid body with respect to an arbitrary axis of rotation is equal to the moment of inertia of the body about a parallel axis through its center of mass plus the product of the total mass and the square of the distance between the center of mass and the axis of rotation.

Finally, the moment of inertia of a surface distribution, with respect to the x-axis, is given by

$$\iint_S \mu(y^2 + z^2)\,d\sigma,$$

where $\mu(u, v)$ is the continuous function of two parameters u and v.

Exercise   Find the moment of inertia of a sphere of unit radius and unit density and occupying region V, about any axis through its center at the origin.

Solution   By symmetry the moment of inertia about any axis through the origin is

$$\mathcal{I} = \iiint_V (y^2 + z^2)\,dx\,dy\,dz,$$

$$= \iiint_V (x^2 + z^2)\,dx\,dy\,dz,$$

$$= \iiint_V (x^2 + y^2)\,dx\,dy\,dz. \qquad (11.115)$$

Adding these three integrals we obtain,

$$3\mathcal{I} = 2\iiint_V (x^2 + y^2 + z^2)\,dx\,dy\,dz.$$

In spherical polar coordinates

$$\mathscr{I} = \frac{2}{3} \int_0^1 r^4 dr \int_0^\pi \sin\theta d\theta \int_0^{2\pi} d\phi = \frac{8\pi}{15}. \qquad \Box$$

Exercise For a beam with edges a, b, c parallel to x-axis, y-axis, z-axis respectively, with unit density and the center of mass at the origin, find the moment of inertia about the x, y plane.

Solution $\displaystyle \int_{-a/2}^{a/2} dx \int_{-b/2}^{b/2} dy \int_{-c/2}^{c/2} z^2 dz = ab\frac{c^3}{12}. \qquad \Box$

Exercise Find the moment of inertia tensor of a right triangular pyramid with constant density ρ shown in Fig. 11.25 about the origin O. Diagonalize this matrix using the technique developed in Chapter 2 to find its eigenvalues and eigenvectors, which define the principal values and principal axes of this moment of inertia tensor.

Solution With $i, j = x, y, z$ we can write, for the elements of the moment of inertia tensor,

$$\mathscr{I}_{ij} = \rho \int_0^{3a/2} dz \int_0^{a-(2z/3)} dy \int_0^{a-(2z/3)-y} dx \begin{pmatrix} y^2 + z^2 & -xy & -zx \\ -xy & z^2 + x^2 & -yz \\ -zx & -yz & x^2 + y^2 \end{pmatrix}. \quad (11.116)$$

We have already found that the total mass of the pyramid is $M = \frac{1}{4}a^3\rho$, or, $\rho = \frac{4M}{a^3}$. Carrying out the integrations in the above equation and using the expression for ρ in terms of the total mass M we get

$$\mathscr{I}_{ij} = \frac{Ma^2}{40} \begin{pmatrix} 13 & -2 & -3 \\ -2 & 13 & -3 \\ -3 & -3 & 8 \end{pmatrix}. \qquad (11.117)$$

In order to obtain the principal moments of inertia about the origin O and the principal axes of inertia, we diagonalize the inertia tensor using the methods of section 5.1. The result is

$$\mathscr{I}_{ij}^{(p)} = \frac{Ma^2}{40} \begin{pmatrix} 15 & 0 & 0 \\ 0 & 5 & 0 \\ 0 & 0 & 14 \end{pmatrix}, \qquad (11.118)$$

with the eigenvectors for the principal axes

$$\hat{\mathbf{i}}_p = \frac{1}{\sqrt{2}}(\hat{\mathbf{i}} - \hat{\mathbf{j}})$$

$$\hat{\mathbf{j}}_p = \frac{1}{\sqrt{6}}(\hat{\mathbf{i}} + \hat{\mathbf{j}} + 2\hat{\mathbf{k}})$$

$$\hat{\mathbf{k}}_p = -\frac{\sqrt{2}}{3}(\hat{\mathbf{i}} + \hat{\mathbf{j}}) + \frac{1}{\sqrt{3}}\hat{\mathbf{k}}, \tag{11.119}$$

where $\hat{\mathbf{i}}, \hat{\mathbf{j}}, \hat{\mathbf{k}}$ are the unit vectors along the x, y, z-axes shown in Fig. 11.25.   □

11.5 Integral Theorems of Gauss and Stokes in Two-dimensions

For a function $f(x)$ of a single variable, the fundamental connection between differentiation and integration is given by the equation

$$\int_{x_0}^{x_1} f'(x)dx = f(x_1) - f(x_0).$$

where the integral is expressed in terms of the values of $f(x)$ at the boundary points.

The corresponding result in two dimensions is called Gauss's theorem, or the divergence theorem. This theorem connects the integral of the divergence of a 2-D vector field $\mathbf{f}(\mathbf{x}) = f(\mathbf{x})\hat{\mathbf{i}} + g(\mathbf{x})\hat{\mathbf{j}}$ in a 2-D region $\mathcal{R}$ with the line integral of the normal component of this field along the boundary curve of $\mathcal{R}$ taken in the positive sense, which we denote by $\mathcal{C}_+$. In two dimensions, this theorem, stated in the form involving functions of several variables, is called Gauss's theorem, or the divergence theorem. When stated in the vector form, the same result is called Stokes theorem. The divergence theorem in 2-D is thus stated as

$$\int\int_{\mathcal{R}} [f_x(x,y) + g_y(x,y)]dxdy = \int_{\mathcal{C}_+} [f(x,y)dy - g(x,y)dx], \tag{11.120}$$

where the boundary $\mathcal{C}$ of the region $\mathcal{R}$ is regarded as an oriented curve $\mathcal{C}_+$ choosing as positive sense on $\mathcal{C}$ the one for which the region $\mathcal{R}$ remains on the left side as we traverse it. As a special case, we note that $f(x,y) = x, g(x,y) = 0$ in Eq. (11.120) gives the area of $\mathcal{R}$ in terms of a line integral on its oriented boundary $\mathcal{C}_+$:

$$A = \int\int_{\mathcal{R}} dxdy = \int_{\mathcal{C}_+} xdy.$$

Similarly, for $f(x,y) = 0, g(x,y) = y$ we obtain

$$A = \int\int_{\mathcal{R}} dxdy = -\int_{\mathcal{C}_+} ydx.$$

The divergence theorem holds good for any 2-D open set $\mathcal{R}$ bounded by one or more closed curves, each consisting of a finite number of smooth arcs and for functions f and g which are $\mathcal{C}^1$ throughout $\mathcal{R}$ and on $\mathcal{C}$ (see Fig. 11.28). We do not give the proof of this theorem in detail, suffice it to say that the proof is based on the method of expressing the double integral as successive single integrals, which we have seen in detail before. We will explore some of the applications of this all-important theorem.

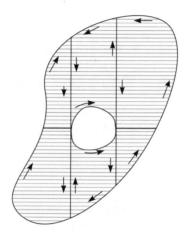

Fig. 11.28 Divergence theorem for connected regions

Stokes theorem

As we have already noted, Stokes theorem in 2-D is obtained by casting the divergence theorem in the vector form. Thus, let the functions $f(x,y)$ and $g(x,y)$ be the components of a 2-D vector field $\mathbf{f}$. Thus, the integrand of the double integral in Eq. (11.120) simply becomes the divergence of $\mathbf{f}$. In order to get a vector expression for line integral in Eq. (11.120), we parameterize the oriented boundary curve $\mathcal{C}_+$ by the arc length s. Here, the sense of increasing s corresponds to the positive orientation of the boundary curve $\mathcal{C}$. The RHS of Eq. (11.143) then becomes

$$\int_{\mathcal{C}} [f(x,y)\dot{y} - g(x,y)\dot{x}]\, ds,$$

where we have put $dx/ds = \dot{x}$ and $dy/ds = \dot{y}$.

We have seen earlier, (see section 9.2), that the vector $\hat{\mathbf{t}}$ with components $\dot{x}$ and $\dot{y}$ has unit length and is in the direction of the tangent in the sense of increasing s and hence in the direction corresponding to the orientation of $\mathcal{C}$. The vector $\hat{\mathbf{n}}$ with components $\xi = \dot{y}$ and $\eta = -\dot{x}$ has unit length, and is orthogonal to the tangent. Moreover, $\hat{\mathbf{n}}$ has the the same position relative to the vector $\hat{\mathbf{t}}$ as the positive x-axis has relative to the positive y-axis. This can be seen from the continuity considerations. Suppose that the tangent to the curve is continuously rotated to make it coincide with the y-axis such that $\hat{\mathbf{t}}$ points in the direction of increasing y. Then, the components of $\hat{\mathbf{t}}$ are $(0,1)$, so that $\hat{\mathbf{n}}$ becomes $(1,0)$ and hence in the positive direction of x-axis. Thus, if a $\pi/2$ clockwise rotation takes positive y-axis into positive x-axis, the vector $\hat{\mathbf{n}}$ is obtained by a $\pi/2$ clockwise rotation from the tangent vector

$\hat{\mathbf{t}}$. Thus, $\hat{\mathbf{n}}$ is the normal pointing to the right side of the oriented curve $\mathcal{C}$ (see subsection 9.2.5). Since in this case $\mathcal{C}_+$ is oriented so as to have region $\mathcal{R}$ on the left side of $\mathcal{C}_+$, we see that $\hat{\mathbf{n}}$ is the outward normal to the region $\mathcal{R}$ (see Fig. 11.29). The components ξ, η of the unit vector $\hat{\mathbf{n}}$ are the direction cosines of the outward normal:

$$\xi = \cos\theta \; ; \; \eta = \sin\theta$$

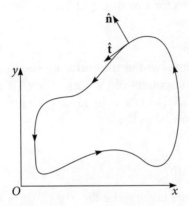

Fig. 11.29 $\hat{\mathbf{n}}$ defines the directional derivatives of x and y

if $\hat{\mathbf{n}}$ subtends an angle θ with the positive x-axis. The components of $\hat{\mathbf{n}}$ are the directional derivatives of x and y in the direction of $\hat{\mathbf{n}}$ as can be seen from $\hat{\mathbf{n}} \cdot \nabla x = \cos\theta$ and $\hat{\mathbf{n}} \cdot \nabla y = \sin\theta$. Denoting these directional derivatives by $\frac{dx}{dn}$ and $\frac{dy}{dn}$ respectively, we can write the divergence theorem in the form:

$$\int\int_{\mathcal{R}} \nabla \cdot \mathbf{f} dx dy = \int_{\mathcal{C}} \left(f\frac{dx}{dn} + g\frac{dy}{dn} \right) ds. \tag{11.121}$$

Here, the integrand on the right is the scalar product $\mathbf{f} \cdot \hat{\mathbf{n}}$ of the vector $\mathbf{f}$ with components f, g and the vector $\hat{\mathbf{n}}$ with components $\frac{dx}{dn}, \frac{dy}{dn}$. Since $\hat{\mathbf{n}}$ is a unit vector, the scalar product $\mathbf{f} \cdot \hat{\mathbf{n}}$ represents the component f_n of the vector $\mathbf{f}$ in the direction of $\hat{\mathbf{n}}$. Thus, the divergence theorem takes the form

$$\int\int_{\mathcal{R}} \nabla \cdot \mathbf{f} dx dy = \int_{\mathcal{C}} \mathbf{f} \cdot \hat{\mathbf{n}} ds = \int_{\mathcal{C}} f_n ds. \tag{11.122}$$

In words, *the double integral of the divergence of a plane vector field over a set $\mathcal{R}$ is equal to the line integral, along the boundary $\mathcal{C}$ of $\mathcal{R}$, of the component of the vector field in the direction of the outward normal.*

There is another form of Stokes theorem in the plane offering an entirely different vector interpretation. To get to it, we put

$$a(x,y) = -g(x,y), \quad b(x,y) = f(x,y).$$

Then, by Eq. (11.120),

$$\int\int_{\mathcal{R}} (b_x - a_y)dxdy = \int_C (a\dot{x} + b\dot{y})ds = \int_{C_+} (adx + bdy). \tag{11.123}$$

We take the two functions a and b to be the components of a vector field $\mathbf{g}$, where $\mathbf{g}$ is obtained at each point from vector $\mathbf{f}$ by its counterclockwise $\pi/2$ rotation. We see that

$$a\dot{x} + b\dot{y} = \mathbf{g} \cdot \hat{\mathbf{t}} = g_t,$$

where g_t is the tangential component of the vector $\mathbf{g}$. The integrand of the double integral in Eq. (11.123) gives the z component of $(\nabla \times \mathbf{g})_z$ of $curl\mathbf{g}$ provided we assume the field $\mathbf{g}$ to continue in the whole of 3-D space coinciding with $\mathbf{g} \equiv (a(x,y), b(x,y))$ on the x, y plane. The Stokes theorem now takes the form,

$$\int\int_{\mathcal{R}} (\nabla \times \mathbf{g})_z dxdy = \int_C g_t ds.$$

Since any plane in space can be taken to be the x, y plane of a suitable coordinate system, we arrive at the following general formulation of Stokes theorem.

$$\int\int_{\mathcal{R}} (\nabla \times \mathbf{g})_n dA = \int_C g_t ds, \tag{11.124}$$

where $\mathcal{R}$ is any plane region in space, bounded by the curve C and $(\nabla \times \mathbf{g})_n$ is the component of the vector $\nabla \times \mathbf{g}$ or $curl\mathbf{g}$ in the direction of the normal $\hat{\mathbf{n}}$ to the plane containing $\mathcal{R}$. Here C has to be oriented in such a way that the tangent vector $\hat{\mathbf{t}}$ points in the counterclockwise direction as seen from the side of the plane toward which $\hat{\mathbf{n}}$ points. In other words, the corresponding rotation of a right handed screw should advance it in the direction of $\hat{\mathbf{n}}$.

If the complete boundary C of $\mathcal{R}$ consists of several closed curves (see Fig. 11.28), these results remain valid provided we extend the line integral over each of these curves oriented properly, so as to leave $\mathcal{R}$ on its left side. If the functions a and b satisfy the condition

$$a_y = b_x,$$

the expression $adx + bdy$ becomes a perfect differential. Since $a_y = b_x$, the double integral over $\mathcal{R}$ in Eq. (11.123) vanishes so that,

$$\int_C (adx + bdy) = 0 \tag{11.125}$$

whenever C denotes the complete boundary of a region $\mathcal{R}$ in which $a_y = b_x$ holds. Further, under these conditions, the integral

$$\int_C (adx + bdy)$$

over a path joining two end points P_0 and P_1 has the same value for all paths in $\mathcal{R}$ joining the end points P_0 and P_1, provided $\mathcal{R}$ is simply connected (see section 11.1).

Exercise   Use the divergence theorem in the plane to evaluate the line integral

$$\int_C f\,du + g\,dv$$

for the following functions and paths taken in the counterclockwise sense about the given region.

(a) $f = au + bv,\ \ g = 0,\ \ u \geq 0\ \ v \geq 0\ \ \alpha^2 u + \beta^2 v \leq 1.$ Ans: $-\frac{b}{\alpha^2\beta^2}.$

(b) $f = u^2 - v^2,\ \ g = 2uv,\ \ |u| < 1,\ \ |v| < 1.$ Ans: 0.

(c) $f = v^n,\ \ g = u^n,\ \ u^2 + v^2 \leq r^2.$ Ans: 0.   □

Exercise   Obtain the formula for the divergence theorem in polar coordinates:

$$\int_{C_+} f(r,\theta)dr + g(r,\theta)d\theta = \int\int_{\mathcal{R}} \frac{1}{r}\left[\frac{\partial g}{\partial r} - \frac{\partial f}{\partial \theta}\right]dS.$$ □

Exercise   Assuming the conditions for the divergence theorem hold, derive the following expressions in polar coordinates for the area of a region $\mathcal{R}$ with boundary C:

$$\frac{1}{2}\int_{C_+} r^2 d\theta,\ \ -\int_{C_+} r\theta\,dr,$$

where in the second formula we assume that $\mathcal{R}$ does not contain the origin.

Hint   Note that $A = \frac{1}{2}\int_{C_+}(xdy - ydx).$ □

Exercise   Apply Stokes theorem in the x,y plane to show that

$$\int\int_{\mathcal{R}} \frac{d(u,v)}{d(x,y)}dS = \int_{C_+} u(\nabla v)\cdot \hat{t}ds,$$

where $\mathbf{x} = \mathbf{x}(u,v)$ is a continuously differentiable $1 - 1$ transformation and $\hat{t}$ is the positively oriented unit tangent vector for C.

Hint   Write $d(u,v)/d(x,y) = (uv_y)_x - (uv_x)_y = \nabla \times (u\nabla v).$ □

Exercise   Let $C_1, C_2,\ldots,C_n$ be non-overlapping simple closed curves in the xy plane and let C be a simple closed curve enclosing all $C_i,\ i = 1,2,\ldots,n$. Let $a(x,y)$ and $b(x,y)$ be continuously differentiable functions such that $a_y = b_x$ outside $C_i,\ i = 1,2,\ldots,n$. If

$$\int_{C_i}(adx + bdy) = m_i,\ \ i, i = 1,2,\ldots,n,$$

then show that

$$\int_{\mathcal{C}} (a\,dx + b\,dy) = \sum_{i=1}^{n} m_i. \tag{11.126}$$

Solution We first make the region interior to $\mathcal{C}$ simply connected by means of cuts as shown in Fig. 11.30. Let Γ be the boundary of the simply connected region so formed, say $\mathcal{R}$, oriented positively, that is, by traversing it keeping region $\mathcal{R}$ on the left. The positive sense on Γ is indicated by the arrows in Fig. 11.30. We have,

$$
\begin{aligned}
\int_{\Gamma} (a\,dx + b\,dy) &= \int_{\mathcal{C}} (a\,dx + b\,dy) - \int_{\mathcal{C}_1} (a\,dx + b\,dy) - \cdots - \int_{\mathcal{C}_n} (a\,dx + b\,dy) \\
&= \int_{\mathcal{C}} (a\,dx + b\,dy) - \sum_{i=1}^{n} m_i. \tag{11.127}
\end{aligned}
$$

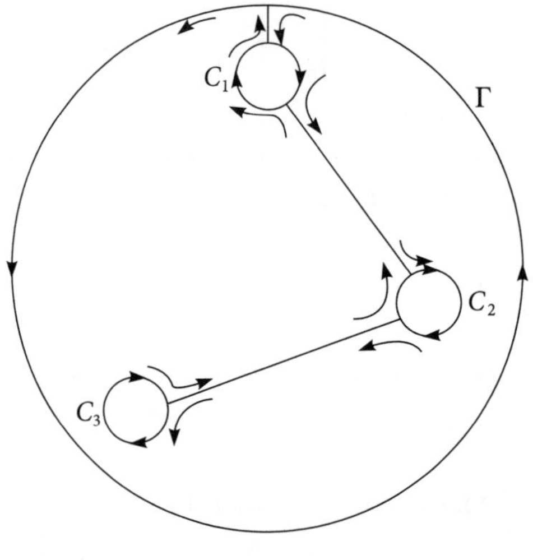

Fig. 11.30 Γ is the boundary of a simply connected region

The integrals along the cuts cancel as they are traversed in opposite directions in going around Γ. The negative signs in Eq. (11.127) occur as the positive sense of traversing individual $\mathcal{C}_i$s is opposite to the positive sense of traversing Γ. Since Γ is the boundary of a simply connected region $\mathcal{R}$ and $a_y = b_x$, in $\mathcal{R}$, Eq. (11.125) holds with $\mathcal{C}$ replaced by Γ and in conjunction with Eq. (11.127) establishes Eq. (11.126). □

11.5.1 Integration by parts in two dimensions: Green's theorem

The divergence theorem, as stated in Eq. (11.121), namely,

$$\int\int_{\mathcal{R}} (f_x + g_y)\,dx\,dy = \int_{\mathcal{C}} \left(f\frac{dx}{dn} + g\frac{dy}{dn} \right) ds \tag{11.128}$$

combined with the rule for differentiating a product immediately gives a prescription for integrating by parts that is basic to the theory of partial differential equations. We substitute for both f and g a product of functions, namely, $f(x,y) = a(x,y)u(x,y)$ and $g(x,y) = b(x,y)v(x,y)$, where the functions a,b,u,v are C^1 in $\mathcal{R}$ as well as on $\mathcal{C}$. Since

$$f_x + g_y = (au_x + bv_y) + (a_x u + b_y v),$$

we can write Eq. (11.128) as

$$\int\int_\mathcal{R} (au_x + bv_y)dxdy = \int_\mathcal{C}\left(au\frac{dx}{dn} + bv\frac{dy}{dn}\right)ds - \int\int_\mathcal{R}(a_x u + b_y v)dxdy. \quad (11.129)$$

To get *Green's first theorem*, we impose $u = v$, $a = \omega_x$ and $b = \omega_y$ for some $\omega(x,y)$. We assume that u is C^1 while ω has continuous second derivatives in the closure of $\mathcal{R}$. This transforms Eq. (11.129) into

$$\int\int_\mathcal{R} (u_x\omega_x + u_y\omega_y)dxdy = \int_\mathcal{C} u\left(\omega_x\frac{dx}{dn} + \omega_y\frac{dy}{dn}\right)ds - \int\int_\mathcal{R} u(\omega_{xx}+\omega_{yy})dxdy.$$

Recognizing

$$\omega_{xx} + \omega_{yy} = \nabla^2\omega \equiv \Delta\omega$$

and that $\frac{dx}{dn}$ and $\frac{dy}{dn}$ are the direction cosines of the outward normal to the boundary $\mathcal{C}$ of $\mathcal{R}$ so that

$$\omega_x\frac{dx}{dn} + \omega_y\frac{dy}{dn} = \frac{d\omega}{dn}$$

is the directional derivative ofω in the direction of the outward normal to $\mathcal{C}$, we obtain, for Green's first theorem,

$$\int\int_\mathcal{R}(u_x\omega_x + u_y\omega_y)dxdy = \int_\mathcal{C} u\frac{d\omega}{dn}ds - \int\int_\mathcal{R} u\Delta\omega dxdy. \quad (11.130)$$

If in addition u has continuous second derivatives, we get from Eq. (11.130), by interchanging the roles of u and ω the equation

$$\int\int_\mathcal{R}(\omega_x u_x + \omega_y u_y)dxdy = \int_\mathcal{C} \omega\frac{du}{dn}ds - \int\int_\mathcal{R} \omega\Delta u dxdy.$$

Subtracting the two equations gives an equation symmetric in u and ω known as *Green's second theorem*:

$$\int\int_\mathcal{R}(\omega\Delta u - u\Delta\omega)dxdy = \int_\mathcal{C}\left(u\frac{d\omega}{dn} - \omega\frac{du}{dn}\right)ds. \quad (11.131)$$

These two theorems of Green are basic in solving the partial differential equation (Laplace equation) $\nabla^2 u = u_{xx} + u_{yy} = 0$ (see books on Electrodynamics like [9, 13]).

11.6 Applications to Two-dimensional Flows

Electrodynamics and fluid mechanics are the two areas of knowledge where the integral theorems we have discussed, (or their 3-D generalizations we will encounter subsequently), find their most natural applications. Here, we deal with some applications to fluid dynamics and leave the electrodynamic version to standard books on the subject [9, 13]. In particular, in this subsection we try and understand the fundamental role of the 2-D integral theorem like the divergence or the Stokes theorem in modelling the motion of a liquid moving in the x, y plane (remember that any plane can be taken to be the x, y plane). We use the velocity field, which is the assignment of the vector $\mathbf{v}(\mathbf{x}, t) \equiv (v_1(\mathbf{x}, t), v_2(\mathbf{x}, t))$ to the position vector $\mathbf{x}$ in the plane at time t, to describe the motion of the liquid on the x, y plane.

Let us first assume that the velocity of the liquid is independent of $(\mathbf{x}, t)$. Then, the amount of liquid crossing a line segment I of length s in the time interval $[t, t + dt]$ fills at $t + dt$ a parallelogram of area $(\mathbf{v} \cdot \hat{\mathbf{n}}) s \, dt$ where $\hat{\mathbf{n}}$ is the unit normal vector to I pointing to the side of I to which the liquid crosses (angle between $\hat{\mathbf{n}}$ and $\mathbf{v}$ is less than $\pi/2$), as depicted in Fig. 11.31.

Exercise Check that the parallelogram is formed by the points $(\tilde{x}, \tilde{y})$ for which the segment with end points $(\tilde{x}, \tilde{y})$ and $(x, y) = (\tilde{x} - v_1 dt, \tilde{y} - v_2 dt)$ has points common with I. $\qquad \square$

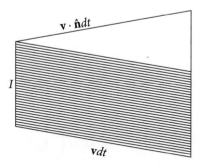

Fig. 11.31 Amount of liquid crossing segment I in time dt for uniform flow of velocity $\mathbf{v}$

We take this area of the parallelogram swept by the liquid crossing the segment I in time dt ($\angle(\hat{\mathbf{n}}, \mathbf{v}) < \pi/2$) to be positive while the corresponding area for the unit vector $\hat{\mathbf{n}}$ such that $\angle(\hat{\mathbf{n}}, \mathbf{v}) > \pi/2$ is taken to be negative. If ρ is the density of the liquid, then $(\mathbf{v} \cdot \hat{\mathbf{n}}) \rho s \, dt$ is the mass of the liquid that crosses I toward the side to which $\hat{\mathbf{n}}$ points.

Now let C be the curve in the x, y plane. We select one of the two possible unit normals along C and call it $\hat{\mathbf{n}}$. In a flow with velocity and density depending on $\mathbf{x}, t$ the integral

$$\int_C (\mathbf{v} \cdot \hat{\mathbf{n}}) \rho \, ds \tag{11.132}$$

represents mass of the liquid crossing $\mathcal{C}$ in unit time toward the side of $\mathcal{C}$ to which $\hat{\mathbf{n}}$ points. This follows by approximating $\mathcal{C}$ by a polygon and the flow for which the velocity is constant across each side of the polygon.

If $\mathcal{C}$ is the boundary of a region $\mathcal{R}$ and if $\hat{\mathbf{n}}$ is the outward normal, the integral represents the mass of the liquid *leaving* $\mathcal{R}$ in unit time. Applying the divergence theorem as in Eq. (11.122) we can express the flow through $\mathcal{C}$ as a double integral

$$\int_{\mathcal{C}} (\mathbf{v} \cdot \hat{\mathbf{n}}) \rho \, ds = \int_{\mathcal{C}} (\rho \mathbf{v}) \cdot \hat{\mathbf{n}} \, ds = \int\int_{\mathcal{R}} \nabla \cdot (\rho \mathbf{v}) \, dx \, dy. \tag{11.133}$$

We can compare this flow of mass through $\mathcal{C}$ out of $\mathcal{R}$ with the change in mass contained in $\mathcal{R}$. The total mass of the liquid contained in the region $\mathcal{R}$ at time t is

$$\int\int_{\mathcal{R}} \rho(\mathbf{x}, t) \, dx \, dy.$$

Thus, in unit time, the loss of mass from $\mathcal{R}$ is given by

$$-\frac{d}{dt} \int\int_{\mathcal{R}} \rho(\mathbf{x}, t) \, dx \, dy = -\int\int_{\mathcal{R}} \frac{\partial \rho}{\partial t}(\mathbf{x}, t) \, dx \, dy.$$

If we assume that the mass is conserved, then mass can only be lost from $\mathcal{R}$ by passing through the boundary $\mathcal{C}$. Hence, by Eq. (11.133) we have

$$\int\int_{\mathcal{R}} \left(\nabla \cdot (\rho \mathbf{v}) + \frac{\partial \rho}{\partial t} \right) dx \, dy = 0. \tag{11.134}$$

Since this identity holds for arbitrary $\mathcal{R}$, if we progressively reduce the area of $\mathcal{R}$ the integral will have the value given by the product of the integrand evaluated at some arbitrary point in $\mathcal{R}$ and the area of $\mathcal{R}$. Since area of $\mathcal{R} > 0$, the integrand must vanish at all points at which the velocity field is defined. Stated more rigorously, if we divide Eq. (11.134) by the area of $\mathcal{R}$ then in the limit as area of $\mathcal{R}$ tends to zero, we get

$$\nabla \cdot (\rho \mathbf{v}) + \frac{\partial \rho}{\partial t} = 0. \tag{11.135}$$

This differential equation expresses the *law of conservation of mass* in the flow. In terms of the components (v_1, v_2) of the velocity vector we can write Eq. (11.135) as

$$\frac{\partial \rho}{\partial t} + v_1 \frac{\partial \rho}{\partial x} + v_2 \frac{\partial \rho}{\partial y} + \rho \left(\frac{\partial v_1}{\partial x} + \frac{\partial v_2}{\partial y} \right) = 0. \tag{11.136}$$

An important special case is that of an *incompressible homogeneous* liquid in which the density ρ has a constant value independent of location and time. In this case, Eqs (11.135), (11.136) reduce to an equation involving the velocity vector alone:

$$\nabla \cdot \mathbf{v} = \frac{\partial v_1}{\partial x} + \frac{\partial v_2}{\partial y} = 0. \tag{11.137}$$

Combining Eqs (11.133) and (11.137) we see that the total amount of an incompressible liquid crossing a closed curve C is zero:

$$\int_C (\mathbf{v} \cdot \hat{\mathbf{n}}) ds = 0. \tag{11.138}$$

Stokes theorem, in the form of Eq. (11.124) applied to the vector field $\mathbf{v}$ has also interesting consequences for the liquid flow. The integral over a closed oriented curve C namely,

$$\int_C \mathbf{v} \cdot \hat{\mathbf{t}} ds$$

where $\hat{\mathbf{t}}$ is the unit tangent vector corresponding to the orientation of C, is called the *circulation* of the liquid around C. By stokes theorem, this circulation is equal to the double integral

$$\int \int_{\mathcal{R}} (\nabla \times \mathbf{v})_z dx dy$$

over the enclosed region $\mathcal{R}$. Hence, the quantity

$$(\nabla \times \mathbf{v})_z = \frac{\partial v_2}{\partial x} - \frac{\partial v_1}{\partial y}, \tag{11.139}$$

called the vorticity of the motion, measures the *density of circulation* at the point $\mathbf{x} \equiv (x, y)$ in the sense that the area integral of the vorticity gives the circulation around the boundary. A flow is called *irrotational* if the vorticity vanishes everywhere, that is, if

$$(\nabla \times \mathbf{v})_z = \frac{\partial v_2}{\partial x} - \frac{\partial v_1}{\partial y} = 0. \tag{11.140}$$

By stokes theorem, the circulation around a closed curve C vanishes if C is the boundary of a region where the motion is irrotational. Since Eq. (11.140) is the condition for $v_1 dx + v_2 dy$ to be a perfect differential, there exists for an irrotational flow in every simply connected region a scalar valued function $\phi(\mathbf{x}, t)$ such that

$$\mathbf{v}(\mathbf{x}) = -\nabla \phi(\mathbf{x}). \tag{11.141}$$

The scalar ϕ, which is determined within a constant, is called a *velocity potential.*

The irrotational motion of an incompressible homogeneous liquid satisfies both, Eqs (11.137) and (11.140). Combining these, we find that the *velocity potential is a solution of Laplace's equation:*

$$\Delta \phi = \phi_{xx} + \phi_{yy} = 0.$$

As an example, we consider the flow corresponding to the solution

$$\phi = a\log r = a\log\sqrt{x^2 + y^2}$$

of the Laplace equation. By Eq. (11.141) the velocity potential has the components

$$v_1 = -\frac{ax}{r^2} \quad v_2 = -\frac{ay}{r^2}$$

and is singular at the origin (see Fig. 11.32(a)). All velocity vectors point towards the origin for $a > 0$, away from the origin for $a < 0$. The velocity of the liquid at a given location does not change with time, although the velocities at different points are different. Such a flow is said to be a *steady flow*. The circulation around any closed curve not passing through the origin vanishes, since vorticity is zero as can be easily checked so that

$$\int_C \mathbf{v}\cdot\hat{\mathbf{t}}\,ds = \int_C v_1\,dx + v_2\,dy = -\int_C d\phi = 0.$$

The amount of liquid passing outward through a simple closed curve C in unit time is

$$\rho\int_C \mathbf{v}\cdot\hat{\mathbf{n}}\,ds = \rho\int_C \left(v_1\frac{dy}{ds} - v_2\frac{dx}{ds}\right) = \rho\int_C v_1\,dy - v_2\,dx = -a\rho\int_C \frac{x\,dy - y\,dx}{x^2 + y^2},$$

where θ is the polar angle from origin.

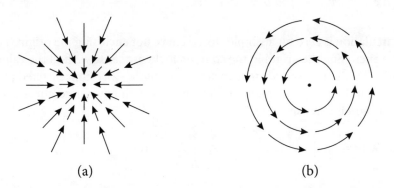

(a)   (b)

Fig. 11.32   (a) Flow with sink and (b) Flow with vortex

Exercise   Show that $\displaystyle\int_C \frac{x\,dy - y\,dx}{x^2 + y^2} = \int_C d\theta.$

Hint   Put $x = \cos\theta$ and $y = \sin\theta$.   □

We assume that C does not pass through the origin. If C encloses the origin and is oriented counterclockwise, $\int_C d\theta = \int_0^{2\pi} d\theta = 2\pi$ while if C does not enclose the origin then the starting and finishing values of θ are the same as we trace the simple closed curve C once, making the limits of the integral the same, so that the value of the integral is zero. Therefore,

$$\rho \int_C \mathbf{v} \cdot \hat{\mathbf{n}} ds = \begin{cases} 0 & \text{if } C \text{ does not enclose the origin} \\ -2\pi a \rho & \text{if } C \text{ encloses the origin.} \end{cases}$$

Thus, the amount of mass flowing through every simple closed curve C enclosing the origin in unit time is the same. For $a > 0$ the origin acts as a *sink* where mass disappears at the rate of $2\pi a\rho$ units in unit time. For $a < 0$ there is a *source* of mass at the origin, giving out mass at the same rate.

Let us now consider a steady flow given by the velocity potential

$$\phi = c\theta = c \tan^{-1} \frac{y}{x}.$$

Despite ϕ being multiple valued, the corresponding velocity field is single valued:

$$v_1 = \frac{cy}{r^2} \quad v_2 = -\frac{cx}{r^2}.$$

The vector field $\mathbf{v}$ is everywhere normal to the radii from the origin (see Fig. 11.32(b)). Again, the velocity field is singular at the origin.

The circulation around a closed curve C has the value

$$\int_C v_1 dx + v_2 dy = -\int_C d\phi = -c \int_C d\theta.$$

Thus, the circulation is zero for a simple closed curve not enclosing the origin. For a simple closed curve encircling the origin in the counterclockwise sense we find the value $-2\pi c$ for the circulation. This corresponds to a vortex of strength $-2\pi c$ concentrated at the origin. On the other hand, the flow of mass in unit time through any closed curve C not passing through the origin is zero, since here

$$\rho \int_C \mathbf{v} \cdot \hat{\mathbf{n}} ds = c\rho \int_C \frac{x dx + y dy}{x^2 + y^2} = c\rho \int_C \frac{dr}{r} = 0.$$

Thus, the origin is not a source or sink of mass.

11.7   Orientation of a Surface

While learning about the line integral of a vector or a scalar valued function along a curve C in a plane or in space, we found that the curve C cannot be treated just as a collection of points in space, but needs to be assigned some *sense* or *orientation*. Similarly, the surface integral, which we will study next, requires an orientation to be assigned to the surface over which the integral is carried out. Thus, we need the definition as well as the understanding of just how to assign an orientation to a surface.

We consider a 2-D surface in the 3-D space which is piecewise smooth, that is, every point $P_0(\mathbf{x}_0)$ of the surface has a neighborhood S which can be represented by a vector valued function of two parameters $\mathbf{x}(u,v)$ having continuous partial derivatives with respect to u and v in S. All points in S are covered by varying $\mathbf{x}(u,v)$ as the parameters u,v vary over an open set γ in the u,v plane such that different (u,v) correspond to different points on S. Further, we want the function $\mathbf{x}(u,v)$ to have the derivatives $\mathbf{x}_u(u,v)$ and $\mathbf{x}_v(u,v)$ with respect to u,v in γ that are continuous and linearly independent. We call such a representation a *regular local* representation of the surface.

We have seen that, the equations

$$x = x(u,v),\ y = y(u,v),\ z = z(u,v),$$

equivalent to $\mathbf{x} = \mathbf{x}(u,v)$, represent a surface provided

$$\mathbf{x}_u \times \mathbf{x}_v \neq \mathbf{0}\ \text{ or }\ |\mathbf{x}_u \times \mathbf{x}_v|^2 > 0.$$

Using identity II, this condition can be converted to

$$|\mathbf{x}_u \times \mathbf{x}_v|^2 = (\mathbf{x}_u \times \mathbf{x}_v) \cdot (\mathbf{x}_u \times \mathbf{x}_v) = \begin{vmatrix} \mathbf{x}_u \cdot \mathbf{x}_u & \mathbf{x}_u \cdot \mathbf{x}_v \\ \mathbf{x}_v \cdot \mathbf{x}_u & \mathbf{x}_v \cdot \mathbf{x}_v \end{vmatrix} > 0,$$

where the determinant in this equation, denoted $\Gamma(\mathbf{x}_u, \mathbf{x}_v)$, is called the Gram determinant. $\Gamma(\mathbf{x}_u, \mathbf{x}_v) = 0$ implies that $\mathbf{x}_u \times \mathbf{x}_v = \mathbf{0}$, that is, $\mathbf{x}_u, \mathbf{x}_v$ are collinear and hence linearly dependent. Conversely, if $|\mathbf{x}_u \times \mathbf{x}_v|^2 = \Gamma(\mathbf{x}_u, \mathbf{x}_v) > 0$, then $\mathbf{x}_u \times \mathbf{x}_v \neq \mathbf{0}$ so that $\mathbf{x}_u, \mathbf{x}_v$ are not collinear and hence are linearly independent. Therefore, the fact that $\mathbf{x}(u,v)$ is a regular local parameterization of the surface implies that $\Gamma(\mathbf{x}_u, \mathbf{x}_v) > 0$, so that $\mathbf{x}_u, \mathbf{x}_v$ are linearly independent.

The vectors $\mathbf{x}_u(u,v)$ and $\mathbf{x}_v(u,v)$ at a point $P = \mathbf{x}(u,v)$ of S are tangential to S at P and span the tangent plane $\pi(P)$ of S at P. Thus, every point of the tangent plane has the position vector $\mathbf{x}_T(u,v) = \mathbf{x}(u,v) + \lambda\mathbf{x}_u(u,v) + \mu\mathbf{x}_v(u,v)$ with suitable coefficients λ and μ.

In order to orient the surface S, we first assign an orientation to the tangent plane $\pi(P)$. Orienting a plane means specifying one of the two sides of it. This can be done by specifying one of the two unit normals to the plane. In order to specify one of the two unit normals to the tangent plane $\pi(P)$ and make it the oriented tangent plane $\pi^*(P)$, we specify an *ordered* pair of linearly independent vectors $\xi(P)$ and $\eta(P)$ in $\pi(P)$. The order of these vectors, $\xi(P), \eta(P)$ or $\eta(P), \xi(P)$ decides which of the two possible directions along the line normal to the plane $\pi(P)$ at P is the direction of the corresponding vector product $\xi(P) \times \eta(P)$ or $\eta(P) \times \xi(P)$ (see Fig. 11.33).

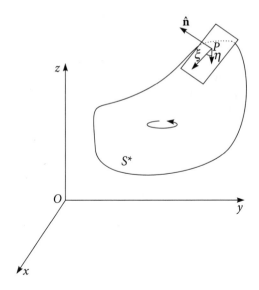

Fig. 11.33   Unit vector $\hat{\mathbf{n}}$ gives the orientation of oriented surface S^* at P

Thus, the orientation of $\pi^*(P)$ is specified in terms of the direction of the vector product of $\xi(P), \eta(P)$, with the order of factors being the same as that of the ordered pair of $\xi(P)$ and $\eta(P)$ chosen to specify the orientation of $\pi^*(P)$. Thus, the oriented tangent plane $\pi^*(P)$ can be specified by the pair $(\pi(P), \hat{\mathbf{n}})$ or $(\pi(P), -\hat{\mathbf{n}})$ where

$$\hat{\mathbf{n}} = \frac{\xi(P) \times \eta(P)}{|\xi(P) \times \eta(P)|} \tag{11.142}$$

or

$$-\hat{\mathbf{n}} = \frac{\eta(P) \times \xi(P)}{|\eta(P) \times \xi(P)|} \tag{11.143}$$

is the unit vector giving the direction of the vector product of $\xi(P)$ and $\eta(P)$ in the chosen order. Since there are only two possible orientations of $\pi(P)$, they can be specified via a dicotomic function $\Omega(\pi^*(P)) = \Omega(\xi(P), \eta(P)) = \pm 1$ where each of the two values corresponds to one of the two possible orientations, but which value corresponds to which orientation is arbitrary (see subsection 1.16.1). Any other ordered pair of independent tangential vectors $\xi'(P), \eta'(P)$ at P determines the same orientation if the angle between the corresponding vector products is less than $\pi/2$, that is,

$$[\xi(P), \eta(P); \xi'(P), \eta'(P)] = (\xi(P) \times \eta(P)) \cdot (\xi'(P) \times \eta'(P)) = \begin{vmatrix} \xi \cdot \xi' & \xi \cdot \eta' \\ \eta \cdot \xi' & \eta \cdot \eta' \end{vmatrix} > 0.$$

where we have used identity II. Generally, we can say that

$$\Omega(\xi(P), \eta(P)) = sgn[\xi(P), \eta(P); \xi'(P), \eta'(P)]\Omega(\xi'(P), \eta'(P)) \tag{11.144}$$

where $sgn(x)$ equals -1 for $x < 0$ and $+1$ for $x \geq 0$ respectively. Equivalently, the the ordered pairs of tangential vectors ξ, η and ξ', η' give the same orientation to π if

$$\hat{\mathbf{n}} \cdot \hat{\mathbf{n}}' > 0$$

where $\hat{\mathbf{n}}$ and $\hat{\mathbf{n}}'$ are the unit vectors specifying the directions of $\xi \times \eta$ and $\xi' \times \eta'$ respectively. Since $\xi(P), \eta(P)$ and $\xi'(P), \eta'(P)$ belong to the same plane, there are only two possibilities: $\hat{\mathbf{n}} \cdot \hat{\mathbf{n}}' = +1$ ($\hat{\mathbf{n}}' = \hat{\mathbf{n}}$) or $\hat{\mathbf{n}} \cdot \hat{\mathbf{n}}' = -1$ ($\hat{\mathbf{n}}' = -\hat{\mathbf{n}}$).

We now use the orientation of the tangent plane to the surface S at a point P on S to define the orientation of the surface S in the following way. We say that the unit normals defining the orientations of the tangent planes $\pi^*(P)$ depend continuously on P, when these normals to the planes $\pi^*(P)$ at the points close to each other (in the Euclidean sense) are themselves close to each other (in the Euclidean sense). That is, given $\epsilon > 0$ however small, there exists $\delta > 0$ such that, $\sqrt{(u - u_1)^2 + (v - v_1)^2} < \delta$ implies $|\hat{\mathbf{n}}(\mathbf{x}(u,v)) - \hat{\mathbf{n}}(\mathbf{x}(u_1,v_1))| < \epsilon$. This is expressed by saying that the the orientation $\Omega(\pi^*(P))$ of tangent plane at P varies continuously as P varies on S. An oriented surface S^* is defined as a surface S with continuously oriented tangent planes $\pi^*(P)$.

It is possible to find another criterion to ascertain the unit vector deciding the orientation of a tangent plane. If $\{\xi, \eta\}$ stands for one of the two ordered pairs drawn out of $\xi(P)$ and $\eta(P)$, then the corresponding unit normal $\hat{\mathbf{n}}$ deciding the orientation of $\pi^*(P)$ is the one which makes the triplet $\{\xi, \eta\}, \hat{\mathbf{n}}$ positively oriented (see section 1.16). This is equivalent to the following inequality,

$$\hat{\mathbf{n}} \cdot \{\xi \times \eta\} = \det(\hat{\mathbf{n}}, \{\xi, \eta\}) = |\{\xi \times \eta\}| > 0. \tag{11.145}$$

Thus, out of the two possible unit vectors perpendicular to $\pi(P)$ at P, the unit vector satisfying inequality Eq. (11.145) decides the orientation of $\pi(P)$. As we show in the next para, this vector also specifies the orientation of a connected surface S. Let $\hat{\mathbf{e}}_1, \hat{\mathbf{e}}_2, \hat{\mathbf{e}}_3$ be the orthonormal basis to which all vectors are referred. Then, if the triplets $(\xi, \eta, \hat{\mathbf{n}})$ and $\hat{\mathbf{e}}_1, \hat{\mathbf{e}}_2, \hat{\mathbf{e}}_3$, have the same orientation, we can write (see section 1.16),

$$\Omega(\xi, \eta, \hat{\mathbf{n}}) = \Omega(\hat{\mathbf{e}}_1, \hat{\mathbf{e}}_2, \hat{\mathbf{e}}_3)$$

and we call this vector $\hat{\mathbf{n}}$, defining the orientation of S^*, the unit normal vector pointing to the *positive side* of the oriented surface S^* or the *positive unit normal* to S^*.

We can now understand how to assign an orientation to a connected surface S. We choose a point P on S, and the pair (ξ, η) in the tangent plane $\pi(P)$, which decides, via Eq. (11.142), one of the two possible unit vectors $\hat{\mathbf{n}}$ and $\hat{\mathbf{n}}'$ specifying the orientation of S at P. This unit vector actually specifies the orientation of the whole surface S, as the following argument shows. At P we have $\hat{\mathbf{n}}' = \epsilon \hat{\mathbf{n}}$, where $\epsilon = \epsilon(P) = \pm 1$. Since the unit vectors $\hat{\mathbf{n}}, \hat{\mathbf{n}}'$ are assumed to vary continuously with P, the same is true for $\epsilon(P) = \hat{\mathbf{n}} \cdot \hat{\mathbf{n}}'$. Thus, ϵ is a continuous function on S having only the values $+1$ or -1. If $\epsilon(P) \neq \epsilon(Q)$ for any two distinct points P and Q on S, it follows from the continuity of ϵ that $\epsilon = 0$ at some point along a curve on S joining P and Q, contradicting the definition of ϵ. As a result, ϵ has same value at all points on S. Thus, any orientation of S is given by either the unit normal $\hat{\mathbf{n}}(P)$ or $\hat{\mathbf{n}}'(P) = -\hat{\mathbf{n}}(P)$. If the positive unit normal corresponding to S^* is $\hat{\mathbf{n}}$, the other possible orientation corresponding to $-\hat{\mathbf{n}}$ as its positive unit normal is called $-S^*$. From Eq. (11.144) we see that

$$\Omega(-S^*) = -\Omega(S^*),$$

where $\Omega(S^*) = \Omega(\xi(P), \eta(P))$ for some tangent plane $\pi(P)$ on S. Thus, the orientation of the positive normal $\hat{\mathbf{n}}$ to a connected surface S at a single point P uniquely determines the positive normal at any other point Q and hence determines the orientation of S. All that we need to do is to continuously carry the positive unit normal at P to Q along a curve on S joining P and Q, so that it coincides with the positive unit normal at Q to S. There are connected surfaces on which a positive unit normal at a point cannot be transported along a curve on the surface, to coincide with the positive unit normal at some other point on the surface. Such a surface cannot be assigned any orientation and is not orientable. The Mobius strip is the most celebrated example of a connected surface that is not orientable.

Orientation of a surface S becomes quite simple if it forms the boundary of a region $\mathcal{R}$ in space. Such a surface can be oriented even if it is not connected, as, for example, the surface forming the boundary of a spherical shell. At each point P on S we can distinguish an *interior normal* pointing into $\mathcal{R}$ from an *exterior normal* pointing away from $\mathcal{R}$. Both these normals vary continuously with P. We can take the exterior normal as the positive normal to define an orientation of S. We call the resulting oriented surface S^* *Oriented positively with respect to $\mathcal{R}$*. Thus, for example, for a spherical shell

$$a \le |\mathbf{x}| \le b$$

the positive oriented boundary S^* of $\mathcal{R}$ has the positive unit normal

$$\hat{\mathbf{n}} = -\mathbf{x}/a \text{ for } |\mathbf{x}| = a \text{ and } \hat{\mathbf{n}} = \mathbf{x}/b \text{ for } |\mathbf{x}| = b.$$

Let a portion of a oriented surface S^* have a regular parametric representation $\mathbf{x} = \mathbf{x}(u, v)$ with (u, v) varying over an open set γ of the u, v plane. Then,

$$\hat{\mathbf{z}} = \frac{\mathbf{x}_u \times \mathbf{x}_v}{|\mathbf{x}_u \times \mathbf{x}_v|} \tag{11.146}$$

defines a unit normal vector for (u, v) in γ. If $\hat{\mathbf{n}}$ is the positive unit normal to S^* we have

$$\hat{\mathbf{n}} = \epsilon \hat{\mathbf{z}}$$

with $\epsilon = \epsilon(u, v) = \pm 1$. By continuity of $\hat{\mathbf{n}}$ and $\hat{\mathbf{z}}$ ϵ is continuous which, when coupled with the fact that $\epsilon = \pm 1$, would mean that ϵ is constant on every connected component of γ. For $\epsilon = 1$, that is, for

$$\Omega(S^*) = \Omega(\mathbf{x}_u, \mathbf{x}_v),$$

we say that S^* is oriented positively with respect to parameters u, v and write

$$\Omega(S^*) = \Omega(u, v).$$

If the same part of S^* has another regular parametric representation in terms of parameters $\bar{u}, \bar{v}$ varying over the region $\bar{\gamma}$, we have, by Eq. (10.65),

$$\mathbf{x}_u \times \mathbf{x}_v = \left(\frac{d(y, z)}{d(u, v)}, \frac{d(z, x)}{d(u, v)}, \frac{d(x, y)}{d(u, v)} \right),$$

or,

$$\mathbf{x}_u \times \mathbf{x}_v = \frac{d(\bar{u}, \bar{v})}{d(u, v)} (\bar{\mathbf{x}}_u \times \bar{\mathbf{x}}_v).$$

Thus, the unit normals $\hat{\mathbf{z}}$ and $\hat{\bar{\mathbf{z}}}$ for the two parametric representations are related by

$$\hat{\mathbf{z}} = sgn \left(\frac{d(\bar{u}, \bar{v})}{d(u, v)} \right) \hat{\bar{\mathbf{z}}}.$$

Thus, S^* is oriented positively with respect to both the parameterizations provided

$$\frac{d(\bar{u}, \bar{v})}{d(u, v)} > 0.$$

As an illustration, we consider the unit sphere S^* with center at the origin, oriented positively with respect to its interior. With $u = x$ and $v = y$ as parameters for $z \neq 0$, we have,

$$\mathbf{x} = \left(u, v, \epsilon \sqrt{1 - u^2 - v^2} \right), \text{ where } \epsilon = sgn\, z.$$

The corresponding unit normal vector $\hat{\mathbf{z}}$ given by Eq. (11.146) becomes

$$\hat{\mathbf{z}} = (\epsilon x, \epsilon y, \epsilon z) = \epsilon \hat{\mathbf{n}}$$

where $\hat{\mathbf{n}}$ is the exterior unit normal. Hence, S^* is oriented positively with respect to the parameters x, y for $z > 0$ and negatively for $z < 0$ (see Fig. 11.34).

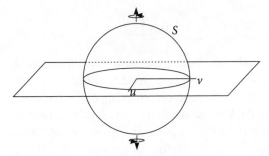

Fig. 11.34   Orientation of S with respect to u, v

We end this subsection by demonstrating the non-orientability of the Mobius strip. We can easily produce Mobius strip by fastening the ends of a rectangular strip of paper after rotating one of the ends by $180°$ (see Fig. 11.35). Starting with the initial rectangle $0 < u < 2\pi$, $-a < v < a$ (where $0 < a < 1$) in the u, v plane, we rigidly move each segment $u =$ constant so that its center moves to the point $(\cos u, \sin u, 0)$ of the unit circle in the x, y plane, the segment is perpendicular to the tangent of the circle at that point and makes the angle $u/2$ with the positive direction of the z-axis, to get the Mobius strip.

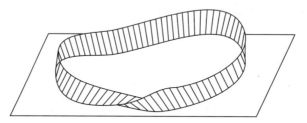

Fig. 11.35   Mobius strip

The assumption $a < 1$ keeps the surface from intersecting itself. The resulting strip has the parametric representation

$$\mathbf{x} = \left(\left(1 + v \sin \frac{u}{2}\right)\cos u,\right.$$

$$\left.\left(1 + v \sin \frac{u}{2}\right)\sin u, v \cos \frac{u}{2}\right)$$

with v restricted to $-a < v < a$. The points $(u,v), (u + 4\pi, v), (u + 2\pi, -v)$ in the u, v plane correspond to the same point on the surface. Making a definite choice of parameters u_0, v_0 for an arbitrary point P on the surface, Eq. (11.147) gives a regular local parametric representation of S for $(u,v) \in \gamma$ given by

$$u_0 - \pi < u < u_0 + \pi, \quad -a < v < a.$$

Along the center line $v = 0$ on the surface, Eq. (11.146) defines a unit normal vector

$$\hat{\mathbf{z}} = \left(\cos u \cos \frac{u}{2}, \sin u \cos \frac{u}{2}, -\sin \frac{u}{2}\right)$$

that varies continuously with u. Starting out with the unit normal $\hat{\mathbf{z}} = (1,0,0)$ at the point $(1,0,0)$ of S corresponding to $u = 0$ and letting u increase from 0 to 2π, we complete a circuit along the center line of the surface, returning to the same point but with the opposite unit normal $\hat{\mathbf{z}} = (-1,0,0)$. We find similarly that carrying a small oriented tangential curve along the circuit, we return to the same point with its orientation reversed. Thus, it is not possible to choose a continuously varying unit normal, or a side of S in a consistent way. In other words, the Mobius strip is not orientable.

Exercise Let S be the mobius strip with the parametric representation given by Eq. (11.147). (a) Show that the line $v = a/2$ divides S into an orientable and a non-orientable set. (b) Show that the line $v = 0$ does not divide S, that is, the set S_1 obtained by removing all points with $v = 0$ from S is still connected. (c) Show that S_1 is orientable.

Solution

(a) The line $v = a/2$ divides S into a part S' $a/2 < v < a$ (or, equivalently, $-a < v < -a/2$) and oriented by $\xi = \mathbf{x}_u$, $\eta = \mathbf{x}_v$ and a part S'' given by $-a/2 < v < a/2$ which is just another Mobius strip.

(b) S_1 is representable by $\Omega(\xi(P), \eta(P))$ with v restricted to the interval $0 < v < a$, where P can be varied continuously over S_1. Obviously, any two points on S_1 can be joined by a curve on S_1 which is the image of the corresponding points (u, v) in the parameter plane.

(c) S_1 is oriented by $\xi = \mathbf{x}_u$, $\eta = \mathbf{x}_v$. □

Exercise Let ξ, η be independent vectors in a plane π. Put $a = |\xi|^2$, $b = \xi \cdot \eta$, $c = |\eta|^2$ form for any θ the vector

$$\mathbf{X}(\theta) = \left(\cos\theta - \frac{b}{\sqrt{ac - b^2}} \sin\theta \right) \xi + \frac{a \sin\theta}{\sqrt{ac - b^2}} \eta.$$

Prove that $\mathbf{X}(\theta)$ is obtained by rotating the vector ξ in the plane π by an angle θ in the sense given by the orientation $\Omega(\xi, \eta)$.

Solution We can easily check that $\mathbf{X}(\theta)$ has length $|\xi|$ and is linearly dependent on ξ, η so that $\mathbf{X}(\theta)$ lies in π. Moreover, $\mathbf{X}(\theta) \cdot \xi / |\xi|^2 = \cos\theta$. The vector $\mathbf{X}(\theta)$ coincides with ξ for $\theta = 0$ and has the direction of η for a certain θ between 0 and π, or, for that θ determined by the relations

$$\cos\theta = \frac{b}{\sqrt{ac}}, \quad \sin\theta = \sqrt{1 - \frac{b^2}{ac}}. \qquad □$$

Summary

We now summarize the relevant points covered in this section. First, an orientable surface S has two possible orientations which are given by the two possible normals to the surface at some point P on it. These are obtained by choosing two non-collinear (linearly independent) vectors ξ and η based at P, spanning the tangent plane to S at P. We form two possible ordered pairs (ξ, η) and (η, ξ) to define two possible unit normals to the tangent plane or to the surface S at P:

$$\hat{\mathbf{n}} = \frac{\xi \times \eta}{|\xi \times \eta|} \; ; \; -\hat{\mathbf{n}} = \frac{\eta \times \xi}{|\eta \times \xi|}.$$

We denote the corresponding oriented surface by S^*. From the above equations it is clear that the triplet $(\xi, \eta, \hat{\mathbf{n}})$ is positively oriented, while the triplet $(\xi, \eta, -\hat{\mathbf{n}})$ is negatively oriented. In order to decide which of these unit normals define the positive orientation of S^*, we first orient the 3-D space containing S^* as follows. We choose a coordinate system defined by the orthonormal basis $(\hat{\mathbf{e}}_1, \hat{\mathbf{e}}_2, \hat{\mathbf{e}}_3)$ to resolve the vectors in some region of space $\mathcal{R}$ and say that $\mathcal{R}$ is positively oriented if this coordinate system is right handed and negatively oriented if it is left handed. If the coordinate system is right handed, it has the same orientation as the triplet $(\xi, \eta, \hat{\mathbf{n}})$ and we say that $\hat{\mathbf{n}}$ defines the positive orientation of S^* and $-\hat{\mathbf{n}}$ defines its negative orientation. On the other hand, if the coordinate system is left handed, it has the same orientation as $(\xi, \eta, -\hat{\mathbf{n}})$ and we say that $-\hat{\mathbf{n}}$ defines the positive orientation of S^* and $\hat{\mathbf{n}}$ defines its negative orientation. In general, a unit vector $\hat{\mathbf{n}}$ defining the positive orientation of S^* is said to be on the positive side of S^*. For a closed surface S at the boundary of a region $\mathcal{R}$ we choose the coordinate system such that the unit normal defining the positive orientation of S^* is its outward normal.

If a surface S is parameterized by a C^1 function $\mathbf{x} = \mathbf{x}(u, v)$, we can replace the pair (ξ, η) by the pair of tangent vectors $(\mathbf{x}_u, \mathbf{x}_v)$ to define the unit vector, via their vector product, giving the orientation of S^*. If this unit vector $\hat{\mathbf{z}}$ defines the positive orientation of S^*, we say that S^* is positively oriented with respect to the parameters u, v.

Now, consider an oriented surface S^* with an oriented and closed boundary curve C^*. Let the unit normal vector $\hat{\mathbf{n}}$ at point P on S decide the orientation of S^*. We drop a perpendicular from P to the plane containing the curve C^* to meet this plane at point O. Let P_1 and P_2 be the points on C^* such that traversing C^* from P_1 toward P_2 is in the same sense defining the orientation of C^*. Then C^* is positively oriented with respect to S^* if the triplet $(\overrightarrow{OP}_1, \overrightarrow{OP}_2, \hat{\mathbf{n}})$ is positively oriented. Further, we say that S^* is positively oriented with respect to the x, y axes if the triplet $(\hat{\mathbf{e}}_1, \hat{\mathbf{e}}_2, \hat{\mathbf{n}})$ is positively oriented.

11.8   Surface Integrals

The orientation of the region over which an integral is carried out is fundamentally connected to its value, although the Riemannian sums involved are defined in terms of quantities like length, area and volume, which are inherently positive quantities. Thus, if we want the additivity rule

$$\int_a^b f(x)dx + \int_b^c f(x)dx = \int_a^c f(x)dx$$

to hold without restricting the relative positions of a, b, c, we have to define $\int_a^b f(x)dx$ both for $a \leq b$ as well as $a \geq b$ by the relation

$$\int_a^b f(x)dx = -\int_b^a f(x)dx. \tag{11.147}$$

Geometrically, the ordered pair of numbers a, b determines an oriented interval I^* on the x-axis with initial point a and the final point b. The value of

$$\int_a^b f(x)dx = \int_{I^*} f(x)dx$$

is the one given by the limit of the Riemann sum (positive for positive f) when the orientation of I^* corresponds to the sense of increasing x, that is, for $a < b$. Interchanging the end points of I^* converts I^* into the interval $-I^*$, with opposite orientation, so that Eq. (11.147) can also be written as

$$\int_{-I^*} f(x)dx = -\int_{I^*} f(x)dx. \tag{11.148}$$

A similar situation prevails regarding the integral over an oriented region $\mathcal{R}^*$ in the x, y plane. When $\mathcal{R}^*$ is oriented positively with respect to the $\hat{e}_1, \hat{e}_2$ basis defining the coordinate system, $\Omega(\mathcal{R}^*) = \Omega(\hat{e}_1, \hat{e}_2)$, the differential area $dxdy$ is positive and the double integral

$$\int\int_{\mathcal{R}^*} f(x,y)dxdy$$

is the limit of the Riemann sums obtained from the subdivisions of the plane into squares of area 2^{-2n}. The integral has a non-negative value for a non-negative f. In case $\Omega(\mathcal{R}^*) = -\Omega(\hat{e}_1, \hat{e}_2) = \Omega(\hat{e}_2, \hat{e}_1)$ resulting in a negative value for the differential area $dydx$ we get

$$\int\int_{\mathcal{R}^*} f dxdy = -\int\int_{\mathcal{R}^*} f dydx,$$

where the integral on the right has the usual meaning as the limit of sums. Thus, we have the rule that

$$\int\int_{-\mathcal{R}^*} f dxdy = -\int\int_{\mathcal{R}^*} f dxdy,$$

where $-\mathcal{R}^*$ is obtained by changing the orientation of $\mathcal{R}^*$. The substitution formula given by Eq. (11.99) becomes, for the oriented region $\mathcal{R}^*$,

$$\int\int_{\mathcal{R}^*} f(x,y)dxdy = \int\int_{T^*} f(x(u,v),y(u,v))\frac{d(x,y)}{d(u,v)}dudv,$$

for smooth $1-1$ mappings

$$x = x(u,v), \ y = y(u,v)$$

of T^* onto $\mathcal{R}^*$ as long as the Jacobian determinant $d(x,y)/d(u,v)$ has the same sign throughout T^*. The sign given by the orientation of $\mathcal{R}^*$ or that of T^* to the corresponding integrals is determined as follows. The rule is that the orientation of $\mathcal{R}^*$ attributes a positive sign to $dxdy$ if the x,y coordinate system has the orientation of $\mathcal{R}^*$ and negative one otherwise. The sign attributed by the orientation of T^* to $dudv$ is then the one that agrees with the relation

$$dxdy = \frac{d(x,y)}{d(u,v)}dudv.$$

Once the proper sign is attached to the differential area $dS = dxdy$ or $dT = dudv$, the rest of the integration amounts to the evaluation of the corresponding double integral.

While learning about line integrals, we came across linear differential forms, also called first order differential forms, which are expressions linear in the differentials dx, dy, dz. A second order differential form is an expression quadratic in the differentials dx, dy, dz and has the form

$$\omega = a(\mathbf{x})dxdy + b(\mathbf{x})dydz + c(\mathbf{x})dzdx$$

where a, b, c are C^1 functions over their domain. Here, we obtain a general form of the surface integral of the second order differential form over an oriented surface S^* in terms of the surface integral of functions over the unoriented surface S. We already know that if S has the parametric representation

$$x = x(u,v),\ y = y(u,v),\ z = z(u,v)$$

and if ξ, η, ζ denote the components of the normal vector

$$\xi = \frac{d(y,z)}{d(u,v)},\ \eta = \frac{d(z,x)}{d(u,v)},\ \zeta = \frac{d(x,y)}{d(u,v)}, \tag{11.149}$$

the area of S is given by

$$A = \int\int_{\mathcal{R}} \sqrt{\xi^2 + \eta^2 + \zeta^2}\,dudv.$$

Here, the integral is over the region $\mathcal{R}$ in the u,v plane corresponding to S The integral is understood in the sense of a double integral with the surface element

$$dS = \sqrt{\xi^2 + \eta^2 + \zeta^2}\,dudv$$

being treated as a positive quantity or, equivalently, $\mathcal{R}$ is given the positive orientation with respect to the u,v system. Orientability of S is not essential for the definition of A.

Exercise   Express the total area of the Mobius strip as an integral, using its parametric representation given by Eq. (11.147). □

More generally, for a function $f(\mathbf{x})$ defined on the surface S, we can form the integral of f over the surface:

$$\int\int_S f\, dS = \int\int_{\mathcal{R}} f\, \sqrt{\xi^2 + \eta^2 + \zeta^2}\, du\, dv. \tag{11.150}$$

The value of this integral is independent of the particular parametric representation used for S and does not involve any orientation of S. It is positive for positive f.

In order to relate the integral of a second order differential form over an oriented surface S^* to the surface integrals of functions over the unoriented surface S as defined by Eq. (11.150), we introduce the direction cosines of the positive normal to S^*

$$\cos\alpha = \frac{\epsilon\xi}{\sqrt{\xi^2+\eta^2+\zeta^2}}, \cos\beta = \frac{\epsilon\eta}{\sqrt{\xi^2+\eta^2+\zeta^2}}, \cos\gamma = \frac{\epsilon\zeta}{\sqrt{\xi^2+\eta^2+\zeta^2}},$$

where ξ, η, ζ are as defined in Eq. (11.149), $\epsilon = \pm 1$ and $\Omega(S^*) = \epsilon\Omega(\mathbf{x}_u, \mathbf{x}_v)$ (see subsection 1.16.1). We can write ω in the form

$$\omega = K\, du\, dv$$

where

$$K = \frac{\omega}{du\, dv} = a\frac{d(y,z)}{d(u,v)} + b\frac{d(z,x)}{d(u,v)} + c\frac{d(x,y)}{d(u,v)} \tag{11.151}$$

so that

$$\int\int_{S^*}\omega = \int\int_{\mathcal{R}^*} K\, du\, dv$$

$$= \int\int_{\mathcal{R}^*}\left(a\frac{d(y,z)}{d(u,v)} + b\frac{d(z,x)}{d(u,v)} + c\frac{d(x,y)}{d(u,v)}\right)du\, dv. \tag{11.152}$$

Exercise Show that the value of this integral of ω over the oriented surface S^* is independent of the particular parametric representation for S^*. □

From Eqs (11.151) and (11.152) we can write

$$K = \frac{\omega}{du\, dv} = \epsilon(a\cos\alpha + b\cos\beta + c\cos\gamma)\sqrt{\xi^2 + \eta^2 + \zeta^2}.$$

By Eq. (11.152)

$$\int\int_{S^*}\omega = \int\int_{\mathcal{R}^*} K\, du\, dv = \epsilon\int\int_{\mathcal{R}} K\, du\, dv.$$

Therefore, Eq. (11.150) yields the identity

$$\iint_{S^*} \omega = \iint_{S^*} a\,dy\,dz + b\,dz\,dx + c\,dx\,dy$$

$$= \iint_S (a\cos\alpha + b\cos\beta + c\cos\gamma)\,dS$$

$$= \iint_{\mathcal{R}} (a\cos\alpha + b\cos\beta + c\cos\gamma)\sqrt{\xi^2 + \eta^2 + \zeta^2}\,du\,dv, \qquad (11.153)$$

which expresses the integral of the differential form ω over the oriented surface S^* as an integral over the unoriented surface S or over the unoriented region $\mathcal{R}$ in the parameter plane. Note, however, that here the integrand depends on the orientation of S^*, since it involves the direction cosines of the normal $\hat{\mathbf{n}}$ to S^* pointing to its positive side. If the oriented surface S^* comprises many parts S_i^* each having a parametric representation $\mathbf{x} = \mathbf{x}(u,v)$ we apply identity Eq. (11.153) to each part and add over different parts to get the same identity for the integral of ω over the whole surface S^*.

The direction cosines of the normal $\hat{\mathbf{n}}$ pointing to the positive side of S^* can be identified with the derivatives of x, y, z in the direction of $\hat{\mathbf{n}}$, so that[4]

$$\iint_{S^*} \omega = \iint_S \left(a\frac{dx}{dn} + b\frac{dy}{dn} + c\frac{dz}{dn} \right) dS \qquad (11.154)$$

or, in vector notation

$$\iint_{S^*} \omega = \iint_S \mathbf{v} \cdot \hat{\mathbf{n}}\,dS, \qquad (11.155)$$

where $\hat{\mathbf{n}} \equiv (\cos\alpha, \cos\beta, \cos\gamma)$ is the unit normal vector on the positive side of S^* and $\mathbf{v}(\mathbf{x})$ is the vector field with components $(a(\mathbf{x}), b(\mathbf{x}), c(\mathbf{x}))$.

The concept of a surface integral can be interpreted in terms of the 3-D flow of an incompressible fluid of unit density. Let the vector field $\mathbf{v}(\mathbf{x})$ be the velocity field of this flow. Then at each point of the surface S^* the product $\mathbf{v} \cdot \hat{\mathbf{n}}$ gives the component of the velocity of the flow in the direction of the normal $\hat{\mathbf{n}}$ to the surface. The expression $\mathbf{v} \cdot \hat{\mathbf{n}}\,dS$ can then be identified with the amount of fluid that flows across the element of surface dS from the negative side of S^* to the positive side in unit time. Note that this quantity may be negative. The surface integral in Eq. (11.155) therefore represents the total amount of fluid flowing across the surface S^* from the negative to the positive side in unit time. Note the fundamental part played by the orientation (distinction between the positive and negative sides) of S^* in the description of the motion of the fluid.

We may also consider the field defined by the integrand of Eq. (11.155) as the field of force $\mathbf{F}(\mathbf{x})$. The direction of the vector $\mathbf{F}$ then gives the direction of the *lines of force* and its

---

[4]We have, $\frac{dx}{dn} = \hat{\mathbf{n}} \cdot \nabla x = [\cos\alpha \ \cos\beta \ \cos\gamma][1 \ 0 \ 0]^T = \cos\alpha$ etc.

magnitude gives the magnitude of the force. The integral in Eq. (11.155) is then interpreted as the total *flux of force* across the surface from the negative to the positive side.

11.8.1 Divergence of a vector field and the surface integral

We wish to express the divergence of a vector field $\mathbf{f}(\mathbf{x})$ at a point P in terms of a surface integral, that is,

$$\nabla \cdot \mathbf{f}\big|_P = \lim_{S \to P} \frac{1}{V} \int_S \mathbf{f} \cdot \hat{\mathbf{n}} ds, \qquad (11.156)$$

where S is a closed surface enclosing volume V. The point P is interior to or on the surface S. The limit $S \to P$ means every point on S approaches P. If this limit exists, the integral in Eq. (11.156) is independent of S and defines the divergence of $\mathbf{f}$ at P. We show that the limit exists if $\mathbf{f}$ can be expanded in Taylor series in the neighborhood of P.

We construct a Cartesian coordinate system (ξ, η, ζ) with its origin at P. As in subsection 11.1.1 we expand $\mathbf{f}(\mathbf{x})$ with $\mathbf{x}$ on the surface S in Taylor series around the origin $\mathbf{0}$ at P. We have,

$$\mathbf{f}(\mathbf{x}) = \mathbf{f}(\mathbf{0}) + \mathbf{x} \cdot \nabla \mathbf{f}(\mathbf{0}) + \mathbf{R},$$

where $\mathbf{R}$ is of the order of $|\mathbf{x}|^2$ and all the derivatives are evaluated at the origin, that is, at point P. Therefore, integrating over the surface S we get

$$\int_S \mathbf{f}(\mathbf{x}) \cdot d\mathbf{s} = \mathbf{f}(\mathbf{0}) \cdot \int_S d\mathbf{s} + \int_S (\mathbf{x} \cdot \nabla) \mathbf{f}(\mathbf{x}) \cdot d\mathbf{s} + \int_S \mathbf{R} \cdot d\mathbf{s}.$$

We first resolve the vector $d\mathbf{s}$ along the basis $(\hat{\mathbf{i}}, \hat{\mathbf{j}}, \hat{\mathbf{k}})$, (see Fig. 11.36)

$$d\mathbf{s} = \hat{\mathbf{i}} ds_\xi + \hat{\mathbf{j}} ds_\eta + \hat{\mathbf{k}} ds_\zeta \qquad (11.157)$$

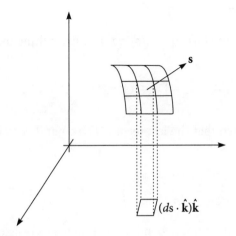

$(d\mathbf{s} \cdot \hat{\mathbf{k}})\hat{\mathbf{k}}$

Fig. 11.36 Illustrating Eq. (11.157)

where the components of $d\mathbf{s}$ are the projections of $d\mathbf{s}$ on yz, zx and xy planes respectively. As in subsection 11.1.1 we express $(\mathbf{x} \cdot \nabla)\mathbf{f}(\mathbf{x}) \cdot d\mathbf{s}$ in terms of the derivatives with respect to (ξ, η, ζ) to get

$$\int_S \mathbf{f} \cdot d\mathbf{s} = \mathbf{f}(0) \cdot \int_S d\mathbf{s} + \frac{\partial f_\xi}{\partial \xi} \int_{S_\xi} \xi \, ds_\xi + \frac{\partial f_\xi}{\partial \eta} \int_{S_\xi} \eta \, ds_\xi + \frac{\partial f_\xi}{\partial \zeta} \int_{S_\xi} \zeta \, ds_\xi$$

$$\frac{\partial f_\eta}{\partial \xi} \int_{S_\eta} \xi \, ds_\eta + \frac{\partial f_\eta}{\partial \eta} \int_{S_\eta} \eta \, ds_\eta + \frac{\partial f_\eta}{\partial \zeta} \int_{S_\eta} \zeta \, ds_\eta$$

$$\frac{\partial f_\zeta}{\partial \xi} \int_{S_\zeta} \xi \, ds_\zeta + \frac{\partial f_\zeta}{\partial \eta} \int_{S_\zeta} \eta \, ds_\zeta + \frac{\partial f_\zeta}{\partial \zeta} \int_{S_\zeta} \zeta \, ds_\zeta + \int_S \mathbf{R} \cdot d\mathbf{s},$$

where (S_ξ, S_η, S_ζ) are the projections of S on the coordinate planes and the last integral goes as $|\mathbf{x}|^4$. We shall show later in an exercise that

$$\int_S d\mathbf{s} = 0.$$

Further,

$$\int_{S_\xi} \xi \, ds_\xi = V,$$

since $\int_{S_\xi} \xi \, ds_\xi$ gives the volume under the upper part minus that under the lower part (see subsection 11.4.2). Similarly,

$$\int_{S_\eta} \eta \, ds_\eta = V = \int_{S_\zeta} \zeta \, ds_\zeta.$$

Moreover, the integrals of the form $\int_{S_\xi} \eta \, ds_\xi$ vanish. Everything put together we get

$$\int_S \mathbf{f} \cdot d\mathbf{s} = \left(\frac{\partial f_\xi}{\partial \xi} + \frac{\partial f_\eta}{\partial \eta} + \frac{\partial f_\zeta}{\partial \zeta} \right) V + O(|\mathbf{x}|^4).$$

Divide both sides by V, (so that the last term is $O(|\mathbf{x}|)$ and goes to zero as $|\mathbf{x}| \to 0$), and take the limit as $|\mathbf{x}| \to 0$ to get

$$\lim_{S \to P} \frac{1}{V} \int_S \mathbf{f} \cdot d\mathbf{s} = \left(\frac{\partial f_\xi}{\partial \xi} + \frac{\partial f_\eta}{\partial \eta} + \frac{\partial f_\zeta}{\partial \zeta} \right) = \nabla \cdot \mathbf{f}.$$

Thus, the limit exists and does not depend on S. It depends only on the derivatives of $\mathbf{f}$ at point P.

Exercise   Let S be a closed surface and let P be an interior point of S or a point on S. For a scalar field f and a vector field $\mathbf{F}$ show that

$$\nabla f = \lim_{S \to P} \frac{1}{V} \int_S f d\mathbf{s}$$

and

$$\nabla \times \mathbf{F} = \lim_{S \to P} \frac{1}{V} \int_S d\mathbf{s} \times \mathbf{F}. \qquad \qquad \square$$

11.9   Diveregence Theorem in Three-dimensions

This is the extension of the Gauss's theorem in two dimensions we proved before. There an integral over a plane region is reduced to a line integral taken around the boundary of the region. In its 3-D version, we consider a closed bounded region $\mathcal{R}$ in space bounded by a surface S. To start with we assume that S is intersected by every straight line parallel to x, y, z axes only at two points, or does not intersect at all. We will remove this assumption later. Let the functions $a(\mathbf{x}), b(\mathbf{x}), c(\mathbf{x})$ be C^1 in $\mathcal{R}$. Consider the integral

$$\int \int \int_{\mathcal{R}} \frac{\partial c}{\partial z} dx dy dz$$

over the region $\mathcal{R}$, oriented positively with respect to x, y, z coordinate system. Due to the assumption made regarding the mesh of straight lines parallel to the axes and the region $\mathcal{R}$, such a region $\mathcal{R}$ can be described by the inequalities

$$z_0(x, y) \le z \le z_1(x, y)$$

where (x, y) varies over the projection B of $\mathcal{R}$ on the x, y plane. We assume that B has an area and that the functions $z_0(x, y)$ and $z_1(x, y)$ are C^1 in B. We can express the volume integral over $\mathcal{R}$ as the succession of integrals

$$\int \int \int_{\mathcal{R}} f dx dy dz = \int \int_B dx dy \int_{z_0}^{z_1} f dz.$$

Here, $f = \partial c / \partial z$ so that the integral over z can be carried out, giving

$$\int_{z_0}^{z_1} \frac{\partial c}{\partial z} = c(x, y, z_1) - c(x, y, z_0) = c_1 - c_0,$$

so that,

$$\int \int \int_{\mathcal{R}} \frac{\partial c}{\partial z} dx dy dz = \int \int_B c_1 dx dy - \int \int_B c_0 dx dy.$$

If we assume that the boundary surface S is positively oriented with respect to the region $\mathcal{R}$, then the part of the oriented boundary surface S^* comprising points of entry $z = z_0(x,y)$ has a negative orientation with respect to x,y coordinates when projected on the x,y plane. On the other hand the part $z = z_1(x,y)$ consisting of points of exit has a positive orientation. To understand this, note that the triplets $(\hat{\mathbf{e}}_1, \hat{\mathbf{e}}_2, \hat{\mathbf{n}})$, one with $\hat{\mathbf{n}}$ at the entry point has negative orientation and the one with $\hat{\mathbf{n}}$ at the exit point has positive orientation (see the summary in section 11.7). Hence, the last two integrals combine to form the integral

$$\iint_{S^*} c(x,y,z)dxdy$$

taken over the whole surface S^*. We thus have,

$$\iiint_{\mathcal{R}} \frac{\partial c}{\partial z} dxdydz = \iint_{S^*} c(x,y,z)dxdy.$$

If a part S'^* of S^* is a cylinder perpendicular to the x,y plane, the normal defining its orientation lies parallel to the x,y plane and has no contribution to the integral on the right.

Exercise Prove this statement.

Hint Take the parametric representation $x = u$, $y = \phi(u)$, $z = v$ for S'^* and then evaluate $\iint_{S^*} c(x,y,z)dxdy$ after transforming it to the integral over u,v. $\qquad \square$

We get the corresponding equations for the components $a(\mathbf{x})$ and $b(\mathbf{x})$ of the vector field with components a,b,c. Adding all the three equations we get the desired result:

$$\iiint_{\mathcal{R}} \left[\frac{\partial a(\mathbf{x})}{\partial x} + \frac{\partial b(\mathbf{x})}{\partial y} + \frac{\partial c(\mathbf{x})}{\partial z} \right] dxdydz = \iint_{S^*} [a(\mathbf{x})dydz + b(\mathbf{x})dzdx + c(\mathbf{x})dxdy].$$

$$(11.158)$$

which is known as Gauss's theorem, or divergence theorem. Using Eq. (11.153) we can write this in the form

$$\iiint_{\mathcal{R}} [a_x + b_y + c_z]dxdydz = \iint_S (a\cos\alpha + b\cos\beta + c\cos\gamma)dS$$

$$= \iint_S \left(a\frac{dx}{dn} + b\frac{dy}{dn} + c\frac{dz}{dn} \right)dS, \qquad (11.159)$$

where, α, β, γ are the angles made by the outward normal $\hat{\mathbf{n}}$ with the positive coordinate axes, corresponding to the positive orientation of S^* with respect to $\mathcal{R}$.

We can lift the restriction stated at the beginning, that is the region $\mathcal{R}$ can be covered by a mesh of straight lines with each line intersecting the boundary surface exactly at two points, if the region $\mathcal{R}$ can be divided onto subregions separately satisfying this restriction and each subregion is bounded by an orientable surface. Then Gauss's theorem separately holds for each subregion. Upon adding, on the left we get a triple integral over the whole region $\mathcal{R}$ and on the right some of the surface integrals combine to form the integral over the oriented surface S, while the others making extra surfaces required to cover each subregion cancel one another. Assuming that we get the same integral independent of the way we divide the region $\mathcal{R}$ into subregions, this procedure generalizes Gauss's theorem to more general regions in space.

Exercise   Use Gauss's theorem to get the volume of a region $\mathcal{R}$ bounded by the surface S^* oriented positively with respect to $\mathcal{R}$.

Answer

$$V = \int\int\int_{\mathcal{R}} dx\,dy\,dz = \int\int_{S^*} x\,dy\,dz = \int\int_{S^*} z\,dx\,dy = \int\int_{S^*} y\,dz\,dx.$$

Hint   To get the first equality, for example, put $a = 0$, $b = 0$, $c = z$ in Eq. (11.158).   □

To get the vector form of the divergence theorem, let $\mathbf{v}$ be the vector field with component functions $a(\mathbf{x}), b(\mathbf{x}), c(\mathbf{x})$. Then, the integrand on the left of Eq. (11.159) is simply the divergence of this field and the integrand on the right is its component along the outward normal, so that

$$\int\int\int_{\mathcal{R}} \nabla \cdot \mathbf{v}\,dV = \int\int_{S^*} \mathbf{v} \cdot \hat{\mathbf{n}}\,dS, \tag{11.160}$$

where $dV = dx\,dy\,dz$ is the differential volume.

Exercise   Show that

$$\int_V f(\nabla \cdot \mathbf{A})d\tau = -\int_V \mathbf{A} \cdot (\nabla f)d\tau + \int_S f\mathbf{A} \cdot d\mathbf{a} \tag{11.161}$$

where f and $\mathbf{A}$ are scalar and vector valued functions respectively, $d\mathbf{a} = da\,\hat{\mathbf{n}}$ is the vector differential area and the surface S encloses volume V.

Hint   Use $\nabla \cdot (f\mathbf{A}) = f(\nabla \cdot \mathbf{A}) + \mathbf{A} \cdot (\nabla f)$ and the divergence theorem.   □

11.10   Applications of the Gauss's Theorem

(a) *Application to fluid flow*

We generalize to three dimensions the results about two dimensional flow of a fluid we obtained before. We deal with two fields, the velocity field $\mathbf{v}(\mathbf{x}, t)$ and the momentum vector (per unit volume) field $\mathbf{A}(\mathbf{x}, t) = \rho(\mathbf{x}, t)\mathbf{v}(\mathbf{x}, t)$. If $\mathcal{R}$ is a fixed region in space bounded by the surface S then the total mass of fluid that flows across a small area ΔS of S from interior to exterior of $\mathcal{R}$ in unit time is approximately $\rho \mathbf{v} \cdot \hat{\mathbf{n}} \Delta S$ where $\mathbf{v} \cdot \hat{\mathbf{n}}$ is the component of the velocity $\mathbf{v}$ in the direction of the outward normal $\hat{\mathbf{n}}$ at a point on the surface element defined by ΔS. Thus, the total amount of fluid flowing across the boundary S of $\mathcal{R}$ from inside to outside in unit time is given by the integral

$$\int\int_S \rho \mathbf{v} \cdot \hat{\mathbf{n}} \, dS$$

over the whole boundary S. By Gauss's theorem, the amount of fluid leaving $\mathcal{R}$ in unit time through the boundary is

$$\int\int\int_{\mathcal{R}} \nabla \cdot (\rho \mathbf{v}) \, dx \, dy \, dz.$$

The total mass of fluid contained in $\mathcal{R}$ at any instant of time is given by

$$\int\int\int_{\mathcal{R}} \rho(\mathbf{x}, t) \, dx \, dy \, dz$$

and the decease in unit time in the mass content of $\mathcal{R}$ is

$$-\frac{d}{dt} \int\int\int_{\mathcal{R}} \rho(\mathbf{x}, t) \, dx \, dy \, dz = -\int\int\int_{\mathcal{R}} \frac{\partial \rho}{\partial t} \, dx \, dy \, dz.$$

By the law of conservation of mass, in the absence of sources or sinks of mass in $\mathcal{R}$, the amount of mass of fluid leaving $\mathcal{R}$ through surface S must be exactly equal to the loss of mass of fluid contained in $\mathcal{R}$. We must then have,

$$\int\int\int_{\mathcal{R}} \nabla \cdot (\rho \mathbf{v}) \, dx \, dy \, dz = -\int\int\int_{\mathcal{R}} \frac{\partial \rho}{\partial t} \, dx \, dy \, dz$$

at any time t for any region $\mathcal{R}$. Dividing both sides of this identity by the volume of $\mathcal{R}$ and taking the limit as the size of $\mathcal{R}$ goes to zero, (as we did in the 2-D case), we get the three dimensional *continuity equation*:

$$\nabla \cdot (\rho \mathbf{v}) + \frac{\partial \rho}{\partial t} = 0,$$

or,

$$\frac{\partial \rho}{\partial t} + \frac{\partial(\rho u)}{\partial x} + \frac{\partial(\rho v)}{\partial y} + \frac{\partial(\rho w)}{\partial z} = 0$$

where $u(\mathbf{x}), v(\mathbf{x}), w(\mathbf{x})$ are the components of $\mathbf{v}(\mathbf{x})$. The continuity equation expresses the law of conservation of mass for the motion of fluids.

If the law of conservation of mass is not invoked, the expression

$$\nabla \cdot (\rho \mathbf{v}) + \frac{\partial \rho}{\partial t}$$

measures the amount of mass created (or annihilated if negative) in unit time per unit volume.

Of particular interest is the case of a homogeneous and incompressible fluid, for which the density is constant both in space and time. For such a constant ρ, we deduce from the continuity equation that,

$$\nabla \cdot \mathbf{v} = \frac{\partial (\rho u)}{\partial x} + \frac{\partial (\rho v)}{\partial y} + \frac{\partial (\rho w)}{\partial z} = 0$$

if mass is to be preserved. From Gauss's theorem it then follows that

$$\int \int_S \rho \mathbf{v} \cdot \hat{\mathbf{n}} dS = 0$$

whenever surface S bounds a region $\mathcal{R}$. Consider, in particular, two surfaces S_1 and S_2 bounded by the same oriented curve C^* in space, and together forming the boundary S of a three dimensional region $\mathcal{R}$. We find that

$$0 = \int \int_S \rho \mathbf{v} \cdot \hat{\mathbf{n}} dS = \int \int_{S_1} \rho \mathbf{v} \cdot \hat{\mathbf{n}} dS + \int \int_{S_2} \rho \mathbf{v} \cdot \hat{\mathbf{n}} dS$$

where, on both S_1 and S_2, $\hat{\mathbf{n}}$ denotes the normal pointing away from $\mathcal{R}$. We can make both S_1 and S_2 into oriented surfaces S_1^* and S_2^* in such a way that the orientation of C^* is positive with respect to both S_1^* and S_2^*. On both these surfaces, let $\hat{\mathbf{n}}^*$ be the unit normal pointing to the positive side. For a right handed orientation of space, this implies that $\hat{\mathbf{n}}^*$ points to that side of the surface from which the orientation of C^* appears counterclockwise. Then, necessarily, $\hat{\mathbf{n}}^* = \hat{\mathbf{n}}$ on one of the surfaces S_1, S_2 and $\hat{\mathbf{n}}^* = -\hat{\mathbf{n}}$ on the other. It follows from the last equation that

$$\int \int_{S_1} \rho \mathbf{v} \cdot \hat{\mathbf{n}}^* dS = \int \int_{S_2} \rho \mathbf{v} \cdot \hat{\mathbf{n}}^* dS.$$

In words, *if the fluid is incompressible and homogeneous and mass is conserved, then the same amount of fluid flows across any two surfaces with the same boundary curve C^* that together bound a three dimensional region in space.* This amount of fluid does not depend on the precise form of the surfaces, it is plausible that it must be determined by the boundary curve C^* alone. We will answer this question in the next subsection by means of stokes theorem.

Application to surface forces and space (body) forces

The forces acting in the continuous media are classified as space or body forces (e.g., gravitational force, electrostatic force) or as surface forces (pressures, tractions). This is not a fundamental distinction and the effect of a force can be expressed in both these forms. The connection between these points of view is given by Gauss's theorem.

The continuous medium we consider is a fluid of density $\rho(\mathbf{x})$, in which there is a pressure $p(\mathbf{x})$ which in general depends on the position $(\mathbf{x})$ in the fluid. This means that the force acting on a portion $\mathcal{R}$ of the fluid exerted by the remaining part of the fluid can be considered as a force acting on each point of the surface S of $\mathcal{R}$ in the direction of the inward drawn normal and of magnitude p per unit surface area. Denoting by dx/dn, dy/dn, dz/dn the direction cosines of the *outward normal* at a point of a surface S of $\mathcal{R}$, the components of the force per unit area are given by

$$-p\frac{dx}{dn}, \quad -p\frac{dy}{dn}, \quad -p\frac{dz}{dn}.$$

Thus, the resultant of the surface forces acting on $\mathcal{R}$ is a force with components

$$F_x = -\int\int_S p\frac{dx}{dn}dS, \quad F_y = -\int\int_S p\frac{dy}{dn}dS, \quad F_z = -\int\int_S p\frac{dz}{dn}dS.$$

By Gauss's theorem (Eq. (11.159)), we can write these components as volume integrals

$$F_x = -\int\int\int_{\mathcal{R}} p_x dxdydz, \quad F_y = -\int\int\int_{\mathcal{R}} p_y dxdydz, \quad F_z = -\int\int\int_{\mathcal{R}} p_z dxdydz.$$

The resultant force $\mathbf{F}$ (a vector) is given by

$$\mathbf{F} = -\int\int\int_{\mathcal{R}} \nabla p \, dxdydz. \tag{11.162}$$

We can express this by saying that the forces in a fluid due to a pressure $p(\mathbf{x})$ may, on the one hand, be regarded as surface forces (pressure) that act with density $p(\mathbf{x})$ perpendicular to each surface element through the point $(\mathbf{x})$ and on the other hand, as space forces, that is, the forces that act on every element of volume with volume density $-\nabla p$.

Consider a fluid in equilibrium under the joint action of forces due to pressure and gravity. Then, the force $\mathbf{F}$ due to pressure must balance the total attractive force $\mathbf{G}$ on the fluid contained in $\mathcal{R}$:

$$\mathbf{F} + \mathbf{G} = 0.$$

If the gravitational force acting on a unit mass at the point $\mathbf{x}$ is given by the vector $\mathbf{g}(\mathbf{x})$, we have,

$$\mathbf{G} = \int\int\int_{\mathcal{R}} \mathbf{g}(\mathbf{x})\rho(\mathbf{x})dxdydz.$$

From equation $\mathbf{F} + \mathbf{G} = \mathbf{0}$, valid for any portion $\mathcal{R}$ of the fluid, we conclude, as we did previously while deriving continuity equations, that the corresponding relation holds for the integrands, that is, that at each point of the fluid the equation

$$-\nabla p + \rho \mathbf{g} = \mathbf{0} \tag{11.163}$$

applies. Since the gradient of a scalar ϕ is perpendicular to the level surfaces of the scalar (given by $\phi = $ constant), we conclude that *for a fluid in equilibrium under pressure and gravity, the gravitational force at each point of a surface of constant pressure p (isobaric surface) is perpendicular to the surface.* If we costumerily assume that the force of gravitational force per unit mass near the surface of the earth is given by $\mathbf{g} = (0,0,-g)$ where g is the (constant) gravitational acceleration, we find from Eq. (11.163) that

$$p_x = 0, \quad p_y = 0, \quad p_z = -g\rho. \tag{11.164}$$

In particular, for a homogeneous liquid of constant density ρ bounded by a *free surface* of pressure zero, Eq. (11.164) tells us that along this free surface,

$$0 = dp = p_x dx + p_y dy + p_z dz = -g\rho dz,$$

implying $dz = 0$ or that *a free surface of a liquid has to be a plane z = constant $= z_0$.* For any point $\mathbf{x}$ in the liquid, by Eq. (11.164), the value of the pressure is

$$p(x,y,z) = -\int_z^{z_0} p_z(x,y,\zeta)d\zeta = g\rho(z_0 - z).$$

Therefore, *at the depth $z_0 - z = h$ the pressure has the value gph.* For a solid partly or wholly immersed in the liquid, let $\mathcal{R}$ denote the portion of the solid lying below the free surface $z = z_0$. We find from Eqs (11.162) and (11.164) that the resultant of the pressure forces acting on the solid equals the buoyancy force with components

$$F_x = 0, \quad F_y = 0, \quad F_z = \int \int \int_{\mathcal{R}} g\rho \, dx dy dz.$$

This force is directed vertically upward and its magnitude equals the weight of the displaced liquid (Archimedes' principle).

11.10.1 Exercises on the divergence theorem

In what follows we denote a position vector by $\mathbf{x}$ and its magnitude $|\mathbf{x}|$ by r. $\mathbf{F}(\mathbf{x})$ and $f(\mathbf{x})$ denote a vector and a scalar field respectively. We assume that both the fields have continuous derivatives of any required order, at all points in their domains. Γ denotes a simple closed curve and S is either a surface with Γ as its boundary or a closed surface enclosing the interior with volume V. $\hat{\mathbf{n}}$ is the outward normal to S.

(1) Show that $\int_S d\mathbf{s} = \mathbf{0}$ over a closed surface.

Solution Let $\mathbf{a}$ be an arbitrary constant vector. Then, by the divergence theorem,

$$\mathbf{a} \cdot \int_S d\mathbf{s} = \int_S \mathbf{a} \cdot d\mathbf{s} = \int_V \nabla \cdot \mathbf{a} d\tau.$$

Since $\mathbf{a}$ is constant, $\nabla \cdot \mathbf{a} = 0$, so that $\mathbf{a} \cdot \int_S d\mathbf{s} = 0$. Since $\mathbf{a}$ is arbitrary, it follows that $\int_S d\mathbf{s} = \mathbf{0}$. $\square$

(2) Show that the volume enclosed by a closed surface is

$$V = \frac{1}{6} \int_S \nabla(r^2) \cdot d\mathbf{s},$$

where $r = |\mathbf{x}|$ and $\mathbf{x}$ is the position vector of a point of $d\mathbf{s}$.

Solution

$$\frac{1}{6} \int_S \nabla(r^2) \cdot d\mathbf{s} = \frac{1}{6} \int_S \nabla(\mathbf{x} \cdot \mathbf{x}) \cdot d\mathbf{s} = \frac{1}{6} \int_S 2((\mathbf{x} \cdot \nabla)\mathbf{x})) \cdot d\mathbf{s}$$

$$= \frac{1}{3} \int_S \mathbf{x} \cdot d\mathbf{s} = \frac{1}{3} \int_V \nabla \cdot \mathbf{x} d\tau = \int_V d\tau = V.$$

where we have used $(\mathbf{x} \cdot \nabla)\mathbf{x} = \mathbf{x}$, $\nabla \cdot \mathbf{x} = 3$ and the divergence theorem. $\square$

(3) Show that

$$\int_S f\hat{\mathbf{n}} d\mathbf{s} = \int_V \nabla f d\tau. \tag{11.165}$$

Solution Let $\mathbf{a}$ be an arbitrary constant vector. We apply the divergence theorem to the vector $f\mathbf{a}$. We get, since f is a scalar,

$$\mathbf{a} \cdot \int_S f\hat{\mathbf{n}} d\mathbf{s} = \int_S \hat{\mathbf{n}} \cdot f\mathbf{a} d\mathbf{s} = \int_V \nabla \cdot f\mathbf{a} d\tau.$$

Further,

$$\nabla \cdot f\mathbf{a} = f\nabla \cdot \mathbf{a} + \mathbf{a} \cdot \nabla f.$$

The first term on RHS is zero as $\mathbf{a}$ is a constant vector. Therefore, integrating we get

$$\int_V \nabla \cdot f\mathbf{a} d\tau = \mathbf{a} \cdot \int_V \nabla f d\tau.$$

Thus,

$$\mathbf{a} \cdot \left[\int_S f\hat{\mathbf{n}}ds - \int_V \nabla f d\tau \right] = 0.$$

Since $\mathbf{a}$ is arbitrary, the second factor in the dot product must vanish, proving Eq. (11.165). $\square$

(4) Show that

$$\int_S \hat{\mathbf{n}} \times \mathbf{F} ds = \int_V (\nabla \times \mathbf{F}) d\tau. \tag{11.166}$$

Solution Let $\mathbf{a}$ be an arbitrary constant vector and apply the divergence theorem to the vector $\mathbf{F} \times \mathbf{a}$. We get,

$$\int_S \hat{\mathbf{n}} \cdot \mathbf{F} \times \mathbf{a} ds = \int_V \nabla \cdot (\mathbf{F} \times \mathbf{a}) d\tau,$$

or,

$$\int_S \mathbf{a} \cdot \hat{\mathbf{n}} \times \mathbf{F} ds = \int_V (\mathbf{a} \cdot \nabla \times \mathbf{F} - \mathbf{F} \cdot \nabla \times \mathbf{a}) d\tau = \int_V \mathbf{a} \cdot \nabla \times \mathbf{F} d\tau.$$

Taking $\mathbf{a}\cdot$ out of these integrals and collecting all the terms on one side we get the result. $\square$

(5) Show that

$$\int_S f\mathbf{F} \cdot d\mathbf{s} = \int_V (f\nabla \cdot \mathbf{F} + \mathbf{F} \cdot \nabla f) d\tau. \qquad \square$$

11.11 Integration by Parts and Green's Theorem in Three-dimensions

Here, we obtain the the generalization of the corresponding result in two dimensions. Applying Gauss's theorem (Eq. (11.159)) to the products of functions au, bv, cw leads to a prescription for integration by parts:

$$\int\int\int_{\mathcal{R}} (au_x + bv_y + cw_z) dxdydz = \int\int_S \left(au\frac{dx}{dn} + bv\frac{dy}{dn} + cw\frac{dz}{dn} \right) dS$$

$$- \int\int\int_{\mathcal{R}} (a_x u + b_y v + c_z w) dxdydz. \tag{11.167}$$

If $u = v = w = U$ and if a, b, c are of the form $a = V_x, b = V_y, c = V_z$ where $U(\mathbf{x})$ and $V(\mathbf{x})$ are scalar valued functions, we obtain *Green's first theorem*

$$\int\int\int_{\mathcal{R}} \nabla U \cdot \nabla V dx dy dz = \int\int_{S} U \frac{dV}{dn} dS - \int\int\int_{\mathcal{R}} U \Delta V dx dy dz, \qquad (11.168)$$

where Δ is the *Laplace operator* defined by

$$\Delta V = \nabla^2 V = V_{xx} + V_{yy} + V_{zz}$$

and dV/dn is the derivative of V in the direction of the *outward* normal:

$$\frac{dV}{dn} = V_x \frac{dx}{dn} + V_y \frac{dy}{dn} + V_z \frac{dz}{dn}.$$

Interchanging U and V in Eq. (11.168) and subtracting the resulting equation from it, we get *Green's second theorem*

$$\int\int\int_{\mathcal{R}} (U\Delta V - V\Delta U) dx dy dz = \int\int_{S} \left(U \frac{dV}{dn} - V \frac{dU}{dn} \right) dS. \qquad (11.169)$$

11.11.1 Transformation of ΔU to spherical coordinates

We can use Green's theorem to express ΔU in terms of spherical polar coordinates. We set $V = 1$ in Green's theorem, (Eq. (11.169)), to get

$$\int\int\int_{\mathcal{R}} \Delta U dx dy dz = \int\int_{S} \frac{dU}{dn} dS = \int\int_{S} \nabla U \cdot \hat{n} dS. \qquad (11.170)$$

The spherical polar coordinate system is defined by

$$x = r \sin\theta \cos\phi, \quad y = r \sin\theta \sin\phi, \quad z = r \cos\theta.$$

We apply Eq. (11.170) to a wedge shaped region $\tilde{\mathcal{R}}$ described by inequalities of the form

$$r_1 < r < r_2, \quad \theta_1 < \theta < \theta_2, \quad \phi_1 < \phi < \phi_2.$$

The boundary S of $\tilde{\mathcal{R}}$ consists of six faces along each of which one of the coordinates r, θ, ϕ has constant value. Applying the formula for transformation of triple integrals we write the left side of Eq. (11.170) as

$$\int\int\int_{\mathcal{R}} \Delta U dx dy dz = \int\int\int_{\tilde{\mathcal{R}}} \Delta U \frac{d(x,y,z)}{d(r,\theta,\phi)} dr d\theta d\phi$$

$$= \int\int\int_{\tilde{\mathcal{R}}} \Delta U r^2 \sin\theta dr d\theta d\phi. \qquad (11.171)$$

In order to transform the surface integral in Eq. (11.170) we introduce the position vector

$$\mathbf{x} \equiv (x, y, z) = (r \sin \theta \cos \phi, r \sin \theta \sin \phi, r \cos \theta)$$

and find that its first derivatives satisfy the relations

$$\mathbf{x}_r \cdot \mathbf{x}_\theta = 0, \quad \mathbf{x}_\theta \cdot \mathbf{x}_\phi = 0, \quad \mathbf{x}_\phi \cdot \mathbf{x}_r = 0$$

$$\mathbf{x}_r \cdot \mathbf{x}_r = 1, \quad \mathbf{x}_\theta \cdot \mathbf{x}_\theta = r^2, \quad \mathbf{x}_\phi \cdot \mathbf{x}_\phi = r^2 \sin^2 \theta. \tag{11.172}$$

Thus, at each point the vector $\mathbf{x}_r$ is normal to the coordinate surface $r = $ constant passing through that point, the vector $\mathbf{x}_\theta$ normal to the surface $\theta = $ constant and the vector $\mathbf{x}_\phi$ normal to the surface $\phi = $ constant. (In other words, the unit vectors in the direction of these vectors form the $\hat{\mathbf{r}}, \hat{\theta}, \hat{\phi}$ basis at that point). More precisely, on one of the faces $r = $ constant $= r_k, k = 1, 2$ of the region $\tilde{\mathcal{R}}$ defined above, the outward normal unit vector $\hat{\mathbf{n}}$ is given by $(-1)^k \mathbf{x}_r$. Hence, on these faces

$$\nabla U \cdot \hat{\mathbf{n}} = (-1)^k \nabla U \cdot \mathbf{x}_r = (-1)^k \frac{\partial U}{\partial r}.$$

Using θ, ϕ as parameters on the face $r = r_k$, we get, for the element of area (see section 10.12)

$$dS = \sqrt{EG - F^2} d\theta d\phi = \sqrt{(\mathbf{x}_\theta \cdot \mathbf{x}_\theta)(\mathbf{x}_\phi \cdot \mathbf{x}_\phi) - (\mathbf{x}_\theta \cdot \mathbf{x}_\phi)} d\theta d\phi = r^2 \sin \theta d\theta d\phi.$$

Thus, the contribution of the two faces $r = r_1$ and $r = r_2$ to the integral of dU/dn over S is represented by the expression

$$\int\int_{r=r_2} r^2 \sin \theta \frac{\partial U}{\partial r} d\theta d\phi - \int\int_{r=r_1} r^2 \sin \theta \frac{\partial U}{\partial r} d\theta d\phi,$$

where integration is over the rectangle

$$\theta_1 < \theta < \theta_2, \quad \phi_1 < \phi < \phi_2.$$

We can write this difference of integrals as the triple integral

$$\int\int\int_{\tilde{\mathcal{R}}} \frac{\partial}{\partial r} \left(r^2 \sin \theta \frac{\partial U}{\partial r} \right) dr d\theta d\phi.$$

Similarly, we find that on a face $\theta = $ constant $= \theta_k, k = 1, 2$

$$\hat{\mathbf{n}} = (-1)^k \frac{1}{r} \mathbf{x}_\theta, \quad dS = r \sin \theta d\phi dr, \quad \frac{dU}{dn} = \frac{(-1)^k}{r} \frac{\partial U}{\partial \theta}$$

and on a face

$$\phi = \text{constant} = \phi_k$$

$$\hat{\mathbf{n}} = (-1)^k \frac{1}{r \sin \theta} \mathbf{x}_\phi, \quad dS = r dr d\theta, \quad \frac{dU}{dn} = \frac{(-1)^k}{r \sin \theta} \frac{\partial U}{\partial \phi}.$$

Combining the contributions of the opposite faces $\theta = \text{constant}$ or $\phi = \text{constant}$, as we did for $r = \text{constant}$, we find the total surface integral to be

$$\iint_S \frac{dU}{dn} dS = \iiint_{\tilde{\mathcal{R}}} \left[\frac{\partial}{\partial r} \left(r^2 \sin \theta \frac{\partial U}{\partial r} \right) + \frac{\partial}{\partial \theta} \left(\sin \theta \frac{\partial U}{\partial \theta} \right) + \frac{\partial}{\partial \phi} \left(\frac{1}{\sin \theta} \frac{\partial U}{\partial \phi} \right) \right] dr d\theta d\phi.$$

Comparing with Eq. (11.171) dividing with the volume of the wedge $\tilde{\mathcal{R}}$ and taking the limit as this volume tends to zero, we can equate the corresponding integrands to get the desired expression for the Laplace operator in the spherical coordinates:

$$\Delta U = \frac{1}{r^2 \sin \theta} \left[\frac{\partial}{\partial r} \left(r^2 \sin \theta \frac{\partial U}{\partial r} \right) + \frac{\partial}{\partial \theta} \left(\sin \theta \frac{\partial U}{\partial \theta} \right) + \frac{\partial}{\partial \phi} \left(\frac{1}{\sin \theta} \frac{\partial U}{\partial \phi} \right) \right]. \quad (11.173)$$

11.12   Helmoltz Theorem

In this subsection, we make use of the Dirac delta function, so we assume that you have read the appendix on the Dirac delta function. In this subsection we use $\mathbf{r}, \mathbf{r}'$ to denote position vectors and define $r = |\mathbf{r}|$ and $r' = |\mathbf{r}'|$. Now consider a vector field $\mathbf{f}(\mathbf{r})$ satisfying the relations

$$\nabla \cdot \mathbf{f}(\mathbf{r}) = d(\mathbf{r}),$$

$$\nabla \times \mathbf{f}(\mathbf{r}) = \mathbf{c}(\mathbf{r}). \quad (11.174)$$

Since the divergence of curl is always zero, the second of the above equations gives

$$\nabla \cdot \mathbf{c} = 0. \quad (11.175)$$

The question we are interested in is this: knowing the functions $d(\mathbf{r})$ and $\mathbf{c}(\mathbf{r})$, can we use Eqs (11.174) and (11.175) to uniquely specify the field $\mathbf{f}(\mathbf{r})$? The answer is yes, provided $d(\mathbf{r})$ and $\mathbf{c}(\mathbf{r})$ tend to zero faster than $1/r^2$ as $r \to \infty$. It turns out that

$$\mathbf{f} = -\nabla u + \nabla \times \mathbf{w}, \quad (11.176)$$

where

$$u(\mathbf{r}) = \frac{1}{4\pi} \int \frac{d(\mathbf{r}')}{\gamma} d\tau', \quad (11.177)$$

and

$$\mathbf{w}(\mathbf{r}) = \frac{1}{4\pi} \int \mathbf{c} \frac{(\mathbf{r}')}{\gamma} d\tau', \tag{11.178}$$

where the integrals are over all space, $d\tau'$ is the differential volume element and $\gamma = |\mathbf{r} - \mathbf{r}'|$. If $\mathbf{f}$ is given by Eq. (11.176), then its divergence is given by, (since divergence of curl is zero), (see Appendix),

$$\nabla \cdot \mathbf{f} = -\nabla^2 u = -\frac{1}{4\pi} \int d\nabla^2 \left(\frac{1}{\gamma}\right) d\tau' = \int d(\mathbf{r}')\delta^3(\mathbf{r} - \mathbf{r}')d\tau' = d(\mathbf{r}).$$

Regarding the curl of the field, we have, since the curl of a gradient is zero,

$$\nabla \times \mathbf{f} = \nabla \times (\nabla \times \mathbf{w}) = -\nabla^2 \mathbf{w} + \nabla(\nabla \cdot \mathbf{w}). \tag{11.179}$$

where we have used Eq. (10.92). The last term yields

$$-\nabla^2 \mathbf{w} = -\frac{1}{4\pi} \int \mathbf{c}\nabla^2 \left(\frac{1}{\gamma}\right) d\tau' = \int \mathbf{c}(\mathbf{r}')\delta^3(\mathbf{r} - \mathbf{r}')d\tau' = \mathbf{c}(\mathbf{r}).$$

Thus, we need to show that the $\nabla(\nabla \cdot \mathbf{w})$ vanishes. Using integration by parts, Eq. (11.161), and noting that the derivatives of γ with respect to primed coordinates differ by a sign from those with respect to unprimed coordinates, we get

$$4\pi\nabla \cdot \mathbf{w} = \int \mathbf{c} \cdot \nabla\left(\frac{1}{\gamma}\right) d\tau' = -\int \mathbf{c} \cdot \nabla'\left(\frac{1}{\gamma}\right) d\tau'$$

$$= \int \frac{1}{\gamma}\nabla' \cdot \mathbf{c}d\tau - \int \frac{1}{\gamma}\mathbf{c} \cdot d\mathbf{a}. \tag{11.180}$$

However, the divergence of $\mathbf{c}$ is zero, by Eq. (11.175) and the surface integral vanishes as $\gamma \to \infty$ as long as $\mathbf{c}(\mathbf{r})$ goes to zero sufficiently rapidly. The rate of divergence of $d(\mathbf{r})$ and $\mathbf{c}(\mathbf{r})$ as $r \to \infty$ is important for the convergence of the integrals in Eqs (11.177) and (11.178). In the large r' limit, where $\gamma \approx r'$, the integrals are of the form

$$\int^\infty \frac{X(r')}{r'} r'^2 dr' = \int^\infty r'X(r')dr',$$

where X stands for d or $\mathbf{c}$ as the case may be. If $X \sim 1/r'$ the integrand is constant so that the integral blows up or if $X \sim 1/r'^2$ the integral is a logarithm and blows up. Evidently, the divergence and the curl of $\mathbf{f}$ must vanish more rapidly than $1/r'^2$ as $r' \to \infty$ for the above proof to hold.

Assuming that the required conditions on $d(\mathbf{r})$ and $\mathbf{c}(\mathbf{r})$ are satisfied, is the solution (11.176) unique? Not in general, because we can add to $\mathbf{f}$ any vector function with vanishing divergence and curl to get the same solution. However, it turns out that there is no function with vanishing divergence and curl everywhere and goes to zero at infinity. So, if we include the requirement that $\mathbf{f}(\mathbf{r}) \rightarrow \mathbf{0}$ as $r \rightarrow \infty$ then solution (11.176) is unique. For example, generally we do expect the electromagnetic fields to go to zero far away from the charge and current distributions which produce them.

We can thus state the all-important Helmoltz theorem rigorously as follows.

If the divergence $d(\mathbf{r})$ and the curl $\mathbf{c}(\mathbf{r})$ of a vector field $\mathbf{f}(\mathbf{r})$ are specified and if they both go to zero faster than $1/r^2$ as $r \rightarrow \infty$, and if $\mathbf{f}(\mathbf{r})$ goes to zero as $r \rightarrow \infty$, then $\mathbf{f}$ is given uniquely by Eq. (11.176).

From Helmoltz theorem it follows that a vector field with vanishing curl is derivable from a scalar potential, while a field with vanishing divergence can be expressed as the curl of some other vector field. For example, in electrostatics, $\nabla \cdot \mathbf{E} = \rho/\epsilon_0$ where ρ is the given charge distribution and $\nabla \times \mathbf{E} = \mathbf{0}$, so

$$\mathbf{E}(\mathbf{r}) = -\nabla V(\mathbf{r}),$$

where V is the scalar electrostatic potential. While in magnetostatics $\nabla \cdot \mathbf{B} = 0$ and $\nabla \times \mathbf{B} = \mu_0 \mathbf{J}$ where $\mathbf{J}$ is the given current distribution, so that

$$\mathbf{B}(\mathbf{r}) = \nabla \times \mathbf{A},$$

where $\mathbf{A}$ is the vector potential.

11.13 Stokes Theorem in Three-dimensions

We generalize this all important theorem to three dimensions. In three dimensions, this theorem connects the integral of the normal component of the curl of a vector field over a curved surface with the integral of the tangential component of the vector field over the boundary curve.

Consider an oriented surface S^* in 3-D space bounded by a closed curve C^* oriented positively with respect to S^*. We choose a right handed coordinate system so that space is oriented positively with respect to x, y, z-axes. Let $\hat{\mathbf{n}}$ denote the unit normal vector at each point of S^* pointing to its positive side, that is, $\hat{\mathbf{n}}$ defines the positive orientation of S^*. Let $\hat{\mathbf{t}}$ be the unit tangent vector to C^* pointing in the direction corresponding to the orientation of C^*. Let $\mathbf{v}(\mathbf{x}) \equiv (a(\mathbf{x}), b(\mathbf{x}), c(\mathbf{x}))$ be a vector field defined in a region of space $\mathcal{R}$ containing the surface S. Stokes theorem asserts that

$$\int\int_S (\nabla \times \mathbf{v}(\mathbf{x})) \cdot \hat{\mathbf{n}} dS = \int_C \mathbf{v} \cdot \hat{\mathbf{t}} ds. \tag{11.181}$$

where on the right we integrate along C, in the direction defined by its orientation, dictated by the choice of $\hat{\mathbf{t}}$, over the arclength ds. The orientations of S and C is imposed on this integration via the choice of the unit vectors $\hat{\mathbf{n}}$ and $\hat{\mathbf{t}}$.

In terms of the components of vectors $\hat{\mathbf{n}}$ and $\hat{\mathbf{t}}$, we can write

$$\iint_S \left[(c_y - b_z)\frac{dx}{dn} + (a_z - c_x)\frac{dy}{dn} + (b_x - a_y)\frac{dz}{dn} \right] dS = \int_C \left(a\frac{dx}{ds} + b\frac{dy}{ds} + c\frac{dz}{ds} \right) ds.$$

$$(11.182)$$

or, using Eq. (11.154),

$$\iint_{S^*} (c_y - b_z)dydz + (a_z - c_x)dzdx + (b_x - a_y)dxdy = \int_{C^*} adx + bdy + cdz. \quad (11.183)$$

Stokes theorem can be made plausible by using the fact that it is true for plane surfaces. If S is a polyhedral surface composed of plane polygonal surfaces, so that the boundary curve C is a polygon, we can apply Stokes theorem to each of the plane surfaces and add the corresponding contributions. Then, the line integrals along all the interior edges of the polyhedron cancel and we obtain the stokes theorem for the polyhedral surface. In order to prove the general statement of the Stokes theorem, we only have to pass to the limit, leading from approximate polyhedra to arbitrary surfaces S bounded by arbitrary curves C. The regorous validation of this passage to the limit could be cumbersome so the proof is generally carried out by transforming the whole surface S into a plane surface and proving that the theorem is preserved under such transformations. We omit the details of this proof and assume the theorem.

We can now settle the question asked in the discussion regarding the incompressible and homogeneous fluid in section 11.10. Since the fluid is incompressible, its divergence is everywhere zero so by Helmoltz theorem it must be given by the curl of some vector field. Now by applying Stokes theorem we can write

$$\iint_S \mathbf{v} \cdot \hat{\mathbf{n}} dS = \iint_S (\nabla \times \mathbf{A}) \cdot \hat{\mathbf{n}} dS = \int_C \mathbf{A} \cdot \hat{\mathbf{t}} ds.$$

Thus, the total amount of fluid passing through any two surfaces with the same boundary curve C is determined by the curve C alone.

Exercise   Show that the arguments leading to Eqs (10.105) and (10.107) can be extended to prove the divergence theorem and Stokes theorem respectively (see Griffiths [9]). Compare with our proofs of these theorems.   □

The following two exercises give two fundamental results based on the Helmoltz theorem and the stokes theorem.

Exercise   Curl-less or irrotational fields. Let $\mathbf{F}$ be a vector field. Show that the following conditions are equivalent.

(a) $\nabla \times \mathbf{F} = \mathbf{0}$ everywhere.

(b) $\mathbf{F}$ is the gradient of some scalar, $\mathbf{F} = -\nabla V(\mathbf{x})$.

(c) $\int_a^b \mathbf{F} \cdot d\mathbf{x}$ is independent of path for any given end points and depend only on the end points in a simply connected region.

(d) $\oint \mathbf{F} \cdot d\mathbf{x} = 0$ for any closed loop.

Solution   (a) $\Rightarrow$ (b) : By Helmoltz theorem. (b) $\Rightarrow$ (c) is proved in section 11.1. (c) $\Rightarrow$ (d): Take any two distinct points P_1 and P_2 on the closed loop. Then,

$$\oint \mathbf{F} \cdot d\mathbf{x} = \int_{P_1}^{P_2} \mathbf{F} \cdot d\mathbf{x} + \int_{P_2}^{P_1} \mathbf{F} \cdot d\mathbf{x} = \int_{P_1}^{P_2} \mathbf{F} \cdot d\mathbf{x} - \int_{P_1}^{P_2} \mathbf{F} \cdot d\mathbf{x} = 0.$$

(d) $\Rightarrow$ (a) by Stokes theorem. □

Exercise   Divergence-less or solenoidal fields.   Show that the following conditions are equivalent.

(a) $\nabla \cdot \mathbf{F} = 0$ everywhere.

(b) $\mathbf{F} = \nabla \times \mathbf{A}$ for some vector field $\mathbf{A}$.

(c) $\int \int_S \mathbf{F} \cdot \hat{\mathbf{n}} dS$ is independent of surface, for any given boundary curve, being equal to the integral of $\mathbf{A}$ along the boundary curve in the positive sense with respect to the surface.

(d) $\int \int_S \mathbf{F} \cdot \hat{\mathbf{n}} dS = 0$ for any closed surface.

Solution   (a) $\Rightarrow$ (b) : By Helmoltz theorem. By Eq. (11.177), $u(\mathbf{r}) = 0$ in Eq. (11.176). (b) $\Rightarrow$ (c) : By Stokes theorem the integral over the surface reduces to that over the boundary curve.   (c) $\Rightarrow$ (d): View the closed surface as two surfaces with common boundary curve. The integral in (c) reduces to the integrals over the boundary curve in the opposite sense for the two surfaces, because the positive orientation of the boundary curve with respect to two surfaces are opposite, so that these integrals cancel each other. (d) $\Rightarrow$ (a): By divergence theorem, condition (d) means the volume integral of $\nabla \cdot \mathbf{F}$ over the region $\mathcal{R}$ enclosed by the surface vanishes. Since this is true for any closed surface enclosing any region $\mathcal{R}$, we can divide by the volume of $\mathcal{R}$ and take the limit as this volume tends to zero to yield condition (a). □

11.13.1   Physical interpretation of Stokes theorem

This is similar to that we have seen in the two dimensional case. We interpret the vector field $\mathbf{v}(\mathbf{x}) \equiv (v_1(\mathbf{x}), v_2(\mathbf{x}), v_3(\mathbf{x}))$ as the velocity field of the flow of a fluid. We call the integral

$$\int_C \mathbf{v} \cdot \hat{\mathbf{t}} ds = \int_{C^*} \mathbf{v} \cdot d\mathbf{x}$$

taken over an oriented closed curve C^* the *circulation* of the flow along this curve. Stokes theorem states that the circulation along C^* equals the integral

$$\int\int_S (\nabla \times \mathbf{v}) \cdot \hat{\mathbf{n}} dS,$$

where S is any orientable surface bounded by C and $\hat{\mathbf{n}}$ is the unit normal to S making it the oriented surface S^* such that the curve C^* is oriented positively with respect to S^*. Suppose we divide the circulation around C by the area of the surface S bounded by C and pass to the limit by making C shrink to a point while remaining the boundary of the surface. For the surface integral of the normal component of curl $\mathbf{v}$ divided by the area, this limit gives the value $(\nabla \times \mathbf{v}) \cdot \hat{\mathbf{n}}$ at the limit point. Thus, we can regard the component of curl $\mathbf{v}$ in the direction of the surface normal $\hat{\mathbf{n}}$ as the *circulation density* of the flow across the surface at the corresponding point.

The vector curl $\mathbf{v}$ is called the *vorticity* of the fluid motion. Therefore, the circulation around a curve C equals the integral of the normal component of the vorticity over a surface bounded by C. The motion is called *irrotational* if the vorticity vector vanishes at every point occupied by the fluid, that is, if the vorticity vector satisfies the relations

$$v_{3y} - v_{2z} = 0, \quad v_{1z} - v_{3x} = 0, \quad v_{2x} - v_{1y} = 0.$$

As a result of Stokes theorem, the circulation in an irrotational motion vanishes along any curve C that bounds a surface contained in the region filled with the fluid.

By the above exercise we know that an irrotational vector field is also conservative. That is,

$$\nabla \times \mathbf{v} = \mathbf{0} \text{ implies } \mathbf{v} = \nabla \phi.$$

Thus, the velocity field of an irrotational fluid flow in a simply connected region implies the existance of a velocity potential $\phi(\mathbf{x})$ satisfying

$$\mathbf{v}(\mathbf{x}) = \nabla \phi(\mathbf{x}).$$

If, in addition the fluid is homogeneous and incompressible we have

$$\nabla \cdot \mathbf{v} = 0.$$

Thus, the velocity potential satisfies the Laplace equation

$$0 = \nabla \cdot \nabla \phi = \nabla^2 \phi = \phi_{xx} + \phi_{yy} + \phi_{zz}.$$

11.13.2 Exercises on Stoke's theorem

In what follows we denote a position vector by $\mathbf{x}$ and its magnitude $|\mathbf{x}|$ by r. $\mathbf{F}(\mathbf{x})$ and $f(\mathbf{x})$ denote a vector and a scalar field respectively. We assume that both the fields have continuous derivatives of any required order, at all points in their domains. Γ denotes a simple closed curve and S is either a surface with Γ as its boundary or a closed surface enclosing the interior with volume V. $\hat{\mathbf{n}}$ is the outward normal to S.

(1) Verify Stoke's theorem for the field

$$\mathbf{F} = z\hat{\mathbf{i}} + x\hat{\mathbf{j}} + y\hat{\mathbf{k}}$$

where Γ is the unit circle in the xy plane bounding the hemisphere $z = \sqrt{1 - x^2 - y^2}$.

Solution

$$\int_\Gamma \mathbf{F}(\mathbf{x}) \cdot d\mathbf{x} = \int_\Gamma z\,dx + \int_\Gamma x\,dy + \int_\Gamma y\,dz.$$

On Γ $z = 0 = dz$ so that

$$\int_\Gamma \mathbf{F}(\mathbf{x}) \cdot d\mathbf{x} = \int_\Gamma x\,dy = \pi.$$

Now

$$\nabla \times \mathbf{F} = \hat{\mathbf{i}} + \hat{\mathbf{j}} + \hat{\mathbf{k}}$$

so that

$$\int_S (\nabla \times \mathbf{F}) \cdot d\mathbf{s} = \int_S \hat{\mathbf{i}} \cdot d\mathbf{s} + \int_S \hat{\mathbf{j}} \cdot d\mathbf{s} + \int_S \hat{\mathbf{k}} \cdot d\mathbf{s} = \pi$$

because

$$\int_S \hat{\mathbf{i}} \cdot d\mathbf{s} = 0 = \int_S \hat{\mathbf{j}} \cdot d\mathbf{s}$$

and

$$\int_S \hat{\mathbf{k}} \cdot d\mathbf{s} = \pi,$$

as the integrals represent the projected areas of the hemisphere on the coordinate planes. Alternatively, we can express $\mathbf{F}$ and $\nabla \times \mathbf{F}$ in terms of spherical polar coordinates and integrate over $\sin\theta\,d\theta\,d\phi$, $0 \le \theta \le \pi/2$, $0 \le \phi < 2\pi$. This establishes Stoke's theorem for the given field. $\qquad\square$

(2) Evaluate $\int_\Gamma \mathbf{F} \cdot d\mathbf{x}$ for $\mathbf{F} = (x^2 - y^2)\hat{\mathbf{i}} + xy\hat{\mathbf{j}}$ and Γ is the arc of $y = x^3$ from $(0,0)$ to $(2,8)$.

Solution First check that the given field is *not* conservative, so that the integral depends on the given curve. However, we can evaluate the given integral over the closed loop enclosing area A

$$\mathcal{C} = \mathcal{C}_1 + \mathcal{C}_2 - \Gamma$$

as shown in Fig. 11.37, by using Stoke's theorem,

$$\int_{\mathcal{C}} \mathbf{F} \cdot d\mathbf{x} = \int_{S} \hat{\mathbf{n}} \cdot \nabla \times \mathbf{F} ds.$$

Since, as a part of $\mathcal{C}$, Γ is negatively oriented, $(-\Gamma)$, we have

$$\int_{\mathcal{C}} \mathbf{F} \cdot d\mathbf{x} = \int_{(0,0)}^{(2,0)} \mathbf{F} \cdot d\mathbf{x} + \int_{(2,0)}^{(2,8)} \mathbf{F} \cdot d\mathbf{x} - \int_{\Gamma} \mathbf{F} \cdot d\mathbf{x}.$$

Or,

$$\int_{\Gamma} \mathbf{F} \cdot d\mathbf{x} = -\int_{S} \hat{\mathbf{n}} \cdot \nabla \times \mathbf{F} ds + \int_{(0,0)}^{(2,0)} \mathbf{F} \cdot d\mathbf{x} + \int_{(2,0)}^{(2,8)} \mathbf{F} \cdot d\mathbf{x}.$$

Or, since $\hat{\mathbf{n}} = \hat{\mathbf{k}}$,

$$\int_{\Gamma} \mathbf{F} \cdot d\mathbf{x} = -\int_{S} 3y ds + \int_{0}^{2} x^2 dx + \int_{0}^{8} 2y dy$$

$$= -\int_{0}^{2}\int_{0}^{x^3} 3y dy dx + \int_{0}^{2} x^2 dx + \int_{0}^{8} 2y dy = \frac{824}{21},$$

where we have evaluated the first integral as repeated single integrals.   □

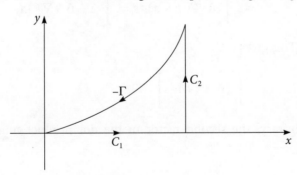

Fig. 11.37   Evaluation of a line integral using Stoke's theorem

(3) Let $\mathbf{F}(\mathbf{x}) = \mathbf{0}$ at every point on a surface S. Show that $\nabla \times \mathbf{F}$ is tangent to S at every point on it.

Solution   Suppose $\nabla \times \mathbf{F}$ is not tangent to S at a point P on S. Then, by continuity, there is some neighborhood of P on S, say S', in which the component of $\nabla \times \mathbf{F}$ along the normal $\hat{\mathbf{n}}$ has the same sign, at every point in S'. Applying Stoke's theorem to S',

$$\int_{\Gamma} \mathbf{F} \cdot d\mathbf{x} = \int_{S'} \hat{\mathbf{n}} \cdot \nabla \times \mathbf{F} ds,$$

where Γ is the boundary of S'. Since $\mathbf{F} = \mathbf{0}$ on S', $\int_{\Gamma} \mathbf{F} \cdot d\mathbf{x} = 0$ on S'. However, $\int_{S'} \hat{\mathbf{n}} \cdot \nabla \times \mathbf{F} ds \neq 0$ on S', since the integrand is not zero by assumption and has the same sign throughout S'. This contradicts Stoke's theorem, so that $\hat{\mathbf{n}} \cdot \nabla \times \mathbf{F} = 0$ or $\nabla \times \mathbf{F}$ must be perpendicular to $\hat{\mathbf{n}}$, that is, tangent to S at P. Since point P was arbitrary, $\nabla \times \mathbf{F}$ is tangent to S at all points on it. □

(4) Show that

$$\int_{\Gamma} f(\mathbf{x}) d\mathbf{x} = \int_{S} \hat{\mathbf{n}} \times \nabla f ds, \tag{11.184}$$

where Γ is the boundary of S.

Solution   Let $\mathbf{a}$ be an arbitrary constant vector. Then, $f(\mathbf{x})\mathbf{a}$ is a vector. By Stoke's theorem,

$$\int_{\Gamma} f(\mathbf{x}) \mathbf{a} \cdot d\mathbf{x} = \int_{S} \hat{\mathbf{n}} \cdot \nabla \times f(\mathbf{x}) \mathbf{a} ds$$

$$= \int_{S} \hat{\mathbf{n}} \cdot (f \nabla \times \mathbf{a} + \nabla f \times \mathbf{a}) ds$$

$$= \int_{S} \hat{\mathbf{n}} \cdot (\nabla f \times \mathbf{a}) ds = \int_{S} \mathbf{a} \cdot (\hat{\mathbf{n}} \times \nabla f) ds$$

as $\nabla \times \mathbf{a} = \mathbf{0}$. This gives

$$\mathbf{a} \cdot \left[\int_{\Gamma} f(\mathbf{x}) d\mathbf{x} - \int_{S} (\hat{\mathbf{n}} \times \nabla f) ds \right] = 0.$$

Since $\mathbf{a}$ is arbitrary, the second factor in the dot product must vanish, proving Eq. (11.184). □

(5) Show that

$$\int_{\Gamma} d\mathbf{x} \times \mathbf{F} = \int_{S} (\hat{\mathbf{n}} \times \nabla) \times \mathbf{F} ds \tag{11.185}$$

where Γ is the boundary of the surface S.

Solution Let **a** be an arbitrary constant vector and consider

$$\int_\Gamma \mathbf{a} \times \mathbf{F} \cdot d\mathbf{x} = \mathbf{a} \cdot \int_\Gamma \mathbf{F} \times d\mathbf{x}.$$

By Stoke's theorem,

$$
\begin{aligned}
\int_\Gamma \mathbf{a} \times \mathbf{F} \cdot d\mathbf{x} &= \int_S \hat{\mathbf{n}} \cdot \nabla \times (\mathbf{a} \times \mathbf{F}) ds \\
&= \int_S \hat{\mathbf{n}} \cdot [\mathbf{a}(\nabla \cdot \mathbf{F}) - (\mathbf{a} \cdot \nabla)\mathbf{F}] ds \\
&= \mathbf{a} \cdot \int_S [(\nabla \cdot \mathbf{F})\hat{\mathbf{n}} - \nabla(\mathbf{F} \cdot \hat{\mathbf{n}})] ds \\
&= -\mathbf{a} \cdot \int_S (\hat{\mathbf{n}} \times \nabla) \times \mathbf{F} ds.
\end{aligned}
$$

All these steps can be proved using Levi-Civita symbols and noting that ∇ does not operate on $\hat{\mathbf{n}}$. Last two equations give

$$\mathbf{a} \cdot \left[\int_\Gamma d\mathbf{x} \times \mathbf{F} - \int_S (\hat{\mathbf{n}} \times \nabla) \times \mathbf{F} ds \right] = 0.$$

Since **a** is arbitrary, the second factor of the dot product must vanish, proving Eq. (11.185).　　　　□

(6) Show that $\left| \int_\Gamma d\mathbf{x} \times \mathbf{x} \right|$, where Γ is a closed curve in the xy plane, is twice the enclosed area A.

Solution In Eq. (11.185) we replace $\hat{\mathbf{n}}$ by $\hat{\mathbf{k}}$ which is the vector normal to xy plane and **F** by **x**. We get,

$$
\begin{aligned}
\int_\Gamma d\mathbf{x} \times \mathbf{x} &= \int_S (\hat{\mathbf{k}} \times \nabla) \times \mathbf{x} ds \\
&= \int_S [\nabla(\hat{\mathbf{k}} \cdot \mathbf{x}) - \hat{\mathbf{k}}(\nabla \cdot \mathbf{x})] ds \\
&= \int_S (\hat{\mathbf{k}} - 3\hat{\mathbf{k}}) ds = -2\hat{\mathbf{k}} \int_S ds = -2\hat{\mathbf{k}} A,
\end{aligned}
$$

where the second equality can be proved using Levi-Civita symbols and noting that $\hat{\mathbf{k}}$ is a constant vector. Thus,

$$\left| \int_\Gamma d\mathbf{x} \times \mathbf{x} \right| = |-2\hat{\mathbf{k}}A| = 2A. \qquad \square$$

(7) For two scalar fields $f(\mathbf{x})$ and $g(\mathbf{x})$ show that

$$\int_\Gamma f(\mathbf{x})\nabla g(\mathbf{x}) \cdot d\mathbf{x} + \int_\Gamma g(\mathbf{x})\nabla f(\mathbf{x}) \cdot d\mathbf{x} = 0. \qquad (11.186)$$

where Γ is a simple closed curve.

Solution   Let $\mathbf{F} = f\nabla g$ and S be a surface with Γ as its boundary. Applying Stoke's theorem we get

$$\int_\Gamma f\nabla g \cdot d\mathbf{x} = \int_S \hat{\mathbf{n}} \cdot \nabla \times (f\nabla g) ds$$

$$= \int_S \hat{\mathbf{n}} \cdot (\nabla f \times \nabla g) ds + \int_S f\hat{\mathbf{n}} \cdot (\nabla \times \nabla g) ds$$

$$= \int_S \hat{\mathbf{n}} \cdot (\nabla f \times \nabla g) ds,$$

because $\nabla \times \nabla g = \mathbf{0}$. Similarly,

$$\int_\Gamma g\nabla f \cdot d\mathbf{x} = -\int_S \hat{\mathbf{n}} \cdot (\nabla f \times \nabla g) ds.$$

Last two equations prove Eq. (11.186). $\qquad \square$

(8) Prove that $\nabla \cdot \nabla \times \mathbf{F} = 0$.

Solution   We will use both, the divergence theorem and the Stoke's theorem. By divergence theorem and referring to Fig. 11.37 we see that

$$\int_V \nabla \cdot \nabla \times \mathbf{F} d\tau = \int_{S_1} \hat{\mathbf{n}} \cdot \nabla \times \mathbf{F} ds_1 + \int_{S_2} \hat{\mathbf{n}} \cdot \nabla \times \mathbf{F} ds_2.$$

Now applying Stoke's theorem to each term on the RHS we get,

$$\int_{S_1} \hat{\mathbf{n}} \cdot \nabla \times \mathbf{F} ds_1 = \int_\Gamma \mathbf{F} \cdot d\mathbf{x}$$

and

$$\int_{S_2} \hat{\mathbf{n}} \cdot \nabla \times \mathbf{F} ds_2 = -\int_{\Gamma} \mathbf{F} \cdot d\mathbf{x}.$$

The sign is reversed while transforming the second integral because the positive directions around the boundaries of the two surfaces are opposite. Hence,

$$\int_{V} \nabla \cdot \nabla \times \mathbf{F} d\tau = 0.$$

Since this equation holds for all volume elements it follows that $\nabla \cdot \nabla \times \mathbf{F} = 0$. $\square$

(9) For a closed surface S, show that

(i) $$\int_{S} \hat{\mathbf{n}} \cdot (\nabla \times \mathbf{F}) ds = 0$$

and

(ii) $$\int_{S} \hat{\mathbf{n}} \times \nabla f ds = \mathbf{0}.$$

Hints (i) Divide S into two parts, S_1 and S_2, with the common boundary curve Γ (see Fig. 11.37) and write

$$\int_{S} \hat{\mathbf{n}} \cdot (\nabla \times \mathbf{F}) ds = \int_{S_1} \hat{\mathbf{n}} \cdot (\nabla \times \mathbf{F}) ds_1 + \int_{S_2} \hat{\mathbf{n}} \cdot (\nabla \times \mathbf{F}) ds_2.$$

Now, apply Stoke's theorem to both the terms on RHS keeping in mind that the positive sense of traversing Γ as the boundary of S_1 is opposite to that traversing Γ as the boundary of S_2. This makes the two terms on RHS cancel after applying Stoke's theorem and the result follows.

(ii) Following the hint for part (i) we can write

$$\int_{S} \hat{\mathbf{n}} \times \nabla f ds = \int_{S_1} \hat{\mathbf{n}} \times \nabla f ds_1 + \int_{S_2} \hat{\mathbf{n}} \times \nabla f ds_2.$$

Now use Eq. (11.184) for the two terms on RHS and then follow rest of the hint for part (i). $\square$

(10) Show that (with Γ as the boundary of S)

$$\int_{\Gamma} f \mathbf{F} \cdot d\mathbf{x} = \int_{S} \hat{\mathbf{n}} \cdot (\nabla f \times \mathbf{F} + f \nabla \times \mathbf{F}) ds. \qquad \square$$

(11) If $\mathbf{F}$ is continuous and $\mathbf{F} \times d\mathbf{x} = \mathbf{0}$ for every closed curve, show that $\mathbf{F}$ is constant. $\square$

Odds and Ends

In this chapter we present an assorted collection of situations to demonstrate how they can be analyzed using vectors. Here, we do not attempt a systematic development of any particular topic. The basic idea is to illustrate how a large variety of problems can be tackled using vectors in a coordinate free way.

12.1 Rotational Velocity of a Rigid Body

We find the rotational velocity of an arbitrarily rotating rigid body. This section is a continuation of our development of rotation operator and its matrix representation. In particular, we freely use the symbols introduced there, without re-defining them here.

Since the rotational velocity of a rigid body is common to all points of the body, it is enough to find the rotational velocity of the position vector $\mathbf{x}(t)$ of a point in the body. Let $\mathbf{x}_0$ denote the value of $\mathbf{x}(t)$ at $t = 0$. We seek a relation of the form

$$\dot{\mathbf{x}} = [\Omega S]\mathbf{x}_0 = \Omega \mathbf{x}. \tag{12.1}$$

and solve for Ω. Note that the time dependence must reside in the operator ΩS. Obviously,

$$\Omega = \dot{S}S^T = \dot{S}S^{-1} \tag{12.2}$$

solves Eq. (12.1) giving $\dot{\mathbf{x}} = \dot{S}\mathbf{x}_0$ where $\dot{S}$ is the time derivative of the operator $S(t)$. Note that we are using the same symbol for the operator and its matrix. This is justified because they are isomorphic. Differentiating $SS^T = I$ we get

$$\dot{S}S^T + S\dot{S}^T = 0. \tag{12.3}$$

Here, we have used the fact that the operations of transpose and differentiation commute. Equations (12.2) and (12.3) lead to

$$\Omega = \dot{S}S^T = -S\dot{S}^T = -\Omega^T \tag{12.4}$$

Thus, the operator Ω is skewsymmetric. We know that every skewsymmetric operator on a 3-D Euclidean space is the operator of vector multiplication by a fixed vector. We denote the corresponding vector for the skewsymmetric operator Ω by ω, so that

$$\Omega \mathbf{x} = \omega \times \mathbf{x} \quad \forall \mathbf{x} \in \mathbb{R}^3.$$

To appreciate this result, consider the matrix of Ω in some basis

$$\begin{bmatrix} 0 & -\omega_3 & \omega_2 \\ \omega_3 & 0 & -\omega_1 \\ -\omega_2 & \omega_1 & 0 \end{bmatrix}.$$

This gives vector $\omega \leftrightarrow [\omega_1 \ \omega_2 \ \omega_3]^T$ as an eigenvector with eigenvalue 0. By applying the matrix Ω to a vector $\mathbf{x} \leftrightarrow [x_1 \ x_2 \ x_3]^T$ we get the vector $\omega \times \mathbf{x} \leftrightarrow [\omega_2 x_3 - \omega_3 x_2 \ \ \omega_3 x_1 - \omega_1 x_3 \ \ \omega_1 x_2 - \omega_2 x_1]^T$.

In order to get the expression for ω we proceed as follows. Put $\theta \hat{\mathbf{n}} \times \mathbf{x} = A\mathbf{x}$ defining operator A. Then, the equation connecting $\mathbf{x}_0$ at $t = 0$ with $\mathbf{x}(t)$ at a later time t, namely,

$$\mathbf{x} = e^{\theta \hat{\mathbf{n}} \times} \mathbf{x}_0$$

can be written, in terms of A as

$$\mathbf{x} = e^A \mathbf{x}_0 \tag{12.5}$$

whence $S = e^A$. It then follows that

$$\Omega = \frac{d}{dt}\left(e^A\right) e^{-A} \tag{12.6}$$

which can be expanded, giving

$$\Omega = \dot{A} + \frac{1}{2!}[A, \dot{A}] + \frac{1}{3!}[A, [A, \dot{A}]] + \cdots \tag{12.7}$$

Here, $[A, B] = AB - BA$ is the commutator of A and B. To prove Eq. (12.7) we define

$$\Omega(\lambda) = \frac{\partial}{\partial t}\left(e^{\lambda A}\right) e^{-\lambda A}$$

where λ is a parameter independent of t. We have $\Omega(0) = 0$ and

$$\frac{\partial \Omega(\lambda)}{\partial \lambda} = \dot{A} + [A, \Omega(\lambda)].$$

The higher derivatives can be evaluated iteratively e.g.,

$$\frac{\partial^2 \Omega(\lambda)}{\partial \lambda^2} = [A, \frac{\partial \Omega(\lambda)}{\partial \lambda}] = [A, \dot{A}] + [A, \Omega(\lambda)],$$

$$\frac{\partial^3 \Omega(\lambda)}{\partial \lambda^3} = [A, [A, \dot{A}]] + [A, \Omega(\lambda)]$$

and proceeding iteratively, we get, for the nth derivative

$$\frac{\partial^n \Omega(\lambda)}{\partial \lambda^n} = \underbrace{[A, [A, [A, [\cdots [A, \dot{A}] \cdots]}_{(n-1)\text{factors}} + [A, \Omega(\lambda)].$$

Expanding $\Omega(\lambda)$ in Taylor series in λ about $\lambda = 0$ and using the above derivatives we get

$$\Omega(\lambda) = \lambda \dot{A} + \frac{\lambda^2}{2!} [A, \dot{A}] + \frac{\lambda^3}{3!} [A, [A, \dot{A}]] + \cdots$$

and Eq. (12.7) follows with $\lambda = 1$.

We must now evaluate the commutator of two skewsymmetric matrices. This is also a skewsymmetric matrix. Further, given a vector $\mathbf{x} \in \mathbb{R}^3$ and A, B skewsymmetric operators, $A\mathbf{x} = \mathbf{a} \times \mathbf{x}$ and $B\mathbf{x} = \mathbf{b} \times \mathbf{x}$ implies $[A, B]\mathbf{x} = (\mathbf{a} \times \mathbf{b}) \times \mathbf{x}$, as you can check. Thus, Eq. (12.7) can be written as (remember $A = \theta \hat{\mathbf{n}} \times$)

$$\Omega \mathbf{x} = \omega \times \mathbf{x} = \sum_{m=0}^{\infty} \frac{[(\boldsymbol{\theta} \times)^m \times \dot{\boldsymbol{\theta}}]}{(m+1)!} \theta \mathbf{x} = \sum_{m=0}^{\infty} \frac{[\theta^{m+1} (\hat{\mathbf{n}} \times)^m \times \dot{\hat{\mathbf{n}}}]}{(m+1)!} \times \mathbf{x} + \dot{\theta} \hat{\mathbf{n}} \times \mathbf{x} \quad (12.8)$$

Here, we define $(\boldsymbol{\theta} \times)^m$ by $\underbrace{\boldsymbol{\theta} \times (\boldsymbol{\theta} \times (\boldsymbol{\theta} \times (\cdots}_{m \text{ factors}}$ and similarly for $(\hat{\mathbf{n}} \times)^m$. Also, we have $\dot{\boldsymbol{\theta}} = \dot{\theta} \hat{\mathbf{n}} + \theta \dot{\hat{\mathbf{n}}}$. To obtain the infinite sum in Eq. (12.8) we note that $\dot{\hat{\mathbf{n}}}$ lies in the plane perpendicular to $\hat{\mathbf{n}}$. Therefore, as we have seen before,

$$\hat{\mathbf{n}} \times (\hat{\mathbf{n}} \times \dot{\hat{\mathbf{n}}}) = -\dot{\hat{\mathbf{n}}}$$

Using this equation in Eq. (12.8) and collecting the coefficients of $\hat{\mathbf{n}} \times \dot{\hat{\mathbf{n}}}$ and $\hat{\mathbf{n}} \theta (\hat{\mathbf{n}} \theta \dot{\hat{\mathbf{n}}})$ we get

$$\omega = \dot{\theta} \hat{\mathbf{n}} + (1 - \cos \theta) \hat{\mathbf{n}} \times \dot{\hat{\mathbf{n}}} - \sin \theta [\hat{\mathbf{n}} \times (\hat{\mathbf{n}} \times \dot{\hat{\mathbf{n}}})],$$

or,

$$\omega = \dot{\theta} \hat{\mathbf{n}} + (1 - \cos \theta) \hat{\mathbf{n}} \times \dot{\hat{\mathbf{n}}} + \sin \theta \dot{\hat{\mathbf{n}}}. \quad (12.9)$$

We see that $\omega \neq \dot{\boldsymbol{\theta}}$ unless $\dot{\hat{\mathbf{n}}} = \mathbf{0}$. Thus, it is more appropriate to call ω 'rotational velocity' rather than 'angular velocity' of the body.

Exercise   A fan operates as shown in Fig. 12.1. A horizontal shaft rotates counterclockwise with constant rotational velocity ω_1 about a vertical stand and the fan blades rotate counterclockwise with constant rotational velocity ω_2 about this shaft. Find the rotational velocity of the fan blade relative to the origin O of the stationary frame as shown in the figure.

Solution   Applying Eq. (12.9) to the first rotation about $\hat{\mathbf{n}}_3$ we get, since $\dot{\hat{\mathbf{n}}}_3 = \mathbf{0}$,

$$\omega_1 = \dot{\hat{\mathbf{i}}}_1 = \omega_1 \hat{\mathbf{n}}_3. \tag{12.10}$$

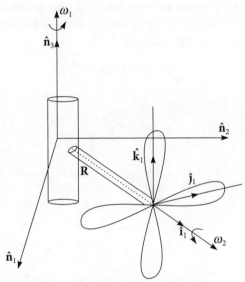

Fig. 12.1   The rotating fan

Now apply Eq. (12.9) to get the rotational velocity of the blade,

$$
\begin{aligned}
\omega &= \omega_2 \hat{\mathbf{i}}_1 + (1 - \cos \omega_2 t)\hat{\mathbf{i}}_1 \times \dot{\hat{\mathbf{i}}}_1 + \sin \omega_2 t \dot{\hat{\mathbf{i}}}_1 \\[4pt]
&= \omega_2 \cos \omega_1 t \hat{\mathbf{n}}_1 + \omega_2 \sin \omega_1 t \hat{\mathbf{n}}_2 \\[4pt]
&\quad + \omega_1 (1 - \cos \omega_2 t)(\cos \omega_1 t \hat{\mathbf{n}}_1 \times \hat{\mathbf{n}}_3 + \sin \omega_1 t \hat{\mathbf{n}}_2 \times \hat{\mathbf{n}}_3) + \omega_1 \sin \omega_2 t \hat{\mathbf{n}}_3 \\[4pt]
&= \omega_2 (\cos(\omega_1 t)\hat{\mathbf{n}}_1 + \sin(\omega_1 t)\hat{\mathbf{n}}_2) \\[4pt]
&\quad + \omega_1 (1 - \cos(\omega_2 t))(\sin(\omega_1 t)\hat{\mathbf{n}}_1 - \cos(\omega_1 t)\hat{\mathbf{n}}_2) + \omega_1 \sin(\omega_2 t)\hat{\mathbf{n}}_3 \\[4pt]
&= (\omega_2 \cos(\omega_1 t) + \omega_1 \sin(\omega_1 t)(1 - \cos(\omega_2 t)))\hat{\mathbf{n}}_1 \\[4pt]
&\quad + (\omega_2 \sin(\omega_1 t) - \omega_1 \cos(\omega_1 t)(1 - \cos(\omega_2 t)))\hat{\mathbf{n}}_2 + \omega_1 \sin(\omega_2 t)\hat{\mathbf{n}}_3.
\end{aligned}
$$

where we have put $\hat{\mathbf{i}}_1 = \cos\omega_1 t\,\hat{\mathbf{n}}_1 + \sin\omega_1 t\,\hat{\mathbf{n}}_2$, used Eq. (12.10) and the fact that $\hat{\mathbf{n}}_1, \hat{\mathbf{n}}_2, \hat{\mathbf{n}}_3$ form a right handed system.   □

Exercise   Suppose a rigid body is rotating in space and you know its instantaneous rotational velocity ω. This does not mean that you know the instantaneous axis of rotation, because ω specifies only its direction, which corresponds to a continuum of parallel lines in space. Obtain the equation of the instantaneous axis of rotation in terms of ω and the instantaneous (inertial) position and velocity vectors of a particle in the rigid body, which is not on the instantaneous axis of rotation.

Solution   [20] In what follows we refer to Fig. 12.2 and use symbols and the quantities specified in this figure, without defining them in the text, as they are self explanatory. Thus, you have to read the solution jointly with Fig. 12.2.

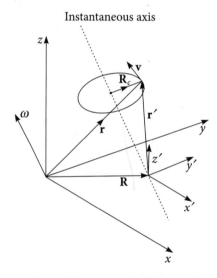

Fig. 12.2   Finding the instantaneous axis of rotation of a rigid body

Let $\mathbf{r}$ and $\mathbf{v}$ denote the position and velocity of the particle as specified in the problem. As all of the velocity $\mathbf{v}$ is taken to be rotational, it follows that

$$\omega \times \mathbf{R_c} = \mathbf{v}.$$

Crossing both sides of the above equation with ω we get

$$\omega \times (\omega \times \mathbf{R_c}) = \omega \times \mathbf{v}.$$

This equation can be transformed to

$$\omega(\omega \cdot \mathbf{R_c}) - \mathbf{R_c}(\omega \cdot \omega) = \omega \times \mathbf{v}.$$

Now $\omega \cdot \mathbf{R_c} = 0$ and $\omega \cdot \omega = |\omega|^2$, so that

$$\mathbf{R_c} = \frac{-(\omega \times \mathbf{v})}{|\omega|^2}.$$

Now

$$\mathbf{r}' = \mathbf{R_c} + \frac{\lambda \omega}{|\omega|} = \frac{\lambda \omega}{|\omega|} - \frac{(\omega \times \mathbf{v})}{|\omega|^2},$$

where λ is a scalar parameter with the dimensions of length. Hence, we have, with $\mathbf{R} = \mathbf{r} - \mathbf{r}'$,

$$\mathbf{R} = \mathbf{r} - \frac{\lambda \omega}{|\omega|} + \frac{(\omega \times \mathbf{v})}{|\omega|^2}.$$

As λ varies, the locus of the tip of this vector generates the line of the instantaneous axis of rotation for a point moving with velocity $\mathbf{v}$ and position vector $\mathbf{r}$ in the rigid body. Since the instantaneous rotational velocity ω is common to the whole rigid body, the instantaneous axis of rotation we have found is also common to all points in the body.

12.2 3-D Harmonic Oscillator

Oscillatory motion is performed by systems close to their *stable equilibrium* configurations under specified force fields. Here, we deal with a particle moving under the action of a force field $\mathbf{f}(\mathbf{x})$. We are concerned with an equilibrium point for the field, that is, the point $\mathbf{x}_0$ such that $\mathbf{f}(\mathbf{x}_0) = 0$. Thus, the particle does not experience any force at $\mathbf{x}_0$. We assume that $\mathbf{x}_0$ is an *isolated* equilibrium point, that is, it has a neighborhood devoid of any equilibrium point other than itself. Shifting the origin to $\mathbf{x}_0$, the condition for equilibrium can be stated as

$$\mathbf{f}(\mathbf{0}) = \mathbf{0}.$$

An equilibrium point is said to be *stable*, if it has a neighborhood at every point of which the particle is accelerated towards the interior of the neighborhood. A famous theorem due to Lagrange states that an equilibrium point is stable if and only if it is a point of local minimum for the potential corresponding to the field.

Thus, we are interested in the bounded motion of a system near a stable equilibrium point. To get this motion, we must first get an approximate form of the force field in a neighborhood of the equilibrium point. This can be achieved if the field $\mathbf{f}(\mathbf{x})$ has a Taylor expansion in some neighborhood of the stable equilibrium point which we have taken to be the origin. We can then write

$$\mathbf{f}(\mathbf{x}) = \mathbf{f}(\mathbf{0}) + \mathbf{r} \cdot \nabla \mathbf{f}(\mathbf{0}) + \frac{1}{2} (\mathbf{r} \cdot \nabla)^2 \mathbf{f}(\mathbf{0}) + \cdots.$$

The first term on RHS vanishes because origin is an equilibrium point, while the second term is linear in $\mathbf{r}$, that is,

$$(\alpha_1 \mathbf{r}_1 + \alpha_2 \mathbf{r}_2) \cdot \nabla \mathbf{f}(\mathbf{0}) = \alpha_1 \mathbf{r}_1 \cdot \nabla \mathbf{f}(\mathbf{0}) + \alpha_2 \mathbf{r}_2 \cdot \nabla \mathbf{f}(\mathbf{0}).$$

Third and further terms are of higher order of smallness and can be neglected. Stability of the equilibrium point is ensured if we impose $\mathbf{r} \cdot \ddot{\mathbf{r}} < 0$, or, equivalently, we use the following *stability condition*,

$$\mathbf{r} \cdot \nabla \mathbf{f}(\mathbf{0}) \le 0,$$

with equality only when $\mathbf{r} = \mathbf{0}$.

If we keep only the second term in the Taylor expansion of the force and neglect all further higher order terms, the corresponding equation of motion is the following second order linear differential equation:

$$m\ddot{\mathbf{r}} = \mathbf{r} \cdot \nabla \mathbf{f}(\mathbf{0}).$$

Since this is a second order equation, it has two linearly independent solutions (that is, they are not proportional to each other) say $\mathbf{r}_1 = \mathbf{r}_1(t)$ and $\mathbf{r}_2 = \mathbf{r}_2(t)$. Since it is linear, any linear combination of these two linearly independent solutions say $\mathbf{r}_n = \alpha_n \mathbf{r}_1(t) + \beta_n \mathbf{r}_2(t)$ is also a solution. This system, governed by a linear force obeying the stability condition, is called a *harmonic oscillator*. This superposition principle makes the analysis of harmonic oscillator manageable. As we will see below, if the force satisfies one additional requirement of being isotropic, the harmonic oscillator equation can be integrated to get exact solutions. On the other hand, if we add the third term in the Taylor series to the equation of motion, the resulting differential equation ceases to be linear. The mathematical analysis of this so called *anharmonic oscillator* becomes very difficult and is generally analysed using perturbation techniques, where the anharmonic term is treated as a small perturbation to the harmonic one.

Let us now specialize to the case where the force $\mathbf{f}$ is not only linear, but also isotropic or central, that is, it is only a function of the magnitude of $\mathbf{r}$ and not of its direction. Thus, $\mathbf{f}(\mathbf{r}) \equiv (f(r), 0, 0)$, expressed in the $\hat{\mathbf{r}}, \hat{\theta}, \hat{\phi}$ basis. It is straightforward to check that in this case

$$\mathbf{r} \cdot \nabla \mathbf{f}(\mathbf{0}) = -kr\hat{\mathbf{r}} = -k\mathbf{r}, \quad \text{where} \quad -k = \left.\frac{df(r)}{dr}\right|_{r=0}.$$

k is called the *force constant* and gives the strength of the isotropic binding force. Note that, if $V(r)$ is the potential function for the isotropic force, $\left.\frac{df(r)}{dr}\right|_{r=0} = -\left.\frac{d^2 V(r)}{dr^2}\right|_{r=0} = -k$. By Lagrange's theorem potential $V(r)$ has a local minimum at $r = 0$ so that $\left.\frac{d^2 V(r)}{dr^2}\right|_{r=0} > 0$, making $k > 0$. This makes $-k < 0$ and satisfies the stability condition. The force $-k\mathbf{r}, (k > 0)$, is commonly called Hooke's law force after Robert Hooke, who invented it to explain the elastic force causing oscillations of a spring. However, one has to remember that the general form of the Hooke's law force is given by the second term in the Taylor expansion of *any* force field near a stable equilibrium position, thus giving an universal approximation to any force field having Taylor expansion near a stable equilibrium point. This explains why Hooke's law is so ubiquitous in physics and engineering applications. By the same argument, Hooke's law is not a fundamental force law, but only a very useful approximation.

Thus, we have to solve the equation

$$\ddot{\mathbf{r}} + \omega_0^2 \mathbf{r} = \mathbf{0} \quad \text{where} \quad \omega_0^2 = \frac{k}{m}. \tag{12.11}$$

It turns out that bounded orbits of the attractive central force $-k\mathbf{r}$ are closed [3, 10, 19], so that the motion in the vicinity of a stable equilibrium point under such a force is periodic. Further, note that the torque exerted by $-k\mathbf{r}$ on the particle is $-k\mathbf{r} \times \mathbf{r} = \mathbf{0}$. Therefore, the angular momentum of the particle must be conserved. This fixes the angular momentum vector $m\mathbf{r} \times \mathbf{v}$ in space confining the position vector $\mathbf{r}$ and the velocity vector $\mathbf{v}$ of the particle to a plane perpendicular to the angular momentum vector. Thus, the motion under such a central force is planar.

In order to get two linearly independent solutions of Eq. (12.11) let us choose one of them as the circular orbit obtained by rotating a vector $\mathbf{a}_+$ *counterclockwise* in the plane of the orbit through the angle $\omega_0 t$ in time t about the unit vector $\hat{\mathbf{n}}$ perpendicular to the plane of the orbit. Using Eq. (6.45) we get,

$$\mathbf{r}_+(t) = \mathcal{R}_{\hat{\mathbf{n}}, \omega_0 t}(\mathbf{a}_+) = \cos \omega_0 t \, \mathbf{a}_+ + \sin \omega_0 t (\hat{\mathbf{n}} \times \mathbf{a}_+). \tag{12.12}$$

To construct the other linearly independent solution we take a vector $\mathbf{a}_-$ in the plane of the orbit and rotate it *clockwise* by the angle $\omega_0 t$ in time t. This amounts to replacing $\hat{\mathbf{n}}$ by $-\hat{\mathbf{n}}$ and $\mathbf{a}_+$ by $\mathbf{a}_-$ in Eq. (12.12). We get,

$$\mathbf{r}_-(t) = \cos \omega_0 t \, \mathbf{a}_- - \sin \omega_0 t (\hat{\mathbf{n}} \times \mathbf{a}_-). \tag{12.13}$$

To get a general solution we add these two linearly independent solutions. We get,

$$\mathbf{r}(t) = \mathbf{a}_0 \cos \omega_0 t + \mathbf{b}_0 \sin \omega_0 t, \tag{12.14}$$

where

$$\mathbf{a}_0 = \mathbf{a}_+ + \mathbf{a}_-$$

and

$$\mathbf{b}_0 = (\mathbf{a}_+ - \mathbf{a}_-) \times \hat{\mathbf{n}}. \tag{12.15}$$

The two constant vectors $\mathbf{a}_0$ and $\mathbf{b}_0$ can have any values. Therefore, Eq. (12.14) is the general solution of Eq. (12.11). If either $\mathbf{a}_0 = \mathbf{0}$ or $\mathbf{b}_0 = \mathbf{0}$, the motion becomes one dimensional with oscillations along the line of the surviving vector. Thus, the motion ceases to be planar and the unit vector $\hat{\mathbf{n}}$ is not uniquely defined, but any unit vector normal to $\mathbf{a}_\pm$ will do.

The vector coefficients $\mathbf{a}_0$ and $\mathbf{b}_0$ can be expressed in terms of initial conditions, that is, the values of the position and velocity vectors at $t = 0$. Putting $t = 0$ in the expressions for $\mathbf{r}(t)$ as in Eq. (12.14) and $\dot{\mathbf{r}}(t)$ obtained by differentiating Eq. (12.14) with respect to t, we get

$$\mathbf{r}_0 \; = \; \mathbf{r}(0) = \mathbf{a}_0$$

$$\mathbf{v}_0 \; = \; \dot{\mathbf{r}}(0) = \omega_0 \mathbf{b}_0. \tag{12.16}$$

An inspection of Eq. (12.14) tells us that it represents a superposition of independent simple harmonic motions along the lines determined by $\mathbf{a}_0$ and $\mathbf{b}_0$ or, via Eq. (12.16) along $\mathbf{r}_0$ and $\mathbf{v}_0$. The resultant motion is elliptical and reduces to one-dimensional simple harmonic motion if $\mathbf{r}_0 = \mathbf{0}$ or $\mathbf{v}_0 = \mathbf{0}$ or, generally, when $\mathbf{r}_0 \times \mathbf{v}_0 = \mathbf{0}$. To see that the orbit is an ellipse we recast Eq. (12.14) as

$$\mathbf{r} = \mathbf{a}\cos\phi + \mathbf{b}\sin\phi, \tag{12.17}$$

where $\mathbf{a}^2 \geq \mathbf{b}^2$, $\mathbf{a} \cdot \mathbf{b} = 0$ and $\phi = \phi(t) = \omega_0 t + \phi_0$. Vectors $\mathbf{a}$ and $\mathbf{b}$ define the major axis and the minor axis of the ellipse respectively.

Exercise   For an oscillator with orbit

$$\mathbf{r}(t) = \mathbf{a}\cos(\omega_0 t + \phi_0) + \mathbf{b}\sin(\omega_0 t + \phi_0),$$

find the major axis $\mathbf{a}$ and the minor axis $\mathbf{b}$ from the initial conditions $\mathbf{r}_0 = \mathbf{r}(0)$ and $\mathbf{v}_0 = \dot{\mathbf{r}}(0)$. Show that, for $0 < \phi_0 < \frac{\pi}{2}$,

$$\mathbf{a} = \mathbf{r}_0 \cos\phi_0 - \frac{\mathbf{v}_0}{\omega_0}\sin\phi_0$$

$$\mathbf{b} = \mathbf{r}_0 \sin\phi_0 + \frac{\mathbf{v}_0}{\omega_0}\cos\phi_0$$

and that ϕ_0 is given by

$$\tan 2\phi_0 = \frac{2\omega_0 \mathbf{r}_0 \cdot \mathbf{v}_0}{\mathbf{v}_0^2 - \omega_0^2 \mathbf{r}_0^2}.$$

Hint   Expand the trigonometric functions in the expression for $\mathbf{r}(t)$ and compare with Eq. (12.14) to get expressions for $\mathbf{a}_0$ and $\mathbf{b}_0$ in terms of $\mathbf{a}$ and $\mathbf{b}$ and invert these equations to get the result. To get the equation for ϕ_0 use $\mathbf{a} \cdot \mathbf{b} = 0$.   □

We may eliminate ϕ_0 by taking $\phi_0 = \omega_0 t_0$ and then shifting the origin in time to t_0. You may recognize Eq. (12.17) to be the equation to an ellipse parameterized by ϕ which we have encountered before (see section 2.4). $\mathbf{a}$ and $\mathbf{b}$ respectively give the major axis and the minor axis of this ellipse (see Fig. 12.3). As we have mentioned above, we can now see that the elliptic orbit of an isotropic harmonic oscillator is periodic in space that is, the particle aquires the same position vector **r** after a fixed period of time T. However, something more is true. Both the state variables **r** and $\dot{\mathbf{r}}$ have exactly the same values at any two times separated by a fixed time interval T called the period of the motion. We express this by saying that the motion of the isotropic harmonic oscillator is periodic. For the elliptical motion, the period T is related to the *natural frequency* of the oscillator ω_0 by

$$\omega_0 T = 2\pi.$$

The motion over a single period is called an *oscillation*. The constant ϕ_0 is called *phase* of an oscillation beginning at $t = 0$. The maximum displacement from the equilibrium point during an oscillation is called its *amplitude*. For the elliptical motion, the amplitude is $A = |\mathbf{a}|$.

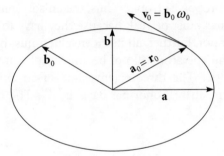

Fig. 12.3   Orbit of an isotropic harmonic oscillator

As we have seen, Eq. (12.14) represents the elliptical motion as a superposition of *two uniform circular motions* with opposite senses. This is illustrated in Fig. 12.4. As we can see from the figure, this relation provides a practical way to construct an ellipse from two circles.

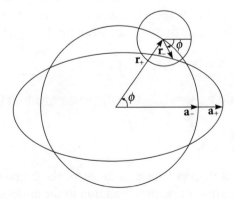

Fig. 12.4   Elliptical orbit as a superposition of coplanar circular orbits

Exercise   Show that the total energy of the oscillator $E = \left(\frac{1}{2}m\dot{\mathbf{r}}^2 + \frac{1}{2}k\mathbf{r}^2 \right)$ is constant in time, and hence a *constant of the motion*. Show further, that $E = \frac{1}{2}k(\mathbf{a}^2 + \mathbf{b}^2)$. In fact energy is an additive constant of motion, that is, the energy of $n > 1$ oscillators is the sum of the energies of individual oscillators. Such additive constants of motion are called *conserved quantities*.   □

Exercise   Learn about the damped harmonic oscillator (an oscillator oscillating in a resistive medium) from a suitable book and try to formulate and solve it using vector methods. Differentiate between three cases: Light damping, heavy damping and critical damping.   □

12.2.1   Anisotropic oscillator

In this case we continue to terminate the Taylor series for the force field near the stable equilibrium point after the term linear in $\mathbf{r}$, so that the force is linear in $\mathbf{r}$. However, we lift the requirement that the force be isotropic. Thus, the anisotropic force is a linear operator on $\mathcal{E}_3$ and all its eigenvalues must be real, because they have to be measurable. Hence, it must be a symmetric operator. Further, all its eigenvalues must be distinct, because, if two of them are equal, then the operator will not be anisotropic on the plane spanned by the corresponding eigenvectors. The three eigenvectors of an anisotropic force are called *principal vectors* and form an orthonormal basis in $\mathcal{E}_3$. The corresponding eigenvalue equations are

$$\mathbf{f}(\mathbf{e}_1) = -k_1\mathbf{e}_1$$

$$\mathbf{f}(\mathbf{e}_2) = -k_2\mathbf{e}_2$$

$$\mathbf{f}(\mathbf{e}_3) = -k_3\mathbf{e}_3$$

where $k_{1,2,3}$ are the positive force constants giving the strength of the binding force along the three principal directions. Now, the superposition principle tells us that we can resolve the general motion along the three principal directions. If $\mathbf{r}_i$ is the component of displacement along $\mathbf{e}_i$, $i = 1, 2, 3$, then we can write for the equation of motion,

$$m\ddot{\mathbf{r}} = m\ddot{\mathbf{r}}_1 + m\ddot{\mathbf{r}}_2 + m\ddot{\mathbf{r}}_3 = -k_1\mathbf{r}_1 - k_2\mathbf{r}_2 - k_3\mathbf{r}_3 = -\sum_i k_i\hat{\mathbf{e}}_i.$$

Since $\mathbf{r}_i$ are orthogonal and $\hat{\mathbf{e}}_i$, $i = 1, 2, 3$ do not change with time, each component must independently satisfy

$$m\ddot{\mathbf{r}}_i = -k_i\mathbf{r}_i, \quad i = 1, 2, 3,$$

whose solutions must be of the same form as those for the isotropic oscillator restricted to one dimensional motion. Thus, the general solution to the anisotropic oscillator is

$$\mathbf{r} = A_1\mathbf{e}_1\cos(\omega_1 t + \phi_1) + A_2\mathbf{e}_2\cos(\omega_2 t + \phi_2) + A_3\mathbf{e}_3\cos(\omega_3 t + \phi_3), \quad (12.18)$$

where, A_k, $k = 1,2,3$ are the amplitudes of oscillation along $\hat{\mathbf{e}}_k$, $k = 1,2,3$ respectively and the three natural frequencies are given by

$$\omega_i = \sqrt{\frac{k_i}{m}}.$$

The orbit corresponding to Eq. (12.18) will be closed and the corresponding motion be periodic only when the ratios ω_1/ω_2 and ω_2/ω_3 are rational numbers. In general, the orbit will not lie in a plane. Since the individual 1-D oscillations are harmonic, energy of each of them is conserved so that the total energy of an anisotropic oscillator is conserved. The corresponding conserved energy is given, with $m = 1$ by

$$\frac{1}{2}\dot{\mathbf{r}}_i^2 + \frac{1}{2}\omega_i^2\mathbf{r}_i^2 = E_i(0) = \frac{1}{2}A_i^2, \; i = 1,2,3,$$

where $E_i(0)$ is the value of the energy at $t = 0$ and A_i is the amplitude of ith oscillation along ith principal axis. The conservation of energy for the anisotropic oscillator becomes

$$\frac{1}{2}\sum_{i=1}^{3}(\dot{\mathbf{r}}_i^2 + \frac{1}{2}\omega_i^2\mathbf{r}_i^2) = \sum_{i=1}^{3}E_i(0) = E.$$

It then follows that the orbit of the anisotropic oscillator will be confined to an ellipsoidal region given by $V(\mathbf{r}_1,\mathbf{r}_2,\mathbf{r}_3) = \sum_{i=1}^{3} V_i(\mathbf{r}_i) = \frac{1}{2}\sum_{i=1}^{3}\omega_i^2\mathbf{r}_i^2 \leq E$ with principal axes $\mathbf{e}_1,\mathbf{e}_2,\mathbf{e}_3$ and centered at the equilibrium point. If $k_3 = 0 = \omega_3$, the orbit will be restricted to $\mathbf{e}_1,\mathbf{e}_2$ plane and is commonly known as a *Lissajous figure*.

Exercise   Write down the energy conservation equations for a 2-D anisotropic oscillator. Show that the rectangle formed by the sides $2A_1$ and $2A_2$ is inscribed in the ellipse (see Fig. 12.5(a)).   □

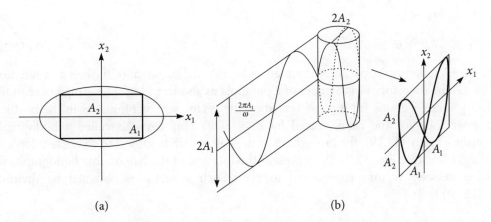

(a)   (b)

Fig. 12.5   (a) The regions $V \leq E$, $V_1 \leq E$ and $V_2 \leq E$ (b) Construction of a Lissajous figure

Exercise Justify, the following procedure to construct an orbit of the anisotropic oscillator in the e_1, e_2 plane, with axes labelled x_1, x_2, $\omega_1 = 1$, $\omega_2 = \omega$, that is, the corresponding Lissajous figure. Consider a cylinder with base $2A_1$ and a strip of width $2A_2$. We draw on the strip a sine wave with period $2\pi A_1/\omega$ and amplitude A_2 and wind the strip onto the cylinder (see Fig. 12.5(b)). The orthogonal projection $(x_1, x_2, x_3) \mapsto (x_1, x_2, 0)$ of the sinusoid wound around the cylinder onto x_1, x_2 plane gives the desired orbit, or the Lissajous figure.   □

Lissajous figures can be conveniently seen on an oscilloscope which displays independent harmonic oscillations along the horizontal and vertical axes.

12.3   Projectiles and Terrestrial Effects

In this section we deal with projectile motion and the effect of earth's rotation on it.[1]

12.3.1   Optimum initial conditions for netting a basket ball

We will now find the optimum speed v_0 and the angle θ_0 with the horizontal for netting a basket ball at height h and distance L. We show that θ_0 is greater than $\pi/4$ by an amount $\arctan(h/L)$.

We analyze the above projectile motion in the velocity space (as explained below). This is conceptually simple, it clearly brings out the basic mechanics and geometry of the situation and saves algebra.

We assume that the ball is to be thrown from the origin at a horizontal distance L from the pole on which the basket mounted at a height h from the horizontal xy plane passing through the origin. Let the initial velocity of the ball be $\mathbf{v}_0$. It will experience a constant force due to gravity, inducing a constant acceleration $\mathbf{g}$ in it, directed vertically downwards. The resulting equation of motion is,

$$\dot{\mathbf{r}} = \mathbf{v} = \mathbf{g}t + \mathbf{v}_0, \tag{12.19}$$

which integrates to

$$\mathbf{r} = \frac{1}{2}\mathbf{g}t^2 + \mathbf{v}_0 t. \tag{12.20}$$

The last equation is the parametric equation for the displacement of the ball as a function of time. The trajectory is a segment of a parabola as shown in Fig. 12.6. To go over to the velocity space, we look for a curve traced by the vector $\mathbf{v} = \mathbf{v}(t)$, just as in the position space we look for the curve traced by $\mathbf{r} = \mathbf{r}(t)$. This curve is called a hodograph. According to Eq. (12.19), the hodograph of the ball, which is subject to a constant force, is a straight line (see Fig. 12.7). To represent the location of the ball on this *hodograph*, we need a velocity vector proportional to $\mathbf{r}(t)$. Such a vector is obtained by dividing Eq. (12.20) by t:

$$\langle \mathbf{v} \rangle(t) = \frac{\mathbf{r}}{t} = \frac{1}{2}\mathbf{g}t + \mathbf{v}_0. \tag{12.21}$$

---

[1] Applications in this and the next section are treated in [10] using geometric algebra.

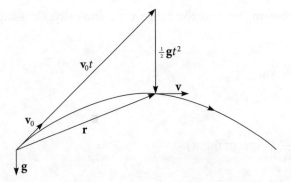

Fig. 12.6   Trajectory in position space

The vector $\langle \mathbf{v} \rangle(t)$ is the average velocity of the ball. Note that $\langle \mathbf{v} \rangle(t)$ and $\mathbf{r}(t)$ have the same direction. Comparing Eqs (12.19) and (12.21), we get a simple relation between the actual velocity and the average velocity:

$$\mathbf{v}(t) = \langle \mathbf{v} \rangle(t) + \frac{1}{2}\mathbf{g}t = \frac{\mathbf{r}}{t} + \frac{1}{2}\mathbf{g}t. \tag{12.22}$$

Figure 12.6 depicts the hodograph given by Eq. (12.21) and also displays Eq. (12.22). We see that the increment in the velocity of the ball in equal intervals of time is equal. Fig. 12.7 contains all the information about the projectile motion, so all questions regarding the motion can be answered by dealing with the triangles in the figure graphically or algebraically.

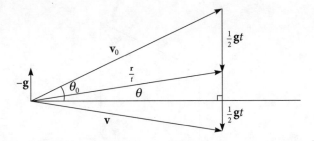

Fig. 12.7   Trajectory in the velocity space

First, consider the question of determining the range r of a target sighted in a direction $\hat{\mathbf{r}}$ (not necessarily along the horizontal) which is hit by a projectile, launched with velocity $\mathbf{v}_0$. This can be done graphically by using the properties of Fig. 12.7. Having laid out $\mathbf{v}_0$ on a graph paper (by choosing appropriate units and scale!) as indicated in Fig. 12.7, one extends a line from the base of $\mathbf{v}_0$, in the direction $\hat{\mathbf{r}}$, to its intersection with the vertical line extending from the tip of $\mathbf{v}_0$. The length of the two sides of the triangle thus constructed are then measured, say v_1 and v_2, to get the magnitude of $\frac{1}{2}\mathbf{g}t$ and $\frac{\mathbf{r}}{t}$ respectively. This gives the time of flight $t = 2v_1/g$ and the range $r = 2(v_1 v_2)/g$. How to get the final velocity is also evident from Fig. 12.7.

To get to our problem, we find the range r algebraically. Crossing Eq. (12.21) with $\mathbf{r}$ we get,

$$\frac{1}{2}t(\mathbf{g}\times\mathbf{r}) = \mathbf{r}\times\mathbf{v}_0,$$

giving

$$t = \frac{2v_0}{g}\frac{|\hat{\mathbf{r}}\times\hat{\mathbf{v}}_0|}{|\hat{\mathbf{g}}\times\hat{\mathbf{r}}|}\;\text{(Time of flight)}.\tag{12.23}$$

Again, crossing Eq. (12.21) with $(-\mathbf{g}t)$, after some simplification, using Eq. (12.23) for t, we get

$$r = \frac{2v_0^2}{g}\frac{(-\hat{\mathbf{g}}\times\hat{\mathbf{v}}_0)\cdot(\hat{\mathbf{v}}_0\times\hat{\mathbf{r}})}{|-\hat{\mathbf{g}}\times\hat{\mathbf{r}}|^2}.\tag{12.24}$$

Using identity II we get,

$$(-\hat{\mathbf{g}}\times\hat{\mathbf{v}}_0)\cdot(\hat{\mathbf{v}}_0\times\hat{\mathbf{r}}) = -\hat{\mathbf{g}}\cdot\hat{\mathbf{r}} + (\hat{\mathbf{v}}_0\cdot\hat{\mathbf{r}})(-\hat{\mathbf{g}}\cdot\hat{\mathbf{v}}_0)$$

$$= \cos\left(\frac{\pi}{2}-\phi\right) + \cos(\theta_0-\phi)\cos\left(\frac{\pi}{2}-\theta_0\right),\tag{12.25}$$

where θ_0 and ϕ are the angles respectively made by $\hat{\mathbf{v}}_0$ and $\hat{\mathbf{r}}$ with the horizontal, as shown in Fig. 12.7.

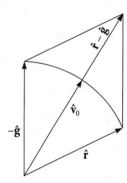

Fig. 12.8   Graphical determination of the displacement r, time of light t and final velocity $\mathbf{v}$

Now we complete the job in the following two steps. First, for a given v_0 and $\hat{\mathbf{r}}$, we find $\hat{\mathbf{v}}_0$ which maximizes the range r in the direction $\hat{\mathbf{r}}$ and also find this maximum range, say $r_{\max}$. Using this $\hat{\mathbf{v}}_0$ and $(r, \hat{\mathbf{r}})$ as given, we solve for v_0 with $r_{\max} = r$. Note that $r = \sqrt{h^2 + L^2}$ and $\hat{\mathbf{r}}$ is specified by $\tan(\phi) = h/L$.

To find the direction $\hat{\mathbf{v}}_0$ which maximizes the range r along $\hat{\mathbf{r}}$, we note that r is maximum when the RHS of Eq. (12.25) is maximum. Since $\hat{\mathbf{r}}$ and $-\hat{\mathbf{g}}$ are fixed directions, we have to maximize the second term on the RHS of Eq. (12.25). This is maximum when $\frac{\pi}{2} - \theta_0 = \theta_0 - \phi$ which implies $\theta_0 = \frac{\pi}{4} + \frac{\phi}{2}$. Thus, $\hat{\mathbf{v}}_0$ is directed along the line bisecting the angle between $\hat{\mathbf{r}}$ and $-\hat{\mathbf{g}}$ (see Fig. 12.8).

Thus,

$$\hat{\mathbf{v}}_0 = \frac{\hat{\mathbf{r}} - \hat{\mathbf{g}}}{|\hat{\mathbf{r}} - \hat{\mathbf{g}}|}. \tag{12.26}$$

Substituting Eq. (12.26) in Eq. (12.24) we get,

$$r_{max} = \frac{2v_0^2}{g} \frac{1}{|\hat{\mathbf{r}} - \hat{\mathbf{g}}|^2} = \frac{v_0^2}{g} \frac{1}{1 + \sin(\phi)}. \tag{12.27}$$

We leave the last equality for you to check. Solving Eq. (12.27) for v_0 with $r_{max} = \sqrt{h^2 + L^2} = r_0$ say, (note that $\sin(\phi) = h/r_0$), we get

$$v_0 = \sqrt{g(r_0 + h)}.$$

Using $\theta_0 = \frac{\pi}{4} + \frac{\phi}{2}$ and $\phi = \arctan(h/L)$ we get

$$\theta_0 = \frac{\pi}{4} + \frac{1}{2} \arctan\left(\frac{h}{L}\right).$$

12.3.2 Optimum angle of striking a golf ball

For non-spinning high speed golf balls the force of air drag is roughly linear with velocity ($\mathbf{F}_D = C\mathbf{v}$). Assume that $C/m = 0.25$ s^{-1}, $m = 0.046$ kg and that the maximum horizontal range of 152 m is obtained with an initial speed of 61 m/sec. We show that the angle of striking has to be 32 degrees with the horizontal, whereas in the absence of any air drag it would have been 45 degrees.

We have to set up and solve the equation of motion for a ball projected with the initial velocity $\mathbf{v}_0$ from origin under the force of linear drag and constant gravity. Let the drag force be given by

$$\mathbf{F}_D = C\mathbf{v} = -m\gamma\mathbf{v}.$$

which defines γ. Then the equation of motion is

$$\dot{\mathbf{v}} = \mathbf{g} - \gamma\mathbf{v}, \tag{12.28}$$

or,

$$(\dot{\mathbf{v}} + \gamma\mathbf{v}) = \mathbf{g}.$$

Noting that $e^{\gamma t}$ is the integrating factor, we get,

$$e^{\gamma t}(\dot{\mathbf{v}} + \gamma \mathbf{v}) = \frac{d}{dt}(e^{\gamma t}\mathbf{v}) = e^{\gamma t}\mathbf{g}.$$

Integrating, we get,

$$e^{\gamma t}\mathbf{v}(t) - \mathbf{v}_0 = \mathbf{g}\int_0^t e^{\gamma t'}dt' = \mathbf{g}\left(\frac{e^{\gamma t}-1}{\gamma}\right).$$

Solving for $\mathbf{v}(t)$, we get,

$$\mathbf{v}(t) = \mathbf{g}\left(\frac{1-e^{-\gamma t}}{\gamma}\right) + \mathbf{v}_0 e^{-\gamma t}. \tag{12.29}$$

The constant γ^{-1} is called relaxation time which is the measure of the time it takes for the retarding force to make the particle forget its initial conditions. If $t \gg \gamma^{-1}$, then $e^{-\gamma t} \ll 1$ so that the first term on the RHS of Eq. (12.29) dominates all others, irrespective of the value of $\mathbf{v}_0$, giving

$$\mathbf{v} = \mathbf{v}_\infty = \gamma^{-1}\mathbf{g}.$$

The value $\mathbf{v}_\infty$ is called the terminal velocity, which can also be obtained by putting $\dot{\mathbf{v}} = 0$ in the equation of motion.

The displacement $\mathbf{r}$ of the ball from the origin is found by directly integrating Eq. (12.29). This gives

$$\mathbf{r} = \mathbf{g}\left(\frac{e^{-\gamma t}+\gamma t-1}{\gamma^2}\right) + \mathbf{v}_0\left(\frac{1-e^{-\gamma t}}{\gamma}\right). \tag{12.30}$$

Let the plane of motion of the ball be the $x-y$ plane with x axis horizontal. Equation (12.30) gives rise to the equations

$$x = v_{0x}\left(\frac{1-e^{-\gamma t}}{\gamma}\right) \tag{12.31}$$

$$y = g\left(\frac{e^{-\gamma t}+\gamma t-1}{\gamma^2}\right) + v_{0y}\left(\frac{1-e^{-\gamma t}}{\gamma}\right). \tag{12.32}$$

At the end of its range, the ball touches the ground, so $y = 0$, making the RHS of Eq. (12.32) equal to zero. This gives a transcendental equation for the time of flight t which does not have a closed form solution. Assuming t to be sufficiently large so as to make $e^{-\gamma t}$ small enough, we expand $e^{-\gamma t}$ in powers of t and retain terms only up to second order so that contribution due to gravity is properly included. We now find the positive root of the resulting quadratic in t and substitute in Eq. (12.31). Putting

$v_{0x} = v_0 \cos\theta_0$ and $v_{0y} = v_0 \sin\theta_0$ where θ_0 is the angle at which the ball is projected and $v_0 = |\mathbf{v}_0|$, we find that we have now got an equation expressing the range x as a function of θ_0. To find θ_0 for the maximum range, we solve $\frac{dx}{d\theta_0} = 0$. Using the given data, we get $\theta_0^{\max} = 32^0$.

Equation (12.28) is useful in the analysis of microscopic motions also. For example, consider an electron (with mass m and charge e) moving in a conductor under the influence of a constant electric field $\mathbf{E}$. The electron's motion is retarded by the collisions with the lattice. We may represent the retardation by the resistive force proportional to the velocity of the electron. If the resistance is independent of the direction in which the electron moves, we say that the conductor is an isotropic medium. We can then write the resistive force in the form $-\mu\mathbf{v}$, where μ is a scalar constant. We are thus led to the equation, (compare with Eq. (12.28)),

$$\dot{\mathbf{v}} = e\mathbf{E} - \mu\mathbf{v}. \tag{12.33}$$

For times large compared to the relaxation time $\tau = m/\mu$, the electron reaches the terminal velocity

$$\mathbf{v} = \left[\frac{e}{\mu}\right]\mathbf{E} \tag{12.34}$$

and the result is a steady current in the conductor. The electric current density $\mathbf{J}$ is given by

$$\mathbf{J} = Ne\mathbf{v}, \tag{12.35}$$

where N is the number density of electrons. Substituting Eq. (12.34) in Eq. (12.35) we get Ohm's law

$$\mathbf{J} = \sigma\mathbf{E}, \tag{12.36}$$

where the conductor's d-c conductivity σ is given by

$$\sigma = Ne^2/\mu. \tag{12.37}$$

Ohm's law holds remarkably well for many conductors over a wide range of currents. The conductivity σ and the electron density N can be measured, so μ can be calculated from Eq. (12.37). Then, the relaxation time can also be calculated and compared with the measured values. These are in general agreement with the extremely short relaxation times observed in metals. Thus, Eq. (12.33) is vindicated to some degree. However, we note that the velocity $\mathbf{v}$ in Eq. (12.33) cannot be regarded as the velocity of an individual electron, whose trajectory must be very irregular as it collides repeatedly with the massive atoms in the lattice. Thus, $\mathbf{v}$ in Eq. (12.33) must be a kind of average electron velocity. Thus, our classical analysis can describe, (if at all), only the average motion in the microscopic domain. Derivation and explanation of equations like Eq. (12.33), pertaining to the electron's motion in a metal, requires statistical mechanics and the basic equations of quantum mechanics.

12.3.3   Effects of Coriolis force on a projectile

A projectile is fired due east from a point on the surface of the earth at a geographical latitude λ with speed v_0 and at an angle of elevation α above the horizontal. We find the lateral deflection of the projectile when it strikes the earth. We also find the change in the range of the projectile due to the rotation of the earth.

We use a rotating frame of reference fixed to the surface of the earth *topocentric frame* to analyse this motion (see Fig. 12.9). We have to account for the inertial forces namely the centrifugal force $m(\omega \times \mathbf{r}) \times \omega$ and Coriolis force $2m(\mathbf{v} \times \omega)$ where ω is the rotational velocity of the earth and $(\mathbf{r}, \mathbf{v})$ are the instantaneous position and velocity of the projectile, as measured in the rotating (topocentric) frame. We add the gravitational and centrifugal accelerations to get,

$$\mathbf{g}_{\text{eff}} = \mathbf{g} + (\omega \times \mathbf{r}) \times \omega.$$

Since the earth's surface is a geoid, $\mathbf{g}_{\text{eff}}$ is normal to it.

Thus, the equation of motion becomes

$$\dot{\mathbf{v}} = \ddot{\mathbf{r}} = \mathbf{g}_{\text{eff}} + 2(\mathbf{v} \times \omega). \tag{12.38}$$

Henceforth, we replace $\mathbf{g}_{\text{eff}}$ by $\mathbf{g}$ so that whenever we write $\mathbf{g}$ we actually mean $\mathbf{g}_{\text{eff}}$. Also we neglect the resistance due to air.

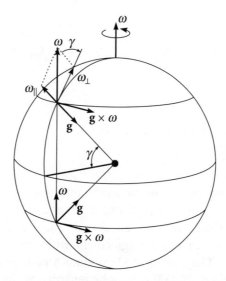

Fig. 12.9   Terrestrial Coriolis effect

From Eq. (12.38) we can compute the effect of Coriolis force on the projectile motion, treating $\mathbf{g}$ to be a constant. The principal source of variation in $\mathbf{g}$ is the deviation of earth's figure from sphericity and the non-uniformity of its mass distribution (density). Another reason is the possible fall from great heights (multiples of earth's radius) which is unrealistic for a surface to surface projectile. Anyway, here we shall treat $\mathbf{g}$ to be a constant. Actually, in the approximation of constant $\mathbf{g}$ and ω Eq. (12.38) can be exactly solved. In our case, however, for typical velocities we have $2|(\mathbf{v} \times \omega)| << \mathbf{g}$ because of the relatively small value for the angular speed of the earth ($\omega = 7.29 \times 10^{-5}$ radians sec^{-1}).

Thus, a perturbation solution is more useful here and we proceed to get it in the following way.

We regard the Coriolis term in Eq. (12.38) as a small perturbing force. Then Eq. (12.38) can be solved by the method of successive approximations. We write velocity $\mathbf{v}$ as an expansion of successive orders in ω,

$$\mathbf{v} = \mathbf{v}_1 + \mathbf{v}_2 + \mathbf{v}_3 + \cdots \tag{12.39}$$

The zeroth order term $\mathbf{v}_1$ is required to satisfy the unperturbed equation $\dot{\mathbf{v}}_1 = \mathbf{g}$, which integrates to

$$\mathbf{v}_1 = \mathbf{g}t + \mathbf{v}_0, \tag{12.40}$$

where $\mathbf{v}_0$ is the initial velocity. Inserting $\mathbf{v}$ to the first order in Eq. (12.38) we get,

$$\dot{\mathbf{v}} = \dot{\mathbf{v}}_1 + \dot{\mathbf{v}}_2 = \mathbf{g} + 2(\mathbf{v}_1 + \mathbf{v}_2) \times \omega.$$

Neglecting the second order term $2\mathbf{v}_2 \times \omega$ this reduces to an equation for $\mathbf{v}_2$ when $\mathbf{v}_1$ is replaced by the RHS of Eq. (12.40),

$$\dot{\mathbf{v}}_2 = 2\mathbf{v}_1 \times \omega = 2(\mathbf{g}t + \mathbf{v}_0) \times \omega.$$

This integrates to

$$\mathbf{v}_2 = (\mathbf{g}t^2 + 2\mathbf{v}_0 t) \times \omega. \tag{12.41}$$

We can determine the higher order corrections $\mathbf{v}_3, \mathbf{v}_4 \cdots$ in a similar way.

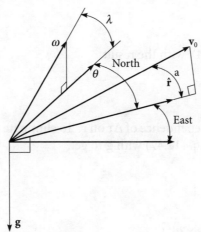

Fig. 12.10   Topocentric directional parameters

Substituting Eqs (12.40) and (12.41) in Eq. (12.39) we get the velocity to the first order in ω as

$$\mathbf{v} = \mathbf{v}_0 + \mathbf{g}t + (\mathbf{g}t^2 + 2\mathbf{v}_0 t) \times \boldsymbol{\omega} \tag{12.42}$$

Integrating this, we get a parametric equation for the displacement

$$\mathbf{r} = \frac{1}{2}\mathbf{g}t^2 + \mathbf{v}_0 t + \Delta\mathbf{r} \tag{12.43}$$

where the deviation $\Delta\mathbf{r}$ from a parabolic trajectory (due to Coriolis force) is given to the first order by

$$\Delta\mathbf{r} = (\mathbf{v}_0 + \frac{1}{3}\mathbf{g}t) \times \boldsymbol{\omega}t^2 + \cdots \tag{12.44}$$

To estimate the magnitude of the correction $\Delta\mathbf{r}$, we observe from Eqs (12.43) and (12.44) that

$$\frac{|\Delta\mathbf{r}|}{|\mathbf{r}|} \approx \omega t \tag{12.45}$$

For the correction to be one percent we must have $\omega t \geq 0.01$ and from the value of ω we find that the time of flight must be at least two minutes, which is more than the time of flight in a typical projectile problem. Hence, we need not consider the corrections of order higher than the first. Indeed, before considering the higher order corrections, the assumption that $\mathbf{g}$ is a constant should be examined.

The expression in Eq. (12.44) for the Coriolis deflection $\Delta\mathbf{r}$ is not in its most convenient form as it is not given as a function of target location $\mathbf{r}$. To circumvent this, we use the zeroth order approximation

$$\mathbf{r} \approx \frac{1}{2}\mathbf{g}t^2 + \mathbf{v}_0 t \tag{12.46}$$

to eliminate $\mathbf{v}_0$ in Eq. (12.44), with the result,

$$\Delta\mathbf{r} = -t\boldsymbol{\omega} \times (\mathbf{r} - \frac{1}{6}\mathbf{g}t^2). \tag{12.47}$$

This shows the directional dependence of $\Delta\mathbf{r}$ on $\mathbf{r}$. To eliminate t from Eq. (12.47) in favour of $\mathbf{r}$ we cross both sides of Eq. (12.47) with $\mathbf{g}$ to get,

$$(\mathbf{r} \times \mathbf{g}) = (\mathbf{v}_0 \times \mathbf{g})t,$$

or,

$$(\mathbf{r} \times \mathbf{g}) \cdot (\mathbf{v}_0 \times \mathbf{g}) = |\mathbf{v}_0 \times \mathbf{g}|^2 t,$$

or,

$$t = \frac{(\mathbf{r} \times \mathbf{g}) \cdot (\mathbf{v}_0 \times \mathbf{g})}{|\mathbf{v}_0 \times \mathbf{g}|^2}.$$
(12.48)

Similarly, again from Eq. (12.46) we have,

$$\frac{1}{2} t^2 = \frac{(\mathbf{r} \times \mathbf{v}_0) \cdot (\mathbf{g} \times \mathbf{v}_0)}{|\mathbf{g} \times \mathbf{v}_0|^2}.$$
(12.49)

Note that

$$\mathbf{r} - \frac{1}{6} \mathbf{g} t^2 = r \left(\hat{\mathbf{r}} - \frac{1}{3} \left[\frac{(\hat{\mathbf{r}} \times \hat{\mathbf{v}}_0) \cdot (\hat{\mathbf{g}} \times \hat{\mathbf{v}}_0)}{|\hat{\mathbf{g}} \times \hat{\mathbf{v}}_0|^2} \right] \hat{\mathbf{g}} \right).$$
(12.50)

This shows that the two terms in Eq. (12.47) are of the same order of magnitude.

To find the change in range due to the Coriolis force we have to find the component of $\Delta\mathbf{r}$ in the direction $\hat{\mathbf{r}}$, which is easily obtained from Eq. (12.47) as

$$\hat{\mathbf{r}} \cdot \Delta\mathbf{r} = \frac{t^3}{6} \hat{\mathbf{r}} \cdot (\boldsymbol{\omega} \times \mathbf{g}).$$
(12.51)

Similarly, the vertical deflection is given by

$$\hat{\mathbf{g}} \cdot \Delta\mathbf{r} = t\mathbf{r} \cdot (\boldsymbol{\omega} \times \hat{\mathbf{g}})$$
(12.52)

The vector $\boldsymbol{\omega} \times \hat{\mathbf{g}}$ is directed west, except at poles, so both Eqs (12.51) and (12.52) vanish for the trajectories to the north or south. They have maximum values for the trajectories to the west. This is due to rotation of the earth in opposite direction while the projectile is in flight.

In most circumstances, resistive forces have a greater effect on the range and vertical deflection than the Coriolis force. The lateral Coriolis deflection is more significant as it will not be masked by resistive forces, that is, the observed lateral deflection is solely due to Coriolis force, as the resistive forces do not have any component in the lateral direction. Of course, resistive forces will change $\Delta\mathbf{r}$ (and also its lateral component) via their influence on the velocity which in turn governs the Coriolis force.

For a target on a horizontal plane, $\mathbf{g} \cdot \mathbf{r} = 0$ and $\hat{\mathbf{g}} \times \hat{\mathbf{r}}$ is a rightward unit vector. From Eq. (12.47), then, the rightward deflection ΔR is given by

$$\Delta R = (\hat{\mathbf{g}} \times \hat{\mathbf{r}}) \cdot \Delta\mathbf{r}$$

$$= -t(\hat{\mathbf{g}} \times \hat{\mathbf{r}}) \cdot \left(\boldsymbol{\omega} \times \left(\mathbf{r} - \frac{t^2}{6} \mathbf{g} \right) \right)$$

$$= -t \left[(\hat{\mathbf{g}} \cdot \boldsymbol{\omega}) \left(\hat{\mathbf{r}} \cdot \left(\mathbf{r} - \frac{t^2}{6} \mathbf{g} \right) \right) - \left(\hat{\mathbf{g}} \cdot \left(\mathbf{r} - \frac{t^2}{6} \mathbf{g} \right) \right) (\hat{\mathbf{r}} \cdot \boldsymbol{\omega}) \right]$$

$$= t\left[-r(\hat{\mathbf{g}} \cdot \boldsymbol{\omega}) - \frac{t^2}{6} g(\hat{\mathbf{r}} \cdot \boldsymbol{\omega}) \right]$$

$$= -rt\omega \cdot \left(\hat{\mathbf{g}} + \frac{t^2 g}{6r} \hat{\mathbf{r}} \right)$$

$$= -rt\omega \cdot \left(\hat{\mathbf{g}} + \frac{1}{3} \frac{(\hat{\mathbf{r}} \times \hat{\mathbf{v}}_0) \cdot (\hat{\mathbf{g}} \times \hat{\mathbf{v}}_0)}{(\hat{\mathbf{g}} \times \hat{\mathbf{v}}_0) \cdot (\hat{\mathbf{g}} \times \hat{\mathbf{v}}_0)} \hat{\mathbf{r}} \right).$$

Here, we have used Eq. (12.49). We now use the identity II and Fig. 12.10 to get

$$\Delta R = rt\omega \cos \lambda \left(\tan \lambda - \frac{1}{3} \tan \alpha \cos \phi \right). \tag{12.53}$$

For nearly horizontal trajectories ($\alpha \approx 0$), the second term in Eq. (12.53) can be neglected, giving $\Delta R = rt\omega \sin \lambda$ which is positive in the northern hemisphere and negative in the southern hemisphere. As a general rule, therefore, the Coriolis force tends to deflect particles to the right in the northern hemisphere and to the left in the southern hemisphere. However, this rule is violated by highly arched trajectories and Eq. (12.53) tells us that for a trajectory satisfying

$$\tan \alpha_0 = \frac{3 \tan \lambda}{\cos \phi}, \tag{12.54}$$

the Coriolis deflection ΔR vanishes. In the northern hemisphere, deflection will be to the left for $\alpha > \alpha_0$ and to the right for $\alpha < \alpha_0$. In the southern hemisphere, these inequalities reverse.

From Eq. (12.48), the time of flight for a target on the horizontal plane is

$$t = \frac{r}{v_0 \cos \alpha}. \tag{12.55}$$

Since the projectile is fired due east, $\phi = \frac{\pi}{2}$, so from Eq. (12.53) we get,

$$\Delta R = rt\omega \sin \lambda. \tag{12.56}$$

We eliminate t from Eq. (12.56) using Eq. (12.55) to get,

$$\Delta R = \left(\frac{r^2}{v_0} \right) \omega \sec \alpha \sin \lambda \tag{12.57}$$

with obvious dependence on the hemisphere.

To get the change in range for a projectile fired due east, we note that the angle between $\hat{\mathbf{r}}$ and $\hat{\omega} \times \hat{\mathbf{g}}$ is π. So $(\boldsymbol{\omega} \times \mathbf{g}) \cdot \hat{\mathbf{r}} = -\omega g \cos \lambda$. Substituting this result and the expression for the time of flight from Eq. (12.55) into Eq. (12.51) we get,

$$\text{Change in range} = -\frac{1}{6}\left(\frac{r}{v_0}\right)^3 \omega g \sec^3 \alpha \cos \lambda$$

which does not depend on the hemisphere.

Exercise   River Brahamaputra flows southwards near Guwahati. Find the difference in water levels at its right and left banks if its width is 5000 meters, the latitude of Guwahati is $26°11'$ and its speed is 10 km/hr.

Solution   It is observed that the Coriolis effect denudes the right banks of large rivers in the northern hemisphere flowing over long stretches more than their left banks. On the rivers in the southern hemisphere, the effect is opposite. The following solution to this exercise will help you understand this.

We set up the topocentric coordinate system with its x-axis along the flow (southwards), y axis along the transverse horizontal direction to the left of the flow (eastward) and the local vertical along the z axis. Let the direction of the flow make an angle ϕ (in the anticlockwise sense) with respect to the geographical north direction. Since the river is flowing southwards, $\phi = \pi$. (Now draw a figure). In this frame, the rotational velocity of the earth and the velocity of the river $\mathbf{v}$ can be resolved as

$$\omega = \omega(\sin \lambda \, \hat{\mathbf{k}} + \cos \lambda \cos \phi \, \hat{\mathbf{i}} - \cos \lambda \sin \phi \, \hat{\mathbf{j}})$$

and

$$\mathbf{v} = v\hat{\mathbf{i}}.$$

Here, $\hat{\mathbf{i}}, \hat{\mathbf{j}}, \hat{\mathbf{k}}$ are the unit vectors along x, y, z axes respectively. With $\phi = \pi$ the Coriolis acceleration $\mathbf{a}_c$ becomes

$$\mathbf{a}_c = 2\mathbf{v} \times \omega = -2v\omega \sin \lambda \, \hat{\mathbf{j}}, \tag{12.58}$$

which is towards the right of the flow (westward). So the total acceleration of the water is $\mathbf{a}_c + \mathbf{g}$ (see Fig. 12.11) with $\mathbf{a}_c$ given by Eq. (12.58). From Fig. 12.11 we see that the angle made by the resultant $\mathbf{a}_c + \mathbf{g}$ with $\mathbf{g}$ (angle α in Fig. 12.11) is given by

$$\tan \alpha = \left(\frac{a_c}{g}\right). \tag{12.59}$$

Now the water surface must be normal to the vector $\mathbf{a}_c + \mathbf{g}$, so it makes angle α with the horizontal. If the level difference is h and width of the river is W we have from Eq. (12.59),

$$\left(\frac{h}{W}\right) = \left(\frac{a_c}{g}\right)$$

or,

$$h = \left(\frac{a_c}{g}\right) W$$

Putting numerical values of all the quantities involved we get the result.

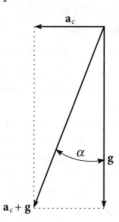

Fig. 12.11 Net acceleration of river water

12.4 Satellites and Orbits

12.4.1 Geometry and dynamics: Circular motion

We show that motion on a circular orbit, conserving angular momentum, corresponds to the force $\mathbf{f} = -\frac{mv^2}{r}\hat{\mathbf{r}}$, where r is the radius of the circle. Note that this is an attractive central force. Further, if Kepler's third law is satisfied, we show that the force must vary inversely as the square of the distance r from the center.

We first make only one assumption, that the angular momentum is conserved. To get the velocity, we differentiate $\mathbf{r} = r\hat{\mathbf{r}}$ with respect to time to get,

$$\dot{\mathbf{r}} = \dot{r}\hat{\mathbf{r}} + r\dot{\hat{\mathbf{r}}}. \tag{12.60}$$

Cross Eq. (12.60) with $\mathbf{r}$ to get,

$$\mathbf{H} = \mathbf{r} \times \dot{\mathbf{r}} = r\mathbf{r} \times \dot{\hat{\mathbf{r}}} = r^2 \hat{\mathbf{r}} \times \dot{\hat{\mathbf{r}}}, \tag{12.61}$$

where $\mathbf{H}$ is the specific angular momentum (angular momentum per unit mass) which is conserved. Cross Eq. (12.61) by $\hat{\mathbf{r}}$ on the right so that

$$\frac{\mathbf{H} \times \hat{\mathbf{r}}}{r^2} = (\hat{\mathbf{r}} \times \dot{\hat{\mathbf{r}}}) \times \hat{\mathbf{r}} = \dot{\hat{\mathbf{r}}}, \tag{12.62}$$

where we have used the identity I and the fact that $\hat{\mathbf{r}} \cdot \dot{\hat{\mathbf{r}}} = 0$. We substitute Eq. (12.62) in Eq. (12.60) to get

$$\dot{\mathbf{r}} = \dot{r}\hat{\mathbf{r}} + \frac{\mathbf{H} \times \hat{\mathbf{r}}}{r}. \tag{12.63}$$

To get the acceleration we differentiate Eq. (12.63) with respect to t and again use Eq. (12.62) and identity I. We have,

$$\ddot{\mathbf{r}} = \left(\ddot{r} - \frac{H^2}{r^3}\right)\hat{\mathbf{r}}. \tag{12.64}$$

Now, we make use of the assumption that the motion is circular. This means $H = rv$, where v is the constant speed of the particle on the circle and also $\dot{r} = 0 = \ddot{r}$. Therefore, the acceleration is

$$\ddot{\mathbf{r}} = -\frac{v^2}{r}\hat{\mathbf{r}}$$

and the force is

$$\mathbf{f} = m\ddot{\mathbf{r}} = -\frac{mv^2}{r}\hat{\mathbf{r}}. \tag{12.65}$$

Let us now assume that Kepler's third law is valid i.e., $\frac{r^3}{P^2}$ is a constant say C, where P is the period of the orbit. For circular motion the period P is related to v by $v = \frac{2\pi r}{P}$ or,

$$v^2 = \frac{4\pi^2 r^2}{P^2}.$$

Putting $\frac{1}{P^2} = \frac{C}{r^3}$ in this equation we get

$$v^2 = 4\pi^2 \frac{C}{r}. \tag{12.66}$$

Put Eq. (12.66) in Eq. (12.65) to get

$$\mathbf{f} = -\frac{4\pi^2 Cm}{r^2}\hat{\mathbf{r}}.$$

Thus, the conservation of angular momentum and Kepler's third law mean that, for circular motion, the force exerted on a moving particle is central, attractive and varies inversely as the square of the radius of the circle.

Exercise The turning points of a satellite orbit are defined by the condition $\mathbf{v} \cdot \mathbf{r} = 0$. Show that, for a turning point, the conservation of Runge–Lenz vector gives the relation

$$\mathbf{r} = \frac{K}{2E'}(\mathbf{e} - \hat{\mathbf{r}}), \tag{12.67}$$

where E' is the specific energy (energy per unit mass) and K is the constant in the gravitational force law.

The conservation of the Runge–Lenz (or the eccentricity) vector $\mathbf{e}$ is given by

$$\mathbf{v} \times \mathbf{H} = K(\mathbf{e} + \hat{\mathbf{r}}), \tag{12.68}$$

where $\mathbf{H}$ is the angular momentum per unit mass (specific angular momentum). Put $\mathbf{H} = \mathbf{r} \times \mathbf{v}$ and use the identity I to get

$$v^2 \mathbf{r} - (\mathbf{r} \cdot \mathbf{v}) = K(\mathbf{e} + \hat{\mathbf{r}}). \tag{12.69}$$

At the turning point $\mathbf{r} \cdot \mathbf{v} = 0$, so the second term on the LHS vanishes. Further, v^2 is related to E' by [19]

$$v^2 = 2\left(E' + \frac{K}{r}\right). \tag{12.70}$$

Substitute this expression for v^2 in Eq. (12.69) to get

$$2\left(E' + \frac{K}{r}\right)\mathbf{r} = K(\mathbf{e} + \hat{\mathbf{r}}),$$

which easily simplifies to Eq. (12.67). It is instructive to sketch this relation on an elliptic or hyperbolic orbit. Note that Eq. (12.67) specifies the turning points only in terms of the conserved quantities. □

12.4.2 Hodograph of an orbit

We find the hodograph for the Keplerian orbit of a satellite/spacecraft, that is, a curve over which the tip of the velocity vector moves as the satellite moves on its orbit.

We know that a Keplerian orbit is a consequence of the conservation of the eccentricity vector given by

$$\mathbf{v} \times \mathbf{H} = K(\mathbf{e} + \hat{\mathbf{r}}), \tag{12.71}$$

so it is no surprise that the hodograph, (which is the orbit in the velocity space), follows directly from it. Take the vector product with $\mathbf{H}$ on both sides of Eq. (12.71) to get

$$\mathbf{H} \times (\mathbf{v} \times \mathbf{H}) = K\mathbf{H} \times (\mathbf{e} + \hat{\mathbf{r}}). \tag{12.72}$$

Using identity I on the LHS of Eq. (12.72) we get,

$$H^2\mathbf{v} - (\mathbf{H}\cdot\mathbf{v})\mathbf{H} = K\mathbf{H}\times(\mathbf{e}+\hat{\mathbf{r}}).$$

Since $\mathbf{H}\cdot\mathbf{v} = 0$, we get,

$$\mathbf{v} = \frac{K}{H}\left(\hat{\mathbf{H}}\times\mathbf{e}+\hat{\mathbf{H}}\times\hat{\mathbf{r}}\right). \tag{12.73}$$

Since $\mathbf{H}\times\mathbf{e}$ is a constant vector, let us put

$$\mathbf{u} = \frac{K}{H}(\hat{\mathbf{H}}\times\mathbf{e}), \tag{12.74}$$

so that

$$\mathbf{v} - \mathbf{u} = \frac{K}{H}\left(\hat{\mathbf{H}}\times\hat{\mathbf{r}}\right) \tag{12.75}$$

or, squaring both sides,

$$(\mathbf{v}-\mathbf{u})^2 = \frac{K^2}{H^2}. \tag{12.76}$$

This equation describes a circle of radius (K/H) centered at point $\mathbf{u}$ given by Eq. (12.74).

Since the centre of the circle is determined by the eccentricity vector as in Eq. (12.74), the distance $u = |\mathbf{u}|$ of the centre from the origin is used to classify the orbits as shown in the following table. In the fourth column, we use $|K|$ to make room for both attractive ($K > 0$) and repulsive ($K < 0$) inverse square law force, (for example, Coulomb force between two like charges, where $K = -q_1 q_2 < 0$), although here we have assumed attractive inverse square law (Newtonian gravity), as we are dealing with spacecrafts and satellites.

Table 12.1   Classification of Orbits with $\mathbf{H} \neq 0$

Conic section	Eccentricity	Energy	Hodograph centre
Hyperbola	$e > 1$	$E' > 0$	$u > \frac{|K|}{H}$
parabola	$e = 1$	$E' = 0$	$u = \frac{|K|}{H}$
Ellipse	$0 < e < 1$	$E' < 0$	$u < \frac{|K|}{H}$
Cirle	$e = 0$	$E' = -\frac{K^2}{2H^2}$	$u = 0$

Thus, the orbit is an ellipse if the origin is inside the circle, or an hyperbola if the origin is outside the circle. For an elliptical orbit the hodograph described by Eq. (12.73) is a single complete circle, as shown in Fig. 12.12 You may check the consistancy of Fig. 12.12 with Eq. (12.73). Notice how, by parallelly moving any velocity vector $\mathbf{v}$ on the hodograph, we can determine the corresponding position $\mathbf{r}$ on the orbit.

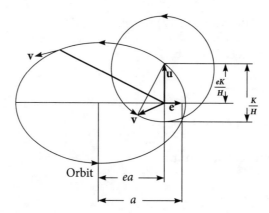

Fig. 12.12   Eliptical orbit and Hodograph

As an application, we find the orbital distance of a satellite as a function of its velocity. First, I leave it for you to show, using Eq. (12.73), Eq. (12.74), the fact that $\mathbf{H} \cdot \mathbf{e} = 0$ and using (twice!) identity II that

$$\mathbf{u} \cdot \mathbf{v} = \frac{K^2}{H^2}(e^2 + \mathbf{e} \cdot \hat{\mathbf{r}}).$$

Now, we know that the eccentricity is related to the specific energy, that is, energy per unit (reduced) mass by

$$e^2 = 1 + \frac{2E'H^2}{K^2}$$

Therefore, after a bit of rearrangement we get,

$$\mathbf{u} \cdot \mathbf{v} - 2E' = \frac{K^2}{H^2}(1 + \mathbf{e} \cdot \hat{\mathbf{r}}).$$

Using the equation to the orbit (in the real space!)

$$(1 + \mathbf{e} \cdot \hat{\mathbf{r}}) = \frac{H^2}{K}\frac{1}{r}$$

we finally get

$$r = r(\mathbf{v}) = \frac{-K}{2E' - \mathbf{u} \cdot \mathbf{v}}$$

as the orbital distance of a satellite as a function of its velocity. Note that both $\mathbf{u}$ and E' are conserved quantities. Thus, knowledge of $\mathbf{u}$ and E' for a particular orbit enables us to determine the orbital distance of the satellite if we know its velocity.

12.4.3 Orbit after an impulse

An impulsive force such as firing of a rocket will produce a change $\Delta\mathbf{v}$ in the velocity of a satellite without a significant change in its position during a short time interval for which the impulse acts. We show that, to the first order, the resulting change in the eccentricity vector of satellite's orbit is given by

$$K\Delta\mathbf{e} = \mathbf{v}\times\Delta\mathbf{H} + \Delta\mathbf{v}\times\mathbf{H}, \qquad (12.77)$$

where $\Delta\mathbf{H} = \mathbf{r}\times\Delta\mathbf{v}$. We use this to determine qualitatively the effect of a radial and a tangential impulse on a circular orbit. We also get the effect of an impulse perpendicular to the orbital plane.

As pointed out, the impulsive force will change the velocity from $\mathbf{v}$ to $\mathbf{v}+\Delta\mathbf{v}$ instantaneously, without any corresponding change in $\mathbf{r}$. Therefore, after the impulse the eccentricity vector will go over to the new (conserved) value given by

$$K\mathbf{e}_{\text{new}} = (\mathbf{v}+\Delta\mathbf{v})\times(\mathbf{r}\times(\mathbf{v}+\Delta\mathbf{v})) - K\hat{\mathbf{r}}.$$

So, the change in the eccentricity vector $\Delta\mathbf{e}$ is given by

$$K\Delta\mathbf{e} = (\mathbf{v}+\Delta\mathbf{v})\times(\mathbf{r}\times(\mathbf{v}+\Delta\mathbf{v})) - \mathbf{v}\times(\mathbf{r}\times\mathbf{v}).$$

Using the distributive property of the cross product and neglecting terms of higher order in $\Delta\mathbf{v}$, the above expression goes over to

$$K\Delta\mathbf{e} = \mathbf{v}\times(\mathbf{r}\times\Delta\mathbf{v}) + \Delta\mathbf{v}\times(\mathbf{r}\times\mathbf{v}) \qquad (12.78)$$

$$= \mathbf{v}\times\Delta\mathbf{H} + \Delta\mathbf{v}\times\mathbf{H} \qquad (12.79)$$

For a circular orbit $\mathbf{e} = \mathbf{0}$, so after the impulse, if $\Delta\mathbf{e} \neq \mathbf{0}$, then a circular orbit will go over to an orbit with eccentricity $\Delta\mathbf{e}$. For a radial impulse to a circular orbit, as shown in Fig. 12.13(a), $\Delta\mathbf{H} = \mathbf{r}\times\Delta\mathbf{v} = \mathbf{0}$, so $K\Delta\mathbf{e} = \Delta\mathbf{v}\times\mathbf{H}$ which is a vector pointing towards east if the direction of $\Delta\mathbf{v}$ is north. The resulting elliptical orbit is shown in Fig. 12.13(b).

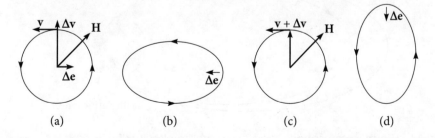

(a)   (b)   (c)   (d)

Fig. 12.13   Orbits after impulse

For a tangential impulse towards west, as shown in Fig. 12.13(c), both the terms in Eq. (12.77) point towards north, pushing the force centre towards north. The resulting elliptical orbit is shown in Fig. 12.13(d).

I leave it for you to show that $\Delta \mathbf{e} = \mathbf{0}$ for an impulse perpendicular to the plane of the orbit. So this impulse does not change the shape of the orbit.

Exercise Atmospheric drag tends to reduce the orbit of a satellite to a circle. For a rough estimate of this effect, suppose that the net effect of the atmosphere is a small impulse at the perigee which reduces the satellite speed by a factor α (see Fig. 12.14). Show that the resulting change in the eccentricity is

$$\Delta \mathbf{e} = -2\alpha(e+1)\hat{\mathbf{e}}. \tag{12.80}$$

For $e = 0.9$ and $\alpha = 0.01$ estimate the number of orbits required to get to a circular orbit. Show that the speed at perigee actually increases with each orbit.

Solution We have to obtain the change in the eccentricity due to impulse at perigee. The general expression for the change in eccentricity due to an impulse $\Delta \mathbf{v}$ is given by Eq. (12.77) with the corresponding definition of $\Delta \mathbf{H}$. In this problem the relevant quantities are,

$$\Delta \mathbf{v} = -\alpha v_+ \hat{\mathbf{v}} \; ; \; \mathbf{r} = r_+ \hat{\mathbf{r}} = a(1-e)\hat{\mathbf{r}} \; ; \; \mathbf{v} = v_+ \hat{\mathbf{v}}.$$

Here, r_+ denotes the distance of perigee from the origin (a focus) and v_+ denotes the speed at perigee. Putting these expressions in Eq. (12.77) and simplifying, we get,

$$K\Delta \mathbf{e} = -2\alpha v_+^2 a(1-e)\hat{\mathbf{e}}. \tag{12.81}$$

To get rid of v_+^2, note that for $\hat{\mathbf{r}} = \hat{\mathbf{e}}$, the conservation law for the eccentricity vector becomes,

$$\mathbf{v} \times \mathbf{H} = v_+^2 a(1-e)\hat{\mathbf{e}} = K(e+1)\hat{\mathbf{e}}. \tag{12.82}$$

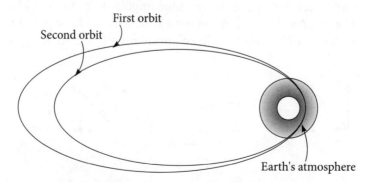

Fig. 12.14 Earth's atmospheric drag on a satellite circularising its orbit

Substitute for $v_+^2 a(1-e)$ from Eq. (12.82) into Eq. (12.81) to get Eq. (12.80). The number of orbits required to get to a circular orbit that is, to reduce the eccentricity to zero, with the given values of α and e is

$$\left|\frac{e}{\Delta e}\right| = \frac{0.9}{0.038} \cong 24.$$

I leave it for you to check the last sentence in the exercise.   □

12.5   A Charged Particle in Uniform Electric and Magnetic Fields

12.5.1   Uniform magnetic field

A uniform magnetic field is constant in space and time within the region in which the charged particle moves. The classical equation of motion of a particle with charge q, mass m and velocity $\mathbf{v}$ in a constant magnetic field $\mathbf{B}$ is

$$m\dot{\mathbf{v}} = \frac{q}{c}\mathbf{v} \times \mathbf{B}. \tag{12.83}$$

We club the constants together by writing

$$\omega \equiv -\frac{q}{mc}\mathbf{B}, \tag{12.84}$$

so that Eq. (12.83) becomes

$$\dot{\mathbf{v}} = \omega \times \mathbf{v}. \tag{12.85}$$

Dotting both sides of Eq. (12.85) with $\mathbf{v}$ we see that $\frac{d}{dt}(\mathbf{v}\cdot\mathbf{v}) = 0$ which means that the magnitude of the velocity of a charged particle moving in constant magnetic field is invariant in time. Thus, we expect vector $\mathbf{v}$ to perform pure rotational motion about the constant magnetic field $\mathbf{B}$ or ω. This is expressed by saying that vector $\mathbf{v}$ precesses around magnetic field $\mathbf{B}$ (see Fig. 12.15).

Taking cue from this observation, we resolve $\mathbf{v}$ into components parallel and perpendicular to ω or $\mathbf{B}$ as

$$\mathbf{v} = \mathbf{v}_\| + \mathbf{v}_\perp. \tag{12.86}$$

We substitute Eq. (12.86) in Eq. (12.85) to get two equations, one for each of $\mathbf{v}_\|$ and $\mathbf{v}_\perp$

$$\dot{\mathbf{v}}_\perp = \omega \times \mathbf{v}_\perp \quad \text{and}$$

$$\dot{\mathbf{v}}_\| = \mathbf{0}. \tag{12.87}$$

The second of these equations can be integrated immediately, giving

$$\mathbf{v}_\|(t) = \mathbf{v}_{0\|}, \tag{12.88}$$

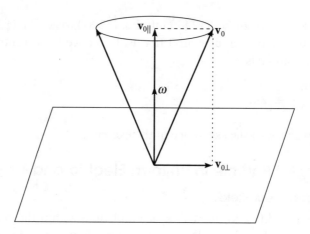

Fig. 12.15   Velocity vector precesses about ω

where $\mathbf{v}_0 = \mathbf{v}_{0\parallel} + \mathbf{v}_{0\perp}$ and $\mathbf{v}_0 = \mathbf{v}(0)$ is the value of $\mathbf{v}(t)$ at $t = 0$.

We have to deal with the first of Eq. (12.87) separately. We know that $\mathbf{v}_\perp$ rotates about ω without any change in its magnitude. We expect a solution of the form

$$\mathbf{v}_\perp(t) = e^{\omega t \hat{\omega} \times} \mathbf{v}_{0\perp} = \cos \omega t \mathbf{v}_{0\perp} + \sin \omega t (\hat{\omega} \times \mathbf{v}_{0\perp}), \tag{12.89}$$

where $\omega = |\omega|$.

Exercise   Show that $\mathbf{v} \cdot (\omega \times e^{\omega t \hat{\omega} \times} \mathbf{v}_{0\perp}) = 0$.

Hint   Show first that $\omega \times e^{\omega t \hat{\omega} \times} \mathbf{v}_{0\perp} = \cos \omega t (\omega \times \mathbf{v}_{0\perp}) - \omega \sin \omega t \mathbf{v}_{0\perp}$. Both terms cancel after dotting with $\mathbf{v}_\perp$ because $\mathbf{v}_\perp \cdot \mathbf{v}_{0\perp} = |\mathbf{v}_\perp|^2 \cos \omega t$ and $\mathbf{v}_\perp \cdot (\omega \times \mathbf{v}_{0\perp}) = \omega |\mathbf{v}_\perp|^2 \sin \omega t$.

From this exercise we find that the vector $e^{\omega t \hat{\omega} \times} \mathbf{v}_{0\perp}$ is normal to both $\mathbf{v}$ and ω. Therefore, it must be proportional to $\dot{\mathbf{v}}$. The proportionality constant is not of any physical consequence and can be taken to be unity. Thus, the solution to Eq. (12.85) is

$$\mathbf{v}(t) = e^{\omega t \hat{\omega} \times} \mathbf{v}_{0\perp} + \mathbf{v}_{0\parallel}$$

$$= \cos \omega t \mathbf{v}_{0\perp} + \sin \omega t (\hat{\omega} \times \mathbf{v}_{0\perp}) + \mathbf{v}_{0\parallel}. \tag{12.90}$$

To get the trajectory of the particle we have to integrate $\mathbf{v}(t)$ with respect to time. We get,

$$\mathbf{r}(t) = \mathbf{x}(t) - \mathbf{x}_0 = \frac{\sin(\omega t)}{\omega} \mathbf{v}_{0\perp} + \frac{\cos(\omega t)}{\omega} (\mathbf{v}_{0\perp} \times \hat{\omega}) + \mathbf{v}_{0\parallel} t \text{ or,}$$

$$\mathbf{r}(\omega t) = \left[\frac{e^{\omega t \hat{\omega} \times} (\mathbf{v}_0 \times \omega)}{\omega^2} \right] + \left[\frac{\mathbf{v}_0 \cdot \omega}{\omega^2} \right] \omega t, \tag{12.91}$$

where $\mathbf{x}_0$ is the constant of integration, so that the state of the particle at $t = 0$ is given by $(\mathbf{x}_0, \mathbf{v}_0)$. We have also used $(\omega \times \mathbf{v}_{0\parallel}) = \mathbf{0}$, and $\mathbf{v}_{0\parallel} = \mathbf{v}_0 \cdot \hat{\omega}\hat{\omega}$. Equation (12.91) is a coordinate free equation of an helix (see Fig. 12.16) with *radius*

$$\mathbf{a} \equiv \frac{(\mathbf{v}_0 \times \omega)}{\omega^2}$$

and *pitch*

$$b \equiv \frac{\mathbf{v}_0 \cdot \omega}{\omega^2}.$$

We can make Eq. (12.91) look like a helix by expressing it in terms of

$$\boldsymbol{\theta} = \theta\hat{\omega} \text{ where } \theta = \omega t. \tag{12.92}$$

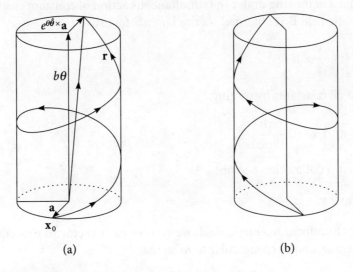

(a)   (b)

Fig. 12.16   (a) Right handed helix (b) Left handed helix

In terms of these variables, Eq. (12.91) takes the form

$$\mathbf{r}(\boldsymbol{\theta}) = e^{\theta\hat{\theta}\times}\mathbf{a} + b\boldsymbol{\theta} \tag{12.93}$$

where $\mathbf{a} \cdot \boldsymbol{\theta} = 0$. The helix is said to be *right handed* if $b > 0$ and *left handed* if $b < 0$ (see Fig. 12.16).

Equation (12.91) gives a circular trajectory if $\mathbf{v}_{0\parallel} = \mathbf{0}$. The radius vector $\mathbf{r}$ rotates with an angular speed $\omega = |q\mathbf{B}|/mc$ called the *cyclotron frequency*. Equation (12.84) tells us that ω has the same (opposite) direction as the magnetic field $\mathbf{B}$ when the charge q is negative (positive). As shown in Fig. 12.17, the circular motion of a negative (positive) charge is right handed (left handed).

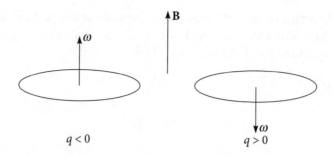

Fig. 12.17   Rotational velocity of a charge q about ω

12.5.2   Uniform electric and magnetic fields

Here, we consider the motion of a point charge q, driven by the simultaneously present uniform electric and magnetic fields. The equation of motion of a charged particle with charge q and mass m moving under the simultaneous action of constant electric field **E** and constant magnetic field **B** is obtained via the Lorentz force as

$$m\dot{\mathbf{v}} = q\left(\mathbf{E} + \frac{\mathbf{v}}{c} \times \mathbf{B}\right). \tag{12.94}$$

We can supress all constants by writing

$$\mathbf{g} = \frac{q}{m}\mathbf{E} \ \text{ and } \ \omega = -\frac{q\mathbf{B}}{mc}, \tag{12.95}$$

so that the equation of motion becomes

$$\dot{\mathbf{v}} = \mathbf{g} + \omega \times \mathbf{v}. \tag{12.96}$$

As in the case of uniform magnetic field, we resolve each vector in this equation into its components parallel and perpendicular to ω so that,

$$\mathbf{v} \ = \ \mathbf{v}_{\parallel} + \mathbf{v}_{\perp},$$

$$\mathbf{g} \ = \ \mathbf{g}_{\parallel} + \mathbf{g}_{\perp}. \tag{12.97}$$

This generates two equations, since $\omega \times \mathbf{v}_{\parallel} = \mathbf{0}$,

$$\dot{\mathbf{v}}_{\parallel} \ = \ \mathbf{g}_{\parallel},$$

$$\dot{\mathbf{v}}_{\perp} \ = \ \mathbf{g}_{\perp} + \omega \times \mathbf{v}_{\perp}. \tag{12.98}$$

Let the velocity at $t = 0$ be $\mathbf{v}(0) = \mathbf{v}_0$ which is also resolved parallel and perpendicular to ω:

$$\mathbf{v}(0) = \mathbf{v}_0 = \mathbf{v}_{0\parallel} + \mathbf{v}_{0\perp}. \tag{12.99}$$

The first of Eq. (12.98) with initial condition Eq. (12.99) can be readily integrated to give,

$$\mathbf{v}_{\|}(t) = \mathbf{g}_{\|}t + \mathbf{v}_{0\|}$$

$$= (\mathbf{g}\cdot\omega)\omega^{-1}t + \mathbf{v}_{0\|}$$

$$= \frac{q}{m}\mathbf{E}_{\|}t + \mathbf{v}_{0\|} = \mathbf{b}t + \mathbf{v}_{0\|} \text{ say,} \qquad (12.100)$$

where $\omega^{-1} = \omega/|\omega|^2$ (see subsection 1.7.1).

To integrate the second of Eq. (12.98) with initial condition Eq. (12.99), we re-write it, using identity I and the fact that $\mathbf{g}_{\perp}\cdot\omega = 0$, as follows.

$$\dot{\mathbf{v}}_{\perp} = \omega\times[(\mathbf{g}_{\perp}\times\omega^{-1}) + \mathbf{v}_{\perp}]. \qquad (12.101)$$

Equation (12.101) is the same as the first of Eq. (12.87) with $\mathbf{v}_{\perp}$ replaced by the expression in the square bracket, which is given by adding a constant vector to $\mathbf{v}_{\perp}$. Therefore, it can be solved in a similar way and is given by

$$\mathbf{v}_{\perp}(t) = e^{\omega t \hat{\omega}\times}\mathbf{a} + \mathbf{c}$$

$$= \cos\omega t\,\mathbf{a} + \sin\omega t(\hat{\omega}\times\mathbf{a}) + \mathbf{c}, \qquad (12.102)$$

with

$$\mathbf{a} = (\mathbf{g}_{\perp}\times\omega^{-1}) + \mathbf{v}_{0\perp} = (\mathbf{g}\times\omega^{-1}) + \mathbf{v}_{0\perp} = \mathbf{v}_{0\perp} - d\,\mathbf{E}\times\mathbf{B}^{-1}$$

(d : a scalar constant) and $\mathbf{c}$ is the constant of integration. Since

$$\mathbf{v}_{\perp}(0) = \mathbf{v}_{0\perp} = (\mathbf{g}_{\perp}\times\omega^{-1}) + \mathbf{v}_{0\perp} + \mathbf{c},$$

we must have

$$\mathbf{c} = -(\mathbf{g}_{\perp}\times\omega^{-1}) = -(\mathbf{g}\times\omega^{-1}). \qquad (12.103)$$

Noting that $(\mathbf{g}_{\perp}\times\omega^{-1}) = (\mathbf{g}\times\omega^{-1})$ and combining Eqs (12.100), (12.102) and (12.103), we can write the solution of Eq. (12.96) as

$$\mathbf{v}(t) = e^{\omega t \hat{\omega}\times}\mathbf{a} + \mathbf{b}t + \mathbf{c}, \qquad (12.104)$$

where the vectors $\mathbf{a}$ and $\mathbf{b}$ are defined above and the vector $\mathbf{c}$ is re-defined as

$$\mathbf{c} = \mathbf{v}_{0\|} - \mathbf{g}\times\omega^{-1} = \mathbf{v}_{0\|} + d\,\mathbf{E}\times\mathbf{B}^{-1}.$$

Integrating Eq. (12.104) with respect to time, we get the equation to the path of the charge q (Exercise) as

$$\mathbf{r}(t) = \mathbf{x}(t) - \mathbf{x}_0 = e^{\omega t \hat{\omega} \times}(\mathbf{a} \times \omega^{-1}) + \frac{1}{2}\mathbf{b}t^2 + \mathbf{c}t, \tag{12.105}$$

where $\mathbf{x}_0$ is the constant of integration, giving the initial position of the particle to be $\mathbf{x}(0) = \mathbf{x}_0 + \mathbf{a} \times \omega^{-1}$. If we take the origin at $\mathbf{x}(0)$, then $\mathbf{x}_0 = \omega^{-1} \times \mathbf{a}$. With this choice of the origin, $\mathbf{r}(0) = \mathbf{a} \times \omega^{-1}$, so the vector $\mathbf{r}$ at $t = 0$ lies on the circle of radius a/ω with its center at the origin and the particle trajectory passes through this point. Note that the vectors $\mathbf{a}$ and $\mathbf{a} \times \omega^{-1}$ lie in the plane perpendicular to ω, while $\mathbf{b}$ is parallel to ω.

It is instructive to write

$$\mathbf{r}(t) = \mathbf{r}_1(t) + \mathbf{r}_2(t), \tag{12.106}$$

where

$$\mathbf{r}_1(t) = \frac{1}{2}\mathbf{b}t^2 + \mathbf{c}t, \tag{12.107}$$

which is an equation to a parabola parameterized by t and

$$\mathbf{r}_2(t) = e^{\omega t \hat{\omega} \times}(\mathbf{a} \times \omega^{-1}), \tag{12.108}$$

which generates a uniform circular motion along a circle of radius $|\mathbf{a} \times \omega^{-1}| = |\mathbf{a}|/|\omega| = a/\omega$.

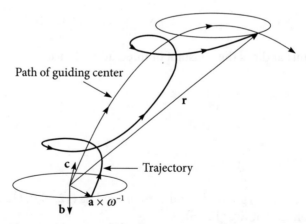

Fig. 12.18   Trajectory of a charged particle in uniform electric and magnetic fields

Thus, we see that the motion of a charged particle under the combined influence of uniform electric and magnetic fields is the composite of two motions, a parabolic motion of the *guiding center* described by Eq. (12.107) and the uniform circular motion around the guiding center along a circle with radius a/ω, in a plane normal to ω, given by Eq. (12.108). The composite motion corresponding to Eq. (12.106) can be viewed as the motion of a point on a spinning disc whose axis is aligned with the vertical and whose center is traversing a parabola. This is depicted in Fig. 12.18 and the corresponding directions of the electric and magnetic fields are shown in Fig. 12.19.

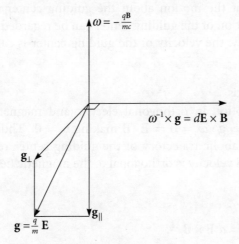

Fig. 12.19 Directions of electric and magnetic fields for Fig. 12.18

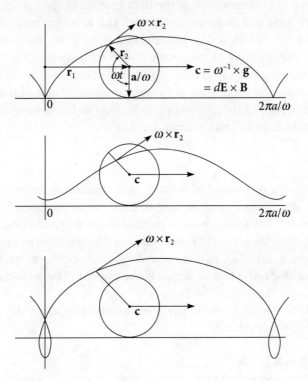

Fig. 12.20 Trochoids traced by a charge q when the electric and magnetic fields are orthogonal

The position vector of the particle relative to the guiding center repeats itself after a period of $2\pi/\omega = 2\pi mc/|q\mathbf{B}|$. Thus, after every such period, the net change in $\mathbf{r}(t)$ can be viewed as a result of only the motion of the guiding center along the parabola. This fact is expressed by saying that the motion about the guiding center averages to zero over a period of $2\pi/\omega$. So motion of the guiding center can be regarded as an average motion of the particle. Accordingly, the velocity of the guiding center is called the *drift velocity* of the particle.

Case of orthogonal fields

The special case of motion in orthogonal electric and magnetic fields has important applications. In this case, $\mathbf{g} \cdot \omega = 0 = \mathbf{E} \cdot \mathbf{B}$ making $\mathbf{b} = 0$. Thus, Eq. (12.107) becomes $\mathbf{r}_1(t) = \mathbf{c}t$ and the parabolic trajectory of the guiding center reduces to a straight line parallel to $\mathbf{c}$. If the initial velocity is orthogonal to the magnetic field,

$$\mathbf{v}_{0\|} = \mathbf{0} \text{ so that}$$

$$\dot{\mathbf{r}}_1 = \mathbf{c} = \omega^{-1} \times \mathbf{g} = d\,\mathbf{E} \times \mathbf{B}^{-1}.$$

Thus, the drift velocity is perpendicular to both the electric and the magnetic field. The particle trajectory is the composition of the drift motion of the center of a circle and the uniform circular motion of a point on this circle. The resulting path of the particle is the curve traced out by a point on a disc at a distance a/ω from the center, rolling without slipping with its center drifting along vector $\mathbf{c}$ with drift speed $|\mathbf{c}| = |\omega^{-1} \times \mathbf{g}| = d\,|\mathbf{E}\times \mathbf{B}^{-1}| = d\,|\mathbf{E}|/|\mathbf{B}|$ and angular speed $\omega = -q|\mathbf{B}|/mc$. This curve is, in general, a trochoid we described in subsection 9.3.2. Now if $\mathbf{r}_2$ is the position vector of the dot on the rolling disc which traces the path of the charged particle, then its linear velocity must match with that of the particle, namely $\mathbf{c}$. Thus, we require that

$$|\omega \times \mathbf{r}_2| = |\mathbf{c}|.$$

In terms of magnitudes of individual vectors, this condition means $r_2 = c/\omega$. Since r_2 depends on fixed quantities c and ω, it has fixed value provided we assume that the initial velocity does not have a component parallel to the magnetic field. Comparison with the radius of the disc a/ω, which depends on the initial velocity, generates three possibilities, namely, $r_2 = a/\omega$, $r_2 < a/\omega$ and $r_2 > a/\omega$. These conditions characterize three classes of trochoids, the first of which is the cycloid. These trochoids are illustrated in Fig. 12.20(a,b,c).

Equation (12.105) tells us that the particle motion coincides with that of the guiding center if $\mathbf{a} = \mathbf{0}$, which is satisfied if

$$\mathbf{v}_0 = \omega^{-1} \times \mathbf{g} = d\,\mathbf{E} \times \mathbf{B}^{-1}. \tag{12.109}$$

The trajectory is a straight line if $\mathbf{E} \cdot \mathbf{B} = 0$. This suggests an effective way to construct a velocity filter for charged particles. Only a particle with initial velocity satisfying condition

Eq. (12.109) will continue moving in its original staight line without any deflection. **E** and **B** fields can be adjusted to select a large range of velocities. The selection is independent of the sign of the charge or the mass of the particle.

12.6 Two-dimensional Steady and Irrotational Flow of an Incompressible Fluid

By irrotational flow, we mean its velocity field satisfies

$$\nabla \times \mathbf{q} = \mathbf{0}.$$

It follows that the velocity field **q** is derivable from a scalar potential $\phi(\mathbf{x})$,

$$\mathbf{q} = -\nabla\phi(\mathbf{x}).$$

Since the flow is steady and the fluid incompressible, its net flow through any closed volume is zero, giving

$$\nabla \cdot \mathbf{q} = \mathbf{0}.$$

This implies

$$\nabla^2 \phi = 0,$$

or, the potential $\phi(\mathbf{x})$ satisfies the Laplace equation in two dimensions

$$\frac{\partial^2 \phi}{\partial x^2} + \frac{\partial^2 \phi}{\partial y^2} = 0.$$

A function $\psi(\mathbf{x})$ which forms a pair of harmonic functions with $\phi(\mathbf{x})$ also satisfies

$$\nabla^2 \phi = 0$$

for such a flow.

Since the flow is 2-D, we can use the isomorphism between the planar vectors and complex numbers and express the flow via the function

$$f(z) = \phi(x,y) + \psi(x,y).$$

Now consider the integral of $f(z)$ along a curve $\mathcal{C}$ in the complex plane

$$\int_{\mathcal{C}} f(z)dz = \int_{\mathcal{C}} (\phi + i\psi)(dx + idy)$$

$$= \int_{\mathcal{C}} (\phi dx - \psi dy) + i \int_{\mathcal{C}} (\psi dx - \phi dy).$$

For an irrotational flow derivable from a potential, we expect this integral to be independent of the chosen curve C and be a function only of the end point coordinates. This is possible if and only if $\phi(x,y)$ and $\psi(x,y)$ satisfy

$$\frac{\partial \phi}{\partial x} = \frac{\partial \psi}{\partial y}, \text{ and } \frac{\partial \psi}{\partial x} = -\frac{\partial \phi}{\partial y},$$

which are the Cauchy–Riemann conditions, necessary and sufficient for the function $f(z)$ to be analytic. We can turn around and say that the real and imaginary parts of an analytic function represent a 2-D irrotational steady flow of an incompressible fluid, as all analytic functions satisfy the Cauchy–Riemann conditions.

It is easy to see that at all points

$$\nabla\phi \cdot \nabla\psi = \left(\hat{\mathbf{i}}\frac{\partial \phi}{\partial x} + \hat{\mathbf{j}}\frac{\partial \phi}{\partial y}\right) \cdot \left(\hat{\mathbf{i}}\frac{\partial \psi}{\partial x} + \hat{\mathbf{j}}\frac{\partial \psi}{\partial y}\right)$$

$$= \frac{\partial \phi}{\partial x}\frac{\partial \psi}{\partial x} + \frac{\partial \phi}{\partial y}\frac{\partial \psi}{\partial y}$$

$$= 0$$

by virtue of the Cauchy–Riemann conditions. Thus, the equipotential surfaces for ϕ and ψ at each point are perpendicular to each other. If $\phi(x,y)$ is taken to be the velocity potential, then the velocity $\mathbf{q} = -\nabla\phi$ must be along the line of constant ψ. Such a curve, with its tangent given by $\nabla\phi$, is called the *stream line*. By Bernoulli's theorem (see for example, [19]), the stream function is constant along all stream lines. So ψ can be treated as the stream function of the problem.

We will now pick up some analytic functions and see what type of flow patterns they represent.

(i) $f(z) = z^2 = (x^2 - y^2) + i2xy$.

Thus,

$$\phi(x,y) = x^2 - y^2 \text{ and } \psi(x,y) = 2xy.$$

The flow pattern is depicted in Fig. 12.21. This is the flow pattern expected around a rectangular corner. (Combine half x axis and half y axis to form a rectangle.)

(ii) $f(z) = z^n, \ n > 2$.

Here,

$$f(z) = (re^{i\theta})^n = r^n e^{in\theta} = r^n \cos(n\theta) + ir^n \sin(n\theta) = \phi + i\psi.$$

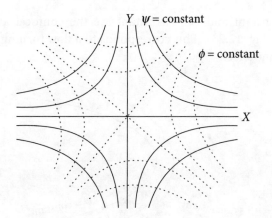

Fig. 12.21   Two-dimensional flow around a 90° corner

This corresponds to a flow pattern around an angle $\alpha = \pi/n$. The case with $n = 3$ is shown in Fig. 12.22.

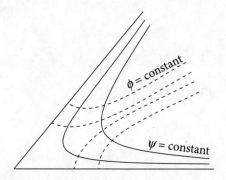

Fig. 12.22   Two-dimensional flow around a 60° corner

(iii) $f(z) = A\sqrt{z}$,

A being a real constant. Here,

$$\phi(x,y) = A\sqrt{r}\cos(\theta/2) \text{ and } \psi(x,y) = A\sqrt{r}\sin(\theta/2).$$

This gives

$$\frac{2\phi^2}{A^2} = 2r\cos^2(\theta/2) = r(1 + \cos\theta) = r + x$$

and

$$\frac{2\psi^2}{A^2} = 2r\sin^2(\theta/2) = r(1 - \cos\theta) = r - x.$$

Hence, $\phi = $ constant and $\psi = $ constant are the confocal and coaxial parabolas respectively (see Fig. 12.23). This corresponds to a flow turning around the edge of a semi-infinite plane sheet.

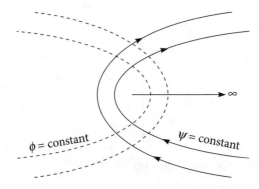

Fig. 12.23   Two-dimensional flow around a Semi-infinite straight line

(iv) $f(z) = -\dfrac{M}{2\pi z}$,

M being a real constant. This gives,

$$\phi = -\frac{M \cos \theta}{2\pi r} \quad \text{and} \quad \psi = \frac{M \sin \theta}{2\pi r}.$$

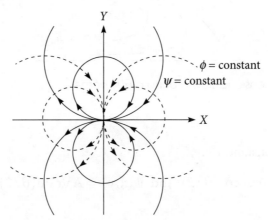

Fig. 12.24   Two-dimensional flow around a 2-D doublet source consisting of a source and a sink of equal strength, at an infinitesimal separation

The resulting flow pattern is shown in Fig. 12.24. This flow represents a doublet source with a source and sink sitting at the origin. The streamlines are like that of some dipole field lines. The source strength M is like the dipole moment of the source.

$f(z) = q_0 z$. This gives the uniform stream with stream velocity q_0 in the direction of the negative x axis.

Appendices

Matrices and Determinants

In this appendix we develop the theory of matrices and determinants, as required by this book, emphasizing their connection with vectors. This approach is not coordinate-free: We have to represent vectors by their coordinates with respect to some basis. This approach has the advantage of being easily generalizable to higher dimensional spaces. Our interest in matrices and determinants stems from their role in understanding of and computations with linear operators and their connection with the orientations of triplets of vectors and of surfaces. In the course of this appendix we may re-derive some of the results we have obtained in the text. Of course, this appendix can be used to explain all instances where we have used matrices and/or determinants. Theory of matrices is an independent, fully developed branch of mathematics worthy of an independent, rewarding and fruitful study. We recommend [12] for such a study.

A.1 Matrices and Operations on them

A matrix is the arrangement of $m \times n$ real or complex numbers in m rows and n columns. In this book, we deal with real matrices with $m, n \leq 3$, although in this appendix we deal with a general $m \times n$ real matrix. The pair (m, n) defines the size of a matrix. We use capital letters to denote a matrix, thus a matrix with m rows and n columns is denoted $A_{m \times n}$ or just A if the suffix $m \times n$ can be left understood. An element in the ith row and jth column in A is denoted a_{ij} and the matrix is written

$$A = [a_{ij}] \quad i = 1, \ldots, m \, ; \, j = 1, \ldots, n.$$

On most occasions the ranges of the subscripts i and j are left understood.

By fixing an orthonormal basis in $\mathscr{E}_n$ we have the isomorphism

$$\mathbf{x} \in \mathscr{E}_n \leftrightarrow \begin{bmatrix} x_1 \\ x_2 \\ \vdots \\ x_n \end{bmatrix} \in M_{n \times 1}, \tag{A.1}$$

where $M_{n\times 1}$ is the space of $n \times 1$ matrices called column vectors. For an orthonormal basis $\hat{\mathbf{e}}_k \ k = 1,\ldots,n$ in $\mathscr{E}_n$ we have the correspondence

$$\hat{\mathbf{e}}_k \leftrightarrow \begin{bmatrix} 0 \\ 0 \\ \vdots \\ 1 \\ \vdots \\ 0 \end{bmatrix} \ ; k = 1,\ldots,n \tag{A.2}$$

where for $\hat{\mathbf{e}}_k$, 1 occurs in the kth row. The transpose of a vector $\mathbf{x}$ is defined by $\mathbf{x}^T = (x_1 \ x_2 \ \ldots \ x_n)$. The transpose of a column vector is the corresponding row vector. Both the column vectors representing $\{\hat{\mathbf{e}}_k\}$, $k = 1,\ldots,n$ and the row vectors representing $\{\hat{\mathbf{e}}_k^T\}$, $k = 1,\ldots,n$ are called "coordinate vectors".

Exercise   Show that the set of all $m \times n$ real matrices forms a linear space of dimension mn.

Hint   Show that this set is isomorphic with the space of all mn-tuples, namely $\mathbb{R}^{mn}$.   □

The rows of a $m \times n$ matrix A can be identified with the vectors $\mathbf{a}_1, \mathbf{a}_2, \ldots, \mathbf{a}_m$ as the vectors in $\mathbb{R}^n$,

$$\mathbf{a}_k = (a_{k1}, a_{k2}, \ldots, a_{kn}) \ ; k = 1, 2, \ldots, m.$$

The matrix A can be written as

$$A = \begin{bmatrix} \mathbf{a}_1 \\ \mathbf{a}_2 \\ \vdots \\ \mathbf{a}_m \end{bmatrix}. \tag{A.3}$$

Given an n dimensional vector $\mathbf{x}$ and a m dimensional vector $\mathbf{y}$,

$$\mathbf{x} \leftrightarrow \begin{bmatrix} x_1 \\ \vdots \\ x_n \end{bmatrix} \ \text{and} \ \mathbf{y} \leftrightarrow \begin{bmatrix} y_1 \\ \vdots \\ y_m \end{bmatrix}, \tag{A.4}$$

the equation

$$A\mathbf{x} = \mathbf{y} \tag{A.5}$$

stands for a system of equations

$$a_{11}x_1 + a_{12}x_2 + \cdots + a_{1n}x_n \;=\; y_1$$

$$a_{21}x_1 + a_{22}x_2 + \cdots + a_{2n}x_n \;=\; y_2$$

$$\vdots$$

$$a_{m1}x_1 + a_{m2}x_2 + \cdots + a_{mn}x_n \;=\; y_m \tag{A.6}$$

The system of simultaneous equations, (Eq. (A.6)), can be written as

$$x_1 \begin{bmatrix} a_{11} \\ a_{21} \\ \vdots \\ a_{m1} \end{bmatrix} + x_2 \begin{bmatrix} a_{12} \\ a_{22} \\ \vdots \\ a_{m2} \end{bmatrix} + \cdots + x_n \begin{bmatrix} a_{1n} \\ a_{2n} \\ \vdots \\ a_{mn} \end{bmatrix} = \begin{bmatrix} y_1 \\ y_2 \\ \vdots \\ y_m \end{bmatrix}. \tag{A.7}$$

Viewed as the system of simultaneous equations, Eq. (A.5) connects the components $(x_1,\ldots,x_n)$ of the vector $\mathbf{x}$ with respect to the basis of vectors defined in the last equation in an n-dimensional subspace to the components of the same vector $(y_1,\ldots,y_m)$ with respect to the basis $\hat{\mathbf{e}}_k$; $k = 1,\ldots,m$. Thus, in this case Eq. (A.5) becomes a passive transformation transforming the components of the same vector from one basis to the other.

We can also view Eq. (A.5) as an active transformation or as a map or a linear operator $A : \mathscr{E}_n \mapsto \mathscr{E}_m$ mapping vectors $\mathbf{x} \in \mathscr{E}_n$ to vectors $\mathbf{y} \in \mathscr{E}_m$. If we shift the origin by a constant vector $\mathbf{b}$ then Eq. (A.5) becomes

$$\mathbf{y} = A\mathbf{x} + \mathbf{b} \tag{A.8}$$

Equation (A.8) defines an affine transformation. This is the most general result of the action of a matrix on a vector.

As an example, the matrix

$$A = \begin{bmatrix} \frac{2}{3} & -\frac{1}{3} \\ -\frac{1}{3} & \frac{2}{3} \\ -\frac{1}{3} & -\frac{1}{3} \end{bmatrix} \tag{A.9}$$

can be actively interpreted as a mapping of vectors $\mathbf{x} = (x_1 x_2)$ in the $(x_1 x_2)$ plane onto the vectors $\mathbf{y} = (y_1, y_2, y_3)$ in the plane defined by

$$y_1 + y_2 + y_3 = 0$$

which is perpendicular to the vector $\mathbf{N} = (1,1,1)$ and which we call π. Geometrically, the point (y_1, y_2, y_3) is obtained by projecting the point $(x_1 x_2, 0)$ perpendicularly to the plane π. Alternatively, the corresponding system of equations

$$y_1 = \frac{2}{3}x_1 - \frac{1}{3}x_2; \quad y_2 = -\frac{1}{3}x_1 + \frac{2}{3}x_2; \quad y_3 = -\frac{1}{3}x_1 - \frac{1}{3}x_2$$

can be interpreted passively as a parametric representation of the plane π, with x_1, x_2 as parameters.

Given a scalar λ we have,

$$\lambda A = [\lambda a_{ij}] \, ; \, i = 1,\ldots,m \, ; \, j = 1,\ldots,n.$$

Two matrices of the same size can be added. The ijth element of the matrix obtained by adding A and B is the addition of the ijth elements of the matrices A and B :

$$A + B = [a_{ij} + b_{ij}]$$

$C = A + B$ implies $c_{ij} = a_{ij} + b_{ij}$. Thus, we can construct a linear combination $\sum_k \lambda_k A_k$ where $A_k \, k = 1,\ldots$ are the matrices of the same size say $m \times n$ and λ_k are scalars. Addition of matrices is associative, $(A+B)+C = A+(B+C)$ and commutative, $A+B = B+A$. It is distributive with respect to the multiplication by a scalar. That is, $\lambda(A + B) = \lambda A + \lambda B$ and $(\alpha + \beta)A = \alpha A + \beta A$, α, β, λ being scalars.

Two matrices can be multiplied provided the number of columns of the left multiplier equals the number of rows of the right multiplier. Then the ijth element of the product is

$$c_{ij} = \sum_k a_{ik} b_{kj}.$$

That is, the ith row of A is is elementwise multiplied with the jth column of B and the corresponding products are summed over, to get the ijth element of the product $C = AB$. Note that, in general, $AB \neq BA$, that is, matrix product is not commutative. In fact only one of the products AB or BA may be defined while the other may not.

Product of matrices can be understood via the composition of mappings. If $\mathbf{y} = A\mathbf{x}$ is the map $A : \mathscr{E}_m \mapsto \mathscr{E}_n$ defined by the matrix $A_{n \times m} = [a_{ji}]$ then by linearity, as shown above, its explicit form is

$$y_j = \sum_{i=1}^{m} a_{ji} x_i.$$

Now suppose $B_{p \times n} = [b_{kj}]$ defines a map $\mathbf{z} = B\mathbf{y}$, $\mathscr{E}_n \mapsto \mathscr{E}_p$, then the vector $\mathbf{z}$ is given by

$$z_k = \sum_{j=1}^{n} b_{kj} y_j = \sum_{j=1}^{n} \sum_{i=1}^{m} b_{kj} a_{ji} x_i = \sum_{i=1}^{m} c_{ki} x_i,$$

where

$$c_{ki} = \sum_{j=1}^{n} b_{kj} a_{ji}; \quad k = 1, \dots, p; \; i = 1, \dots, m.$$

Thus, $\mathbf{z} = C\mathbf{x}$ where $C = BA = [c_{ki}]$ is the matrix with p rows and m columns defined by the last equation. Accordingly, we take the matrix C defined above to be the product BA of matrices A and B in that order.

The matrix product is associative and distributive with respect to matrix addition. Thus, for three matrices A, B, C with appropriate sizes,

$$(AB)C = A(BC)$$

and

$$A(B + C) = AB + AC.$$

Note that, in the last equation, matrices B and C must be of the same size, so if the product AB is defined, so is AC. The last equation is valid with multiplication in the reverse order. For the mappings of vectors determined by matrices, we can write

$$(A + B)\mathbf{x} = A\mathbf{x} + B\mathbf{x}; \quad (\lambda A)\mathbf{x} = \lambda(A\mathbf{x}); \quad A(B + C)\mathbf{x} = AB\mathbf{x} + AC\mathbf{x}.$$

From the definition of the scalar product of two vectors in terms of their coordinates, we see that $\mathbf{x} \cdot \mathbf{y} = x^T y$ where x and y are the column vectors ($n \times 1$ matrices) representing the vectors $\mathbf{x}$ and $\mathbf{y}$. For an orthonormal basis $\{\hat{\mathbf{e}}_k\}$, $k = 1, \dots, n$ we have

$$\hat{\mathbf{e}}_i^T \cdot \hat{\mathbf{e}}_k = [0 \; 0 \; \cdots \; 1 \; \cdots \; 0] \begin{bmatrix} 0 \\ 0 \\ \vdots \\ 1 \\ \vdots \\ 0 \end{bmatrix} = \begin{cases} 0 & \text{for } i \neq k, \\ 1 & \text{for } i = k. \end{cases} \tag{A.10}$$

where 1 is at ith place in the left multiplier and at kth place in the right multiplier. Thus, coordinate vectors are orthonormal, as they should be. In general, for any two orthogonal vectors, we have,

$$\mathbf{x} \cdot \mathbf{y} = x^T y = 0.$$

We end this subsection by defining the transpose of a matrix. The transpose of a $m \times n$ matrix A is the $n \times m$ matrix A^T obtained by interchanging the rows and columns of A. Thus, the ijth element of A^T, denoted a_{ij}^T is the same as the jith element of A giving us the defining equation

$$a_{ij}^T = a_{ji}.$$

The transpose A^T of a $n \times n$ square matrix A is also a $n \times n$ square matrix.

A.2 Square Matrices, Inverse of a Matrix, Orthogonal Matrices

Square matrices are those having equal number of rows and columns and are extremely important in applications. The order of a square matrix is the number of rows or columns. Any two square matrices of the same order n can be added or multiplied. We can form powers of such a matrix

$$A^2 AA, \ A^3 = AAA, \cdots.$$

The zero matrix O of order n is the matrix all of whose elements are zero. All the rows (columns) of zero matrix are zero vectors $\mathbf{0} = (0, 0, \ldots, 0)^T$ of n dimensional space. It has the obvious properties

$$A + O = A = O + A, \ AO = OA = O$$

for all nth order matrices A and

$$O\mathbf{x} = O \ \text{for all} \ \mathbf{x} \in \mathscr{E}_n.$$

The unit matrix of order n, denoted I is the matrix representing the identity mapping

$$I\mathbf{x} = \mathbf{x} \ \text{for all} \ \mathbf{x} \in \mathscr{E}_n.$$

In particular, for any orthonormal basis in $\mathscr{E}_n$ we must have

$$I\hat{\mathbf{e}}_k = \hat{\mathbf{e}}_k \ \ k = 1, 2, \ldots, n,$$

from which we can conclude that the column (row) vectors in I are given by the coordinate vectors as in Eq. (A.2).

$$I = (\hat{\mathbf{e}}_1, \hat{\mathbf{e}}_2, \cdots, \hat{\mathbf{e}}_n) = \begin{bmatrix} 1 & 0 & 0 & \cdots & 0 \\ 0 & 1 & 0 & \cdots & 0 \\ \vdots & \vdots & \vdots & & \vdots \\ 0 & 0 & 0 & \cdots & 1 \end{bmatrix}. \tag{A.11}$$

The nth order unit matrix I is the multiplicative identity for matrix multiplication. That is,

$$IA = AI = A$$

for all nth order matrices A.

Given a nth order matrix A, the matrix A^{-1} satisfying

$$A^{-1}A = I = AA^{-1}$$

is called the *inverse* of A. A nth order matrix A for which A^{-1} exists is called *invertible*. We state and prove the following properties of a nth order invertible matrix.

(i) The inverse of a nth order invertible matrix A is unique.

Proof   If possible, let B and C be two distinct inverses of A satisfying $AB = BA = I = AC$. Then we have,

$$B - C = BA(B - C) = B(AB - AC) = BO = O$$

so that $B = C$.   □

(ii) A nth order matrix A is invertible if and only if $A\mathbf{x} = \mathbf{0}$ implies $\mathbf{x} = \mathbf{0}$, or, if and only if $\mathbf{x} \neq \mathbf{0}$ implies $A\mathbf{x} \neq \mathbf{0}$.

Proof   (*if part*). We are given that $A\mathbf{x} = \mathbf{0}$ implies $\mathbf{x} = \mathbf{0}$. We show that the corresponding map $A : \mathscr{E}_n \mapsto \mathscr{E}_n$ is both one to one and onto and hence invertible. If possible, let $\mathbf{x}_1 \neq \mathbf{x}_2$ with $A\mathbf{x}_1 = A\mathbf{x}_2$. This means, by linearity of A that $A(\mathbf{x}_1 - \mathbf{x}_2) = \mathbf{0}$ so that A maps a non-zero vector $\mathbf{x}_1 - \mathbf{x}_2$ to the zero vector, contradicting the axiom. Therefore, $A\mathbf{x}_1 = A\mathbf{x}_2$ implies $\mathbf{x}_1 = \mathbf{x}_2$ or, in other words, A is one to one. Since the images of two distinct vectors in $\mathscr{E}_n$ under the map A are distinct, and since the map A is defined for all vectors in $\mathscr{E}_n$, the image set of A coincides with its domain $\mathscr{E}_n$ or, in other words, A is onto. Therefore, the inverse of the map A exists and the corresponding matrix is the inverse of the matrix A.

(*only if part*). We are given that A is invertible. Then $A\mathbf{x} = \mathbf{0} \implies A^{-1}A\mathbf{x} = \mathbf{0} \implies \mathbf{x} = \mathbf{0}$. A matrix mapping a non-zero vector to the zero vector is called *singular*. Thus, a matrix is invertible if and only if it is *non-singular*   □

(iii) A nth order matrix A is invertible if and only if its determinant is not zero.

Proof   (*if part*) The determinant of a square matrix is the product of its eigenvalues. If the determinant is zero, then at least one of the eigenvalues of A is zero. Since the eigenvector is non-zero, the corresponding eigenvalue equation reads $A\mathbf{x} = 0\mathbf{x} = \mathbf{0}$, so that A maps a non-zero vector to the zero vector and hence must not be invertible. Alternatively, if $\det(A) \neq 0$, the system $AX = Y$ has unique solution $BY = X$. Substituting, these two equations into each other we get $AB = I = BA$ which means $B = A^{-1}$.

(*only if part*) We are given that A is invertible. Therefore, $A^{-1}A = I$ so that $\det(A^{-1}A) = \det(A^{-1})\det(A) = \det(I) = 1$ which means $\det(A) \neq 0$.   □

(iv) A nth order matrix A is invertible if and only if it maps every basis to some basis.

Proof   (*if part*) We are given that A maps a linearly independent set $\mathbf{x}_1, \mathbf{x}_2, \ldots, \mathbf{x}_n$ to the linearly independent set $A\mathbf{x}_1, A\mathbf{x}_2, \ldots, A\mathbf{x}_n$. Consider $\mathbf{x} = \sum_{k=1}^{n} a_k \mathbf{x}_k$ such that

$A\mathbf{x} = \sum_{k=1}^{n} a_k A\mathbf{x}_k = \mathbf{0}$. Since $\{A\mathbf{x}_k\}$; $k = 1,\ldots,n$ are linearly independent, this equation is satisfied only when all a_ks are zero, in which case $\mathbf{x} = \sum_{k=1}^{n} a_k \mathbf{x}_k = \mathbf{0}$. Thus, $A\mathbf{x} = \mathbf{0}$ implies $\mathbf{x} = \mathbf{0}$ or A is invertible.

(*only if part*) We are given that A is invertible, so that $A\mathbf{x} = \sum_{k=1}^{n} a_k A\mathbf{x}_k = \mathbf{0}$ implies $\mathbf{x} = \sum_{k=1}^{n} a_k \mathbf{x}_k = \mathbf{0}$. Since $\{\mathbf{x}_k\}$ is a basis, the last equation makes all a_ks zero, which means, via the previous equation, that the set $A\mathbf{x}_1, A\mathbf{x}_2,\ldots, A\mathbf{x}_n$ is linearly independent. □

(v) A nth order matrix A is invertible if and only if the column vectors of A are linearly independent.

Proof From Eq. (A.7) it is clear that $A\mathbf{x} = \mathbf{0}$ for $\mathbf{x} \neq \mathbf{0}$ if and only if the column vectors of A are linearly dependent. □

Exercise Show that a matrix is singular if and only if its determinant vanishes. □

We have defined and used orthogonal matrices in connection with the rotation of a vector about a direction in space. The orthogonal matrices correspond to linear operators or transformations that preserve length or distance between points in space. If two points P, Q in space with coordinates (x_i, y_i), $i = 1,\ldots,n$ go over to points P', Q', with coordinates (x_i', y_i'), $i = 1,\ldots,n$ under an orthogonal transformation defined by the orthogonal matrix $R = [a_{ij}]$, then we require that

$$d^2(P,Q) = \sum_{i=1}^{n}(x_i - y_i)^2 = \sum_{i=1}^{n}(x_i' - y_i')^2 = d^2(P',Q'). \tag{A.12}$$

Putting $x_i' = \sum_j a_{ij}x_j$ and $y_i' = \sum_k a_{ik}x_k$ in Eq. (A.12) you can check that Eq. (A.12) is satisfied provided

$$\sum_{i=1}^{n} a_{ij}a_{ik} = \delta_{jk}, \tag{A.13}$$

where δ_{jk} is the Kronaker delta, which is zero when $j \neq k$ and is 1 if $j = k$, or,

$$\mathbf{a}_j \cdot \mathbf{a}_k = \delta_{jk}. \tag{A.14}$$

That is, the jth and the kth column vectors of R are orthonornal. Since a set of orthogonal vectors is essentially linearly independent, the n column vectors of R form an orthonormal basis of the n dimensional space. Thus, every orthogonal matrix is invertible, by virtue of (v) above. In fact Eq. (A.13) can be written as

$$\sum_{i=1}^{n} a_{ji}^T a_{ik} = \delta_{ik},$$

or,

$$R^T R = I = RR^T. \tag{A.15}$$

Thus, the transpose of an orthogonal matrix equals its inverse.

More generally, the orthogonal transformation preserves the scalar product:

$$R\mathbf{x} \cdot R\mathbf{y} = \mathbf{x} \cdot \mathbf{y}. \tag{A.16}$$

Exercise   Show that an orthogonal matrix R must have $\det(R) = \pm 1$.

Solution   We have, $\det(R^T R) = \det(R^T) \det(R) = (\det(R))^2 = \det(I) = 1$ which gives $\det(R) = \pm 1$. □

The set of orthogonal 3×3 matrices with $\det(R) = +1$ represents all possible rotations in 3-D Euclidean space. This result is due to Euler (see section 6.6). In fact, the correspondence between the the rotations and orthogonal matrices with $\det(R) = +1$ is an isomorphism:

$$\mathscr{R}_1 \circ \mathscr{R}_2 = \mathscr{R} \implies [R_1][R_2] = [R],$$

where $[R_1], [R_2]$ and $[R]$ represent the corresponding rotations.

The passive and active interpretations of the orthogonal transformations are described in the text (see section 6.4).

A.3   Linear and Multilinear Forms of Vectors

Our next task in this appendix is to define determinants and formulate their principal properties. We need some general albraic notions to do this job.

A function $f(\mathbf{x})$ of vector argument $\mathbf{x}$ is called a *linear form* in $\mathbf{x}$ if

$$f(\lambda \mathbf{x} + \mu \mathbf{y}) = \lambda f(\mathbf{x}) + \mu f(\mathbf{y})$$

for any vectors $\mathbf{x}, \mathbf{y}$ and scalars λ, μ. Thus, for example, $f(\mathbf{x}) = f(x_1, x_2, x_3) = ax_1 - bx_2 + cx_3$ is a linear form, while $f(\mathbf{x}) = |\mathbf{x}| = \sqrt{x_1^2 + \cdots + x_n^2}$ is not. More generally, a linear form is the one satisfying

$$f(\lambda_1 \mathbf{x_1} + \cdots + \lambda_m \mathbf{x_m}) = \lambda_1 f(\mathbf{x_1}) + \cdots + \lambda_m f(\mathbf{x_m})$$

valid for any m vectors $\mathbf{x_1}, \ldots, \mathbf{x_m}$ and scalars $\lambda_1 \ldots, \lambda_m$. In fact we can write any vector $\mathbf{a}$ as a normal form involving a basis $\hat{\mathbf{e}}_1, \cdots, \hat{\mathbf{e}}_n$:

$$\mathbf{a} = a_1 \hat{\mathbf{e}}_1 + \cdots + a_n \hat{\mathbf{e}}_n \equiv (a_1, a_2, \ldots, a_n).$$

Thus, $f(\mathbf{a})$ has the form

$$f(\mathbf{a}) = a_1 f(\hat{\mathbf{e}}_1) + \cdots + a_n f(\hat{\mathbf{e}}_n) = c_1 a_1 + c_2 a_2 + \cdots + c_n a_n,$$

where c_i are the constant values $c_i = f(\hat{\mathbf{e}}_i)$. We define the vector $\mathbf{c} \equiv (c_1, c_2, \ldots, c_n)$ to get

$$f(\mathbf{a}) = \mathbf{c} \cdot \mathbf{a}.$$

Thus, *the most general linear form in a vector* $\mathbf{a}$ *is the scalar product of* $\mathbf{a}$ *with with a suitable constant vector* $\mathbf{c}$.

A function $f(\mathbf{x}, \mathbf{y})$ of two vectors $\mathbf{x} \equiv (x_1, \ldots, x_n)$, $\mathbf{y} \equiv (y_1, \ldots, y_n)$ is called a *bilinear form* in $\mathbf{x}, \mathbf{y}$ if f is a linear form in $\mathbf{x}$ for fixed $\mathbf{y}$ and a linear form in $\mathbf{y}$ for fixed $\mathbf{x}$. Thus, we require that

$$f(\lambda \mathbf{x} + \mu \mathbf{y}, \mathbf{z}) = \lambda f(\mathbf{x}, \mathbf{z}) + \mu f(\mathbf{y}, \mathbf{z})$$

$$f(\mathbf{x}, \lambda \mathbf{y} + \mu \mathbf{z}) = \lambda f(\mathbf{x}, \mathbf{y}) + \mu f(\mathbf{x}, \mathbf{z}) \tag{A.17}$$

for any vectors $\mathbf{x}, \mathbf{y}, \mathbf{z}$ and scalars λ, μ. The simplest example of a bilinear form is the vector product

$$f(\mathbf{a}, \mathbf{b}) = \mathbf{a} \cdot \mathbf{b}.$$

Here, the rules Eq. (A.17) reduce to the associative and distributive laws for the scalar product. More generally, we find,

$$
\begin{aligned}
f(\alpha \mathbf{a} + \beta \mathbf{b}, \gamma \mathbf{c} + \delta \mathbf{d}) &= \alpha f(\mathbf{a}, \gamma \mathbf{c} + \delta \mathbf{d}) + \beta f(\mathbf{b}, \gamma \mathbf{c} + \delta \mathbf{d}) \\
&= \alpha \gamma f(\mathbf{a}, \mathbf{c}) + \alpha \delta f(\mathbf{a}, \mathbf{d}) + \beta \gamma f(\mathbf{b}, \mathbf{c}) + \beta \delta f(\mathbf{b}, \mathbf{d}) \tag{A.18}
\end{aligned}
$$

Thus, we can deal with the binary forms as we deal with ordinary products in multiplying out expressions. Using the decomposition of a vector in terms of a basis $\hat{\mathbf{e}}_1, \cdots, \hat{\mathbf{e}}_n$, we get, for the most general bilinear form in $\mathbf{a}, \mathbf{b}$,

$$f(\mathbf{a}, \mathbf{b}) = \sum_{j,k=1}^{n} a_j b_k f(\hat{\mathbf{e}}_j, \hat{\mathbf{e}}_k) = \sum_{j,k=1}^{n} c_{jk} a_j b_k \tag{A.19}$$

with constant coefficients

$$c_{jk} = f(\hat{\mathbf{e}}_j, \hat{\mathbf{e}}_k).$$

For $\mathbf{b} = \mathbf{a}$, the bilinear form f goes over to the *quadratic form*

$$f(\mathbf{a}, \mathbf{a}) = \sum_{j,k=1}^{n} c_{jk} a_j a_k.$$

It is now straightforward to generalize to the multilinear forms in m vectors $\mathbf{a}_1, \mathbf{a}_2, \ldots, \mathbf{a}_m$ along with their components

$$\mathbf{a}_1 \equiv (a_{11}, a_{21}, \ldots, a_{n1}); \; \mathbf{a}_2 \equiv (a_{12}, a_{22}, \ldots, a_{n2}); \; \ldots \mathbf{a}_m \equiv (a_{1m}, a_{2m}, \ldots, a_{nm}).$$

The function f is a multilinear form $f(\mathbf{a}_1, \mathbf{a}_2, \ldots, \mathbf{a}_m)$ in $\mathbf{a}_1, \mathbf{a}_2, \ldots, \mathbf{a}_m$ if it is a linear form in each vector when the others are held fixed. We can also consider f as a function of a $n \times m$ matrix

$$A = [\mathbf{a}_1, \mathbf{a}_2, \ldots, \mathbf{a}_m] = [a_{jk}],$$

where $\mathbf{a}_1, \mathbf{a}_2, \ldots, \mathbf{a}_m$ are its column vectors. Generalizing the bilinear case, the most general multilinear form in $\mathbf{a}_1, \mathbf{a}_2, \ldots, \mathbf{a}_m$ is given by

$$f(\mathbf{a}_1, \mathbf{a}_2, \ldots, \mathbf{a}_m) = \sum_{j_1, j_2, \ldots, j_m = 1, \ldots, n} c_{j_1 j_2 \cdots j_m} a_{j_1 1} a_{j_2 2} \cdots a_{j_m m} \tag{A.20}$$

where

$$c_{j_1 j_2 \cdots j_m} = f(\hat{\mathbf{e}}_{j_1}, \hat{\mathbf{e}}_{j_2}, \ldots, \hat{\mathbf{e}}_{j_m}).$$

Exercise   Write explicitly Eq. (A.20) for $m = 3, 4, 5$ and $n = 3$. Construct explicitly the $n \times m$ matrix in each case.   □

A.4   Alternating Multilinear Forms: Determinants

A function of several arguments, which could be vectors or scalars, is called *alternating* if it just changes its sign as a result of interchanging any two of its arguments. Examples of alternating functions of scalar arguments are $\phi(x, y) = y - x$, $\phi(x, y, z) = (z - y)(z - x)(y - x)$. A function f of two n-dimensional vectors $\mathbf{a}_1, \mathbf{a}_2$ is alternating if

$$f(\mathbf{a}_1, \mathbf{a}_2) = -f(\mathbf{a}_2, \mathbf{a}_1)$$

for all $\mathbf{a}_1, \mathbf{a}_2$. This implies that

$$f(\mathbf{a}, \mathbf{a}) = 0.$$

Consider a 2-dimensional space and an alternating function $f(\mathbf{a}_1, \mathbf{a}_2)$ with $\mathbf{a}_1 = (a_{11}, a_{21})$, $\mathbf{a}_2 = (a_{12}, a_{22})$. Then,

$$f(\hat{\mathbf{e}}_1, \hat{\mathbf{e}}_1) = f(\hat{\mathbf{e}}_2, \hat{\mathbf{e}}_2) = 0, \; f(\hat{\mathbf{e}}_2, \hat{\mathbf{e}}_1) = -f(\hat{\mathbf{e}}_1, \hat{\mathbf{e}}_2).$$

It then follows from Eq. (A.19) that

$$f(\mathbf{a}_1, \mathbf{a}_2) = f(a_{11}\hat{\mathbf{e}}_1 + a_{21}\hat{\mathbf{e}}_2, a_{12}\hat{\mathbf{e}}_1 + a_{22}\hat{\mathbf{e}}_2)$$

and using the fact that f is alternating, the right side of this equation can be written

$$(a_{11}a_{22} - a_{12}a_{21})f(\hat{\mathbf{e}}_1, \hat{\mathbf{e}}_2) = c \begin{vmatrix} a_{11} & a_{12} \\ a_{21} & a_{22} \end{vmatrix} = c \, \det(\mathbf{a}_1, \mathbf{a}_2), \qquad (\text{A.21})$$

where $c = f(\hat{\mathbf{e}}_1, \hat{\mathbf{e}}_2)$ and we take the last equality as the definition of the determinant of the second order of the matrix whose columns comprise the components of vectors $\mathbf{a}_1, \mathbf{a}_2$. Thus, *every bilinear alternating form of two vectors $\mathbf{a}_1, \mathbf{a}_2$ in two-dimensional space differs from the determinant of the matrix with columns $\mathbf{a}_1, \mathbf{a}_2$ by a constant factor c.*

More generally, an alternating bilinear form of two vectors in n-dimensional space can be written

$$f(\mathbf{a}_1, \mathbf{a}_2) = \sum_{j,k=1}^{n} c_{jk} a_{j1} a_{k2},$$

where

$$c_{jk} = -c_{kj}, \quad c_{jj} = 0.$$

Combining the terms with subscripts which differ only by a permutation, we can express f as the linear combination of second order determinants.

$$f(\mathbf{a}_1, \mathbf{a}_2) = \sum_{\substack{j,k=1 \\ j<k}}^{n} c_{jk} \begin{vmatrix} a_{j1} & a_{k1} \\ a_{j2} & a_{k2} \end{vmatrix}. \qquad (\text{A.22})$$

The alternating function of three vectors, $f(\mathbf{a}_1, \mathbf{a}_2, \mathbf{a}_3)$ changes sign whenever any two of its arguments are exchanged. More generally, its sign is changed when the number of exchanges of the pairs of its arguments is odd, and its sign does not change if the number of corresponding exchanges are even. f vanishes if two of its arguments are equal.

Exercise Construct all possible permutations of the arguments $\mathbf{a}_1, \mathbf{a}_2, \mathbf{a}_3$ of an alternating form which change its sign and which do not change its sign. ☐

Let

$$\mathbf{a}_1 \equiv (a_{11}, a_{21}, a_{31}), \ \mathbf{a}_2 \equiv (a_{12}, a_{22}, a_{32}), \ \mathbf{a}_3 \equiv (a_{13}, a_{23}, a_{33})$$

be three 3-D vectors. The general alternating trilinear form f in $\mathbf{a}_1, \mathbf{a}_2, \mathbf{a}_3$ is

$$f(\mathbf{a}_1, \mathbf{a}_2, \mathbf{a}_3) = \sum_{j,k,r=1}^{3} c_{jkr} a_{j1} a_{k2} a_{r3},$$

where, using the conditions under which an alternating form changes or does not change sign and the conditions under which it vanishes, we have,

$$c_{jkr} = f(\hat{\mathbf{e}}_j, \hat{\mathbf{e}}_k, \hat{\mathbf{e}}_r) = \varepsilon_{jkr} f(\hat{\mathbf{e}}_1, \hat{\mathbf{e}}_2, \hat{\mathbf{e}}_3),$$

where ε_{jkr} are simply the Levi-Civita symbols which by now we know so well.

Exercise Show that $\varepsilon_{jkr} = sign(\phi(j,k,r))$ where $\phi(j,k,r) = (r-k)(r-j)(k-j)$. □

We can now write the expression for $f(\mathbf{a}_1, \mathbf{a}_2, \mathbf{a}_3)$ explicitly using the definition of $\{c_{jkr}\}$. We have,

$$\begin{aligned} f(\mathbf{a}_1, \mathbf{a}_2, \mathbf{a}_3) &= (a_{11}a_{22}a_{33} + a_{12}a_{23}a_{31} + a_{13}a_{21}a_{32} \\ &\quad - a_{13}a_{22}a_{31} - a_{11}a_{23}a_{32} - a_{12}a_{21}a_{33}) f(\hat{\mathbf{e}}_1, \hat{\mathbf{e}}_2, \hat{\mathbf{e}}_3) \end{aligned} \quad \text{(A.23)}$$

or,

$$f(\mathbf{a}_1, \mathbf{a}_2, \mathbf{a}_3) = c \begin{vmatrix} a_{11} & a_{12} & a_{13} \\ a_{21} & a_{22} & a_{23} \\ a_{31} & a_{32} & a_{33} \end{vmatrix}, \quad \text{(A.24)}$$

where $c = f(\hat{\mathbf{e}}_1, \hat{\mathbf{e}}_2, \hat{\mathbf{e}}_3)$ is a constant. Therefore, *the most general trilinear alternating form in three 3-dimensional vectors* $\mathbf{a}_1, \mathbf{a}_2, \mathbf{a}_3$ *differs from the determinant of the matrix with columns* $\mathbf{a}_1, \mathbf{a}_2, \mathbf{a}_3$ *by a constant factor c*. Note that

$$f(\hat{\mathbf{e}}_1, \hat{\mathbf{e}}_2, \hat{\mathbf{e}}_3) = \det(\hat{\mathbf{e}}_1, \hat{\mathbf{e}}_2, \hat{\mathbf{e}}_3) f(\hat{\mathbf{e}}_1, \hat{\mathbf{e}}_2, \hat{\mathbf{e}}_3)$$

so that

$$\det(\hat{\mathbf{e}}_1, \hat{\mathbf{e}}_2, \hat{\mathbf{e}}_3) = 1$$

as it should be.

Generalization to higher order matrices is now straightforward. Consider a $n \times n$ matrix

$$A = \begin{bmatrix} a_{11} & a_{12} & \cdots & a_{1n} \\ a_{21} & a_{22} & \cdots & a_{2n} \\ \vdots & \vdots & & \vdots \\ a_{n1} & a_{n2} & \cdots & a_{nn} \end{bmatrix}, \quad \text{(A.25)}$$

with column vectors $\mathbf{a}_1, \mathbf{a}_2, \ldots, \mathbf{a}_n$. Let f be a multilinear alternating form in $\mathbf{a}_1, \mathbf{a}_2, \ldots, \mathbf{a}_n$ as given by Eq. (A.20) where the coefficients $c_{j_1 j_2 \cdots j_n}$ have the form $c_{j_1 j_2 \cdots j_n} = f(\hat{\mathbf{e}}_{j_1}, \hat{\mathbf{e}}_{j_2}, \ldots, \hat{\mathbf{e}}_{j_n})$. Since f is an alternating form, these coefficients are given by

$$c_{j_1 j_2 \cdots j_n} = f(\hat{\mathbf{e}}_{j_1}, \hat{\mathbf{e}}_{j_2}, \ldots, \hat{\mathbf{e}}_{j_n}) = \varepsilon_{j_1 j_2 \cdots j_n} f(\hat{\mathbf{e}}_1, \hat{\mathbf{e}}_2, \ldots, \hat{\mathbf{e}}_n),$$

where $\varepsilon_{j_1 j_2 \cdots j_n} = -1$ whenever $j_1 j_2 \cdots j_n$ is obtained from $1, 2, \ldots, n$ by odd number of pairwise exchanges (odd permutation of $1, 2, \ldots, n$), $\varepsilon_{j_1 j_2 \cdots j_n} = +1$ whenever $j_1 j_2 \cdots j_n$ is obtained from $1, 2, \ldots, n$ by even number of pairwise exchanges (even permutation of $1, 2, \ldots, n$) and $\varepsilon_{j_1 j_2 \cdots j_n} = 0$ if any two of $j_1 j_2 \cdots j_n$ are equal. Thus, $\varepsilon_{j_1 j_2 \cdots j_n}$ are the set of n^n symbols each with n subscripts which can be defined to be the Levi-Civita symbols with n subscripts.

Exercise Find the values of ε_{321}, ε_{2143}, ε_{4231}, ε_{54321}. □

Exercise Show that $\varepsilon_{j_1 j_2 \cdots j_n} = \text{sign}(\phi(j_1, j_2, \ldots, j_n))$ where $\phi(j_1, j_2, \ldots, j_n) = \Pi_{\substack{j,k=1,\ldots,n \\ j<k}}(x_k - x_j)$. □

We define the determinant of the matrix A in Eq. (A.25) as

$$\det(A) = \begin{vmatrix} a_{11} & a_{12} & \cdots & a_{1n} \\ a_{21} & a_{22} & \cdots & a_{2n} \\ \vdots & \vdots & & \vdots \\ a_{n1} & a_{n2} & \cdots & a_{nn} \end{vmatrix} = \sum_{j_1 \cdots j_n} \varepsilon_{j_1 j_2 \cdots j_n} a_{j_1 1} a_{j_2 2} \cdots a_{j_n n}. \tag{A.26}$$

where $j_1 \ldots j_n$ runs over the set of permutations of $1, 2, \ldots, n$ (see the following exercise).

Exercise Show that there are $n!$ terms in the expansion of an nth order determinant given by Eq. (A.26).

Solution We have to show that there are $n!$ non-zero values of $\varepsilon_{j_1 j_2 \cdots j_n}$. Since no two values of the subscripts can be the same, we have n choices for j_1, $n-1$ choices for $j_2 \ldots n-k$ choices for $j_k \ldots$ so that the total number of distinct $\varepsilon_{j_1 j_2 \cdots j_n}$ are $n(n-1)(n-2) \cdots (n-k) \cdots 1$ or $n!$ which is the same as the number of terms in the required expansion. This makes the nth order determinant a nth degree form in the a_{jk} consisting of $n!$ terms. □

Exercise Show that determinant is linear in each of its columns separately. □

A.5 Principal Properties of Determinants

Equation (A.26) gives the explicit formula for the determinant of a $n \times n$ matrix, or the nth order determinant, in terms of its n^2 elements a_{jk}. As shown above, this determinant is an nth degree form having $n!$ terms. Apart from the Levi-Civita symbols, each term is a product of n elements one from each column and each row. Although, the expaqnsion in Eq. (A.26) is explicitly computable, it has too many terms to keep track of ($5! = 120$ for a fifth order determinant and $10! = 36,28,800$ for a tenth order determinant) to be useful for numerical computations and more efficient ways of evaluating determinants have been devised.

From the fact that any nth order determinant is proprtional to a n degree *alternating* multilinear form in n vectors $\mathbf{a}_1, \mathbf{a}_2, \ldots, \mathbf{a}_n$ in an n-dimensional space, we infer that for the corresponding matrix A with these vectors as its column vectors, the determinant changes sign if we interchange any two of its columns. Thus, *the determinant of a square matrix A changes sign if we interchange any two columns of A; in particular, the determinant of a square matrix A with two identical columns vanishes.* Using the linearity of the determinant in each of its columns separately, we find that *multiplying one column of the matrix A by a factor λ has the effect of multiplying the determinant of A by λ.* For example,

$$\det(\lambda \mathbf{a}_1, \mathbf{a}_2, \ldots, \mathbf{a}_n) = \lambda \det(\mathbf{a}_1, \mathbf{a}_2, \ldots, \mathbf{a}_n).$$

In particular, for $\lambda = 0$ and arbitrary $\mathbf{a}_1$ we find

$$\det(\mathbf{0}, \mathbf{a}_2, \ldots, \mathbf{a}_n) = 0,$$

with the same result for any other column so that *the determinant of a matrix A vanishes if any column of A is the zero vector.* Multiplying all elements of A by λ amounts to multiplying every column of A by λ so that

$$\det(\lambda A) = \lambda^n \det(A).$$

From the multilinearity of determinants, we conclude more generally that

$$\det(\mathbf{a}_1 + \lambda \mathbf{a}_2, \mathbf{a}_2, \ldots, \mathbf{a}_n) = \det(\mathbf{a}_1, \mathbf{a}_2, \ldots, \mathbf{a}_n) + \lambda \det(\mathbf{a}_2, \mathbf{a}_2, \ldots, \mathbf{a}_n) = \det(\mathbf{a}_1, \mathbf{a}_2, \ldots, \mathbf{a}_n)$$

since the matrix $(\mathbf{a}_2, \mathbf{a}_2, \ldots, \mathbf{a}_n)$ has two identical columns. Generally, *the value of the determinant of the matrix A does not change if we add a multiple of one column to a different column.* However, if we multiply a column by λ and add it to the *same* column, then the value of the determinant changes by the factor $1 + \lambda$.

We now show that *the determinant of the product of two nth order matrices A and B is the product of their determinants.* To see this, note that if $C = AB$ the resulting matrix C is given by

$$C = \begin{bmatrix} \mathbf{a}_1 \cdot \mathbf{b}_1 & \mathbf{a}_1 \cdot \mathbf{b}_2 & \cdots \mathbf{a}_1 \cdot \mathbf{b}_n \\ \mathbf{a}_2 \cdot \mathbf{b}_1 & \mathbf{a}_2 \cdot \mathbf{b}_2 & \cdots \mathbf{a}_2 \cdot \mathbf{b}_n \\ \vdots & \vdots & \vdots \\ \mathbf{a}_n \cdot \mathbf{b}_1 & \mathbf{a}_n \cdot \mathbf{b}_2 & \cdots \mathbf{a}_n \cdot \mathbf{b}_n \end{bmatrix}, \tag{A.27}$$

where $\mathbf{a}_1, \mathbf{a}_2, \ldots, \mathbf{a}_n$ are the *row vectors* of A while $\mathbf{b}_1, \mathbf{b}_2, \ldots, \mathbf{b}_n$ are the *column vectors* of B. From Eq. (A.27) we see that, keeping A fixed, $\det(C)$ is a linear form in column vectors $\{\mathbf{b}_k\}$ of B. Further, this is an alternating form because interchanging two columns of B corresponds exactly to interchanging the corresponding columns of C. Hence, $\det(C)$ is an alternating multilinear form in the column vectors of the matrix B. Consequently,

$$\det(C) = \gamma \det(B),$$

where γ is the value of $\det(C)$ when $\mathbf{b}_k = \hat{\mathbf{e}}_k$ $k = 1,\dots,n$ or when B is the unit matrix I. Now, if $B = I$, then $C = AB = AI = A$ so that $\gamma = \det(A)$. Thus we get,

$$\det(AB) = \det(A)\det(B). \tag{A.28}$$

Exercise Show that $\det(A^{-1}) = 1/(det(A))$. $\square$

We shall now show that a square matrix A and its transpose A^T have the same determinant:

$$\det(A) = \det(A^T). \tag{A.29}$$

To see this, note that in the expansion of the determinant (Eq. (A.26)) we can rearrange the factors in each term according to the first subscripts (e.g., $a_{31}a_{12}a_{23} = a_{12}a_{23}a_{31}$) so that,

$$a_{j_1 1}a_{j_2 2}\dots a_{j_n n} = a_{1k_1}a_{2k_2}\dots a_{nk_n}. \tag{A.30}$$

where $k_1,k_2,\dots,k_n$ is again a perpmutation of $1,2,\dots,n$.

Exercise Show that $\varepsilon_{j_1 j_2 \cdots j_n} = \varepsilon_{k_1 k_2 \cdots k_n}$.

Solution We have to show that the permutations $j_1 j_2 \cdots j_n$ and $k_1 k_2 \cdots k_n$ of $1,2,\dots,n$ are either *both* even or *both* odd. This follows from the observation that these permutations are inverses of each other. $\square$

Equation (A.30) and the above exercise immediately lead to

$$\det(A) = \sum_{k_1 k_2 \dots k_n} \varepsilon_{k_1 k_2 \cdots k_n} a_{1k_1} a_{2k_2} \dots a_{nk_n} = \det(A^T).$$

An immediate consequence of Eq. (A.29) is that a determinant can be considered to be an alternating multilinear form of its row vectors. In particular, determinant changes its sign if we interchange any two rows. Another consequence is that if $\det(A) \neq 0 \neq \det(A^T)$ then the matrix A^T is invertible, so that the column vectors of A^T or the row vectors of A also form a linearly independent set.

Combining Eqs (A.28) and (A.29) we get

$$\det(A)\det(B) = \det(A^T)\det(B) = \det(A^T B).$$

Combining this result with Eq. (A.27) we get, for the matrices A, B defined via their column vectors, $A = (\mathbf{a}_1,\mathbf{a}_2,\dots,\mathbf{a}_n)$ and $B = (\mathbf{b}_1,\mathbf{b}_2,\dots,\mathbf{b}_n)$,

$$\det(A)\det(B) = \det(A^T B) = \begin{vmatrix} \mathbf{a}_1\cdot\mathbf{b}_1 & \mathbf{a}_1\cdot\mathbf{b}_2 & \cdots \mathbf{a}_1\cdot\mathbf{b}_n \\ \mathbf{a}_2\cdot\mathbf{b}_1 & \mathbf{a}_2\cdot\mathbf{b}_2 & \cdots \mathbf{a}_2\cdot\mathbf{b}_n \\ \vdots & \vdots & \vdots \\ \mathbf{a}_n\cdot\mathbf{b}_1 & \mathbf{a}_n\cdot\mathbf{b}_2 & \cdots \mathbf{a}_n\cdot\mathbf{b}_n \end{vmatrix}. \tag{A.31}$$

A.5.1   Determinants and systems of linear equations

Determinants can be used to find whether a set of n vectors $\mathbf{a}_1, \mathbf{a}_2, \ldots, \mathbf{a}_n$ in n-dimensional space are depemdent, or, equivalently, when a square matrix A with column vectors $\mathbf{a}_1, \mathbf{a}_2, \ldots, \mathbf{a}_n$ is singular. We show that a *square matrix A is singular if and only if its determinant is zero.*

If A is singular, then its column vectors $\mathbf{a}_1, \mathbf{a}_2, \ldots, \mathbf{a}_n$ are linearly dependent. Thus, one of the column vectors, say $\mathbf{a}_1$ can be expressed in terms of the others:

$$\mathbf{a}_1 = \lambda_2 \mathbf{a}_2 + \lambda_3 \mathbf{a}_3 + \cdots + \lambda_n \mathbf{a}_n.$$

It then follows from the multilinearity of determinants that

$$
\begin{aligned}
\det(A) &= \det(\lambda_2 \mathbf{a}_2 + \lambda_3 \mathbf{a}_3 + \cdots + \lambda_n \mathbf{a}_n, \mathbf{a}_2, \ldots, \mathbf{a}_n) \\
&= \lambda_2 \det(\mathbf{a}_2, \mathbf{a}_2, \ldots, \mathbf{a}_n) + \lambda_3 \det(\mathbf{a}_3, \mathbf{a}_2, \mathbf{a}_3, \ldots, \mathbf{a}_n) + \cdots \\
&\quad + \lambda_n det(\mathbf{a}_n, \mathbf{a}_2, \mathbf{a}_3, \ldots, \mathbf{a}_n) \\
&= 0,
\end{aligned}
\tag{A.32}
$$

since each of the matrices has a repeated column.

Conversely, if A is non-singular, it is invertible and we have

$$\det(AA^{-1}) = \det(A)\det(A^{-1}) = \det(I) = 1$$

so that $\det(A) \neq 0$, which completes the proof.

Now consider the system of equations

$$AX = Y$$

where X and Y are $n \times 1$ column vectors and A is an $n \times n$ matrix with column vectors $\mathbf{a}_1, \mathbf{a}_2, \ldots, \mathbf{a}_n$. This system of equations can be re-expressed as

$$x_1 \mathbf{a}_1 + x_2 \mathbf{a}_2 + \ldots + x_n \mathbf{a}_n = \mathbf{y}.$$

Then, it is straightforward to show (Exercise) that

$$\det(\mathbf{a}_1, \ldots, \mathbf{a}_{k-1}, \mathbf{y}, \mathbf{a}_{k+1}, \ldots, \mathbf{a}_n) = x_k \det(\mathbf{a}_1, \mathbf{a}_2, \ldots, \mathbf{a}_n), \ k = 1, 2, \ldots, n.$$

If the matrix A is non-singular, we can divide by its determinant and get the solution $x_1, x_2, \ldots, x_n$ expressed in terms of determinants:

$$x_1 = \frac{\det(\mathbf{y}, \mathbf{a}_2, \ldots, \mathbf{a}_n)}{\det(\mathbf{a}_1, \mathbf{a}_2, \ldots, \mathbf{a}_n)}, \ \ x_2 = \frac{\det(\mathbf{a}_1, \mathbf{y}, \ldots, \mathbf{a}_n)}{\det(\mathbf{a}_1, \mathbf{a}_2, \ldots, \mathbf{a}_n)},$$

$$\ldots, x_n = \frac{\det(\mathbf{a}_1, \mathbf{a}_2, \ldots, \mathbf{y})}{\det(\mathbf{a}_1, \mathbf{a}_2, \ldots, \mathbf{a}_n)}.$$

This is *Crammer's rule* for the solution of n linear equations in n unknowns.

A.5.2   Geometrical interpretation of determinants

We start by showing how various properties of the vector product are related to determinants. We start with the definition

$$\det(\mathbf{a}, \mathbf{b}, \mathbf{c}) = \begin{vmatrix} a_1 & b_1 & c_1 \\ a_2 & b_2 & c_2 \\ a_3 & b_3 & c_3 \end{vmatrix} = \begin{vmatrix} a_1 & a_2 & a_3 \\ b_1 & b_2 & b_3 \\ c_1 & c_2 & c_3 \end{vmatrix}. \tag{A.33}$$

Written out as an alternating linear form in vector $\mathbf{c}$ we have, (see Eq. (A.23)),

$$\det(\mathbf{a}, \mathbf{b}, \mathbf{c}) = (a_2 b_3 - a_3 b_2) c_1 + (a_3 b_1 - a_1 b_3) c_2 + (a_1 b_2 - a_2 b_1) c_3 = \mathbf{z} \cdot \mathbf{c},$$

where $\mathbf{z} \equiv (z_1, z_2, z_3)$ is the vector with components

$$z_1 = a_2 b_3 - a_3 b_2 = \begin{vmatrix} a_2 & b_2 \\ a_3 & b_3 \end{vmatrix},$$

$$z_2 = a_3 b_1 - a_1 b_3 = \begin{vmatrix} a_3 & b_3 \\ a_1 & b_1 \end{vmatrix},$$

$$z_3 = a_1 b_2 - a_2 b_1 = \begin{vmatrix} a_1 & b_1 \\ a_2 & b_2 \end{vmatrix}.$$

From the components of $\mathbf{z}$ it is clear that $\mathbf{z} = \mathbf{a} \times \mathbf{b}$. Therefore,

$$\det(\mathbf{a}, \mathbf{b}, \mathbf{c}) = \mathbf{c} \cdot (\mathbf{a} \times \mathbf{b}).$$

If we cyclically permute the factors on the right side, we have to interchange the columns (or rows) of the determinant on the left twice, leaving the determinant invariant. Thus,

$$\det(\mathbf{a}, \mathbf{b}, \mathbf{c}) = \mathbf{a} \cdot (\mathbf{b} \times \mathbf{c}) = \mathbf{c} \cdot (\mathbf{a} \times \mathbf{b}) = \mathbf{b} \cdot (\mathbf{c} \times \mathbf{a}). \tag{A.34}$$

The components z_i of the vector $\mathbf{z} = \mathbf{a} \times \mathbf{b}$ are themselves second order determinants and hence are bilinear alternating forms of vectors $\mathbf{a}, \mathbf{b}$. This immediately leads to the laws of vector multiplication stated in the text (see Eq. (1.10)).

The property $\mathbf{a} \times \mathbf{a} = \mathbf{0}$ follows from $\mathbf{a} \times \mathbf{b} = -\mathbf{b} \times \mathbf{a}$. More generally, the vector product two vectors $\mathbf{a} \times \mathbf{b}$ vanishes if $\mathbf{a}$ and $\mathbf{b}$ are linearly dependent, as we have seen in the text. To prove this using determinants we note that by Eq. (A.34) $\mathbf{a} \times \mathbf{b} = \mathbf{0}$ implies

$$\det(\mathbf{a}, \mathbf{b}, \mathbf{c}) = 0 \text{ for all vectors } \mathbf{c},$$

which just means that $\mathbf{a}, \mathbf{b}, \mathbf{c}$ are dependent for all $\mathbf{c}$. Since we can always choose $\mathbf{c}$ which is linearly independent of $\mathbf{a}, \mathbf{b}$, we conclude that $\mathbf{a} \times \mathbf{b} = \mathbf{0}$ implies that $\mathbf{a}$ and $\mathbf{b}$ are linearly dependent or are proportional to each other.

From the equations $(\mathbf{a} \times \mathbf{b}) \cdot \mathbf{a} = \det(\mathbf{a}, \mathbf{b}, \mathbf{a}) = 0$ and $(\mathbf{a} \times \mathbf{b}) \cdot \mathbf{b} = \det(\mathbf{a}, \mathbf{b}, \mathbf{b}) = 0$ we see that $\mathbf{a} \times \mathbf{b}$ is perpendicular to both $\mathbf{a}$ and $\mathbf{b}$.

Exercise   Show that

$$|\mathbf{a} \times \mathbf{b}|^2 = |\mathbf{a}|^2 + |\mathbf{b}|^2 - (\mathbf{a} \cdot \mathbf{b})^2,$$

Hint   Write left side in terms of the components of $\mathbf{a} \times \mathbf{b}$.   □

Using the above exercise we get

$$|\mathbf{a} \times \mathbf{b}| = \sqrt{|\mathbf{a}|^2|\mathbf{b}|^2 - |\mathbf{a}|^2|\mathbf{b}|^2 \cos \theta} = |\mathbf{a}|\,|\mathbf{b}| \sin \theta,$$

where θ is the angle between $\mathbf{a}$ and $\mathbf{b}$ and equals the area of the parallelogram spanned by $\mathbf{a}$ and $\mathbf{b}$. Using the above exercise the square of the area $\mathcal{A}^2$ of the parallelogram spanned by vectors $\mathbf{a}, \mathbf{b}$ can be written elegantly in terms of a determinant as

$$\mathcal{A}^2 = (\mathbf{a} \cdot \mathbf{a})(\mathbf{b} \cdot \mathbf{b}) - (\mathbf{a} \cdot \mathbf{b})(\mathbf{b} \cdot \mathbf{a}) = \begin{vmatrix} \mathbf{a} \cdot \mathbf{a} & \mathbf{a} \cdot \mathbf{b} \\ \mathbf{b} \cdot \mathbf{a} & \mathbf{b} \cdot \mathbf{b} \end{vmatrix}. \tag{A.35}$$

The determinant appearing in this equation is called the *Gram determinant* of vectors $\mathbf{a}, \mathbf{b}$ and denoted $\Gamma(\mathbf{a}, \mathbf{b})$. It is clear from the derivation that

$$\Gamma(\mathbf{a}, \mathbf{b}) \geq 0$$

for all vectors $\mathbf{a}, \mathbf{b}$ and that equality holds only if $\mathbf{a}$ and $\mathbf{b}$ are linearly dependent.

We can derive a similar expression for the square of *the volume V of a parallelopiped spanned by three vectors* $\mathbf{a}, \mathbf{b}, \mathbf{c}$. This volume V is the product of the area $\mathcal{A}$ of one of its faces multiplied by the corresponding altitude h. Choosing for $\mathcal{A}$ the area of the parallelogram spanned by the vectors $\mathbf{a}$ and $\mathbf{b}$, we get

$$V^2 = h^2 \mathcal{A}^2 = h^2 \Gamma(\mathbf{a}, \mathbf{b}) = h^2 \begin{vmatrix} \mathbf{a} \cdot \mathbf{a} & \mathbf{a} \cdot \mathbf{b} \\ \mathbf{b} \cdot \mathbf{a} & \mathbf{b} \cdot \mathbf{b} \end{vmatrix}. \tag{A.36}$$

Let the vectors $\mathbf{a}, \mathbf{b}, \mathbf{c}$ be the position vectors of the points P_1, P_2, P_3 respectively and let P denote the foot of the perpendicular to the $\mathbf{a}, \mathbf{b}$ plane dropped from P_3. Then h in Eq. (A.36) is the length of the vector $\mathbf{d} = \overrightarrow{PP}_3$ The position vector of the point P, say $\mathbf{p}$, lies in the $\mathbf{a}, \mathbf{b}$ plane so that

$$\mathbf{p} = \lambda \mathbf{a} + \mu \mathbf{b}.$$

Hence, the vector $\mathbf{d}$ can be expressed as

$$\mathbf{d} = \mathbf{c} - \mathbf{p} = \mathbf{c} - \lambda \mathbf{a} - \mu \mathbf{b} \tag{A.37}$$

with suitable constants λ, μ. Since $\mathbf{d}$ is perpendicular to $\mathbf{a}, \mathbf{b}$ plane, it must satisfy

$$\mathbf{a} \cdot \mathbf{d} = 0 = \mathbf{b} \cdot \mathbf{d}.$$

This leads to a system of linear equations for λ and μ:

$$\lambda \mathbf{a} \cdot \mathbf{a} + \mu \mathbf{a} \cdot \mathbf{b} = \mathbf{a} \cdot \mathbf{c}, \quad \lambda \mathbf{b} \cdot \mathbf{a} + \mu \mathbf{b} \cdot \mathbf{b} = \mathbf{b} \cdot \mathbf{c}. \tag{A.38}$$

The determinant of these equations is just the Gram determinant $\Gamma(\mathbf{a}, \mathbf{b})$. Assuming $\mathbf{a}$ and $\mathbf{b}$ to be independent vectors, (otherwise $V = 0$), we have $\Gamma(\mathbf{a}, \mathbf{b}) \neq 0$. There is, then, a unique solution λ, μ to Eq. (A.38) and hence a unique vector $\mathbf{d}$ perpendicular to $\mathbf{a}, \mathbf{b}$ plane with initial point in that plane. The length of that vector is the required distance h so that, by Eq. (A.37) and using orthogonality of $\mathbf{d}$ with vectors $\mathbf{a}$ and $\mathbf{b}$, we have,

$$h^2 = \mathbf{c} \cdot \mathbf{c} - \lambda \mathbf{c} \cdot \mathbf{a} - \mu \mathbf{c} \cdot \mathbf{b}.$$

This gives the volume V of the parallelopiped spanned by vectors $\mathbf{a}, \mathbf{b}, \mathbf{c}$ in terms of vectors $\mathbf{a}, \mathbf{b}, \mathbf{c}$ as

$$V^2 = (\mathbf{c} \cdot \mathbf{c} - \lambda \mathbf{a} \cdot \mathbf{c} - \mu \mathbf{b} \cdot \mathbf{c}) \Gamma(\mathbf{a}, \mathbf{b}). \tag{A.39}$$

This expression can be written more elegently as the Gram determinant formed from the vectors $\mathbf{a}, \mathbf{b}, \mathbf{c}$:

$$V^2 = \begin{vmatrix} \mathbf{a} \cdot \mathbf{a} & \mathbf{a} \cdot \mathbf{b} & \mathbf{a} \cdot \mathbf{c} \\ \mathbf{b} \cdot \mathbf{a} & \mathbf{b} \cdot \mathbf{b} & \mathbf{b} \cdot \mathbf{c} \\ \mathbf{c} \cdot \mathbf{a} & \mathbf{c} \cdot \mathbf{b} & \mathbf{c} \cdot \mathbf{c} \end{vmatrix} = \Gamma(\mathbf{a}, \mathbf{b}, \mathbf{c}). \tag{A.40}$$

We show the identity of Eqs (A.39) and (A.40) for V^2, using the fact that the value of the determinant $\Gamma(\mathbf{a}, \mathbf{b}, \mathbf{c})$ is unaltered if we subtract from the last column λ times the first column and μ times the second column. Doing this and using Eq. (A.38) we get,

$$1\Gamma(\mathbf{a}, \mathbf{b}, \mathbf{c}) = \begin{vmatrix} \mathbf{a} \cdot \mathbf{a} & \mathbf{a} \cdot \mathbf{b} & 0 \\ \mathbf{b} \cdot \mathbf{a} & \mathbf{b} \cdot \mathbf{b} & 0 \\ \mathbf{c} \cdot \mathbf{a} & \mathbf{c} \cdot \mathbf{b} & \mathbf{c} \cdot \mathbf{c} - \lambda \mathbf{c} \cdot \mathbf{a} - \mu \mathbf{c} \cdot \mathbf{b} \end{vmatrix}. \tag{A.41}$$

Expanding this determinant in terms of the last column leads immediately to the expansion in Eq. (A.39).

Equation (A.40) shows that the volume V of the parallelopiped spanned by the vectors $\mathbf{a}, \mathbf{b}, \mathbf{c}$ does not depend on the choice of the face and of the corresponding altitude used in the computation, because the value of $\Gamma(\mathbf{a}, \mathbf{b}, \mathbf{c})$ does not change when we permute $\mathbf{a}, \mathbf{b}, \mathbf{c}$. For example, $\Gamma(\mathbf{a}, \mathbf{b}, \mathbf{c})$ is invarient under the exchange of first two rows and the first two columns.

Equation (A.39) can be written as

$$\Gamma(\mathbf{a}, \mathbf{b}, \mathbf{c}) = |\mathbf{d}|^2 \Gamma(\mathbf{a}, \mathbf{b}).$$

It follows that

$$\Gamma(\mathbf{a}, \mathbf{b}, \mathbf{c}) \geq 0$$

for any vectors $\mathbf{a}, \mathbf{b}, \mathbf{c}$. The equality sign can only hold if either $\Gamma(\mathbf{a}, \mathbf{b}) = 0$ or $\mathbf{d} = \mathbf{0}$. The first of these equations implies that $\mathbf{a}$ and $\mathbf{b}$ are dependent. The second of these equations would mean $\mathbf{c} = \lambda \mathbf{a} + \mu \mathbf{b}$ so that $\mathbf{c}$ depends on $\mathbf{a}$ and $\mathbf{b}$. Hence, *the Gram determinant vanishes if and only if the vectors $\mathbf{a}, \mathbf{b}, \mathbf{c}$ are dependent.*

Our derivation of the expression for V^2 (Eq. (A.40)) is valid for any n-dimensional space (n finite). If we restrict to 3-dimensional space, Eq. (A.40) follows immediately from Eq. (A.31)

$$V^2 = \det(\mathbf{a}, \mathbf{b}, \mathbf{c}) \det(\mathbf{a}, \mathbf{b}, \mathbf{c}) = \Gamma(\mathbf{a}, \mathbf{b}, \mathbf{c}).$$

Dirac Delta Function

Consider the vector valued function

$$\mathbf{f}(\mathbf{r}) = \frac{\hat{\mathbf{r}}}{r^2}$$

which blows up at the origin. We know that this function is proportional to the electrostatic field produced by a point charge at the origin. It is easy to see that at any $\mathbf{r} \neq \mathbf{0}$, the divergence of $\mathbf{f}$, $\nabla \cdot \mathbf{f}$, is zero:

$$\nabla \cdot \mathbf{f} = \frac{1}{r^2}\frac{\partial}{\partial r}\left(r^2 \frac{1}{r^2}\right) = \frac{1}{r^2}\frac{\partial}{\partial r}(1) = 0.$$

However, at $r = 0$ $\frac{1}{r^2}$ blows up and $\left(r^2 \frac{1}{r^2}\right)$ becomes indeterminate. Further, the surface integral of $\mathbf{f}(\mathbf{r})$ over a sphere of radius R, centered at the origin, is

$$\int \mathbf{f}(\mathbf{r}) \cdot d\mathbf{s} = \int \left(\frac{\hat{\mathbf{r}}}{R^2}\right) \cdot (R^2 \sin\theta d\theta d\phi \hat{\mathbf{r}})$$

$$= \left(\int_0^\pi \sin\theta d\theta\right)\left(\int_0^{2\pi} d\phi\right) = 4\pi.$$

Thus, the surface integral remains finite despite the singularity at the origin. Now, we require on physical grounds that the electrostatic field due to a point charge must obey the divergence theorem. Hence, we must have

$$\int \nabla \cdot \mathbf{f} dV = 4\pi$$

for any volume containing the origin. Since $\nabla \cdot \mathbf{f} = 0$ everywhere except at $\mathbf{r} = \mathbf{0}$, all the contribution to this integral must come from $\nabla \cdot \mathbf{f}$ at the origin. Thus, $\nabla \cdot \mathbf{f}$ has the bizarre property that it vanishes everywhere except at one point, the origin, and yet its integral over any volume containing that point is 4π. Such a behavior is not expected of any ordinary function. The object required to salvage the situation can be constructed as follows. We require the linear space $\mathscr{D}$ of infinitely differentiable (C^∞) and square integrable functions $\phi : \mathscr{E}_3 \mapsto \mathbb{R}$ with compact support.[1] Then the required object is the functional $\delta^3(\mathbf{r})$: $\mathscr{D} \mapsto \mathbb{R}$ defined via

$$\int_V \phi(\mathbf{r})\delta^3(\mathbf{r})dV = \phi(\mathbf{0}) \in \mathbb{R}, \tag{B.1}$$

or, shifting the origin to $\mathbf{a}$,

$$\int_V \phi(\mathbf{r})\delta^3(\mathbf{r}-\mathbf{a})dV = \phi(\mathbf{a}) \in \mathbb{R}, \tag{B.2}$$

where we have assumed that the point $\mathbf{0} \in V$ in the first case, while the point $\mathbf{a} \in V$ in the second, failing which the corresponding integrals vanish. Taking $\phi(\mathbf{r}) = 1$ in Eq. (B.1) we get,

$$\int_V \delta^3(\mathbf{r})dV = 1. \tag{B.3}$$

Of course, all of the above three equations hold unconditionally, if all the integrals are over all space. The functional $\delta^3(\mathbf{r})$ defined via the above three equations is an instance of a mathematical structure called distributions, but is given the name 'Dirac delta function' after its inventor, P.A.M Dirac, although it is not a function in its usual sense.

Thus, the apperent paradox regarding the application of the divergence theorem to the electrostatic field due to a point charge at the origin is resolved if we recognize

$$\nabla \cdot \left(\frac{\hat{\mathbf{r}}}{r^2}\right) = 4\pi\delta^3(\mathbf{r}), \tag{B.4}$$

so that

$$\int \nabla \cdot \left(\frac{\hat{\mathbf{r}}}{r^2}\right)dV = 4\pi \int \delta^3(\mathbf{r})dV = 4\pi. $$

More generally,

$$\nabla \cdot \left(\frac{\widehat{\mathbf{r}-\mathbf{r}'}}{|\mathbf{r}-\mathbf{r}'|^2}\right) = 4\pi\delta^3(\mathbf{r}-\mathbf{r}'), \tag{B.5}$$

where, the differentiation is with respect to $\mathbf{r}$ while $\mathbf{r}'$ is held constant. Since

$$\nabla\left(\frac{1}{|\mathbf{r}-\mathbf{r}'|}\right) = -\left(\frac{\widehat{\mathbf{r}-\mathbf{r}'}}{|\mathbf{r}-\mathbf{r}'|^2}\right), \tag{B.6}$$

---

[1] The support of a function is the set of points in its domain at which its value is different from zero and a set is said to be compact if it is close and bounded.

it follows that

$$\nabla^2\left(\frac{1}{|\mathbf{r}-\mathbf{r}'|}\right) = -4\pi\delta^3(\mathbf{r}-\mathbf{r}').$$

(B.7)

In order to construct the delta function for one dimensional physical phenomena, we need the linear space $\mathscr{D}$ of functions of a single variable which are continuously differentiable at all orders, and have compact support. Then, the Dirac delta function is the functional $\delta(x):\mathscr{D}\mapsto\mathbb{R}$ defined via

$$\int_{-\infty}^{\infty}\phi(x)\delta(x)dx = \phi(0),$$

(B.8)

and

$$\int_{-\infty}^{\infty}\phi(x)\delta(x-a)dx = \phi(a),$$

(B.9)

or, with $\phi(x)=1$,

$$\int_{-\infty}^{\infty}\delta(x)dx = 1.$$

(B.10)

The 3-D delta function $\delta^3(\mathbf{r})$ and 1-D delta function $\delta(x)$ can be connected by evaluating the integral over volume by successive evaluation of three single integrals.

$$\int_{\text{all space}}\delta^3(\mathbf{r})dV = \int_{-\infty}^{\infty}\int_{-\infty}^{\infty}\int_{-\infty}^{\infty}\delta(x)\delta(y)\delta(z)dxdydz = 1.$$

Thus, we can write

$$\delta^3(\mathbf{r}) = \delta(x)\delta(y)\delta(z).$$

(B.11)

Exercise!   Show that

$$\delta(kx) = \frac{1}{|k|}\delta(x),$$

where k is any non-zero constant. (In particular, $\delta(-x)=\delta(x)$.)

Solution   For $\phi(x)\in\mathscr{D}$ consider

$$\int_{-\infty}^{\infty}\phi(x)\delta(kx)dx.$$

We change the variables to $y = kx$ giving $x = (1/k)y$ and $dx = dy/k$. With this change of variables we get

$$\int_{-\infty}^{\infty} \phi(x)\delta(kx)dx = \pm\frac{1}{k}\int_{-\infty}^{\infty} \phi(y/k)\delta(y)dy = \frac{1}{|k|}\phi(0),$$

where $\pm$ corresponds to $k > 0$ and $k < 0$ respectively, so that $\pm\frac{1}{k}$ can be replaced by $\frac{1}{|k|}$. This means

$$\int_{-\infty}^{\infty} \phi(x)\delta(kx)dx = \int_{-\infty}^{\infty} \phi(x)\left[\frac{1}{|k|}\delta(x)\right]dx.$$

This is the required result. □

We can define the derivative of the delta function, denoted $\delta'(x)$, in the following way. For $\phi(x) \in \mathscr{D}$ we write, integrating by parts,

$$\int_{-\infty}^{\infty} \phi(x)\delta'(x)dx = \phi(x)\delta(x)\Big|_{-\infty}^{\infty} - \int_{-\infty}^{\infty} \phi'(x)\delta(x) = \phi'(0),$$

as the first term on the right vanishes because $\phi(x)$ has compact support and the prime denotes diffrentiation with respect to x. Thus we get,

$$\int_{-\infty}^{\infty} \phi(x)\delta'(x)dx = -\phi'(0). \tag{B.12}$$

Exercise! Consider the Heaviside function on $\mathbb{R}$

$$H(x) = \begin{cases} 1, & x \geq 0 \\ 0, & x < 0 \end{cases} \tag{B.13}$$

which defines the functional (distribution) on $\mathscr{D}$ by

$$T_H(\phi) = \int_{-\infty}^{\infty} H(x)\phi(x)dx = \int_0^{\infty} \phi(x)dx.$$

Show that the delta function is the derivative of T_H.

Solution We again integrate by parts to get

$$T_H'(\phi) = -T_H(\phi') = -\int_0^{\infty} \phi'(x)dx = \phi(0) = \delta(\phi).$$

Note that $\phi(\infty) = 0$ because ϕ has compact support. □

Exercise! Prove the following properties of the delta function.

(i) $\delta'(x) = -\delta'(-x)$.

(ii) $x\delta(x) = 0$.

(iii) $x\delta'(x) = -\delta(x)$.

(iv) $\delta(x^2 - a^2) = (2a)^{-1}[\delta(x-a) + \delta(x+a)], \quad a > 0$.

(v) $\int \delta(a-x)\delta(x-b)dx = \delta(a-b)$.

(vi) $f(x)\delta(x-a) = f(a)\delta(x-a)$.

Here, a prime denotes differentiation with respect to the argument. □

There are various expressions involving limits and integrals which mimic delta function and are called various representations of delta function. We do not deal with them because we have not used them in this book. However these are very useful in many branches of physics and can be found in standard text books on quantum mechanics (see e.g., [6]). The standard reference on distributions is the book by Kesavan [14].

Bibliography

1. Ahlfors, L. V. 1979. *Complex Analysis*. New York: Tata McGraw-Hill.

2. Antia, H. M. 1991. *Numerical Methods for Scientists and Engineers*. New Delhi: Tata McGraw-Hill Publishing Company.

3. Arnold, V. I. 1989. *Mathematical Methods of Classical Mechanics*. New York: Sprienger-Verlag.

4. Ashcroft, N. W., and Mermin, N. D. 1976. *Solid State Physics*. Fort Worth: Harcourt Brace College Publishers.

5. Courant, R., and John, F. 1974. *Introduction to Calculus and Analysis*. Vol. I & II. New York: John Wiley and Sons.

6. Cohen-Tannoudji, C., Diu, B., and Laloe, F. 1991. *Quantum Mechanics*. Vol. I & II. Wiley-VCH.

7. Doran, C. J. L., and Lasenby, A. N. 2003. *Geometric Algebra for Physicists*. Cambridge: Cambridge University Press.

8. Fleisch D. 2011. *A Student's Guide to Vectors and Tensors*. Cambridge: Cambridge University Press.

9. Griffiths, D. J. 1999. *Introduction to Electrodynamics*. New Delhi: Prentice-Hall of India Pvt. Ltd.

10. Hestenes, D. 1986. *New Foundations for Classical Mechanics*. Dordrecht: Kluwer Academic Publishers.

11. Hestenes, D., Sobczyk, G. 1987. *Clifford Algebra to Geometric Calculus: A Unified Language for Mathematics and Physics*. (*Fundamental Theories of Physics*). Dordrecht: Springer.

12. Horn, R. A., and Johnson, C. R. 1985. *Matrix Analysis*. Vol. I & II. Cambridge: Cambridge University Press.

13. Jackson, J. D. 1999. *Classical Electrodynamics*. New York: John Wiley and Sons.

14. Kesavan, S. 1989. *Topics in Functional Analysis and Applications*. New Delhi: Wiley.

15. Lang, S. 1973. *Calculus of Several Variables*. Reading, Massachusetts: Addison-Wesley.

16. Munk, W. H., and Macdonald, G. J. F. 1960. *The Rotation of the Earth*. Cambridge: Cambridge University Press.

17. Rajaraman, V. 2009. *Computer Oriented Numerical Methods*. New Delhi: Prentice-Hall of India.

18. Raju, C. K. 2007. *Cultural Foundations of Mathematics: The Nature of Mathematical Proof and the Transmission of Calculus from India to Europe in the 16th c. CE*. Delhi: Pearson Longman

19. Rana, N. C., and Joag, P. S. 1991. *Classical Mechanics*. New Delhi: Tata McGraw-Hill Publishing Company Limited.

20. Rosenberg, C.B. *Private communication*.

21. Schey, H. M. 2005. *Div, Grad, Curl, and all that: an informal text on Vector Calculus*. 4th Ed. New York: W. W. Norton

22. Schwartz, M., Green, S. and Rutledge, W. A. 1960. *Vector Analysis with Applications to Geometry and Physics*. New York: Harper & Brothers.

23. Shorter, L. R. 2014. *Problems and Worked Solutions in Vector Analysis*. Mineola, New York: Dover Publications, Inc.

24. Stacey, F. D. 1969. *Physics of the Earth*. New York: John Wiley & Sons Inc.

25. Sudarshan, E. C. G., and N. Mukunda. 1974. *Classical Dynamics: A Modern Perspective*. New York: Wiley.

26. Zwikker, C. 1950. *Advanced Plane Geometry*. Amsterdam: North Holland Publishing Company.

Index